INTERSCIENCE MONOGRAPHS ON CHEMISTRY

Organic Chemistry Section

EDITOR: George A. Olah
Dow Chemical Company
Framingham, Massachusetts

Interscience Monographs on Chemistry

INORGANIC CHEMISTRY SECTION

Edited by F. Albert Cotton

Goodenough, "Magnetism and the Chemical Bond"

PHYSICAL CHEMISTRY SECTION

Edited by I. Prigogine

Sulfonation and Related Reactions

BY EVERETT E. GILBERT

ALLIED CHEMICAL CORPORATION

GENERAL CHEMICAL DIVISION

MORRISTOWN, NEW JERSEY

INTERSCIENCE PUBLISHERS 1965

a division of John Wiley & Sons, Inc., New York · London · Sydney

Library of Congress Catalog Card Number 65-14728
Printed in the United States of America

Editor's Introduction

The chemical literature in recent years increasingly emphasized multi-author monographs covering broader topics or review articles as part of the numerous "Advances" or "Progress" series. Both fill important needs and became integral parts of our libraries as valuable reference sources. By their nature and price they, however, rarely can reach the desks of individual chemists for their personal use. They also reflect the fact, that the ever growing chemical literature makes it increasingly difficult for individual authors to cover larger fields in a comprehensive and critical way.

To contribute a chapter or to write a review article frequently involves an effort comparable to that of writing a monograph on the topic. There is a genuine and growing need for authentic monographs written by experts actively engaged in research in their respective fields of specialization. These can provide not only a review of the topic, but more importantly, they can critically evaluate the field, point out the major and most important advances achieved, and also possible new avenues of approaches where further future research is most needed. These smaller monographs using improved technical methods can be produced faster and cheaper than multi-author collective volumes, where the "slowest" author or editor inevitably determines the speed of publication. Individual monographs also give full recognition to the author, which is not always possible, if for no other than technical reasons, in edited volumes.

The foregoing were the main reasons which caused the editor and the publishers to initiate a series of monographs in Organic Chemistry. Similar monographs are being published in the field of Inorganic and Physical Chemistry. The Organic Chemistry Section of the Interscience Monographs on Chemistry will be accessible to the average chemist for his own use at reasonable prices and will provide titles of current interest in a wide scope. It is hoped that the high standard and timeliness of these volumes aimed at by the authors, the editors, and the publisher will make them a useful addition to the chemical literature.

GEORGE A. OLAH

November 2, 1964

Preface

No general work on the organic derivatives of sulfur trioxide has appeared since the publication of C. M. Suter's basic treatise *The Organic Chemistry of Sulfur*, which covered the literature through 1941. This book represents an effort to overcome this need.

The author's approach has been selective, rather than all-inclusive, with the general objective of supplying background information of possible value to the laboratory chemist. Recent trends have been emphasized. Chief among these is the recognition that, although the conventional rules of aromatic orientation are followed under kinetically controlled conditions during sulfonation with sulfuric acid or oleum, these rules are not always followed under conditions which are thermodynamically controlled. This effect is made possible by the reversible nature of the sulfonation reaction, a characteristic which has enough other implications to warrant consideration in a separate chapter. Another effect noted increasingly in all aspects of sulfonate preparation, as well as in desulfonation, is the importance of steric requirements. Many examples are noted of the steric assistance or hindrance to be expected in reactions involving moieties as large as sulfur trioxide or sulfite ion. Emphasis is also placed upon recent studies involving the reactions of sulfur trioxide itself, and of its various adducts with organic compounds. An effort is made in appropriate cases to bring together isolated facts into possibly meaningful form in such a way as to indicate trends or generalizations. Chapter 5 on sulfoalkylation and related indirect procedures may constitute an example of this approach, since the broad utility of this general preparative method appears to have been largely unappreciated in the past.

Most of the work discussed in this book has emanated from industrial laboratories, or from European universities, and the approach so far has been largely synthetic and descriptive. This area of research has, with a few notable exceptions, been largely neglected in American universities. This situation has perhaps been aggravated by the frequent difficulty encountered in analyzing sulfonation reaction mixtures, and the unfortunate fact that the newer methods of instrumental analysis are often not easily applicable. The physical and mechanistic aspects of sulfonation have as yet been little studied. Reference is made herein to the relatively few cases in which mechanisms have been suggested, in the hope that such might stimulate further thought in this direction. It was almost a century ago that August Kekulé, in referring to organic chemistry generally, said, "At the present stage of the development of our science, mechanistic interpretations should be made."

The author has attempted to cover the significant developments to the middle of 1964, as obtained through the major American, British, and German journals, and through *Chemical Abstracts*. Much of the material in Chapters 1, 2, 6, and 7 was based on the author's article "The Reactions of Sulfur Trioxide, and of its Adducts, with Organic Compounds," which appeared in *Chem. Rev.* **62,** 549 (1962). The annual reviews on sulfonation in Industrial and Engineering Chemistry, covering the period 1941–1963, provided much information for Chapters 3, 4, 5, and 8. These reviews were written by Mr. G. F. Lisk prior to 1951, and thereafter by Mr. E. P. Jones and the author of this book. It was Dr. George A. Olah who first suggested to the writer that the material in these reviews might provide the basis for a book.

The writer feels much indebted to various individuals for reviewing sections of the manuscript and making many useful suggestions. These include: Ludwig Audrieth, Horst Baumann, Irwin Douglass, George Drake, Jr., Basil Farah, John Guthrie, Harry Kaplan, Harold Kwart, Vincent Lamberti, Charles Martin, George Olah, Paul Peterson, Remsen Schenck, Otto Scherer, James Sprague, Alexander Stirton, Bernard Sukornick, Benjamin Veldhuis, Emil Wildman, and Otto Wurzburg. It is a pleasure to acknowledge the assistance of Mrs. Fabienne Berard, who did most of the typing.

Nomenclature conforms to *Chemical Abstracts* or to that used by the original author. The term "sulfonate" is often used herein in referring to a sulfonic acid or a salt thereof.

EVERETT E. GILBERT

Contents

CHAPTER 1

THE REAGENTS

I. INTRODUCTION

In this chapter are considered the preparation and properties of the main reagents used for the direct introduction of the -SO3H group, for sulfonation, sulfation, or sulfamation, as discussed in Chapters 2, 6, and 7, respectively. All of these reagents can, in the broader sense, be thought of as compounds of SO3, with the ease of its release to the organic material being sulfonated varying from one reagent to another. All of them are inorganic - suitably modified in many cases by complexing with an appropriate organic base. The preparation and properties of "organic sulfonating agents" are discussed separately in Chapter 5.

Several noteworthy developments with respect to new or improved sulfonating reagents have occurred in recent years. Among these may be mentioned the introduction of stabilized, liquid SO3 in 1947 as an article of commerce, an event concurrent with greatly increased production of certain industrial sulfonates - especially surface-active agents, lubricant additives, and ion-exchange resins, resulting in increased interest in the stronger and more efficient reagents. Laboratory research and industrial practice have established acceptable methods for its handling and use. At the opposite end of the spectrum, new reagents of exceptional mildness have appeared for the sulfation of sensitive compounds. In this category is included especially that derived from dimethylformamide, which in itself combines two highly desirable attributes of extraordinary solvency for organic compounds and for SO3-triethylamine and other similar complexes and mild basicity allowing the compound itself to form complexes with SO3 and ClSO3H. Tetrahydrofuran, and dimethyl sulfoxide, likewise weak bases with unusual solvency, may see similar applications in the future. The new SO3-trialkylphosphate adducts have displayed novel and promising results in sulfonating polystyrene and alkenes.

Progress has also been made in greater understanding and wider application of older systems. Physicochemical studies have given more detailed knowledge of the composition of oleum, and work with the SO3-pyridine complex has revealed new or broadened uses for it in sulfating dyes, carbohydrates, and sterols, and for sulfonating polycyclic compounds and acid-sensitive heterocyclics. The SO3-dioxane complex, developed in 1938, has continued to be one of the most favored adducts for laboratory use, especially for the sulfonation of alkenes. Sulfamic acid, introduced commercially about 1936, has suffered from high price and low reactivity compared with the other reagents, but the second objection has been overcome in part by the finding that greatly enhanced reactivity results from the addition of various organic bases.

II. SULFUR TRIOXIDE AND ITS HYDRATES

A. Sulfur Trioxide

The chemistry of SO_3 is complicated and not completely understood. It exists in the monomeric and in several polymeric forms (1).

The SO_3 molecule is planar, triangular, and symmetrical. It is a resonance hybrid in which the oxygen atoms are equivalent (44a). The S—O bond is unusually short, indicating considerable double bond character. Although the exact distribution of electrons between sulfur and oxygen is uncertain, the behavior of SO_3 in chemical reactions indicates that the sulfur atom is strongly electron-deficient, since a marked tendency exists toward increasing the number of electrons in the outer shell from eight to ten, or even to twelve, as in SF_6. Formulas 1-0-A and 1-0-B represent possible canonical forms. At the same time, the oxygen atoms are electron-rich. The SO_3 molecule has accordingly been aptly described (66) as a "Lewis acid on one side (i. e., the sulfur), and a Lewis base on the other (oxygen)," i.e., it is amphoteric. This condition explains the ease with which SO_3 polymerizes, and its activity as a sulfonating agent, with the acidic sulfur atom attacking electron-rich (basic) systems, and the basic oxygen atoms accepting acidic protons.

Sulfur trioxide vapor is monomeric, as are also dilute solutions in SO_2, CCl_4, SO_2Cl_2, and other solvents (55); in more concentrated solutions, there is an increasing quantity of the trimeric, or γ form (formula 1-0-C). Freshly distilled SO_3 is a water-white liquid, indicated by Raman spectral analysis to comprise approximately 90% of the trimeric form and 10% monomer. Others (123) have reported 20% trimer and 80% monomer. Some of the properties of liquid SO_3 are summarized in Table 1-1 (1, 3, 50).

If the freshly distilled liquid is exposed to even a trace of moisture, or is kept standing in a sealed ampoule at room temperature for a short time, it reverts to solid polymers of various possible chain lengths (formula 1-0-D) and degrees of crosslinking, with correspondingly varied physical properties. Although solid SO_3 has been used to a minor extent in the laboratory for making complexes, and for conversion to SO_3 vapor by heating, it has not been considered a commercially practical compound because of its variability, difficulty in handling, and the high increase in vapor pressure occurring during vaporization (1a, 50). The discovery that liquid SO_3 could be stabilized satisfactorily against polymerization to solids by the addition of a small quantity (as low as 0.1%) of various compounds - especially

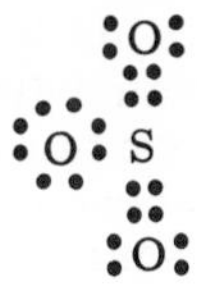

$$\begin{array}{ccc} \ddot{\text{:O:}} \\ \ddot{} \\ \text{:O:} \ \text{S} \\ \ddot{} \\ \ddot{\text{:O:}} \end{array}$$

(A)

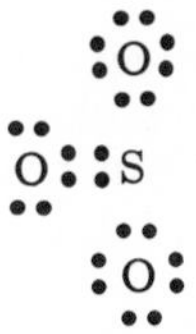

$$\begin{array}{c} \ddot{\text{:O:}} \\ \ddot{} \\ \ddot{\text{O:}} \ \text{:S} \\ \ddot{} \\ \ddot{\text{:O:}} \end{array}$$

(B)

(1-0)

$$\begin{array}{c} O_2 \\ \diagup \ S \ \diagdown \\ O \qquad O \\ | \qquad | \\ SO_2 \qquad SO_2 \\ \diagdown \ O \ \diagup \end{array}$$

$$\left(-O\overset{\displaystyle O}{\underset{\displaystyle O}{\overset{\|}{\underset{\|}{S}}}}-O-\overset{\displaystyle O}{\underset{\displaystyle O}{\overset{\|}{\underset{\|}{S}}}}-O-\overset{\displaystyle O}{\underset{\displaystyle O}{\overset{\|}{\underset{\|}{S}}}}- \right)_x$$

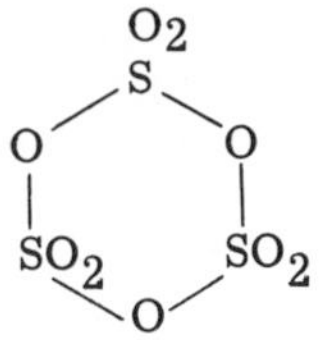

(C) 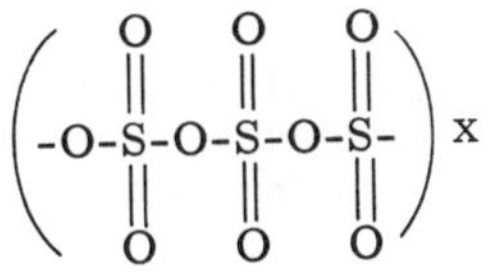   (D)

TABLE 1-1

Some Physical Properties of Liquid Sulfur Trioxide

Boiling point (°C)	44.5
Melting point (°C)	16.8
Density (20 °C)	1.9224
Specific heat (cal./g., 25 − 30 °C)	0.77
Heat of dilution (cal./g.)	504
Heat of vaporization (cal./g.)	127.4
Viscosity (centipoises 30 °C)	1.524

derivatives of boron, phosphorus, or sulfur - resulted in its commercial introduction (30, 50). Since then, many patents have appeared describing numerous different types of inorganic and organic stabilizers, and several companies in various parts of the world have begun to market it.

For laboratory purposes, the use of SO_3 in liquid form may involve the freshly distilled, or the stabilized commercial material. It differs from sulfuric acid and oleum in being miscible in all proportions with liquid SO_2, and with many chlorinated, and chlorinated-fluorinated organic solvents. These include chloroform, carbon tetrachloride, methylene chloride, 1, 1, 1-trichloroethane, and pentachloroethane (4). Some of these solvents will react with SO_3, as shown in Table 6-7, depending upon the purity of the solvent and the nature of the stabilizer. Compounds of boron and mercury catalyze their interaction. The presence of fluorine confers stability, as with fluorotrichloroethane and 1, 1-difluorotetrachloroethane. Tetrachloroethylene and hexachlorobutadiene are also miscible with SO_3, and do not react easily with it; fluorinated alkenes, on the other hand, can form sultones, as indicated in Chapter 2. Even organic compounds which react easily with SO_3 can be used as solvents for compounds which react more easily, provided the reagent is added to a mixture of the two organic compounds. Propane and n-butane have been used in this way with detergent alkylates (98), as has chlorobenzene with petroleum lubricant extracts (53). Nitromethane has been employed recently as an SO_3 solvent (6, 33, 41) with favorable results. Solutions in the range 25 - 40% by weight of SO_3 are stated to decompose slowly at room temperature, but to be stable for at least 4 hr. at 0 °C (41). Others (115) report that mixtures of SO_3 and nitromethane can decompose violently at room temperature, forming CO_2, NO_2, and SO_2; under controlled conditions at 15% yield of nitromethanesulfonic acid is formed. It seems probable that an SO_3-nitromethane complex is formed, but this has not been mentioned in any of the reports to date. Carbon disulfide is miscible with SO_3 in all proportions. Upon standing for a short time at room temperature, or immediately upon warming, reaction occurs:

$$SO_3 + CS_2 \longrightarrow COS + SO_2 + S \qquad (1\text{-}1)$$

Carbon disulfide has, however, been used as reaction solvent for the sulfation of cellulose with SO_3. Vaporization of the SO_3, and dilution with dry air to about 10% strength, is also a standard laboratory procedure, as indicated in Chapters 2 and 6. Vaporized SO_3 is a much milder reagent than the undiluted liquid, even though the total heat of reaction with the former is more than that with the latter by the value for the heat of condensation. Regardless of the degree of subdivision, undiluted liquid SO_3 reacts so rapidly and exothermically that localized charring occurs with all but the most stable organic compounds. The vapor, on the other hand, is milder because it is much more widely distributed. On a commercial scale, the stabilized liquid is mixed with a solvent such as liquid SO_2, or - more commonly - is vaporized and mixed with dry air. The vapor form is also obtained commercially by distillation from oleum, from sulfuric acid plant-converter gas, which contains 5 - 15% SO_3, or by burning sulfur and oxidizing the SO_2 obtained in this manner to SO_3.

B. Sulfur Trioxide Hydrates

Sulfur trioxide has a strong affinity for water. So high is this degree of affinity, and so great is the evolution of heat in mixing the two materials - about 500 cal. for the conversion of 1 g. liquid SO_3 to liquid H_2SO_4 (cf., Table 1-1) - that water in its relation to SO_3 may be regarded as a basic substance.

Recent Raman (56) spectral studies have shown that oleum contains $HO-(SO_3)_x-H$, where x = 1, 2, 3, and 4, and also SO_3 monomer and trimer at the higher strengths. Other spectral studies indicate that the activity coefficient of SO_3 is almost independent of composition over the range 3 - 60% oleum (40). Recent studies of sulfonation kinetics, cited in Chapter 2, indicate that monomeric SO_3 is the true reactive species in oleum and sulfuric acid, as well as in liquid SO_3, and that the water present in the hydrates functions merely as a complexing agent and solvent. The physical properties of the SO_3 hydrates have been described in detail (39, 54a, 56a); some of these for 100% acid are given in Table 1-2.

TABLE 1-2

Some Physical Properties of 100% Sulfuric Acid

Boiling range	290 - 317°C
Freezing point	10.37°C
Density ($\frac{15}{4}$)	1.8356
Specific heat (22.5°C)	0.332
Heat of vaporization (Kcal./kg.)	122.32
Viscosity (centipoise, 25°C)	25.54

The major problem in sulfonating with SO_3 hydrates, therefore, involves finding practical procedures for overcoming the affinity between SO_3 and water so that the former becomes free to react with the organic compound. A similar problem is involved in using all the other reagents mentioned subsequently in this chapter, except that the complexing agent is a different material in each case. The profound effect produced by the hydration of SO_3 is qualitatively indicated in

Table 1-3, where sulfuric acid and SO_3 are compared as sulfonating agents for aromatic hydrocarbons. The oleums, as would be expected, occupy intermediate positions. The major advantages cited for SO_3 in Table 1-3, namely, rapid and complete reaction, and no energy requirement for completing sulfonation, have prompted increasing interest in this reagent. The disadvantages (high heat of reaction with consequent decomposition or side reactions, and high viscosity) can often be overcome by choice of reaction conditions or the use of a solvent.

TABLE 1-3

Comparison of Sulfuric Acid and SO_3 for
Sulfonating Aromatic Hydrocarbons

Factor Compared	H_2SO_4	SO_3
Reaction rate	Slow	Instantaneous
Heat input	Requires heat for completion	Strongly exothermic throughout
Extent of reaction	Partial	Complete
Side reactions	Minor	Sometimes extensive
Viscosity of reaction mixture	Low	Sometimes high
Boiling point	290 - 317°C	44.5°C
Solubility in halogenated solvents	Very low	Miscible

The unusual ability of sulfuric acid to protonate electron-rich centers invites special comment. Although a strong acid, it is more properly regarded as an amphoteric substance (54a), which is capable of protonating its own electron-rich oxygen atoms ("autoprotolysis"). (As noted in the preceding section, SO_3 is also amphoteric, with the sulfur atom functioning as the acidic - i. e., electron-deficient - moiety.) Autoprotolysis largely explains the high electrical conductivity of the acid. Its ability to protonate other electron-rich systems explains its remarkable solvent power for most types of organic compounds, especially those containing oxygen or nitrogen. In many cases the organic compounds can be recovered unchanged by dilution with water, since protonation tends to deactivate the compound, which otherwise might undergo sulfonation or oxidation.

III. SULFUR TRIOXIDE COMPLEXES WITH ORGANIC COMPOUNDS

A. General Discussion

The sulfur atom in SO_3, being a strong electron acceptor or Lewis acid, combines with electron donors or Lewis bases, to form coordination compounds, also known as "adducts" or "complexes:"

$$(1-2)$$

The bases employed may be tertiary amines – including those which are fairly strong (i.e., - trimethyl- or triethylamines), or considerably weaker (pyridine or dimethylaniline). Other even weaker bases include tertiary amides, ethers, and thioethers. The stability of the complex in general varies directly with the strength of the base used. Basic strengths of several amines used for preparing SO_3 complexes are given in Table 1-4 (61). When the adduct is employed for sulfonating an organic compound, the SO_3 is released and the base forms the salt of the new acid:

$$RH + SO_3 \cdot Base \longrightarrow RSO_3H \cdot Base \qquad (1-3)$$

TABLE 1-4

Basic Strengths of Some Amines Used for SO_3 Complexes

Amines	pKa, H_2O
Trimethylamine	10.72
Triethylamine	10.74
Dimethylaniline	5.06
Diethylaniline	6.56
Pyridine	5.22
2-Methylpyridine	5.96
2,6-Dimethylpyridine	6.72
N-Ethylmorpholine	7.70

Sulfation and sulfamation with the complexes proceed similarly. Even the weakest complex is a much milder reagent than free SO_3. It is thus possible to moderate the reactivity of SO_3 to any desired degree by the correct choice of a complexing basic material. Basic strength is not the only factor determining the reactivity of an SO_3 complex, however. Trimethylamine, although equal in basic strength to triethylamine, yields a complex which is more stable and less reactive (5). Likewise, an increasing degree of methylation in the 2- and 6-positions of pyridine does not greatly affect basic strength, but does markedly increase product yields in certain sulfamation reactions, as discussed in Chapter 7.

B.   Sulfur Trioxide-Pyridine

This complex has often been prepared by direct reaction of SO_3 with the base. A 90% yield was noted by adding pyridine to solid SO_3 suspended in carbon tetrachloride (15, 20). A quantitative yield of theoretical assay was obtained with chloroform as solvent (111). Addition of pyridine in 1, 2-dichloroethane at 0 °C to SO_3 dissolved in the same solvent gave a 95% yield (99). The Soviet investigator, A. P. Terent'ev, who has worked extensively with this adduct, adds equivalent dry pyridine, with cooling and stirring to SO_3 in 1, 2-dichloroethane; the product is filtered and dried rapidly at 100 °C (113). A 97% yield assaying 93 - 96% resulted from the addition of liquid SO_3 to SO_2-pyridine dissolved in liquid SO_2 (52); these reaction conditions are extremely mild. Addition of liquid SO_3 to pyridine gives a product of 87% purity (93). This method has been used with chloroform as solvent, employing 30 mole-% excess pyridine, filtering the solid complex, washing it with chloroform and drying in a desiccator (59). Sulfur trioxide can be vaporized into pyridine (35). The complex has also been prepared by bringing together the two components in equivalent quantities without a solvent, either in a heavy-duty mixer below 20 °C (112), or as finely divided mists or vapors entrained in dry air (23, 24).

Sulfur trioxide-pyridine has been prepared with reagents other than SO_3. Reaction of pyridine with $ClSO_3H$ immediately yields SO_3-pyridine and a mole of pyridinium chloride (15, 102, 122):

$$ClSO_3H + 2 \ C_5H_5N \longrightarrow SO_3 \cdot C_5H_5N + C_5H_5N \cdot HCl \qquad (1\text{-}4)$$

With chloroform as solvent at 0 °C (102, 111) a 62% yield is obtained; the insoluble complex separates and can be filtered, while the pyridinium chloride remains dissolved in the filtrate. A common sulfating mixture for carbohydrates, sterols, and other sensitive compounds, is $ClSO_3H$ added to excess pyridine, no effort being made to remove the pyridinium chloride. It has been suggested, however, that the pyridinium chloride, at least in one case, has a detrimental effect if present during sulfation (81). Sulfur trioxide and $ClSO_3H$ are reported to form adducts of the same purity (about 92%) and melting point (97 - 100°) (94). Heating dry sodium pyrosulfate with pyridine for 30 min. at 95°C also yields the complex (10). Potassium pyrosulfate, either anhydrous at 115°C (14), or in cold aqueous solution (19), can also be used. Ethyl chlorosulfonate forms the adduct (15, 122).

$$2 \, C_5H_5N + C_2H_5OSO_2Cl \longrightarrow SO_3 \cdot C_5H_5N + C_5H_5N \cdot ClC_2H_5 \qquad (1\text{-}5)$$

It has also been made by adding ice to a mixture of pyridine and sulfuryl chloride (17):

$$3 \, C_5H_5N + SO_2Cl_2 + H_2O \longrightarrow SO_3 \cdot C_5H_5N + 2 \, C_5H_5N \cdot HCl \qquad (1\text{-}6)$$

Sulfur trioxide-pyridine is available commercially (1b, 2, 45a).

The pyridine complex is a white solid variously reported to melt at 97 - 100 (94), 121 (111), 137 (83), 155 (122), and at 175°C (15). These data all refer to preparations of crude product, since no method for purifying SO_3-pyridine has yet been suggested, aside from trituration with ice water to remove pyridinium sulfate (15). The lack of purification methods is explainable by its salt-like character, with its consequent low volatility and low solubility in nearly all common solvents, as mentioned below.

It is quite stable to, and insoluble in, cold water and cold aqueous alkali, but rapidly decomposes completely upon warming in both media (15). It is insoluble (i. e., less than 1% by weight) in pyridine, nitrobenzene, cyclohexane, methylcyclohexane, n-hexane, chloroform, carbon tetrachloride, dioxane, ethyl ether, n-butyl benzenesulfonate, and acetone, all at 25°C (93). It is soluble in dimethylformamide (4), and forms at least a 20 wt. -% solution in liquid SO_2 at -10°C (4). The complex also dissolves in concentrated sulfuric, perchloric, and hydrochloric acids (18), from all of which it can be precipitated unchanged by dilution with cold water.

Sulfur trioxide-pyridine has been used extensively as a laboratory reagent for sulfating alcohols, sterols, and carbohydrates (cf., Chapter 6), for sulfamating amines, amides, and proteins (Chapter 7), and for sulfonating acid-sensitive heterocyclic compounds and alkadienes (Chapter 2). These reactions are run at moderate temperatures, usually below 120°C in the presence of excess pyridine or a solvent such as 1, 2-dichloroethane. The solid complex can be reacted with

some compounds by melting the two together in the range 150 - 200 °C.
Sulfamations and phenol sulfations can be run in cold aqueous alkaline
solution. It has been used for sulfating on a semimicro scale (49).
Even upon prolonged heating at 150 °C, this complex does not react
with paraffins, cycloparaffins, nonterminal olefins, benzene and its
homologues, stilbene, anthracene, fluorene, or triphenylethylene
(113). Slow reaction occurs with terminal olefins, resulting in a poor
yield of sulfonate. It does not react with long-chain carboxylic acids.
At 170 °C, it sulfonates naphthalene, phenol, and aniline (16), but
these reactions can be effected more rapidly with other cheaper reagents. It has been used somewhat commercially for sulfating oleyl
alcohol and the leuco forms of vat dyestuffs, and is now being employed for sulfamating cyclohexylamine. Complete removal of residual
pyridine from the final products is essential because of its unpleasant
and persistent odor.

Pyridine also forms a complex with two moles of SO_3. It has been
prepared by the addition of SO_3 to pyridine dissolved in liquid SO_2 (52),
or by the addition of SO_3 to SO_3-pyridine suspended in 1, 2-dichloro-
ethane (114). It melts at 83 - 5 °C (114). The second mole of SO_3 is
much more reactive than the first. Work with this adduct has been
very limited; the Soviet group headed by A. P. Terent'ev has employed
it for sulfonating heterocyclic compounds, and aliphatic esters, nitriles and acids (see Chapter 2). This complex is designated herein
as "(2 SO_3)-pyridine."

C. Sulfur Trioxide-Dioxane

Dioxane can react with one or two moles of SO_3:

$$O(CH_2CH_2)_2O \xrightarrow{SO_3} SO_3 \cdot O(CH_2CH_2)_2O \xrightarrow{SO_3}$$

$$SO_3 \cdot O(CH_2CH_2)_2O \cdot SO_3$$

$$(1-7)$$

There is some recent evidence that dioxane can react with even more
than two moles of SO_3 (82). Nearly all of the fairly extensive work
with this complex has been done with the 1:1 product, and it is this
material which is referred to herein as "SO_3-dioxane." The preparation and reactions of SO_3-dioxane have been reviewed recently (46).

Although early work (109) indicated that the two adducts have similar properties and reactivity, there is indication that the SO_3-to-
dioxane ratio may play a role, at least in sulfonating aromatic hydrocarbons. The 2:1 adduct sulfonates benzene at room temperature in
one day (107, 109); however, in the presence of a large excess of dioxane, the 1:1 material did not react in 72 hr. , even at elevated temper-

ature (93). The 2:1 complex sulfonates polystyrene rapidly and completely at 5°C (9), but if more than two moles of dioxane are used per mole of SO$_3$, the reaction is extremely slow and incomplete. As is pointed out below, the complexes with bis(2-chloroethyl)ether and with triethyl phosphate behave similarly.

Liquid SO$_3$ can be added carefully with cooling to undiluted dioxane (54, 93), or to a mixture of dioxane and 1, 2-dichloroethane (9, 103). Sulfur trioxide vapor can be passed into a mixture of dioxane and 1, 2-dichloroethane (107, 109), or carbon tetrachloride (107); the solid adduct crystallizes and can be filtered. With ClSO$_3$H below 20°C dioxane form an oxonium salt (see Section IV) (110); at 20°C HCl is evolved, and SO$_3$-dioxane is formed.

Sulfur trioxide-dioxane, being unstable, is usually prepared immediately before use. The solid adduct can decompose violently after standing for some time at room temperature (102); upon heating, it decomposes at 75°C (109). At 0°C in solution it has been found to decompose to the extent of 9% in 0. 5 hr. , and 13% in 20 hr. (32). Upon contact with water, the complex is immediately converted to dioxane and sulfuric acid (109). It is, therefore, considerably more reactive and less stable than SO$_3$-pyridine.

Since its discovery in 1938, SO$_3$-dioxane has been employed extensively in the laboratory, mainly for sulfonating alkenes (see Chapter 2), and for sulfating alcohols (Chapter 6). To a lesser extent it has been used for sulfamating aromatic amines (Chapter 7), and sulfonating aromatic and petroleum hydrocarbons.

Like dioxane, 1, 4-benzodioxane complexes with one or with two moles of SO$_3$ (92).

D. Sulfur Trioxide-Trimethylamine

This complex has been prepared by the direct vapor phase interaction of SO$_3$ and trimethylamine without a solvent (36). However, solvents such as chloroform (85), 1, 2-dichloroethane (97), or liquid SO$_2$ (52) have usually been employed. Use of the latter entails exceptionally mild conditions, since the reaction is run at -10°C with the solvent functioning as a refluxing autorefrigerant, and the heat of reaction is reduced by first forming the SO$_2$-amine complex. Alternative preparative methods have involved reaction of the amine with ClSO$_3$H (64) using chlorobenzene as solvent at 10°C or with cold aqueous SO$_3$-pyridine (16). It has also been made by treating dimethyl sulfate with tetramethylsulfamide (73) or by simply heating methyl dimethylsulfamate (117), as discussed in Section VII. This complex has been (5) and is (2) available on a semi-commercial scale.

Sulfur trioxide-trimethylamine is a stable solid melting with decomposition at 239°C (36). It has low solubility in organic solvents with which it does not react; 3 g. dissolve in 100 ml. acetone at 56°C (5). However, it is soluble in dimethylformamide (4), and liquid SO$_2$ gives an 18. 5 wt. -% solution at 0°C (36). At 25°C, 1. 5 g. dissolves in 100 ml. water; at 50°C, 10. 8 g. dissolves (5). It dissolves in per-chloric acid (18).

This complex is the most stable of those studied to date, consider-ably more so than that derived from pyridine, as a result of the greater basic strength of trimethylamine compared with that of pyridine, as shown in Table 1-4. This high degree of stability permits its use in aqueous systems. At 50°C in the presence of 25 wt. -% water, it is 6. 4% hydrolyzed in 24 hr. (5). A kinetic study of the hydrolysis by water has shown it to be independent of pH and to be first order (97). The rate of hydrolysis in aqueous sodium hydroxide is given in Table 1-5 (5). Usually, loss of this reagent by hydrolysis is minor, since the compound being sulfated in aqueous medium reacts more easily.

The trimethylamine complex has been used in the laboratory for sul-fating alcohols, starch, leuco vat dyestuffs, and phenols (Chapter 6), and for sulfamating aromatic amines and proteins (Chapter 7). Many of these reactions can be conducted in aqueous medium, which is com-mercially advantageous. A potential disadvantage in some cases is the persistent and unpleasant odor of small residual quantities of the free amine.

TABLE 1-5

Hydrolysis of SO_3-Trimethylamine in Aqueous Sodium Hydroxide

(0. 18 g. per g. water for 24 hr. at room temperature)

% NaOH	% Hydrolyzed
0. 93	10. 3
4. 5	46. 4
8. 6	88. 4

E. Sulfur Trioxide-Triethylamine

This complex has been prepared by the interaction of SO_3 vapor with that of the amine (25), by adding liquid SO_3 to the amine dissolved in carbon tetrachloride (83, 85), or by adding $ClSO_3H$ to the amine in chlorobenzene at 10°C (64).

The behavior of this complex is similar to that of the trimethylamine analogue (5). Although the two bases have nearly the same strength, as shown in Table 1-3, the adduct from triethylamine is less stable and more reactive, as might be expected from the greater steric require-ment and the lower degree of chemical stability of the ethyl group, as compared with methyl. The triethylamine complex melts at 93°C, but it has been recommended that it be stored under refrigeration (5). It is fairly soluble in acetone and in 1, 2-dichloroethane, therein differing from the trimethylamine complex. At 25°C, 2.7 g. dissolves in 100 ml. water, which is double the solubility of the other adduct. Both complexes are sufficiently stable to be used in aqueous medium. The adduct sulfates polysaccharides in dimethylformamide solution even at 0°C, an interesting technique which should find wider application where extremely mild conditions are required (124). The triethylamine adduct has a high oral toxicity (5). It has been (5) and is (2, 69) available in research quantities. The use of this adduct presents less of an odor problem than those of pyridine or trimethylamine.

F.   Sulfur Trioxide-Dimethylaniline

Direct reaction of the base with SO_3 yields this complex (125), which is also formed by adding the SO_3 to the base dissolved in liquid SO_2 (52). However, two investigators report difficulty in preparing the adduct using SO_3, even when employing a solvent (35, 93). The base also reacts with a half-molar proportion of $ClSO_3H$ using as reaction solvents carbon disulfide (35), or chloroform at 0°C (102, 125); this procedure gives a 62% yield. Ethyl chlorosulfonate (125) and potassium pyrosulfate (35) likewise give this complex.

This complex melts at 85 - 90°C (83). Upon heating at 60°C, however, it rearranges to the para sulfonic acid (125). It has been used to a limited extent for sulfating alcohols, phenols and leuco dyes, and for sulfamating alkylaryl amines. It resembles SO_3-pyridine in general reactivity, since - as indicated in Table 1-3 - the two bases have about the same strength. However, the dimethylaniline complex decomposes above 60°C, while SO_3-pyridine has been used even at 170°C.

G.   Sulfur Trioxide-Thioxane

This complex is formed by reacting either SO_3 or $ClSO_3H$ with thioxane in carbon tetrachloride or 1,2-dichloroethane (86, 87). The 1:1 adduct is a solid melting with decomposition at 124°C. It is slightly soluble in carbon tetrachloride, chloroform, 1,2-dichloroethane, and ethers, but is easily soluble in thioxane itself, from which it may be recrystallized. Like dioxane, thioxane also forms a 1:2 adduct which melts at 99°C with evolution of SO_3; its solubility behavior resembles that of the 1:1 complex, to which it is converted by content with thioxane, since the oxygen atom is more basic than sulfur. Limited study of the 1:1 complex (86, 87) has shown that, like the dioxane analogue, it sulfonates alkenes and sulfates alcohols. It may, therefore, have no advantages over the dioxane complex, except that - with a melting point about 50°C higher - it may be more chemically stable.

H.   Sulfur Trioxide-Bis(2-Chloroethyl) Ether

This complex, made by adding SO_3 to the ether (8, 108), has been used for sulfating higher secondary alcohols (72) at -10°C, and for sulfonating polystyrene at -2°C using 1, 2-dichloroethane as solvent (8).   In the latter case, the reaction is too violent if less than 1. 5 moles ether is used per mole SO_3, and too slow and incomplete with more than three.

I.   Sulfur Trioxide-2-Methylpyridine

Chloroform was used as solvent for preparing this complex, made by adding liquid SO_3 at 10 - 20°C (111).   It has also been prepared from $ClSO_3H$ and excess base (106) below 30°C, the by-product pyridinium chloride not being removed in this case.   The adduct, and the 2, 6-dimethyl analogue, are stated to give considerably higher yields than SO_3-pyridine in sulfamating certain aromatic amines (cf. , Chapter 7) (106).

Mixed methylpyridines react with SO_3 without a solvent in a heavy-duty mixer at 0 - 40°C (112).

J.   Sulfur Trioxide-Quinoline

This complex has been prepared by the addition of liquid SO_3 to quinoline dissolved in 1, 2-dichloromethane (93), or by heating the base with an alkali metal pyrosulfate (13).   The former procedure gave a product of 84 -88% purity, which was found (93) to be insoluble in hot or cold o-dichlorobenzene, n-butyl benzene-sulfonate, n-hexane, methylcyclohexane, ethyl ether, dioxane, tetrachloroethylene, acetone, or amyl acetate.   In dimethylformamide it is slightly soluble cold, but very soluble hot.   It does not sulfonate benzene or xylene, but dissolves readily in 2-aminoethanol, probably with reaction.

K.   Sulfur Trioxide-Dimethylformamide

Addition of liquid (43, 93, 126), or vaporized (71) SO_3 to excess liquid amide, with stirring and cooling, is the usual procedure for preparing this complex.   In one case (51), 2 lb. of SO_3 was added dropwise to 11 liters of amide in 4 - 5 hr. at 0 - 5°C.   The adduct can also be made from the amide and methyl chlorosulfonate (44).   The excess amide functions as an excellent solvent, not only for the adduct itself, but for an exceptionally wide variety of organic compounds.   A 2. 5N solution is completely stable for 2 months at -40°C; at -5°C, 3% decomposes in 1 month (42).   Another report (51) states that its efficiency is unimpaired after 4 months at $0°C$, even though it turns yellow and finally orange. The stability of this complex, and the fact that its solution in excess amide is a liquid which can be pipetted conveniently (71,126) are unusual advantages, since the common amine complexes are only slightly soluble in their parent amines, and the dioxane adduct has poor stability. Since dimethylformamide is a very weak base, this adduct is highly reactive, even below room temperature. It has not been isolated and characterized, although it does separate as a white solid from concentrated solutions. Comparatively little work has as yet been done with this unusual complex. It has been shown to sulfamate amino groups and to sulfate hydroxyl groups in chitosan (126), to sulfate leuco dyes (95), and to form acyl sulfates from peptides (42, 70, 71) and from lysergic acid (51). Other SO_3 complexes (with trimethyl- or triethylamines, or dioxane) are unsuitable for this acylation of peptides (1a). This complex is an efficient and rapid cyclodehydrating reagent for making azlactones (11) and butenolides (12), without attack of other sensitive groups in the molecule.

The SO_3-formamide complex is cited in Section M.

L. Sulfur Trioxide-Triethyl Phosphate

This new complex (118 - 121) is best prepared by adding freshly distilled SO_3 at $15°C$ to the phosphate, either pure or mixed with 1, 2-dichloroethane or carbon tetrachloride. The 1:1 complex is a stable solid melting at $18°C$; it dissolves readily in dimethylformamide, triethyl phosphate, aromatic hydrocarbons and chlorinated aliphated hydrocarbons. It liberates heat on mixing with water or with pyridine presumably from the formation of H_2SO_4 and SO_3-pyridine, respectively.

The phosphoryl oxygen, being electron-rich, is the one which reacts, strongly exothermically, with SO_3 to form the 1:1 adduct. The three ester oxygens can also complex, with less evolution of heat in each case, forming the 2:1, 3:1, and 4:1 SO_3-to-phosphate adducts. Similar complexes have also been made from trimethyl-, tributyl-, and triphenyl phosphates; in the last case ring sulfonation occurs when using more than one mole of SO_3.

As with the dioxane and bis(2-chloroethyl)ether adducts, the reactivity of the phosphate complexes depends upon the ratio of SO_3 to phosphate. Alcohols are sulfated by the 1:1 adduct without color formation at $45°C$; as expected, the higher complexes effect sulfation with some color formation. The tributyl phosphate complex has been used to sulfonate alkenes with total formation of alkenesulfonate using the 1:1 compound at a 2:1 molar ratio of complex to alkene; other SO_3 adducts form mixtures of alkenesulfonates and hydroxyalkanesulfonates.

The behavior of the trialkyl phosphate complexes with aromatic hydrocarbons is of special interest. The 1:1 compound dissolves in, but does not react with, aromatic hydrocarbons even at $75°$ C (119), but the higher adducts sulfonate them at $25°$ C, and the 1:1 complex reacts above $80°$ C. In all cases tried, from 20 - 40% of the product was the ethylsulfonate ester when using the triethyl phosphate complex. It seems probable that reactions of the following type are involved:

$$(RO)_3 PO + SO_3 \longrightarrow (RO)_2 (ROSO_2 O) PO \qquad (1-8)$$

(R = alkyl)

$$R'H + (RO)_2 (ROSO_2 O) PO \longrightarrow R'SO_2 OR +$$

$$(RO)_2 POOH \qquad (1-9)$$

(R' = aryl)

Polystyrene, even of high molecular weight, is sulfonated without crosslinking to water-soluble products, a result found difficult to achieve with other reagents in the past. This is explained, at least in part, by the fact that sulfonation of the polymer also occurs by introduction of the ester sulfonate group, which is probably less susceptible to crosslinking by sulfone formation than the corresponding sulfonic acid. Acyl sulfates of other types are known to depress undesired sulfone formation, as discussed in Chapter 2.

These interesting new adducts will no doubt find extensive future application. Complexes derived from phosphines and phosphine oxides are mentioned in the following section.

M.   Miscellaneous Complexes

Reaction of SO_3 with the base has been employed to prepare adducts from tri-n-propylamine (79), tri-n-butylamine (83), and from N-alkylated morpholines (methyl, ethyl, and n-butyl) (62, 75, 112). The complex of pentamethylguanidine, a strong base, is preferably prepared using SO_3-triethylamine rather than free SO_3 (65); this complex dissolves in water forming a stable, neutral solution. The N, N-dimethylbenzylamine adduct is made from $ClSO_3H$ with chloroform as solvent at $0°$ C (58).

Sulfur trioxide-poly (2-vinylpyridine) is the first complex derived from a polymeric base (103a). Since the use of complexes made from insoluble polymers could have advantages in the recovery and recycle of the complexing agent, this concept may see considerable future development.

Amide-SO_3 adducts include those made from N-methylacetanilide, N, N-dimethyl-4-toluenesulfonamide, tetramethylurea, N, N-dimethylurethane, formylmorpholide, tetramethyladipamide, N, N-dimethylbenzamide (43), N-alkyl ethylene carbamates (104, 105), and dimethylcyanamide (63). These adducts have not been compared with that of dimethylformamide, respecting utility and properties. Sulfur trioxide-formamide, a solid melting at 50 °C, is formed from $ClSO_3H$ and the amide at 20 °C (91a). It is soluble in excess liquid formamide (m. p. 3 °C), and decomposes upon warming with the formation of HCN. Some degradation was noted when this complex was used to sulfate amylose.

N-Propyl-, N-isopropyl-, and N-benzylpiperidine oxides are stated to form the SO_3-amine complexes by reaction with SO_2 (7). However, another report (74) states that the amine oxide-SO_2 complexes are different from the amine-SO_3 adducts. Triethylamine oxide was converted to a SO_3 adduct (74) by reaction with SO_3-triethylamine. The pyridine oxide adduct was made by treating the oxide-hydrochloride with SO_3 (21).

The SO_3-trimethylphosphine oxide complex has been known for some time (37), but systematic study of the SO_3 adducts of the triphenyl and tricyclohexyl derivatives of N, P, As, SB, and Bi, as well as their oxides and sulfides, is more recent (22). The triphenylphosphine adduct is a stable solid, m. p. 191 °C, resonance-stabilized by double bond delocalization. The Bi compounds form stable complexes, but those from As are unstable, and triphenylamine preferably undergoes sulfonation, as expected. Triphenylantimony is converted to the oxide, which forms a complex.

Diethyl ether forms adducts with SO_3 at 2:1, 1:1, and 1:2 molar ratios (88), as shown by breaks in the specific conductivity-composition curve; high conductivity was attributed to ion-pair formation. As indicated in Chapter 6, these adducts easily rearrange to diethyl sulfate and its sulfonated derivatives. Diethyl sulfide forms a complex (48), which has been studied only briefly. Tetrahydrofuran yields an adduct by direct reaction with SO_3 (93), but no further work was done with it. The unusually high basicity and solvent power of tetrahydrofuran, compared to other ethers, should make this system (complex dissolved in excess ether) of exceptional future interest.

Carbonyl oxygen, like that in the above-mentioned oxides of organic phosphines, amines, and stibines, and in the phosphate esters, is capable of coordinating with SO_3. Acetone is thus stated to form a complex at -20 °C in the presence of an inert solvent (31); low temperature is essential, since acetone sulfonates easily. Anthraquinone forms 1:1 and 1:2 complexes (45). Similarly, polycyclic mono- and diketones (benzanthrone, benzonaphthone and similar compounds) give adducts (77) with one mole of SO_3 complexing with each carbonyl group.

A second mole of SO_3 will add, but it is much more loosely bound. 2, 6-Dimethyl-γ-pyrone forms an SO_3 complex (84), but its properties have not been reported.

Complex formation with nitro compounds would be expected as consistent with their character as weak Lewis bases. Nitromethane, used occasionally as a solvent for SO_3 as mentioned in Section II-A, probably forms an adduct, but this has not been proved. Two molar proportions of SO_3 complex with 2-nitropropane, forming a hygroscopic, crystalline adduct slowly decomposing at room temperature (4); it sulfonates benzene in poor yield.

Dimethyl sulfone and sulfolane form complexes (4). The latter, a 1:1 adduct, is a hydroscopic solid insoluble in sulfolane and in nonpolar solvents. The methyl groups of dimethyl sulfone do not react with SO_3 even above 200°C. Dimethyl sulfoxide forms an unstable complex (4). This adduct, dissolved in excess sulfoxide, may find uses where the extraordinary solvent power of the latter is an asset.

IV. HALOSULFONIC ACIDS

Chlorosulfonic acid, $ClSO_3H$, is a liquid boiling at 152°, and freezing at -80°C (100). It dissolves readily in halogenated organic solvents which also contain hydrogen, e. g., chloroform, methylene chloride, and 1, 2-dichloroethane, and in nitrobenzene and liquid SO_2. These solvents are sometimes used with this reagent both industrially and in the laboratory, but in many of its reactions no solvent is needed. It is only slightly soluble in carbon disulfide, carbon tetrachloride, tetrachloroethylene, or 1, 1, 2-trifluorotrichloroethane, i. e., halogenated solvents which do not contain hydrogen.

This compound, being a strong acid, is usually written $ClSO_3H$, i. e., the half acid chloride of sulfuric acid. However, the formula $SO_3 \cdot HCl$, indicating it to be the HCl complex of SO_3, would be more accurately descriptive of its method of preparation (direct reaction of the two compounds), its behavior at the boiling point (dissociation into the two compounds), and its reaction with many organic compounds (introduction of SO_3 with liberation of HCl). The formula $ClSO_3H$ is, however, consistent with its behavior with alkenes using a nonpolar solvent (Eq. 1-10), and with the conversion of sulfonic acids to sulfonyl chlorides (Eq. 1-12):

$$RCH = CHR' + ClSO_3H \longrightarrow RCH_2CH(OSO_2Cl)R' \qquad (1\text{-}10)$$

Chlorosulfonic acid, as mentioned in Chapter 6, is a favored laboratory and industrial reagent for sulfating alcohols. The HCl formed is evolved as a gas. It is also employed for preparing aromatic sulfonyl chlorides, as indicated in Chapter 2. Two steps are involved:

$$RH + ClSO_3H \longrightarrow RSO_2OH + HCl \qquad (1\text{-}11)$$

$$RSO_2OH + ClSO_3H \rightleftharpoons RSO_2Cl + HOSO_2OH \qquad (1\text{-}12)$$

As noted in Chapter 7, $ClSO_3H$ has been used for sulfamating amines, and, as indicated in Section III of this chapter, it has often been employed in the laboratory for making SO_3-amine complexes, with or without subsequent separation of the mole of amine hydrochloride formed per mole of SO_3 complex obtained. For all of these purposes, except reaction 1-12, there has been a trend toward the substitution of SO_3 for $ClSO_3H$ in industrial operation.

The complexes of $ClSO_3H$ with weak bases, namely ethers and amides, merit special mention. The system $ClSO_3H$-diethyl ether has been employed for sulfating alcohols, as noted in Chapter 6. Product color and yield are considerably better than those obtained using the acid alone in the case of lauryl alcohol, and, in fact, are superior to those made with any other reagent. These results indicate that the mixture is a much milder reagent than the acid alone, as a result of complex - or oxonium salt - formation. Chlorosulfonic acid-ethylene glycol diethyl ether was similarly employed for the sulfation of a nitrogenous polysaccharide.

Chlorosulfonic acid-diethyl ether is made by adding the acid dropwise to excess ether at $0\,^{\circ}C$ with stirring and cooling (29). Heat is evolved as the oxonium compound is formed. If the mixture is allowed to warm, a complex series of reactions occur, with the formation of ethyl chloride and diethyl sulfate as the main products. This reagent, as shown in Chapter 2, converts alkenes to chlorinated sulfonic acids or to alkenesulfonic acids (Eq. 1-13), an entirely different result from that noted when using a nonpolar solvent, such as chloroform, or no solvent at all, as indicated in Equation 1-10:

$$
RCH{=}CHR' \xrightarrow{\text{ClSO}_3\text{H} \cdot \text{Et}_2\text{O}}
\begin{cases}
\underset{\underset{\text{Cl}}{|}}{RCH}-\underset{\underset{SO_2OH}{|}}{CHR'} \\[2ex]
\quad\quad \Big\downarrow -HCl \\[1ex]
RCH{=}\underset{\underset{SO_2OH}{|}}{CR'}
\end{cases}
\qquad (1\text{-}13)
$$

A difference in the two reagent systems is also noted with 2-phenyl-1, 3-indandione (105a), since $ClSO_3H$ in a nonpolar solvent sulfonates only the phenyl group, whereas $ClSO_3H$-diethyl ether or $ClSO_3H$-dioxane reacts with the hydrogen atom on the carbon between the two carbonyl groups. Styrene, indene and coumarin form the chlorinated sulfonic acids by Equation 1-13 with $ClSO_3H$-diethyl ether, but only ring sulfonation occurs in a nonpolar solvent (58a). Chlorosulfonic acid-dioxane converts isobutylene to the unsaturated disulfonic acid (110) only at about 20°C, in contrast to the pure acid, which reacts at -80°C. This difference is interpreted as evidence of complex formation. On the other hand, the ethers - unlike the amines - apparently do not convert $ClSO_3H$ into a mixture of base hydrochloride and SO_3-base complex, since SO_3-dioxane reacts with isobutylene at 0°C, while $ClSO_3H$-dioxane is active only at 20°C. The system tetrahydrofuran-$ClSO_3H$, which would be even milder than those cited above, has not been studied.

Urea reacts with $ClSO_3H$ in liquid SO_2 forming a complex (67) which has been employed to a limited extent for sulfating oleyl alcohol industrially, as indicated in Chapter 6. Minimal attack of the double bond occurs. Dimethylformamide-$ClSO_3H$ has recently found favor as a mild reagent for the sulfation of complex phenolic compounds (38). This system should prove of considerable future utility, assuming that it is intermediate in reactivity between the SO_3-amide adduct and the amide solution of SO_3-triethylamine. Both of these combinations, as indicated earlier in this chapter, are already finding uses. With formamide at 20°C, $ClSO_3H$ forms the SO_3 complex (91a), a solid melting at 50°C discussed in Section III-M.

Physicochemical and other studies of these weak base-$ClSO_3H$ systems would be of interest to elucidate their compositions and to determine under what conditions they revert to mixtures of the base hydrochlorides and the SO_3 adducts.

Fluorosulfonic acid, b.p. 162°C, resembles $ClSO_3H$ in its method of preparation and general reactivity (79a). It is stated to be the strongest pure acid yet studied (54a), and - in contrast to $ClSO_3H$ - is extremely stable thermally. However, FSO_3H has shown no special advantages over $ClSO_3H$ as an SO_3 donor for sulfonation, and it has the objections of being somewhat less reactive and more expensive, and of liberating HF during reaction. As indicated in Chapter 6, it reacts easily with alkenes forming fluorosulfonates. It forms sulfonyl fluorides with aromatic compounds or their sulfonic acids (cf. Chapter 2). Certain of these have proved interesting as sulfoarylating agents, as pointed out in Chapter 5.

Bromosulfonic acid is known, but it is too unstable to be of practical interest, since it decomposes below room temperature (44a).

V. SULFAMIC ACID

Sulfamic acid, NH_2SO_3H, is a stable, nonhygroscopic, high-melting (205°C) crystalline solid with an acid strength comparable to that of nitric or sulfuric acids (57, 116). It is moderately soluble in water, and easily so in dimethylformamide, but insoluble in concentrated H_2SO_4 and in various organic liquids. It is available commercially (57, 116), being prepared as follows:

$$NH_2CONH_2 + H_2SO_4 + SO_3 \longrightarrow 2\ NH_2SO_3H + CO_2 \uparrow \quad (1\text{-}14)$$

Sulfamic acid is also made by hydrolysis, with sulfuric acid, of the NH_3-SO_3 reaction mixture (116).

In its reactions involving sulfation and sulfonation, sulfamic acid generally resembles the SO_3-tertiary amine complexes. It may, in fact, be conveniently be regarded as an ammonia-SO_3 complex, $NH_3 \cdot SO_3$ (18), even though it is not so prepared, and even though the formula NH_2SO_3H more correctly denotes its role as a strongly acid analogue of sulfuric acid. In one important way it differs from the SO_3-tertiary amine complexes, however. They can be employed for sulfamation or sulfation at low temperature in aqueous alkaline medium, while sulfamic acid and its salts have, in all applications to date, been employed only at elevated temperatures in anhydrous medium. It has been used primarily for sulfation (Chapter 6), and sulfamation (Chapter 7), and to a quite minor extent for sulfonating alkenes, aliphatic ketones and phenolic ethers (Chapter 2). The ammonium salts are formed during sulfation or sulfonation:

$$ROH + NH_3 \cdot SO_3 \longrightarrow ROSO_3H \cdot NH_3 \quad (1\text{-}15)$$

Three factors have tended to limit interest in the use of sulfamic acid, both for laboratory and for industrial purposes. An important consideration has been its considerably higher cost compared to the other reagents. Its chemical inertness, taken with its strongly acid character, has meant that objectionable decomposition of the organic compound can occur at temperatures necessary to effect reaction which are often in the range 150-200°C. As shown in Chapter 6, sulfamic acid gives notably unsatisfactory results in the sulfation of lauryl alcohol. On the other hand, its inertness is an advantage in sulfating alkylphenol-ethylene oxide condensates, since other reagents give objectionable ring sulfonation. In this case, the mildly basic ether groups appear to buffer the system against acid attack, and to permit lowering the reaction temperature to 125°C, but color formation is a problem even under these less drastic conditions. Sulfamic acid and its salts have been used commercially for sulfamating cyclohexylamine, but these reagents are being supplanted by the cheaper SO_3-pyridine, the use of which necessarily entails efficient recovery and recycle of the organic base.

The observation that sulfation and sulfamation reactions with sulfamic acid could be substantially accelerated, and the reaction temperature considerably reduced, by adding pyridine, other tertiary amines, or even weak bases such as urea or acetamide, has extended its range of usefulness considerably. Cellulose cannot be sulfated with sulfamic acid in the absence of urea, and secondary alcohols likewise give poor results in the absence of pyridine. Sterols have also been sulfated by this procedure.

VI. ACYL SULFATES

Sulfur trioxide reacts with acetic acid below 0 °C to form "acetyl sulfate" (90), which may comprise a mixture of several species resulting from the equilibria:

$$2 CH_3COOH + SO_3 \rightleftharpoons CH_3COOSO_3H + CH_3COOH \rightleftharpoons$$

$$(CH_3CO)_2O + H_2SO_4 \qquad\qquad (1\text{-}16)$$

A similar mixture results from acetic anhydride and sulfuric acid (68, 78, 90, 96). Recent opinions differ regarding the actual existence of mono- and diacetyl sulfates. A kinetic investigation has suggested that both species exist (68), while a cryoscopic study of mixtures of acetic or benzoic anhydrides with sulfuric acid (76) led to the conclusion that the existence of acyl sulfates seems improbable and that the anhydrides function by simply abstracting water from sulfuric acid or oleum by the following overall reaction:

$$(RCO)_2O + 3 H_2SO_4 \rightleftharpoons 2 RCOOH_2^+ + HS_2O_7^- + HSO_4^- \qquad (1\text{-}17)$$

The fact that perfluorinated acids, as stated below, form acyl sulfates which can be distilled as stable entities indicates that this species can exist, at least in certain cases. The term "acyl sulfate" will accordingly be used herein.

Acetyl sulfate readily sulfonates aromatic hydrocarbons with a minimum of sulfone formation, as mentioned in Chapter 2. It has also been used to sulfonate heterocyclic compounds. Alicyclic ketones and alkenes are sulfonated by this reagent, the latter forming acetoxysulfonates:

$$RCH{=}CHR' + CH_3COOSO_3H \longrightarrow CH_3COOCHRCHR'SO_3H \qquad (1\text{-}18)$$

Phenolic ethers also containing an olefinic moiety can be preferentially ring-sulfonated without attack of the double bond (121a). As shown in Chapter 6, alcohols are sulfated by acetyl sulfate, and cellulose can be simultaneously acetylated and sulfated. Urea can be sulfamated with this reagent. Amines and phenols, on the other hand, are acetylated (90).

Propionic, butyric and 3-methylbutyric acids react similarly with SO$_3$ (89). The butyric compound sulfonates benzene and sulfates alcohols, but in the latter case differs from acetyl sulfate in also forming some butyrate (91). Perfluorinated acids form stable, distillable acyl sulfates (47).

Benzoic acid is similarly converted to benzoyl sulfate in 1, 2-dichloroethane solvent at room temperature (80). This sulfate is used to sulfonate polystyrene, with subsequent recovery and reuse of the benzoic acid. It has also been made from benzoyl chloride and H$_2$SO$_4$ in carbon tetrachloride (112a). It forms 3-sulfobenzoic acid upon heating.

VII. ALKYL SULFATES

Alkyl sulfates are of theoretical, and even of some practical, interest as sulfating and sulfonating reagents. Salicyclic acid, upon heating with dimethyl sulfate, rapidly undergoes ring sulfonation to form the sulfonic acid and the methyl sulfonate; the hydroxyl and carboxyl groups also undergo methylation (101). Anisole, diphenyl ether, triphenylamine and N-methyldiphenylamine similarly form mixtures of the sulfonic acid and the methyl sulfonate (26-28). Anthraquinone gave the sulfonic acid at 170°C (45b). 2-Thionaphthol underwent alkylation, but did not sulfonate (27), and benzyl methyl ether did not react at all. N-Methyl-2-pyridone and related compounds sulfonate in the 5-position with dimethyl sulfate at 200°C (60). Two types of reactions appear to be occurring (27):

$$(CH_3O)_2SO_2 \rightleftharpoons (CH_3)_2O + SO_3 \qquad (1-19)$$

$$RH + (CH_3O)_2SO_2 \longrightarrow RSO_2OCH_3 + CH_3OH \qquad (1-20)$$

Both dimethyl ether and methanol were actually isolated as products. Reaction 1-19, to the right, is simply the reverse of the method used to prepare the sulfate (cf., Chapter 6). Diethyl sulfate behaves similarly, but the sulfonic acid expectedly predominates since the ethyl group is more labile than methyl. Dimethyl sulfate also functions as an SO$_3$ donor and methylating agent in the following case (73):

$$(CH_3O)_2SO_2 + (CH_3)_2NSO_2N(CH_3)_2 \longrightarrow 2 (CH_3)_3N \cdot SO_3 \qquad (1-21)$$

This overall reaction may proceed in two steps:

$$(CH_3O)_2SO_2 + (CH_3)_2NSO_2N(CH_3)_2 \longrightarrow 2\ (CH_3)_2NSO_2OCH_3 \quad (1\text{-}22)$$

$$(CH_3)_2NSO_2OCH_3 \longrightarrow (CH_3)_3N \cdot SO_3 \quad (1\text{-}23)$$

Reaction 1-23 is known (117).

The alkyl sulfates can also function as sulfating agents by alkyl interchange. One such case, run at 130°C, readily proceeds to completion by distillation of a volatile reaction product (34):

$$CH_3COOCH_2CH_2OCOCH_3 + (CH_3O)_2SO_2 \longrightarrow \begin{matrix} CH_2-O \\ | \qquad \quad \diagdown \\ \qquad \qquad SO_2 + \\ | \qquad \quad \diagup \\ CH_2-O \end{matrix}$$

$$\qquad \qquad \qquad \qquad \qquad \qquad \qquad (1\text{-}24)$$

$$2\ CH_3COOCH_3$$

It seems probable that the sulfation of cellulose with a mixture of isopropanol, or other alcohols as mentioned in Chapter 6, with sulfuric acid, also occurs by alkyl interchange:

$$Cell\text{-}CH_2OH + ROSO_3H \rightleftharpoons Cell\text{-}CH_2OSO_3H + ROH \quad (1\text{-}25)$$

VIII. SULFONIC ACIDS (TRANS-SULFONATION)

Sulfonic acids, like organic sulfates as indicated in the preceding section, are capable of functioning as sulfating and sulfonating reagents. Reference is made in Chapter 6 to the use of naphthalenesulfonic acids for sulfating certain alcohols. The use of one aromatic sulfonic acid to sulfonate another, known as "transsulfonation," apparently involves desulfonation-resulfonation (47a), as discussed in Chapter 8. The well-known conversion of α-naphthalenesulfonic acid to the β-isomer apparently occurs by a mechanism of this type. Trans-sulfonation is also apparently involved in the quantitative conversion of α-sulfostearic acid to stearic acid by refluxing in ortho-dichlorobenzene (cf., Chapter 8).

REFERENCES

1.   Abercromby, D. C., R. A. Hyne, and P. F. Tiley, J. Chem. Soc.,
     1963, 5832.
1a. Albertson, N. F., Organic Reactions, 12, Wiley, New York,
     1962, p. 255.
1b. Aldrich Chemical Co., Milwaukee, Wis.
2.   Allied Chemical Corporation, Baker & Adamson Dept.,
     Morristown, N. J.
3.   Allied Chemical Corporation, General Chemical Division,
     Technical Service Bulletin SO_3-B, 1959.
4.   Allied Chemical Corporation, General Chemical Division, Un-
     published research data.
5.   American Cyanamid Co., "Trialkylamine-Sulfur Trioxide
     Compounds," New York, 1955.
6.   Appel, R., and W. Huber, Chem. Ber., 89, 386 (1956).
7.   Auerbach, M., and R. Wolffenstein, Ber., 32, 2507 (1899).
8.   Baer, M., U. S. Patent 2,533,210; Chem. Abstr., 45, 3651
     (1951).
9.   Baer, M., U. S. Patent 2,533,211; Chem. Abstr., 45, 3651
     (1951).
10. Baldwin, A. W., and E. E. Walker, U. S. Patent 2,146,392;
     Chem. Abstr., 33, 3495 (1939).
11. Baltazzi, E., and E. A. Davis, Chem. Ind. (London), 1962, 929.
12. Baltazzi, E., and E. A. Davis, Chem. Ind. (London), 1962,
     1653.
13. Barnes, R. S., J. E. G. Harris, and J. Thomas, British Patent
     317,736; Chem. Abstr., 24, 2308 (1930).
14. Barnes, R. S., J. E. G. Harris, and J. Thomas, U. S. Patent 1,921,
     497; Chem. Abstr., 27, 5158 (1933).
15. Baumgarten, P., Ber., 59B, 1166 (1926).
16. Baumgarten, P., Ber., 59B, 1976 (1926).
17. Baumgarten, P., Ber., 60, 1177 (1927).
18. Baumgarten, P., Ber., 62B, 820 (1929).
19. Baumgarten, P., Ber., 64B, 1502 (1931).
20. Baumgarten, P., German Patent 514,821; Chem. Abstr., 25,
     2156 (1931).
21. Baumgarten, P., and H. Erbe, Ber., 71, 2603 (1938).
22. Becke-Goehring, M., and H. Thielemann, Z. Anorg. Allgem.
     Chem., 308, 33 (1961).
23. Beckett, E. G., J. E. G. Harris, B. Wylam, and J. Thomas, British
     Patent 294,507; Chem. Abstr., 23, 1909 (1929).
24. Beckett, E. G., J. E. G. Harris, B. Wylam, and J. Thomas, U. S.
     Patent 1,835,841; Chem. Abstr., 26, 999 (1932).
25. Beilstein, F., and E. Wiegand, Ber. 16, 1264 (1883).
26. Belov, V. N., J. Gen. Chem. USSR (English Transl.), 11, 750
     (1941); Chem. Abstr., 36, 418 (1942).

27.   Belov, V. N. , and M. Z. Finkel'shtein, J. Gen. Chem. USSR (English Transl.), 16, 1248 (1946); Chem. Abstr. , 41, 3065 (1947).

28.   Belov, V. N. , and E. I. Shepelenkova, J. Gen. Chem. USSR (English Transl.), 11, 757 (1941); Chem. Abstr. , 36, 419 (1942).

29.   Bert, L. , Compt. Rend. , 222, 898 (1946).

30.   Bevington, C. F. P. , and J. L. Pegler, Chem. Soc. Spec. Publ. No. 12, 283 (1958).

31.   Blaser, B. , M. Rugenstein, and G. Tischbirek, U. S. Patent 2, 764, 576; Chem. Abstr. , 51, 6218 (1957).

32.   Bordwell, F. G. , and G. W. Crosby, J. Am. Chem. Soc. , 78, 5367 (1956).

33.   Boyland, E. , J. Chem. Soc. , 1962, 5217.

34.   Brunken, J. , G. Glockner, and E. J. Poppe, Veroeffentl. Wiss. Photolab. AGFA (Wolfen), 9, 61 (1961); Chem. Abstr. , 57, 16027 (1962).

35.   Burckhardt, G. N. , and A. Lapworth, J. Chem. Soc. , 1926, 684.

36.   Burg, A. B. , J. Am. Chem. Soc. , 65, 1629 (1943).

37.   Burg, A. B. , and W. E. McKee, J. Am. Chem. Soc. , 73, 4590 (1951).

38.   Butenandt, A. , E. Biekert, N. Koga, and P. Traub, Z. Physiol. Chem. , 321, 258 (1960); Chem. Abstr. , 55, 16553 (1961).

39.   Carter, B. A. , in Kirk-Othmer, Encyclopedia of Chemical Technology, 13, 1st ed., Interscience, New York, 1954, p. 458.

40.   Cerfontain, H. , Rec. Trav. Chim. , 80, No. 3, 257 (1961).

41.   Christensen, N. H. , Acta Chim. Scand. , 15, 1507 (1961).

42.   Clayton, D. W. , J. A. Farrington, G. W. Kenner, and J. M. Turner, J. Chem. Soc. , 1957, 1398.

43.   Coffey, S. , G. W. Driver, D. A. W. Fairweather, and F. Irving, British Patent 642, 206; Chem. Abstr. , 45, 3412 (1951).

44.   Coffey, S. , D. A. W. Fairweather, D. E. Hathaway, and F. H. Slinger, U. S. Patent 2, 563, 819; Chem. Abstr. , 45, 9881 (1951).

44a.   Cotton, F. A. , and G. Wilkinson, Advanced Inorganic Chemistry, Interscience, New York, 1962.

45.   Courtot, C. , and J. Bonnet, Compt. Rend. , 182, 855 (1926).

45a.   Distillation Products Industries, Eastman Organic Chemicals Dept. , Rochester, New York.

45b.   Dokunikhin, N. S. , and L. A. Gaeva, Zh. Vses. Khim. Obshchestva im. D. I. Mendeleeva, 6, 234 (1961); Chem. Abstr. , 55, 19877 (1961).

46.   Dombrovskii, A. V. , Usp. Khim. , 30, 1453 (1961); Chem. Abstr. , 56, 9678 (1962).

47.   Dowdall, J. F. , U. S. Patent 2, 628, 253; Chem. Abstr. , 48, 1425 (1954).

47a.   Drews, H. , S. Meyerson, and E. K. Fields, J. Am. Chem. Soc. , 83, 3871 (1961).

48. Fairweather, D. A. W. , British Patent 630, 459; Chem. Abstr. , 44, 3276 (1950).
49. Fieser, L. F. , J. Am. Chem. Soc. , 70, 3232 (1948).
50. Flint, G. , in Kirk-Othmer, Encyclopedia of Chemical Technology, 13, 1st ed. , Interscience, New York, 1954, p. 501.
51. Garbrecht, W. L. , J. Org. Chem. , 24, 368 (1959).
52. Gilbert, E. E. , and H. R. Nychka, U. S. Patent 2, 928, 836; Chem. Abstr. , 54, 12165 (1960).
53. Gilbert, E. E. , and B. Veldhuis, U. S. Patent 2, 769, 836; Chem. Abstr. , 51, 9143 (1957).
54. Gilbert, E. E. , B. Veldhuis, E. J. Carlson, and S. L. Giolito, Ind. Eng. Chem. , 45, 2065 (1953).
54a. Gillespie, R. J. , in Friedel-Crafts and Related Reactions, G. A. Olah, ed. , Interscience, New York, 1963.
55. Gillespie, R. J. , and E. A. Robinson, Can. J. Chem. , 39, 2189 (1961).
56. Gillespie, R. J. , and E. A. Robinson, Can. J. Chem. , 40, 658 (1962).
56a. Gmelins Handbuch der anorganischen Chemie; VIII Ed. ; System No. 9, Teil B: Sulfur, Verlag Chemie, Weinheim, 1960.
57. Grasselli Chemicals Dept. , E. I. Du Pont de Nemours & Co. , Inc. , Wilmington, Del.
58. Grillot, G. P. , and R. N. Ciccarelli, J. Org. Chem. , 26, 1665 (1961).
58a. Grotowsky, P. H. , U. S. Dept. Commerce, OTS Rept. 75, 372, 1935.
59. Guisley, K. B. , and P. M. Ruoff, J. Org. Chem. , 26, 1248 (1961).
60. Haack, E. , German Patent 597, 452; Chem. Abstr. , 28, 5083 (1934).
61. Hall, H. K. , Jr. , J. Phys. Chem. , 60, 63 (1956).
62. Hardy, W. B. , U. S. Patent 2, 502, 839; Chem. Abstr. , 44, 5923 (1950).
63. Hardy, W. B. , U. S. Patent 2, 774, 761; Chem. Abstr. , 51, 4724 (1957).
64. Hardy, W. B. , and E. M. Hardy, U. S. Patent 2, 649, 452; Chem. Abstr. , 48, 1014 (1954).
65. Hardy, W. B. , and H. Z. Lecher, Canadian Patent 532, 618.
66. van der Heijde, H. B. , in Organic Sulfur Compounds, N. Kharasch, ed. , Pergamon Press, New York, 1961.
67. Henkel et Cie. GmbH, German Patent 918, 985; Chem. Zentr. , 126, 687 (1955).
68. Jeffery, E. A. , and D. P. N. Satchell, J. Chem. Soc. , 1962, 1913.
69. K and K Laboratories, Jamaica, New York.
70. Kenner, G. W. , U. S. Patent 2, 766, 225; Chem. Abstr. , 51, 2853 (1957).

71.   Kenner, G. W. , and R. J. Stedman, J. Chem. Soc. , 1952, 2069.
72.   Law, G. H. , and R. W. McNamee, U. S. Patent 2, 088, 027;
      Chem. Abstr. , 31, 6673 (1937).
73.   Lecher, H. Z. , and W. B. Hardy, U. S. Patent 2, 386, 693;
      Chem. Abstr. , 40, 591 (1946).
74.   Lecher, H. Z. , and W. B. Hardy, J. Am. Chem. Soc. , 70, 3789
      (1948).
75.   Lecher, H. Z. , M. Scalera, and E. M. Hardy, U. S. Patent 2, 402,
      647; Chem. Abstr. , 40, 5774 (1946).
76.   Leisten, J. A. , J. Chem. Soc. , 1955, 298.
77.   Lukin, A. M. , J. Soc. Dyers Colourists, 68, 468 (1952).
78.   Mal'kova, T. V. , Zh. Obshch. Khim. , 30, No. 7, 2113, 2120
      (1960); Chem. Abstr. , 55, 9016 (1961).
79.   Mamlock, L. , and R. Wolffenstein, Ber. 34, 2499 (1901).
79a. McCarter, W. S. W. , in Kirk-Othmer, Encyclopedia of Chem-
      ical Technology, 6, 1st. ed. , Interscience, New York 1951,
      p. 734.
80.   McRae, W. A. , and S. S. Alexander, U. S. Patent 2, 962, 454;
      Chem. Abstr. , 55, 8703 (1961).
81.   Meyer, K. H. , R. P. Piroue, and M. E. Odier, Helv. Chim.
      Acta, 35, 574 (1952).
82.   Mezhenni, Ya. F. , and N. Ya. Kovganich, Zh. Obshch. Khim. ,
      30, 1755 (1960); Chem. Abstr. , 55, 10172 (1961).
83.   Moede, J. A. , and C. Curran, J. Am. Chem. Soc. , 71, 852
      (1949).
84.   Muth, F. , in Houben-Weyl, Methoden der Organischen
      Chemie, Vol. 9, 4th ed. , Thieme Verlag, Stuttgart, 1955,
      p. 429.
85.   National Starch Products Inc. , British Patent 755, 461;
      Chem. Abstr. , 51, 8460 (1957).
86.   Nawiasky, P. , and G. E. Sprenger, U. S. Patent 2, 219, 748;
      Chem. Abstr. , 35, 1067 (1941).
87.   Nawiasky, P. , and G. E. Sprenger, U. S. Patent 2, 335, 193;
      Chem. Abstr. , 38, 2666 (1944).
88.   Paul, R. C. , and S. P. Narula, J. Sci. Ind. Res. (India), 20B,
      184 (1961); Chem. Abstr. , 55, 20912 (1961).
89.   Paul, R. C. , S. P. Narula, and P. Meyer, J. Indian Chem. Soc. ,
      39, No. 4, 297 (1962); Chem. Abstr. , 57, 5794 (1962).
90.   van Peski, A. J. , Rec. Trav. Chim. , 40, 103 (1921).
91.   van Peski, A. J. , Rec. Trav. Chim. , 40, 736 (1921).
91a. Pfannemueller, B. , in Houben-Weyl, Methoden der Organi-
      schen Chemie, Vol. 14/2, 4th ed. , Thieme Verlag, Stutt-
      gart, 1963.
92.   Quaedvlieg, M. , in Houben-Weyl, Methoden der Organischen
      Chemie, Vol. IX, 4th ed. , Thieme Verlag, Stuttgart, 1955,
      p. 343.

93.   Ratcliff, G. A. , Ph. D. Dissertation, Cornell University,
        Ithaca, New York, Dissertation Abstr. , 14, 2018 (1954).
94.   Reitz, H. C. , R. E. Ferrel, H. S. Olcott, and H. Fraenkel-Conrat,
        J. Am. Chem. Soc. , 68, 1031 (1946).
95.   Robson, A. C. , and F. H. Slinger, U. S. Patent 2, 553, 475;
        Chem. Abstr. , 45, 7357 (1951).
96.   Russell, J. , and A. E. Cameron, J. Am. Chem. Soc. , 60, 1345
        (1938).
97.   Ryss, I. G. , and L. P. Bogdanova, Zh. Neorgan. Khim. , 7, 1316
        (1962); Chem. Abstr. , 57, 6852 (1962).
98.   Schmerling, L. , U. S. Patent 2, 524, 086; Chem. Abstr. , 45,
        375 (1951).
99.   Scully, J. F. , and E. V. Brown, J. Org. Chem. , 19, 894 (1954).
100.   Shedd, D. P. , in Kirk-Othmer, Encyclopedia of Chemical
        Technology, 3, 1st ed. , Interscience, New York, 1949,
        p. 885.
101.   Simon, L. J. , and M. Frerejacque, Compt. Rend. , 177, 533
        (1923).
102.   Sisler, H. H. , and L. F. Audrieth, Inorg. Syn. , 2, 173 (1946).
103.   Smith, C. W. , U. S. Patent 2, 566, 810; Chem. Abstr. , 46,
        2576 (1952).
103a.   Smith, H. E. , and C. K. Russell, U. S. Patent 3, 057, 855:
        Chem. Abstr. , 58, 652 (1963).
104.   Smith, J. L. , and R. C. Harrington, Jr. , U. S. Patent 2, 891,
        962; Chem. Abstr. , 54, 1546 (1960).
105.   Smith, J. L. , and R. C. Harrington, Jr. , U. S. Patent 2, 957,
        014; Chem. Abstr. , 55, 19786 (1961).
105a.   Strakov, A. , E. Gudriniece, A. Ievins, and G. Vanags, Zh.
        Obshch. Khim. , 30, 3967 (1960); Chem. Abstr. , 55, 22251
        (1961).
106.   Sureau, R. F. M. , and P. M. J. Obellianne, U. S. Patent 2, 789,
        132; Chem. Abstr. , 51, 15571 (1957).
107.   Suter, C. M. , U. S. Patent 2, 098, 114; Chem. Abstr. , 32, 191
        (1938).
108.   Suter, C. M. , and P. B. Evans, J. Am. Chem. Soc. , 60, 536
        (1938).
109.   Suter, C. M. , P. B. Evans, and J. M. Kiefer, J. Am. Chem.
        Soc. , 60, 538 (1938).
110.   Suter, C. M. , and J. D. Malkemus, J. Am. Chem. Soc. , 63, 978
        (1941).
111.   Taras, J. , U. S. Patent 2, 507, 944; Chem. Abstr. , 45, 873
        (1951).
112.   Taras, J. , U. S. Patent 2, 739, 150; Chem. Abstr. , 50, 15600
        (1956).
112a.   Tauber, S. J. , and N. N. Lowry, J. Org. Chem. , 27, 2659
        (1962).

113.   Terent'ev, A. P. , and A. V. Dombrovskii, J. Gen. Chem. USSR
       (English Transl.), 19, 1467 (1949); Chem. Abstr. , 44, 1481
       (1950).
114.   Terent'ev, A. P. , and G. M. Kadatskii, Zh. Obshch. Khim. , 22,
       153 (1952); Chem. Abstr. , 46, 11178 (1952).
115.   Terent'ev, A. P. , L. A. Yanovskaya, A. M. Berlin, and E. A.
       Borisov, Vestn. Mosk. Univ. , 8, No. 6, Ser. Fiz. -Mat. i.
       Estesteven. Nauk, No. 4, 117 (1953); Chem. Abstr. , 49,
       8092 (1955).
116.   Torrey, G. G. , in Kirk-Othmer, Encyclopedia of Chemical
       Technology, 1st ed. , Interscience, New York, 1954,
       p. 285.
117.   Traube, W. , H. Zander, and H. Gaffron, Ber. , 57B, 1049
       (1924).
118.   Turbak, A. F. , U. S. Patent 3, 072, 703; Chem. Abstr. , 58,
       10080 (1963).
119.   Turbak, A. F. , Paper presented at the 139th American Chem-
       ical Society Meeting, St. Louis, Mo. , March 21-30, 1961.
120.   Turbak, A. F. , Paper presented at the 144th American Chem-
       ical Society Meeting, Los Angeles, Calif. , April, 1963.
121.   Turbak, A. F. , Ind. Eng. Chem. , Prod. Res. Develop. , 1, 275
       (1962).
121a. Union Carbide Corp. , French Patent 1, 312, 330.
122.   Wagner, J. , Ber. , 19, 1157 (1886).
123.   Walrafen, G. E. , and T. F. Young, Trans. Faraday Soc. , 56,
       1419 (1960).
124.   Whistler, R. L. , and W. Spencer, Arch. Biochem. Biophys. ,
       95, 36 (1961).
125.   Willcox, O. W. , Am. Chem. J. , 32, 446 (1904).
126.   Wolfram, M. L. , and T. M. S. Han, J. Am. Chem. Soc. , 81,
       1764 (1959).

CHAPTER 2

SULFONATION WITH COMPOUNDS
OF SULFUR TRIOXIDE

I. INTRODUCTION

This chapter is concerned with the preparation of sulfonates (i. e., compounds in which the sulfur atom is directly attached to carbon) by the direct reaction of the reagents discussed in Chapter 1 with organic compounds. This approach, being the simplest and most direct, has, therefore, by a wide margin, been the one most commonly employed both in the laboratory and in commercial practice for the manufacture of detergents, dye intermediates, ion-exchange resins, sulfonated oils, and other sulfonates of industrial interest. Primary emphasis is placed upon recent developments, with major consideration being devoted to the uses of the newer reagents, especially SO_3 and its adducts with organic compounds for sulfonating alkenes, many aliphatic compounds containing carbonyl groups, polycyclic aromatics, and acid-sensitive heterocyclic compounds.

With aromatic compounds, the recent use of SO_3 and other strong reagents has prompted theoretical and empirical study of the factors involved in the resulting undesired side-reaction of sulfone formation, and has led to new methods for the direct preparation of aromatic sulfonic anhydrides. Although aromatic sulfonation with sulfuric acid or oleum has long been known to be a reversible reaction (as discussed in Chapter 8), it has now become clear that a number of sulfonate isomers formerly considered "abnormal" can be made with these reagents if the reactions are allowed to reach equilibrium by the application of suitably high temperatures or long periods of reaction. This development appears significant both practically and theoretically. Sulfonation under conditions of lower acidity (i. e., with free SO_3 or with an SO_3 adduct of an organic compound), on the other hand, is less easily reversible, which has advantageously given simpler product mixtures with polycyclic hydrocarbons than when acid or oleum were used.

II. SULFONATION OF ALIPHATIC AND ALICYLIC COMPOUNDS

A. Saturated Compounds

1. HYDROCARBONS

Paraffinic and cycloparaffinic hydrocarbons react with sulfonating agents, but neither easily nor in a clean-cut manner, with oxidation being the primary effect. Under mild conditions, tertiary alkanes undergo oxidation to carbonium ions (152), followed by hydrogen ex-

31

change via a chain reaction. At higher temperatures, methyl groups migrate, presumably also by a carbonium-ion mechanism, while hydrocarbons which do not contain tertiary hydrogen atoms are comparatively unaffected. As the temperature is raised or reagent strength is increased, these compounds also react. Dehydration and oxidation with SO_2 formation accompany sulfonation (393), yielding complex mixtures containing hydroxyl and carbonyl compounds, carboxylic acids, and unsaturated compounds, as well as their derived sulfates, sulfonic acids, sulfones, sultones, and sulfonate esters. Methane at 260°C, using $HgSO_4$ catalyst, forms methanesulfonic acid, methanedisulfonic acid, and methyl methanesulfonate (363). Propane, n-butane, and isobutane, in the range 60 - 300°C, form polyhydroxylsulfonic acids with the hydroxyl groups partly sulfated (402). Hexane, heptane, and octane, all of unknown structure, were sulfonated at reflux with SO_3 vapor (487); they gave "disulfonic acids," together with much oxidation. An "isohexane" of uncertain structure was sulfonated to the extent of 50% with SO_3 dissolved in liquid SO_2 at -10°C (204); n-dodecane did not react under the same conditions.

Cycloparaffins behave similarly. Cyclohexane reacts with 20 and 60% oleums at 10°C with evolution of over 1 mole of SO_2 per mole reacted, forming complex sulfonation-oxidation-polymerization products similar to those obtained from cyclohexene (368). Dicyclohexyl and cyclohexyl methylcyclopentane behave likewise. Decahydronaphthalene is also oxidized with oleum in the cold (368) or with SO_3 vapor at 193°C (81). The cis isomer is preferentially attacked, yielding approximately 2 moles SO_2 per mole reacted; the final reaction product comprises sulfonated and oxidized polymers of unknown composition, with little appearing as naphthalenesulfonic acids. 12-Methylperhydroretene ("abietane") reacts likewise with SO_3 at 0°C (478).

This type of reaction has been used for preparative purposes in only two cases. Cyclohexane, with SO_3 at room temperature for 8 hr. undergoes dehydrogenation, ring cleavage, polymerization, and sulfonation to form a carbyl sulfate which was hydrolyzed to a hydroxylsulfonate by the following overall sequence (134):

$$C_6H_{12} \xrightarrow{\substack{(1)SO_3 \\ (2)H_2O}} HO_3SCH_2CHOH(CH{=}CH)_{13}CHOHCH_2SO_3H +$$

$$H_2SO_4 + SO_2 \qquad (2\text{-}0)$$

The product from this remarkable series of reactions is stated to be a blood anticoagulant comparable in activity to heparin. 1-Hexadecanol is reported to form a similar material with $ClSO_3H$. The structural assignments may be questioned, since it seems unlikely that reactive polyunsaturated systems of this kind would be stable in the presence of SO_3 or H_2SO_4.

Although not of preparative utility, these types of reactions have proved of practical interest in other respects. Sludge formation during the sulfonation of petroleum fractions occurs partly in this manner (148). The adhesiveness and printability of polyethylene is improved by surface oxidation-sulfonation; reaction undoubtedly occurs mainly at the tertiary carbon atoms. Of the many patents which have appeared on various procedures for achieving this effect, two which may be cited as typical, involve treating a polyethylene fabric with 3% oleum at 50°C (468), and polyethylene sheeting at room temperature with SO_3 dissolved in tetrachloroethylene (145). Chlorosulfonic acid was found best for sulfonating low-pressure polyethylene film (457). Although alkanes will react with SO_3 and are not miscible with it, reaction is sufficiently slow so that they can be employed satisfactorily as sulfonation solvents for other compounds which react more easily, especially at low temperatures; n-butane (39) and n-hexane (150) have been used in this manner.

Halogenated aliphatic and cycloaliphatic hydrocarbons undergo sulfation, as discussed in Chapter 6.

2. CARBOXYLIC ACIDS

Acetic anhydride reacts with sulfuric acid, and acetic acid with SO_3, to form "acetyl sulfate," as discussed in Chapter 1, Section VI. When acetyl sulfate is warmed, rearrangement and further reaction occur, resulting in the ultimate disappearance of sulfate ion and the formation of a mixture of compounds of which sulfoacetic acid, HO_3SCH_2COOH, is a constituent. However, the yield is low and the procedure has not been recommended for preparative use. The kinetics and mechanism of this reaction have been studied (210); the conversion of the mono- and diacetyl sulfates to the sulfonic acid was concluded to be rate-determining. Ketene and SO_3-dioxane are stated to form the anhydride of sulfoacetic acid (362):

$$CH_2:C:O + SO_3 \longrightarrow \begin{array}{c} CH_2\!-\!C\!:\!O \\ | \qquad | \\ SO_2\!-\!O \end{array} \qquad (2\text{-}1)$$

This compound was not isolated as such, but as its anilide. The reaction is generally similar to β-sultone formation between SO_3 and alkenes, discussed in Section I-B - 1. Treatment of acetic acid with SO_3, or acetic acid or anhydride with oleum (84) yields methanetrisulfonic acid:

$$CH_3COOH + 3 SO_3 \longrightarrow \left[(HO_3S)_3CCOOH\right] \longrightarrow$$

$$\qquad (2\text{-}2)$$

$$(HO_3S)_3CH + CO_2$$

Unlike the monosulfonation of acetic acid, this reaction proceeds in good yield and can be employed for preparative purposes. It is interesting that methanedisulfonic acid has not been made in good yield by this route.

Unlike acetic acid, chloroacetic acid is monosulfonated smoothly with SO_3 vapor in 95% yield at 70 - 140°C (19, 364). As indicated in Chapter 5, the acid chloride of this sulfo acid has been studied industrially for sulfoacylating dyes. Bromoacetic acid can be sulfonated similarly in 70% yield (15).

Propionic (20) and butyric (16, 307) acids form the acyl sulfates below 0°C; they also rearrange in poor yields to the α-sulfo acids. However, with $(2SO_3)$-pyridine, butyric acid is reported to be sulfonated quantitatively (440). In contrast to their acetic analogues, 2-chloro- and 2-bromopropionic acids (21), give only 25 - 30% yields of the halogenerated α-sulfo acids upon treatment with SO_3 at 100 - 120°C.

The lower fatty acid chlorides (C1-4) follow a generally similar pattern upon treatment with $ClSO_3H$ (235). The acylated chlorosulfonate, $RCOOSO_2Cl$, is first formed, followed by α sulfonation. Acetyl chloride is more difficult to sulfonate than the higher acid chlorides, and it forms a much larger proportion of condensation products by side reactions.

The long-chain fatty acids (C9 and higher) differ from the lower acids in that the former can be α-sulfonated easily and in good yields. Cheap availability of the acids has led to substantial industrial interest in their sulfonation, first in Germany, and more recently in the United States, as shown in a series of papers by A. J. Stirton and co-workers; this work has been reviewed and summarized (383). α-Sulfo acids of this type are commercially available (9).

Several reagents are capable of α sulfonating the saturated fatty acids. A comparative study (477) has shown that the addition of liquid SO_3 to the acid in a halogenated solvent appears most practical. Chlorosulfonic acid behaves similarly, but it requires a higher temperature, does not give a lighter-colored product, and was concluded to have no advantage. Sulfur trioxide-dioxane in carbon tetrachloride yields a sulfonate of exceptionally light color. No reaction occurred with SO_3-pyridine, sulfamic acid, or $ClSO_3H$-urea. It is interesting that sulfuric acid and stearic anhydride did not form the sulfonate; it, therefore, differs in this respect from acetic anhydride. Free SO_3 is the reagent most commonly employed. The molten acids, such as pelargonic (477) or palmitic (171) acids, can be treated without a solvent with SO_3 vapor at 75 - 100°C. This method gives colored by-products, which can, however, be easily removed by recrystallization of the monosodium salts from water (477). However, solvent procedures are usually preferred as yielding lighter-colored products. Lauric acid has been sulfonated in refluxing butane (39) and stearic acid in liquid SO_2 (90, 272). Tetrachloroethylene (169) and carbon tetrachloride (97, 201, 477) have been used for sulfonating pelargonic, lauric, myristic, palmitic, stearic, and behenic acids in crude yields ranging from 60 to 97%. The

SO_3 in these cases was added in liquid form, although the vapor gives a lighter-colored product (477). The German industrial process for sulfonating a technical palmitic-stearic acid mixture, dissolved in five weights of carbon tetrachloride, involved addition of vaporized SO_3 at 25 - 30°C (169), finally raising the temperature to 60°C to complete reaction. A similar procedure was employed to sulfonate montanic acid (97), hardened palm kernel acid (201), and the C7-9 fatty acid made by the oxidation of paraffin wax (198). A petroleum naphthenic acid has been sulfonated with SO_3 vapor in 66% yield (319).

Sulfur trioxide-dioxane, used at 60°C for 1 hr., yields unusually light-colored α-sulfo acid from 9,10-dichloro- and 9,10-dihydroxy-stearic acids (477). In the second case, 5 moles of SO_3 were employed, and the sulfated product was hydrolyzed to the desired dihydroxysulfo-stearic acid.

The α-sulfopalmitic and -stearic acids, because of their cheapness and commercial availability, are of interest as sulfoacylating agents, as discussed in Chapter 5. They have also been converted to salts (475), ester salts (35, 384, 473, 474), and amide-salts (476), all of which were evaluated as detergents. Sulfopelargonic ester salts are good wetting agents (477).

Sulfur trioxide-dioxane selectively sulfonates phenylalkanoic acids on the carbon atom adjacent to the carboxyl group, rather than on the aromatic ring. Ring sulfonation is, however, observed with other reagents such as sulfuric acid (450). Phenylacetic, 3-phenylpropanoic, 6-phenylcaproic and phenylstearic (477) acids give good yields of the α-sulfo acids. Diphenylacetic and cyclohexylacetic acids do not react, and 2-phenylbutanoic acid gives a poor yield; these observations are consistent with the large steric requirements of the entering sulfonic group. 4-Phenylbutanoic acid cyclizes to α-tetralone, which then sulfonates as expected on the carbon atom adjacent to the carbonyl group.

Aliphatic dicarboxylic acids are also sulfonated with SO_3. With 1 mole at 110-120°C, succinic acid is simply dehydrated to its anhydride (22). With 2.5 - 4.0 moles, it yields mono- and disulfonic acids together with unsulfonated material; more than 4.0 moles forms mono- and disulfonic acids together with some maleic anhydride produced by dehydrogenation. Succinic anhydride is left half unreacted by 0.9 mole SO_3 at 110°C; the other half is converted to mono- and disulfonates. Methylsuccinic acid reacts with two moles to form the monosulfonic acid by replacement of the tertiary hydrogen atom (17); the second mole is consumed in forming the acid anhydride. Propane-1,1,2-tricarboxylic acid yields the isomeric sulfonate with decarboxylation (18):

$$CH_3CH(COOH)CH(COOH)_2 \xrightarrow{\quad SO_3 \quad}$$

$$(2\text{-}3)$$

$$CH_3CH(COOH)CH(SO_3H)(COOH) \ + \ CO_2$$

Apparently replacement of the more sterically hindered, but more reactive, hydrogen atom precedes decarboxylation, although some replacement of the other hydrogen atom does occur, as indicated by the
formation of disulfonate. Higher aliphatic dicarboxylic acids (glutaric,
adipic, azelaic, and sebacic) have been sulfonated with SO_3 using tri-
chloroacetic acid as solvent (140).

The mechanism of the α sulfonation of carboxylic acids has apparently not been considered. Presumably, it is similar to that proposed
for ketones, as expressed in Equation 2-5.

The conversion of amino acids to acyl sulfates with SO_3-dimethyl-
formamide, intermediate to the preparation of peptides, is mentioned
in Chapter 1.

3. ESTERS

Carboxylic esters undergo protonation with sulfuric acid (152). On
pouring into water, either the free carboxylic acid or the original ester
is recovered, depending upon its structure. The mechanism of acidolysis, and its probable relationship to ester structure, has been discussed (152). Alkyl-oxygen fission is favored over acyl-oxygen fission.

Ester cleavage also often occurs upon treatment with SO_3 (7). Methyl
laurate forms α-sulfolauric acid and dimethyl sulfate with SO_3 in liquid
SO_2 (273). Aliphatic esters of acetic, acrylic, crotonic, and succinic
acids are also cleaved (219). The first step in the cleavage process is
no doubt formation of a complex between SO_3 and the electron-rich
carbonyl oxygen atom, followed by a similar reaction between a second
mole of SO_3 and the other less basic oxygen. As noted in Chapter 1,
SO_3 can also cleave phosphate esters. Sulfonate esters behave similarly (212, 219), as do also ethyl and amyl benzoates (120). Even the
stable aromatic esters phenyl benzoate undergoes cleavage with excess
SO_3 (119).

It is, therefore, noteworthy that in some cases the sulfonation of
esters has been reported to occur without cleavage. Three ethyl esters
(acetate, propionate, and butyrate) yielded disulfonates with three reagents (440). Sulfur trioxide gave 45, 48, and 15% yields, $(2SO_3)$-
pyridine 100% from the first two compounds and SO_3-dioxane 100% disulfonate from the first and last. Diethyl malonate, on the other hand,
formed 50% monosulfonate with SO_3-dioxane; a disulfonate would not be
expected on steric grounds. The formation of di-, rather than monosulfonates, is a noteworthy difference from the free acids, which, except for acetic acid, form only the mono compounds. Diethyl adipate
has been mono- and disulfonated with apparent retention of the ester
groups using $ClSO_3H$ in a chlorinated solvent (73). γ-Butyroactone, an
internal ester, reacts with SO_3 in chloroform at $0°C$ to form the monosulfonate (236). At $100°C$, without a solvent, it gives a disulfonic acid.

4. NITRILES

As indicated in Chapter 7, initial attack by SO_3 on both aliphatic and aromatic nitriles occurs as expected at the more electron-rich nitrogen atom, forming cyclic N-sulfonated derivatives by Equation 7-24. Although acetonitrile is stated to form a compound of this kind, it is also reported (440) to form the nitrile α-monosulfonic acid in 35, 28, and 70% yields with SO_3,$(2SO_3)$-pyridine and SO_3-dioxane. Propionitrile similarly forms 80% α-sulfonitrile with $(2SO_3)$-pyridine, and 3-methyl-butyronitrile 25% with SO_3-dioxane (440). Long-chain fatty nitriles (e. g. , lauric and palmitic) are also reported to form the α-sulfonitriles upon treatment with SO_3 under mild conditions (183, 184) in solvent such as tetrachloroethylene, but no analytical data are presented which would exclude attack on the nitrile group. Attack of the cyclic N-sulfonate by excess SO_3 seems likely, with formation of a salt of the corresponding α-sulfonated acid during workup under aqueous conditions.

5. KETONES

Like carboxylic acids, the aliphatic and alicyclic ketones sulfonate easily on the carbon atom adjacent to the carbonyl group:

$$RCH_2COR' \xrightarrow{\quad SO_3 \quad} RCH(SO_3H)COR' \qquad (2\text{-}4)$$

The data are summarized in Table 2-1. When R' is methyl and R is alkyl, substitution occurs on the $-CH_2-$ group (312). Even ketones with tertiary hydrogen atoms, such as di-(isopropyl)ketone, sulfonate in good yield. Pivalophenone did not react, as would be expected from the absence of a hydrogen atom on the carbon atom next to the carbonyl moiety. Dibenzoylmethane did not react at $5°C$ (449), but was found by others to undergo sulfonation at $25°C$ (161). Among the ketones also containing carbocylic rings, ring sulfonation was reported for 2-aceto-naphthone and 2-(3, 4-dimethoxyphenyl)-1, 3-indandione. In the second case this is not surprising, since the aromatic ring is made extremely susceptible to sulfonation by the presence of the two methoxyl groups. 2-Phenyl-1, 3-indandione, and related compounds, gave ring sulfonate exclusively when employing $ClSO_3H$ in a halogenated solvent, but yielded the desired compound with the milder reagents acetyl sulfate or $ClSO_3H$ in ethyl ether. The heterocyclic rings in 1- and 2-acetofuran, and in 2-acetopyrrole do sulfonate to some extent, although this did not occur in 2-acetothienone (446).

Sulfur trioxide-dioxane has proved the favored reagent, as used in the range 5 - $50°C$, with 1, 2-dichloroethane as reaction solvent. In some cases (452) the desired sulfonic acid can be precipitated by simply cooling the reaction mixture. Acetyl sulfate has been employed especially with diketones and steroid ketones; it has desirably proved milder and more selective than $ClSO_3H$.

The mechanism of ketone sulfonation is regarded as similar to that of their acid-catalyzed bromination (446). As shown in Equation 2-5, where A = SO_3 and B = dioxane, the first step involves complex formation between the electron-rich carbonyl oxygen atom and the electron-deficient sulfur atom. Several such complexes are mentioned in Chapter 1.

$$\underset{\substack{\| \\ O \\ \delta^-}}{\overset{\delta^+}{\bar{R}CCH_3}} \xrightarrow{A} \underset{\substack{| \\ O \\ | \\ A^-}}{\overset{+}{RCCH_3}} \xrightarrow{B}$$

$$\underset{\substack{| \\ O \\ | \\ A^-}}{RC{:}CH_2} \; (+BH^+) \longrightarrow \underset{\substack{\| \\ O}}{RCCH_2A^-}$$

(2-5)

Several terpenic ketones behave abnormally. Camphor, even though it does have hydrogen atoms on a carbon adjacent to the carbonyl group, is sulfonated by acetyl sulfate preferably on a methyl group (471). Fenchone (isomeric with camphor) has no hydrogen atoms on the adjacent carbon, but it is sulfonated by acetyl sulfate on a methyl group located in the same position as in camphor (237). Another investigator (444) obtained the same sulfonate in 65% yield from fenchone with SO_3 vapor, but noted no reaction with acetyl sulfate. These anomalies cannot be attributed to the use of acetyl sulfate, since it sulfonates 1-keto-1,2, 3,4-tetrahydrophenanthrene, and several steroidal ketones, normally on the adjacent carbon atoms.

6. ALDEHYDES

Saturated aldehydes resemble ketones and carboxylic acids in undergoing sulfonation with SO_3-dioxane on the carbon atom adjacent to the carbonyl group, presumably by a mechanism similar to that cited above for ketones:

$$RCH_2CHO + SO_3 \longrightarrow RCH(SO_3H)CHO \qquad (2-6)$$

As indicated in Table 2-2, disulfonates have been obtained in some cases by using two molar proportions of reagent. Apparently no attempt has

TABLE 2-1

Sulfonation of Saturated Aliphatic and Alicyclic Mono- and Diketones[a]

Compound	Monosulfonic acid yield, %	Reference
Monoketones		
Acetone	53, 70, 84, 100[b]	312, 434, 446
Methyl ethyl, -isobutyl, -n-hexyl	73 - 87	312
Methyl tert-butyl	70	446
Diethyl	67	312
Di-(n-propyl)	80, 95, 100[b]	312, 434
Di-(isopropyl)	59, 90	312, 434
C13-17	- (ClSO$_3$H, AC)	197
Palmitone, etc.	- (SO$_3$ in CCl$_4$)	172
Coconut ketones	- (SO$_3$ in SO$_2$)	93
Acetophenone	70, 90, 93	430, 434, 446
4-Methylacetophenone	-	431
4-Ethyl-, 4-isopropylacetophenone	79, 87	430
4-Methoxy-, 4-ethoxyacetophenone	80, 84	430
4-Chloro-, 4-bromoacetophenone	56, 58	430
2, 4-Dimethyl-, 2, 4, 6-trimethyl-acetophenone	70, 77	431, 446
α-Chloro-, α-fluoroacetophenone	77, 46	449
Propiophenone	70	446
Isobutyrophenone	63, 70	446, 452
Pivalophenone	0	446
2-Acetonaphthone	Mono- and di-	446
2-Acetothienone	70	446
Camphor	-(AC)	471
α-Chloro-d-camphor	-(ClSO$_3$H)	456

continued

TABLE 2-1 (Continued)

Compound	Monosulfonic acid yield, %	Reference
Monoketones (continued)		
Dihalogenated camphors	-(oleum)	290
Fenchone	65(SO_3 vapor)	444
Fenchone	0(AC), -(AC)	237, 444
Tropolone	-(oleum)	191
Hinokitiol and halogenated derivatives	-(NH_2SO_3H)	295
Cyclopentanone	-($ClSO_3H$)	351
Cyclohexanone	70, 84	434, 446
1-Tetralone	70	451
1-Keto-1, 2, 3, 4-tetrahydro-phenanthrene	85(AC), 71(AC)	99
Androsterone and isoandrosterone acetates	-(AC), 63(AC)	99
Estrone acetate	74(AC)	99
Coprostan-3-one, cholestan-3-one	-(AC)	485, 486
Progesterone	-(AC)	485
Diketones		
5-Phenyl-1, 3-cyclohexanedione	65(AC)	161, 162, 165
5, 5-Dimethyl-1, 3-cyclohexane-dione	42-97(AC); 92(SO_3)	101, 161, 162, 168
1, 3-Indandione	Good, -(AC)[b]	161 - 163
Anhydro-bis-1, 3-indandione	-(AC)	162, 164
2-Aryl-1, 3-indandiones	-(AC)	386
2-Phenyl-1, 3-indandione	77(AC), 52 ($ClSO_3H$ with ethyl ether)	161, 162, 385
2-(3, 4-Dimethoxyphenyl)-1, 3-indandione	5(AC), plus 30% sultone	387

continued

TABLE 2-1 (Continued)

Compound	Monosulfonic acid yield, %	Reference
Diketones (continued)		
Perinaphthindan-1, 3-indandione	-, -(AC)	161, 162
Dibenzoylmethane	-, 0	161, 449
o-Diacetylbenzene	0	449
m-Diacetylbenzene	59[b]	449
p-Diacetylbenzene	53[b]	449
Cholestan-3, 6-dione	-(AC)	486

[a]All sulfonations were done with SO_3-dioxane, except as otherwise indicated; AC = acetyl sulfate; - indicates yield not given.

[b]Disulfonate yield using 2:1 molar ratio.

been made to use other reagents. Aldehydes without hydrogen on a carbon atom adjacent to the carbonyl group, such as formaldehyde or chloral, form cyclic sulfates as pointed out in Chapter 6.

7. MISCELLANEOUS SATURATED ALIPHATIC AND ALICYCLIC COMPOUNDS

Methanesulfonic acid reacts with SO_3 under mild conditions to form the pyrosulfonic acid, its solvate $CH_3SO_3SO_3H \cdot 2\ CH_3SO_3H$, and methanesulfonic anhydride (337). Under more drastic conditions (3 hr at 145°C), an 85% yield of disulfonic acid is obtained (91):

$$CH_3SO_3H + SO_3 \longrightarrow CH_2(SO_3H)_2 \qquad (2-7)$$

The CH_3SO_2-group in sulfones, on the other hand, is unreactive, as noted with methyl-4-tolyl sulfone (using SO_3-dioxane) (446), and with dimethyl sulfone (employing SO_3, even at 230°C) (7).

Nitromethane formed 15% monosulfonic acid with SO_3, 4% with $(2SO_3)$-pyridine, and 6% with SO_3-dioxane (440); nitrocyclohexane correspondingly gave yields of 26, 22, and 20%. Sulfur trioxide-pyridine did not react with either compound. By analogy to the sulfonation

TABLE 2-2

Sulfonation of Saturated Aliphatic Aldehydes with SO_3-Dioxane

Aldehyde	Monosulfonate yield, %	Reference
Acetaldehyde	39, 80[a]	434
1-Propanal	55	434
1-Butanal	61, 78[a]	434
2-Methyl-1-propanal	75, -[a]	434, 446
2-Methyl-1-butanal	78[a]	434
1-Heptanal	65	434
1-Octanal	60, -	434, 446
1-Decanal	43, 34[a]	434
Phenylacetaldehyde	57, 41[a]	434, 446

[a]Indicates yield of disulfonate at 2:1 molar ratio; - indicates yield not given.

mechanism cited for ketones (Eq. 2-5), the nitro compounds may react via their aci- forms. This type of mechanism was also suggested in Chapter 3 for α sulfonation of aliphatic nitro compounds with SO_2Cl_2. As pointed out in Chapter 1, the nitroalkanes initially form SO_3 complexes with free SO_3, although such may not form when using SO_3-puridine, or SO_3-dioxane.

B.   Unsaturated Compounds

1. GENERAL DISCUSSION

All classes of unsaturated compounds sulfonate easily, forming the various types of compounds shown in Figure 2-1. Included are ethylene, acetylene, and polyene compounds, any of which can contain a wide variety of other functional groups.

Much of the work on the sulfonation of unsaturated compounds has come from three sources. C. M. Suter, F. G. Bordwell, and collaborators in the United States have studied the sulfonation of alkyl and aryl ethylenes with SO_3-dioxane, and the latter has begun a promising attack

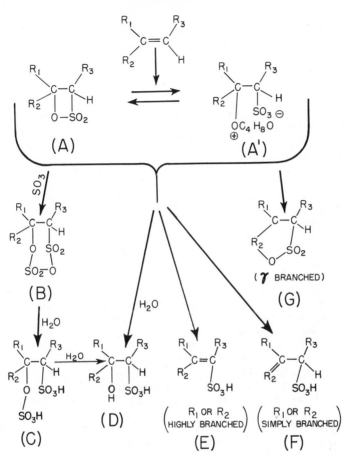

Fig. 2-1. Alkene sulfonation products.

toward elucidating the mechanism and basic chemistry of these often
complicated reactions. A. P. Terent'ev in the Soviet Union has employed SO_3-pyridine with cycloalkenes, alkadienes, and alkene derivatives, the primary emphasis being preparative. Industrial chemists
have used free SO_3, generally with a solvent, to prepare surface-active
agents from commercially-available, long-chain olefins; this work has
been largely empirical. A solvent often employed in these last studies
is liquid SO_2 at its boiling point ($-10°C$). The system $ClSO_3H$-diethyl
ether has also been used industrially.

    A β-sultone (Formula A, Fig. 2-1), or its dioxane-solvated carbo-
nium ion (Formula A'), is now considered the primary alkene sulfonation product (43, 46-50). Similar products are presumably formed from
free SO_3 and from other SO_3 complexes. This type of sultone was

actually isolated from styrene (44, 50), and from a series of fluorinated ethylenes (cf., Table 2-8). Although 1-butene and long-chain terminal alkenes are stated to form the β-sultones in liquid SO_2 (185), or without using a solvent (31a), efforts made to date to prepare the one from ethylene have failed - a "polymeric sultone" being formed instead per Equation 2-9. These β-sultones are quite reactive and unstable, and can form one or more of the several types of final products shown in Figure 2-1 depending upon various factors, including reactant-reagent ratio (48), reaction temperature (47, 327), method of product workup (48), and degree of polymerization or water content of the SO_3 used (100, 121). Long reaction times (at low temperature) or high temperatures (at short times) favor the formation of type E sulfonates (454). In the case of branched-chain alkenes, the type and position of chain branching, with steric factors of primary influence, determine which of structures E, F, or G will be formed (43, 46); heteroconjugation of doubly-bonded carbon with sulfonate and hyperconjugation of it with alkyl groups also play a role (46). With ring-halogenated styrenes, the type and position of the ring substituent determines what products are formed (68), as shown in Table 2-4. Inductive effects of ring substituents appear to determine sulfate-sulfonate (type C) yields, since they become less as the fluorine atom is farther removed from the olefinic bond of the styrene. Furthermore, the yields of type C products from the meta-substituted styrene decrease as the electronegativity of the meta substituent diminishes. Total electronic effect (inductive plus resonance) of the meta and para substituents (Hammett σ values) appears to correlate with yield of olefinic (type E) sulfonates.

The nature of the complexing reagent can also determine what types of products are formed, as shown in Table 2-3 (454). The runs shown were made under identical conditions using a long-chain α-olefin, at a 1:1:1 molar ratio of SO_3, complexing agent and olefin. The trialkyl-phosphate adducts can, under the proper conditions, form the alkene-sulfonate exclusively. Sulfur trioxide-dioxane, on the other hand, has always given mixtures.

TABLE 2-3

Influence of Complexing Agent on Alkene Sulfonation Products

Complexing agent	% Hydroxysulfonate (Type D)	% Alkenesulfonate (Type E)
Tributyl phosphate	19	81
Bis-(2-chloroethyl) ether	59	41
Dioxane	59	41

Products of type B (sulfate-sulfonic anhydride, or "a carbyl sulfate") have been isolated only in the cases of ethylene and 1,1-difluoroethylene (with both of which no other products are formed), of trifluoroethylene and methallyl chloride (which give mixtures), of tetrafluoroethylene and hexafluoropropylene, which give some product B with undistilled SO_3, but none with the freshly-distilled material, and possibly of cyclohexene (125). However, this type of unstable anhydride may be intermediate in many alkene sulfonations where the more stable compounds C or D are actually isolated as the final products.

The usual types of final products isolated after aqueous neutralization of the reaction mixture are alkenesulfonates (structure E or F), or a hydroxylsulfonate (also called an "isethionate") of structure D, the last forming from sultone A by hydrolysis, either directly, or via compounds B and C. Compounds of type C (sulfate-sulfonates, or "ethionates") are unstable in aqueous medium and usually are isolated only with special precautions, as with cyclohexene (48), cyclopentene (48), methylenecyclohexene (412), halo- (68) or nitrostyrenes (68) (see Table 2-4), and vinyl ethers, as discussed in Section II-B-4.

Five-membered ring sultones of type G can in some cases be obtained in fair yield from the corresponding γ-branched alkenes, as shown in Table 2-5 (43).

Steric factors, besides often determining sulfonate structure, can also prevent alkene sulfonation, as with 1,1-diphenyl-2-methyl-1-propene (45). Polybutylene mixtures (7) sulfonate only to the extent of about 25%, the remainder apparently being too sterically hindered to react, since the double bonds are internally situated. Tetrachloroethylene does not sulfonate, probably for the same reason, although tetrafluoroethylene does.

Chlorosulfonic acid reacts easily with olefinic compounds, with the system $ClSO_3H$ - ethyl ether being favored in a number of industrial studies, as indicated in Table 2-6. The primary product formed from $ClSO_3H$-ether is thought to be the chlorinated sulfonic acid, formed by reaction 1-13, but the halogen is so labile that the olefinic or hydroxy sulfonate is the species often actually isolated. Undecylenic acid thus forms a hydroxysulfonic acid (28), and oleic acid either a chlorinated sulfonic acid, or the unsaturated sulfonic acid (29). Without a solvent, or with a nonpolar solvent, the primary product is stated to be the chlorosulfonate ester, formed by Equation 1-10 (268). Since such esters also react with olefins, the overall sequence in the case of propylene is as follows (129):

$$CH_3CH{:}CH_2 \xrightarrow{\ ClSO_3H\ } CH_3CH(CH_3)OSO_2Cl \xrightarrow{\ CH_3CH{:}CH_2\ }$$

$$CH_3CH(CH_3)OSO_2CH_2CHClCH_3 \xrightarrow{\ H_2O\ } \qquad (2\text{-}8)$$

$$CH_3CHOHCH_2SO_3H \ + \ CH_3CHOHCH_3 \ + \ HCl$$

TABLE 2-4

Halogenated Styrenes with SO_3-Dioxane

Compound	Yield, %		
	Sulfate-sulfo-nate (Type C)	Olefinic sulfo-nate (Type E)	Hydroxyl sul-fonate (Type D)
2-Fluorostyrene	58	30	12
3-Fluorostyrene	39	9	53
4-Fluorostyrene	15	68	18
2,4-Difluorostyrene	39	25	35
3-(Trifluoromethyl) styrene	59	7	34
3-(Trifluoromethyl)-4-fluorostyrene	0	0	100
2-Chlorostyrene	10	5	85
3-Chlorostyrene	16(15[a])	10(18[a])	74(67[a])
4-Chlorostyrene	0	38	60
2-Bromostyrene	0	6	94
3-Bromostyrene	0	8	92
4-Bromostyrene	2	33	65
3-Nitrostyrene	69[a]	4[a]	27[a]
4-Nitrostyrene	88[a]	6[a]	6[a]
Styrene	0	69	31

[a]Data from reference 447; all other data from reference 68.

Workup of the product in aqueous medium would by hydrolysis give a maximum 50% yield of a salt of 2-hydroxypropanesulfonic acid, the same product potentially obtainable in theoretical yield by use of the $ClSO_3H$-diethyl ether system. 2-Pentene, with $ClSO_3H$ in chloroform, gave the olefinic sulfonic acid (269). Since the yield was only 37%, the mechanism of reaction 2-8 may apply here also. Ethyl chlorosulfonate, $ClO_2SOC_2H_5$, adds across the double bond of oleic acid, forming a compound of structure $-CHClCH(SO_2OC_2H_5)-$, which was hydrolyzed to the hydroxysulfonate (178); this is further evidence of the plausibility of reaction sequence 2-8.

TABLE 2-5

Sultones From γ-Branched Alkenes

Alkene	Yield, %
3-Methyl-1-butene	53
3,3-Dimethyl-1-butene	71
2,3,3-Trimethyl-1-butene	76
3,3-Dimethyl-2-phenyl-1-butene	73
4-Methyl-2-pentene	82
4,4-Dimethyl-2-pentene	51

2. ALKYL AND ARYL ETHYLENES; CYCLOALKENES

This category includes compounds with only hydrogen or carbon atoms attached to the doubly-bonded carbons. Compounds studied with the main products formed, are listed in Table 2-6. All of the starting materials are hydrocarbons, except for a few compounds with halogen not on a doubly-bonded carbon, and ring-substituted styrenes. It is noted that, although SO_3-dioxane has been the preferred reagent, their range has extended from highly reactive (free SO_3) to fairly unreactive (sulfamic acid, SO_3-pyridine). As indicated in Chapter 6, sulfuric acid effects the sulfation of alkenes.

Ethylene forms only a type B product, carbyl sulfate, by reaction with two moles of SO_3. Production of the β-sultone would be of decided commercial interest, since the second mole of SO_3 in carbyl sulfate is wasted as sulfate ion in its useful reactions, as discussed in Chapter 5. An ingenious attempt to accomplish this has involved the interaction of carbyl sulfate with ethylene (125), which yields an allegedly equally useful polymer of the β-sultone:

$$x/2 \ CH_2{:}CH_2 + x/2 \quad \begin{array}{c} \diagup CH_2 \!\!-\!\! CH_2 \\ O \qquad\qquad SO_2 \\ \diagdown SO_2 \!\!-\!\! O \diagup \end{array} \qquad (2\text{-}9)$$

$$(-OCH_2CH_2SO_2-)_x$$

On the other hand, 1-butene is stated to yield the sultone by reaction with SO_3 in SO_2, followed by distillation in vacuo (185).

TABLE 2-6

Sulfonation of Alkyl and Aryl Ethylenes and Cycloalkenes

Compound	Reagent[a]	Type major product(s)	Reference
C2			
Ethylene	VA	B	59
Ethylene	LI	B	128
Ethylene	CE	No reaction	266
C3			
Propylene	DI	D	398
Propylene	CE	D	266
Propylene	$ClSO_3H$	D or E	129
Allyl chloride	LI	D	330
C4			
1- and 2-Butenes	CE	D	266
1-Butene	LI	A	185
Isobutylene	PY	E, F (di)	416
Isobutylene	DI	E, F (di)	396, 399
Isobutylene	DI	F (mono)	12, 396
Isobutylene	AC	F (mono)	382
Methallyl chloride	DI	D	330
Methallyl chloride	DI	B, F	397
Methallyl chloride	TH	E or F	283
Methallyl chloride	$ClSO_3Na$	E	397
C5			
2-Methyl-1-butene	DI	F	46
3-Methyl-1-butene	DI	G	43
2-Methyl-2-butene	DI	F	46
2-Methyl-2-butene	PY	E, F (di)	416

continued

TABLE 2-6 (Continued)

Compound	Reagent[a]	Type major product(s)	Reference
2-Pentene	ClSO$_3$H	E	269
2-Pentene	DI	Not given	395
2-Pentene	TH	E or F	284
Cyclopentene	DI	C, D	48
C6			
3,3-Dimethyl-1-butene	DI	G	43
4-Methyl-1-pentene	DI	E	46
4-Methyl-2-pentene	DI	G	43
1-Hexene	DI	C, D	47
1-Methylcyclopentene	DI	E	367
Methylenecyclopentane	DI	F	11
Cyclohexene	DI	C, D, E	48
Cyclohexene	DI	E	367
Cyclohexene	PY	C	408, 412
Cyclohexene	AC	D, E	369, 382
C7			
2,3,3-Trimethyl-1-butene	DI	G	43
4,4-Dimethyl-1-pentene	DI	E	46
4,4-Dimethyl-2-pentene	DI	G	43
Heptene mixture	LI	Not given	204
Methylenecyclohexane	PY	C	408, 412
Methylenecyclohexane	DI	F	12
C7-17 alkenes	LI	Not known	315
C8			
2,4,4-Trimethyl-1-pentene	DI	E	46
2,4,4-Trimethyl-2-pentene	DI	E	46
Diisobutylene	TH	E or F	283, 284

continued

TABLE 2-6 (Continued)

Compound	Reagent[a]	Type major product(s)	Reference
"Isooctene"	TH	E or F	283
Cyclooctene	AC	E	382
Styrene	PY	E	408, 412, 418, 419
Styrene	DI	D or E	51, 327
Styrene	DI	E	52
Styrene	DI	A	50
Styrene	DI	D	68
Styrene	CE	D	160
Styrene	NH_2SO_3H	E	316
1-, 2-, 3-Monochloro-, Mono-bromo-, and Monofluoro-styrenes	DI	(Table 2-4)	
2, 4-Difluorostyrene	DI	(Table 2-4)	
3- and 4-Nitrostyrenes	DI	(Table 2-4)	
C9			
1-Nonene	DI	D	398
"Isononylene"	CE	E	266
Propylene trimer	LI	E or F	333
1-Phenyl-1-propene	DI	E	400
2-Phenyl-1-propene	DI	E, F (di)	400
2-Phenyl-1-propene	DI, PY	E, F (di)	418
3-Phenyl-1-propene	DI	D	418
3-(Trifluoromethyl)-styrene	DI	(Table 2-4)	
3-(Trifluoromethyl)-4-fluoro-styrene	DI	(Table 2-4)	
Indene	PY	E	408, 412
Indene	CE	E	160

continued

TABLE 2-6 (Continued)

Compound	Reagent[a]	Type major product(s)	Reference
C10			
Camphene	PY	E	103, 408, 412
Camphene	AC	G	13
1- and 6-Nitrocamphenes	AC	G	14
Diamylene	TH	E or F	283
2-Benzyl-1-propene	DI	F	53
Anethole, isosafrole	NH_2SO_3H	E	316
C12			
1-Dodecene	LI	Not given	109
3,3-Dimethyl-2-phenyl-1-butene	DI	G	43
Triisobutylene	DI	E or F	396
Triisobutylene	TH	E or F	283
Propylene tetramer	LI	E or F	333
1-Vinylnaphthalene	PY	Sulfone of E	418
C12-18 α alkenes	c	D and/or E	454
C14			
n-Tetradecene	LI	Not given	109
1,1-Diphenylethylene	DI	E	49
1,1-Diphenylethylene	PY	E	418
C14-18 α-olefins	VA	D	173a
C15			
C15-18 propylene polymer	CE	E	3
C16			
1-Hexadecene	DI	D	395, 398
1-Hexadecene	$ClSO_3H$	E	109
Hexadecene	LI	D	128

continued

TABLE 2-6 (Continued)

Compound	Reagent[a]	Type major product(s)	Reference
Cetene	SO_3	E or F	239
1,1-Diphenyl-2-methyl-1-propene	DI	No reaction	45
Tetraisobutylene	LI	D	329
Tetraisobutylene	TH, DI	E or F	283
Diisooctylene	AC	Not given	170
C17			
1-Heptadecene	DI	D	395, 398
Heptadecene	TH	Not given	283
2-Methyl-2-hexadecene	DI	E or F	396
C17-22 polybutylene	AC	Not given	3
C18			
Octadecene	AC	D	169
Octadecene	$ClSO_3H$	Not given	109
1-Chloro-9-octadecene	TH	E or F	283
1-Chloro-9-octadecene	AC	Not given	170
C19			
Abietene	b	Not given	478
Miscellaneous			
Cracked alkene mixture	AC	D and, or E	205
Alkene polymer (mol. wt. 1100)	VA	Not given	150
Diamylene polymer	TH	Not given	284
Polyisobutylene	TH	E or F	284
Polybutylene (mol. wt. 420)	VA	Not known	7
Petroleum olefin (mol. wt. 450 - 600)	CE	E	267
Natural rubber	CE	E	344

[a]Reagents are abbreviated as follows: DI: SO_3-dioxane; PY: SO_3-pyridine; TH: SO_3-thioxane; VA: SO_3 vapor; LI: SO_3 in liquid SO_2: AC: acetyl sulfate; CE: $ClSO_3H$ in ethyl ether.

[b]SO_3 in tetrachloroethane.

[c]Used DI, SO_3-bis-(2-chloroethyl) ether, and SO_3-tributyl phosphate.

Type E sulfonates prepared from styrene with SO_3-pyridine (418), and from long-chain α-olefins with SO_3-tributyl phosphate (454) have the trans configuration, as would be expected from the substantial steric requirement of the reaction as discussed before.

Detergents of good surface activity, foaming power, and biodegradability can be made in good yields by hydrolysis of the reaction products of SO_3 with C14-18 long-chain α-olefins (173a). The final products are sodium 2-hydroxylsulfonates (type D).

3. HALOGENATED ETHYLENES

All the halogenated ethylene derivatives listed in Table 2-7 form sulfonates, except tetrachloroethylene, which undergoes oxidation instead, but only slowly and at elevated temperature. Trichloroacetyl chloride is formed, possibly via an epoxide intermediate. Failure of this compound to sulfonate may be explained by the large steric requirementments of the chlorine atoms, since tetrafluoroethylene does form a sulfonate. Because of its stability, complete miscibility with SO_3, and its favorable boiling point ($121°C$), tetrachloroethylene is a useful sulfonation solvent. One investigator has reported, however, that a solution of stabilized SO_3 in this solvent increases 37% in acid value on standing for twelve days at room temperature (317). Trichloroethylene, on the other hand, reacts easily with SO_3 on the carbon holding the single chlorine atom. The five halides forming aldehydic and ketonic sulfonates can be regarded as reacting normally, since a halogen atom on the same carbon as a hydroxyl group in a product of structure D would be expected to generate a carbonyl group. The two monobrominated ethylenes shown in Table 2-7 sulfonate on different carbon atoms, possibly for steric reasons. Hexachlorobutadiene resembles tetrachloroethylene in being miscible with SO_3, and in not reacting with it at room temperature (7); hexachlorocyclopentadiene, on the other hand, reacts easily with SO_3 and with $ClSO_3H$, as noted in Section II-B-8. Halogenated alkanes form sulfates and related compounds, as indicated in Chapter 6.

Fluorinated ethylenes (Table 2-8) present several features of unusual interest. All of them, except $F_2C:CH_2$, form β-sultones - a type of compound isolated only recently in the two other cases of styrene and 1-butene, as discussed before.

$$F_2C:CRR' + SO_3 \longrightarrow \begin{array}{c} F_2C-CRR' \\ | \quad\; | \\ O-SO_2 \end{array} \qquad (2\text{-}10)$$

The oxygen atom is always attached to the F_2C- group, except in the case of $F_2C:CFCl$, where the two possible sultones are formed in equal amounts (121, 211). With $F_2C:CH_2$, a quantitative yield of carbylsulfate type (structure B) product is formed; 34% was formed from $F_2C:CFH$. Only two other carbyl sulfates had been isolated previously.

TABLE 2-7

Sulfonation of Chlorinated and Brominated Ethylenes

Compound	Reagent	Product	Reference
$CH_2:CHCl$	SO_3-pyridine	Acetaldehydesulfonic acid	409
$ClCH:CHCl$	Liquid SO_3	Monochloroacetaldehyde-sulfonic acid	250
$BrCH:CHBr$	Liquid SO_3	Monobromoacetaldehyde-sulfonic acid	328
$Cl_2C:CHCl$	Liquid SO_3	Trichloroethyl trichloro-vinylsulfonate	139
$Cl_2C:CCl_2$	Liquid SO_3	Trichloroacetyl chloride	314
$C_6H_5CCl:CH_2$	SO_3-pyridine	Benzoylmethanesulfonic acid	418
$C_6H_5CH:CHBr$	SO_3-dioxane	1-Bromo-2-phenylethene-1-sulfonic acid	451
$(CH_3)_2C:CHBr$	SO_3-pyridine	Dimethylacetaldehyde-sulfonic acid	409

Two investigators (100, 121) have noted that the history of the SO_3 used affects the types of products formed. Tetrafluoroethylene and hexa-fluoropropylene form the sultones with freshly-distilled SO_3, but un-distilled material gives substantial amounts of carbyl sulfate in both cases. This difference may reflect a varying degree of polymerization of the SO_3, an effect not previously noted in alkene sulfonation. It may also result from the presence of a trace of moisture, since the addition of water to freshly distilled SO_3 produces the same effect.

4. VINYL ETHERS AND ESTERS

These materials were sulfonated at 100°C with SO_3-pyridine, form-ing the products shown in Table 2-9. In all cases, the sulfur atom be-came attached to the carbon without oxygen. With the vinyl ethers, sulfate-sulfonates (formula C) were isolated; being typical formals, they were converted to the aldehydic sulfonates with aqueous hydro-chloric acid:

$$HO_3SCH_2CH(OR)OSO_3H \xrightarrow{H_2O} HO_3SCH_2CHO + ROH + H_2SO_4 \quad (2\text{-}11)$$

Intermediates of type C were not isolated from the vinyl esters.

TABLE 2-8

Sultones From Fluorinated Ethylenes

Compound	Yield, %	Reference
$F_2C:CF_2$	100	100, 121
$F_2C:CFCl$	86	100, 121, 211
$F_2C:CCl_2$	56	121
$F_2C:CFH$	60	100, 121
$F_2C:CH_2$	0	121
$ClFC:CClF$	80	121, 211
$F_2C:CFCF_3$	85, 94	100, 121, 137, 211
$F_2C:CFC_4H_9$	Good	121
$F_2C:CF(CF_2)_6H$	Good	121
$F_2C:CF(CF_2CClF)_xCF_2Cl$ (x = 1 to 4)	72 - 82	211
$F_2C:CFCF_2CFCl_2$	73	211
$F_2C:CFC_5F_{11}$	58	137
$F_3CCl:CClCF_3$	60	211

5. KETONES AND ALDEHYDES

The limited work done with these compounds using SO_3-dioxane is summarized in Table 2-10. It appears that some of the unsaturated ketones, like the saturated analogues discussed in Section II-A-5, sulfonate on a carbon atom adjacent to the carbonyl group, but that such may, or may not, occur on the doubly-bonded carbon. The saturated and unsaturated ketones are also similar in forming either mono- or disulfonates; with mesityl oxide, higher temperatures favor disulfonation. The two xyloquinones, as pointed out in Section III-A-8, resemble the unsaturated ketones both structurally, and in manner of sulfonation. Benzoquinone and toluquinone, on the other hand, form hydroxysulfonates like alkenes.

TABLE 2-9

Vinyl Ethers and Esters with SO_3 - Pyridine

Compound	Product Isolated	Reference
Vinyl acetate	Acetaldehydesulfonic acid	428, 429
Vinyl butyl ether	Acetaldehydesulfonic acid; also sulfate-sulfonate	408, 428, 433
Vinyl isoamyl ether	Acetaldehydesulfonic acid; also sulfate-sulfonate	408, 433
Isobutenyl acetate	Dimethylacetaldehydesulfonic acid	428, 429
Isopropenyl acetate	Acetonesulfonic acid	428, 429

　　　The sulfonation of α,β- and β,γ -unsaturated ketones with acetyl sulfate (1 mole H_2SO_4 with 2 moles acetic anhydride) at $0°C$ is of special interest.　With two α,β-unsaturated steroid (Δ^4-cholesten-3-one (485) and 7-ketocholestene (486) sulfonation occurs not on an available adjacent carbon atom, as with the saturated ketones, but on a carbon atom separated from the keto group by the vinyl moiety.　Many other such ketones similarly sulfonate on the third carbon removed from the carbonyl group, but they cyclize to sultones:

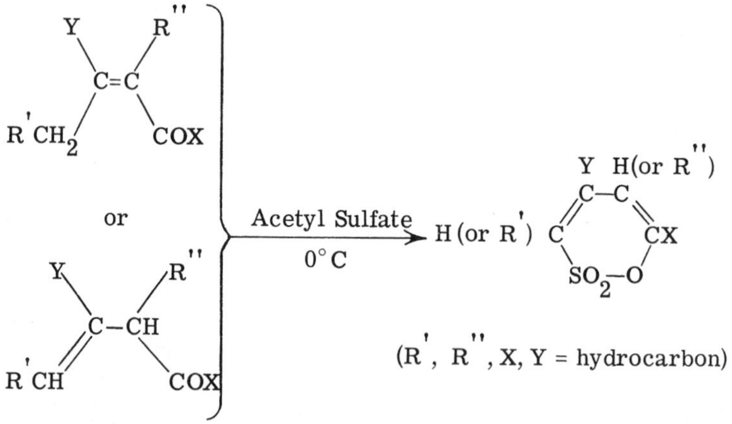

(2-12)

$(R', R'', X, Y = hydrocarbon)$

　　　The double bond can be in an open chain, or part of a ring.　The scope of this reaction has been well reviewed by Mustafa up to 1954 (278), and it has been used subsequently (181, 230).

　　　Sulfur trioxide-pyridine is stated to be unsuitable for sulfonating unsaturated aldehydes (105).

TABLE 2-10

Unsaturated Aldehydes and Ketones with SO_3-Dioxane

Compound	Products	Temp.	Yield, %	Reference
$(CH_3)_2C{:}CHCOCH_3$	$(CH_3)_2C{:}C(SO_3H)COCH_3$	0	50	104
$(CH_3)_2C{:}CHCOCH_3$	Mono- and disulfonates	35	-	104
$(CH_3)_2C{:}CHCOCH_3$	Disulfonate	70	50	104
$C_6H_5CH{:}CHCOCH_3$	$C_6H_5CH{:}CHCOCH_2SO_3H$	50	65	104
$(C_6H_5CH{:}CH)_2CO$	Mono- and disulfonates	50	73	104
$[(CH_3)_2C{:}CH]_2CO$	Monosulfonate	50	37	104
C15 to 57 Isophorones	Unidentified	40	-	258
Oleone[a]	Unidentified	-	-	172
$CH_2{:}CHCHO$	$HO_3SCH{:}CHCHO$	0	98	104
$CH_3CH{:}CHCHO$	$CH_3C(SO_3H){:}CHCHO$	0	75	104
$C_6H_5CH{:}CHCHO$	Monosulfonate	60	12	104

[a]SO_3 in CCl_4 used.

6. ALKENOIC ACIDS, ESTERS, AND GLYCERIDES

Maleic anhydride gives an 85% yield of sulfomaleic anhydride upon heating at 50°C with SO_3 (23); fumaric acid forms the same product. Crotonic acid at 50°C yields 90% of a sulfonate of unstated structure (340). These acids are resonance-stabilized.

Alkenoic acids without resonance stabilization react with SO_3 at a lower temperature. In liquid SO_2 as solvent at -10°C, undecylenic acid gave 80% unsaturated sulfonate, and 10% each of hydroxysulfonate and sulfate-sulfonate (332, 340), all of unproved structure. Under similar conditions, oleic acid formed 54, 28, and 17% of the same three types of products. In both cases, 1 - 1.25 moles of SO_3 were used per mole of acid, and the total yield of sulfonate was 85 - 90%. Sulfooleic acid, a commercial surface-active agent, has been manufactured by this type of process (407).   Since this product has a carbon-sulfur bond, it is much more stable than the conventional type of "sulfonated" oleic acid made with concentrated H_2SO_4, which contains the relatively weak sulfate linkage, as indicated in Chapter 6.   Oleic acid has also been sulfonated with 2 molar proportions of SO_3 at 50°C with nitrobenzene as solvent (171); a hydroxysulfonate is stated to be the final product. Tetrachloroethylene has also been employed as solvent for this sulfonation (6); SO_3 (2 moles), dissolved in this solvent, was added dropwise at 10°C.   Another procedure involves the use of acetyl sulfate (33, 169, 195).   The acetoxysulfonate presumably is formed; it hydrolyzes to the hydroxysulfonate upon treatment with water.   Undecylenic acid, with $ClSO_3H$-ethyl ether followed by hydrolysis, forms the hydroxysulfonic acid (28).   Oleic acid with the same reagent gives either the chlorinated saturated sulfonic acid, or the unsaturated sulfonic acid derived from it by dehydrochlorination (29).

Oleic esters, on the other hand, react with SO_3 quite differently from the acid in liquid SO_2 (332, 340).   At 1:1 molar ratio, half the ester remains unchanged, while the other half reacts with 2 moles of SO_3, presumably forming a product of type B, which hydrolyzes to types C and D during workup.   The ester groups are inferred to remain intact during the sulfonation and workup, an interesting observation in view of their pronounced tendency to undergo cleavage with SO_3, as discussed in Section II-A-3.   Sulfur trioxide requirements can therefore be halved in producing sulfooleic esters, if the sulfo acid is esterified, rather than sulfonating the ester directly (332).   As noted in Chapter 6, butyl oleate is sulfated with concentrated H_2SO_4 without destruction of the ester linkage.

Oleic triglyceride (olive oil) has been sulfonated with SO_3-dioxane (394, 395), below room temperature, and with acetyl sulfate, made from SO_3 and glacial acetic acid, at -20°C (195).   The latter reagent presumably yields an acetoxysulfonate similar to that formed from oleic acid.

The "sulfonation" of castor oil (the triglyercide of ricinoleic (12-hydroxyoleic) acid) with concentrated H_2SO_4 has, as pointed out in Chapter 6, long been practiced commercially on an entirely empirical basis for making leather- and textile-treating aids.   The reagent is used in excess, and the products, being sulfates rather than sulfonates, are unstable.   When an equal weight of SO_3 is used, with petroleum ether as solvent, a product with considerably improved properties results (281), more so than when using lesser quantities of SO_3 or other reagents; this corresponds to approximately 12 moles SO_3 per mole castor oil.   Patents describe treatment of castor oil with SO_3 in tetrachloroethylene (300), of acetylated castor oil with excess SO_3 in liquid SO_2 (157), of ricinoleic acid with SO_3 in carbon tetrachloride below 0°C (220), and of ricinoleic acid amide with SO_3 in liquid SO_2 (173). Castor oil has been reacted with acetyl sulfate at 30°C (63), as has ricinoleic acid at low temperature (195).   This treatment presumably sulfates the hydroxyl group and converts the olefinic moiety to acetoxy sulfonate.

Dimerized linoleic acid and tall oil acids were sulfonated with SO_3 in liquid SO_2 (332), and abietic acid (as gum rosin) was treated likewise in tetrachloroethane (478).

In nearly all of this work on fatty acids and their derivatives, no reaction products were identified; the work was empirical, with the objective of obtaining products with surface activity. Apparently none of these approaches is in commercial use, except in the case of oleic acid.

7. ALKENAMINE DERIVATIVES

Surface-active agents were prepared by treatment of 21 fatty amides of methallylamine (291) with acetyl sulfate. The same reagent was used with N-dodecyl-N'-allylthiourea (336). N-Methyl-N-allylaniline was sulfonated with SO_3 in carbon tetrachloride (112); the SO_3-amine complex initially formed in this case is sufficiently loose as not to render sulfonation difficult. It is interesting that reaction occurs with the olefinic group rather than with the ring, in spite of the fact that the latter is easy to sulfonate.

8. ALKADIENES AND CYCLOALKADIENES

1,3-Butadiene, as shown in Table 2-11, give type E sulfonates with SO_3-pyridine in the known cases. Cyclopentadiene, on the other hand, forms a product of structure F, which can be explained by the unusually high reactivity of the methylene hydrogen atoms, or by the high degree of mobility of the ring unsaturation. Hexachlorocyclopentadiene resembles tetrachloroethylene (Table 2-7) in forming an oxygen-containing product, rather than undergoing sulfonation. Guaiazulene, which contains fused methylcyclopentadiene and cycloheptatriene rings, has given three different products. It undergoes replacement of a hydrogen atom on the cyclopentadiene ring with SO_3-dioxane (445) or with acetyl sulfate. Oleum, on the other hand, leads to substitution of another hydrogen atom on the same ring, and of one on the methyl group (262).

9. ALKYNES

Acetylene reacts with SO_3 in liquid SO_2 at a 1:4 molar ratio, presumably forming a product of type B, which upon hydrolysis yields the expected acetaldehydedisulfonic acid (146, 147) isolated as the monohydrate:

$$(2-13)$$

TABLE 2-11

Alkadienes and Cycloalkadienes

Compound	Reagent	Product	Reference
Butadiene	SO_3-pyridine	Diene-1-sulfonate	408, 411, 415
Butadiene	$ClSO_3H$-ether	Unsaturated sulfonate	266
Hexachlorobuta-diene	SO_3 liquid	No reaction	7
2-Methylbutadiene	SO_3-pyridine	Diene-1-sulfonate	408, 411, 415
2,3-Dimethylbuta-diene	SO_3-pyridine	Diene-1-sulfonate	411, 415
2,3-Dimethylbuta-diene	SO_3-dioxane	2,3-Dimethyl-4-hydroxy-2-butene-1-sulfonic acid sultone	43
1,4-Dimethylbuta-diene	SO_3-pyridine	2-Hydroxy-3-hexene-1-sulfonic acid (?)	408
1,1,4,4-Tetra-methylbutadiene	SO_3-pyridine	A disulfonic acid	408
1,3-Cyclopenta-diene	SO_3-pyridine	Diene-5-sulfonate	414
Guaiazulene	Various	(See text)	262, 445
1,3-Hexachloro-cyclopentadiene	SO_3 liquid	$C_{10}Cl_{10}O$	142
Alloocimene dimer	SO_3 vapor	A sulfonate	335
Butadiene with isobutylene	SO_3 in liquid SO_2	Sulfonated co-polymer	40
4-Phenylbuta-diene	SO_3-pyridine	Diene-1-sulfonate	410, 413

The aldehyde group is typically reactive, and has been employed to convert this sulfonate to numerous derivatives, as indicated in Chapter 5.

With SO_3-dioxane at $40°C$, acetylene reacts at lower ratios (106), to give a mixture of two products:

$$HC\equiv CH + SO_3 \longrightarrow HC\equiv CSO_3H \qquad (2\text{-}14)$$

$$HC\equiv CH \xrightarrow{2\ SO_3} \underset{HC}{\overset{SO_2-O}{\big|}} = \underset{CH}{\overset{SO_2}{\big|}} \xrightarrow{H_2O} \left[\underset{HC}{\overset{H}{\underset{\big|}{\big|}}} = \underset{CH}{\overset{O\ SO_2OH}{\underset{\big|}{\big|}}} \right] \longrightarrow$$

$$\underset{HC}{\overset{O}{\big|}} - \underset{CH_2}{\overset{SO_2OH}{\big|}} + H_2SO_4 \qquad (2\text{-}15)$$

1-Hexyne similarly yields 59% of the corresponding acetylenic sulfonate without forming any carbonyl derivative. Phenylacetylene, on the other hand, gave only the analogous sulfonated acetophenone, or unidentified products (326). Sodium phenylacetylide gave no definite products. This reaction deserves further study, since acetylenic sulfonates, with one doubtful exception (234), were previously unknown.

10. PHOSPHORUS YLIDS

These compounds react with SO_3-dioxane as follows (289):

$$(C_6H_5)_3\overset{+}{P}-\overset{-}{C}RR' \xrightarrow{SO_3} (C_6H_5)_3\overset{+}{P}-\underset{\overset{|}{SO_3^-}}{C}RR' \xrightarrow[(R=H)]{Base}$$

$$\text{(A)}$$

$$(C_6H_5)_3P\text{:}C(SO_3Na)R' \qquad (2\text{-}16)$$

$$\text{(B)}$$

$$(R' = CH_3CO\text{--}, C_6H_5CO\text{--}, -COOCH_3)$$

The betaines (2-16-A) were isolated, and converted to sulfonates in 80% yield or better when R was hydrogen. With R and R' both phenyl, the betaine was formed, but it did not yield a sulfonate. Unlike normal phosphorus ylides, compound 2-16-B, because of the high electro-negativity of the sulfonate group, does not react with aldehydes to form olefinic sulfonates and triphenyl phosphine oxide. This synthesis may be capable of extension to others of the many ylides of this type now known.

III. SULFONATION OF AROMATIC COMPOUNDS

A. Benzene Derivatives

1. KINETICS, MECHANISM, ORIENTATION; COMPLETING THE REACTION

Kinetic and mechanistic studies of the sulfonation of aromatic compounds have led to the conclusion that it is an S_E2 reaction with monomeric SO_3 as the effective reacting species, not only with SO_3 itself, but also when sulfuric acid or oleum are used. Since the detailed evidence has been well reviewed by others (216, 285, 286), only the general conclusions will be considered herein. A monograph on this subject is projected by H. Cerfontain, who has published extensively in this and related areas.

In the low-strength oleums, the rate expression is (286, 469):

$$\text{Rate } \alpha \text{ (ArH) } (SO_3)$$

As the SO_3 content of the oleum is increased, the order with respect to SO_3 steadily increases, approaching 2 for pure SO_3, as has been shown by studies of the reaction of SO_3 with various aromatic compounds in nitrobenzene solution (111, 462, 465); the data are summarized in Table 2-12. The rate expression then becomes

$$\text{Rate } \alpha \text{ (ArH) } (SO_3)^2$$

This led to the suggestion (462, 465) that dimeric SO_3 (S_2O_6) might be the effective species. However, the data could also correspond to successive reaction with 2 moles of monomeric SO_3 - one attacking the ring, the other then protonating the incipient sulfonate group and also functioning as a base for removal of the proton, forming a pyrosulfonate:

$$C_6H_6 + SO_3 \rightleftharpoons \qquad \qquad (2\text{-}17)$$

(A)

$$2\text{-}17\text{-}A + SO_3 \rightleftharpoons$$

$$(2\text{-}18)$$

TABLE 2-12

Relative Rates of Sulfonation with SO_3 in Nitrobenzene

Compound	Velocity constant k, 40°C (liters/g. mole sec.)	Ratio
Benzene	44. 8	100
4-Nitroanisole	6. 29	14
1-Nitronaphthalene	3. 27	7
Chlorobenzene	2. 4	5
Bromobenzene	2. 1	5
1,3-Dichlorobenzene	$4. 36 \times 10^{-2}$	< 1
4-Nitrotoluene	$9. 53 \times 10^{-4}$	< 1
Nitrobenzene	$7. 85 \times 10^{-6}$	< 1

As discussed in the next section, the pyrosulfonate is an important intermediate, since it sulfonates a second mole of aromatic compound and leads to sulfone formation. A similar mechanism seems to hold for SO_3 hydrates (228), but reaction 2-18 would then involve some other basic species for proton removal, for example HSO_4^-, or $H_2S_2O_7$.

Well-defined complexes presumed to have structures generally like that of 2-17-A are formed from SO3 and electron-rich polycyclic hydrocarbons such as perylene (299a). Sulfuric acid gives protonated complexes from these hydrocarbons. Sulfur trioxide complexes are also formed in which the hydrocarbon moiety is present as a monopositive ion.

Sulfonation has been thought to differ from nitration and bromination, in that the former has shown a deuterium isotope effect of 1. 4 - 2. 1 using oleum, whereas the other two processes do not give this effect. More recently, however, it has been found that benzene does not show an isotope effect in sulfonation with SO_3 (77a). This means that in SO_3 sulfonation, as with nitration and halogenation, the proton-removal step is not rate-controlling. The question is also raised as to whether different mechanisms are involved with the two different reagents.

The proposal (218) that in sulfuric acid an acid solvate of SO3 is the active species is considered possible (216), but less likely than that free SO_3 is involved.

As shown in Tables 2-12 and 2-13, the rates of sulfonation of various types of aromatic compounds vary widely. Furthermore, the relative rates, compared to benzene as 100, vary greatly depending upon whether SO_3 or H_2SO_4 is used as the reagent, as well as upon the specific reaction conditions. Thus chlorobenzene and bromobenzene react at about

TABLE 2-13

Relative Rates of Sulfonation with H_2SO_4 in Nitrobenzene

Compound	Velocity constant ($k \times 10^6$, $40°C$)	Ratio
o-Xylene	-	1775[a]
Naphthalene	141. 3	910[b]
m-Xylene	116. 7	752[b]
Toluene	78. 7	507[b]
Ethylbenzene	-	482[a]
Isopropylbenzene	-	335[a]
tert-Butylbenzene	-	284[a]
1-Nitronaphthalene	26. 1	169[b]
4-Chlorotoluene	17. 1	110[b]
Benzene	15. 5	100[b]
Chlorobenzene	10. 6	69[b]
Bromobenzene	9. 5	61[b]
m-Dichlorobenzene	6. 7	43[b]
4-Nitrotoluene	3. 3	21[b]
p-Dibromobenzene	1. 0	7[b]
p-Dichlorobenzene	0. 98	6[b]
1, 2, 4-Trichlorobenzene	0. 73	5[b]
Nitrobenzene	0. 24	2[b]

[a]Reference 286.

[b]Reference 390.

the same rate with either reagent, but this rate is 60 - 70% of that of benzene with H_2SO_4, and only 5% of the rate of benzene with SO_3. Recent work has shown that H_2SO_4 sulfonates toluene 31 times as fast as benzene (114), but with nitrobenzene as solvent, toluene reacts only about 5 times as fast with H_2SO_4, as indicated in Table 2-13. In liquid SO_2, toluene reacts 29. 5 times as fast with SO_3 as benzene (324). This study also showed that bromobenzene reacts 3. 1 times as fast as benzene; the date of Tables 2-12 and 2-13 indicates that the former reacts more slowly. Recent kinetic studies (76, 217) of the sulfonation of toluene, ethylbenzene, isopropylbenzene, and tert-butylbenzene with acid of 72 - 89% strength show a decline in the relative rate constants in the order given, probably because of increasing steric hindrance in the ortho position. For example, at 25°C with 85.8% acid the rates of the last three compounds relative to toluene are 0.80, 0.52, and 0.33; dealkylation was noted only with the tert-butyl compound.

Electron-withdrawing groups (nitro, sulfonyl, carbonyl) are meta-directing and make sulfonation difficult, while electron-donating groups (alkyl, alkoxy, alkylthio, hydroxy, and amino) render sulfonation easy and are ortho-para-directing. The amino group can, however, also be meta-directing, as discussed in Section III-A-4. Halogen is also anomalous, since it is electron-withdrawing and slows sulfonation, but is ortho-para directing. This effect has been explained by the ability of the halogen atom to form a quasi double bond with the ring carbon atom in the same manner as phenols and aromatic amines (189). These remarks apply to sulfonations conducted under normal laboratory conditions. As indicated subsequently in this chapter, and in Chapter 8, the use of drastic conditions can give the so-called abnormally oriented isomers as major products from some ortho-para directing, as well as meta-directing groups.

The reagents of most practical interest for ring sulfonation are SO_3, its hydrates, and $ClSO_3H$. Sulfur trioxide complexes with organic compounds have proven of limited utility for this purpose, since only the more active compounds, e.g., polycyclic hydrocarbons (Section III-C), react with the more active complexes (e.g., SO_3-dioxane). On the other hand, the complexes have proved highly useful for the sulfation of phenols (Chapter 6) and for the sulfamation of aromatic amines (Chapter 7).

Benzene and other aromatic compounds, can be sulfonated with concentrated H_2SO_4, but as the concentration of the water increases during reaction, the rate of sulfonation steadily decreases, the reaction rate being inversely proportional to the square of the water concentration. Reaction ceases when the acid concentration reaches a level characteristic of each compound, in the case of benzene about 78% H_2SO_4. As indicated in Chapter 8, this corresponds to the acid concentration at which the rates of sulfonation and desulfonation are equal. It is sometimes called the "π factor," as discussed more fully elsewhere (143).

Much thought has been devoted to methods for carrying the sulfonation reaction to completion. One approach involves removal of the water as formed, the net result being substantially quantitiative utilization of both hydrocarbon and acid. This can be accomplished by repeated passage of the vaporized hydrocarbon through the acid, thereby removing the water formed during sulfonation as the azeotrope. This partial-pressure distillation procedure, although time-consuming, combines excellent yields with comparative simplicity of operation and has been an industrial approach for sulfonating low-boiling, stable aromatic hydrocarbons such as benzene, toluene, and the xylenes. The method can be extended to higher-boiling compounds by adding a suitably inert, comparatively low-boiling azeotroping agent such as carbon tetrachloride or petroleum naphtha. Another procedure, also used industrially, is the use of excess acid, such that the acid concentration remains above the π value until all of the hydrocarbon has reacted. This procedure is simple and the yields based on the hydrocarbon are nearly quantitative, but the excess acid must be neutralized and the resulting salt separated and discarded or utilized.

Two other procedures for completing sulfonation with H_2SO_4 are of interest. Spryskov (372) showed that the π-factor concept does not hold at high temperatures and pressures. At 162°C in 9 hr. using excess benzene, the residual acid was only 38% H_2SO_4, as opposed to the approximately 78% π value. Similarly, he sulfonated naphthalene to 25% spent acid, and even lower, as opposed to a π value of 64% (cf. Table 2-19). Subsequent work (358) showed that the time could be reduced by using emulsive agitation, and, in fact, could be taken as low as 5 min. by operating at 200 - 225°C (213). At 1:1 molar ratio the yield of sulfonic acid was good, in agreement with the observations of Spryskov; there was no disulfonation or sulfone formation. This approach seems a fairly conclusive solution to the problem, provided corrosion-proof equipment for operating under pressure is available.

The second approach for completing sulfonation involves a chemical method for removing the water as formed (58) by the following reaction:

$$H_2O \; + \; SOCl_2 \longrightarrow 2 \; HCl \; + \; SO_2 \qquad (2\text{-}19)$$

This procedure gives sulfonic acid yields of 73 - 99% at room temperature from benzene, toluene, o- and p-xylenes, ethylbenzene, fluoro-, chloro-, and bromobenzenes. Paradichlorobenzene, 2-chlorotoluene, and 4-nitrotoluene yielded 28% or less, while nitrobenzene and iodobenzene formed none. It will be noted that these results are roughly in agreement with those quoted in Table 2-13, regarding the influence of substituting groups on the rate of sulfonation. This appears a convenient and simple procedure for laboratory use.

2. HYDROCARBONS

a. Benzene Monosulfonation; Sulfone Formation

Potentially, the most attractive and practical procedure for sulfonating benzene and other aromatics is by direct reaction with SO_3, since the process is instantaneous, smoothly exothermic, and can involve simple mixing of the two liquids. No expenditure of energy is necessary to separate SO_3 from water, as when using the SO_3 hydrates. The chemical factors involved when using SO_3 are, however, complicated and will be discussed in some detail. At least three products are always formed: benzenemonosulfonic acid, diphenyl sulfone, and

H_2SO_4; others may be formed, the proportions of each depending upon various factors. With both reagents in the vapor phase, a 50% yield of sulfone is obtained at 150 - 200°C (69), and 30% at 70 - 80°C (279). With excess SO_3 under the latter conditions, the product comprises 35% each of the benzenemono- and disulfonic acids, and 30% of mixed mono- and disulfonic acids of diphenyl sulfone (279). At low temperature with excess SO_3, the sulfonic acid anhydride is a major product (7). Addition of SO_3, either as a liquid or vapor, to liquid benzene gives 15 - 18% sulfone, but addition of liquid benzene to liquid SO_3 yields 7.5% (151). Use of chloroform as solvent reduces the sulfone to about 2% (88, 245). Liquid SO_2 has been studied most extensively as the solvent for this reaction, because of its favorable boiling point and cost, and because it dissolves both reagents and products (70, 71, 159, 245, 334). One of these studies (334) has led to several conclusions regarding the probable course of the reaction at 1:1 molar ratio, as well as the extent and possible mechanism of sulfone formation. The reaction is seen as occurring in two steps:

$$C_6H_6 + 2 \ SO_3 \longrightarrow C_6H_5SO_2OSO_3H \qquad (2\text{-}20)$$

(Benzenepyrosulfonic acid)

$$C_6H_5SO_2OSO_3H + C_6H_6 \begin{cases} \xrightarrow{A} C_6H_5SO_2C_6H_5 + H_2SO_4 \\ \xrightarrow{B} 2 \ C_6H_5SO_3H \end{cases} \qquad (2\text{-}21)$$

This scheme is thought (334) to explain several facts, for the reasons given: (a) the addition of the hydrocarbon to the SO_3 gives about half as much sulfone as the reverse procedure (71, 151, 245, 334), because of mass action; (b) most of the total heat of reaction is evolved as the first mole of benzene is added, since reactions 2-21-A and -B should be less exothermic than 2-20; (c) the addition of 1 - 5 wt.-% of acetic acid, or other organic acids, reduces sulfone formation from the 7 - 18% level to the 1 - 6% range (141, 334), since reaction 2-22 and 2-23-B are thought to predominate.

$$C_6H_5SO_2OSO_3H + CH_3COOH \longrightarrow C_6H_5SO_3H + CH_3COOSO_3H \quad (2\text{-}22)$$

$$CH_3COOSO_3H + C_6H_6 \begin{cases} \xrightarrow{A} CH_3COC_6H_5 + H_2SO_4 \\ \xrightarrow{B} C_6H_5SO_3H + CH_3COOH \end{cases} \qquad (2\text{-}23)$$

(Recycle to reaction 2-22)

It is noted that only about half of the benzenesulfonic acid is formed by direct reaction of benzene with SO_3 (reaction 2-20), the other half resulting from reaction 2-21-B. Reaction 2-23-A, which would be analogous to sulfone formation as in reaction 2-21-A, does occur but only to a very slight extent (7). That reaction 2-21 largely controls the quantity of sulfone formation is shown by an increase in its yield from 6.5 - 18.3% as the temperature is raised from -9 to 75°C, with reaction 2-20 being run at -9°C in all cases (334). The pyrosulfonate mechanism is also considered probable in the gas phase (179).

This hypothesis has the weakness that the key intermediate, benzene-pyrosulfonic acid, has never been isolated or characterized. Attempts to prepare it by treating 1 mole of benzene with 2 moles of SO_3 in liquid SO_2 have, on the other hand, given substantial yields of the sulfonic acid anhydride (7). This general procedure, has in fact, been used for the preparation of a series of aromatic sulfonic acid anhydrides (Section III-A-9), and the reaction, therefore, appears general (78). Definite evidence for the existence of a pyrosulfonate does come, however, from a Raman spectral and freezing-point study of mixtures of methanesulfonic acid and SO_3 (337). Methanesulfonic anhydride was isolated from the same mixture. Equilibria of the following types may therefore be involved:

$$2\ C_6H_5SO_2OSO_3H \rightleftharpoons (C_6H_5SO_2)_2O + H_2SO_4 + SO_3 \qquad (2\text{-}24)$$

$$C_6H_5SO_2OSO_3H + C_6H_5SO_3H \rightleftharpoons (C_6H_5SO_2)_2O + H_2SO_4 \qquad (2\text{-}25)$$

A sequence similar to that outlined above, and also involving a pyrosulfonate intermediate, likewise has been suggested to explain sulfone formation in sulfonations with chlorosulfonic acid (256). The concept that pyro compounds of this general type lead to sulfone formation may receive support from the observation that pyrosulfonate esters, made from SO_3 and the sulfonate ester, give good yields of sulfones (212, 460):

$$RSO_2OR' + SO_3 \longrightarrow RSO_2OSO_2OR' \qquad (2\text{-}26)$$

$$RSO_2OSO_2OR' + R''H \longrightarrow RSO_2R'' + R'OSO_2OH \qquad (2\text{-}27)$$

The fact that little or no sulfone is formed in sulfonations with sulfuric acid is also consistent with the pyrosulfonate theory of their formation, since the pyro compounds are decomposed by water. Not everyone has accepted this theory, however. The older suggestion that sulfone is formed by direct interaction of anhydrous benzenesulfonic acid with benzene is still held (378). Structural factors are also important in sulfone formation, since the amount formed decreases markedly as the

number of alkyl groups on the ring is increased, or with increasing
length of a single substituting group. Sulfone formation with 2-bromo-
ethylbenzene is promoted by adding 5 - 9 wt. -% of boric oxide (107).

Although direct continuous reaction of benzene with SO_3 is rapid
and smooth, and, therefore, attractive industrially, high sulfone formation has prohibited its commercial use. Aside from the work cited
before, there has been no systematic study of the chemistry of sulfone
formation. Empirically developed chemical "sulfone inhibitors," such
as the acetic acid already mentioned, and also including propionic and
peracetic acids (141), acetic anhydride (141), sodium sulfate (404, 464),
pyridine (60), and clay (60), are only partially effective. However, the
addition of SO_3 to benzenesulfonic acid containing a large proportion of
sodium sulfate, followed by the addition of benzene (464), is stated to
give low sulfone; most of the reaction product is then recycled. Another
expedient involves reaction of the benzene with sulfuric acid, which
gives no sulfone; the sulfuric acid, diluted by water of reaction, is now
refortified by adding SO_3 and recycled. This type of operation, as
exemplified by the Dennis-Bull and similar processes (143), has been
used somewhat commercially, but the actual reagent is sulfuric acid
rather than SO_3.

Benzene is not sulfonated by SO_3 complexes made from: thioxane, in
24 hr. at 40°C (283); dimethylformamide (317); pyridine, at 150°C
(412); dioxane, in 7.5 hr. at 65°C, or in 73 hr. at 23°C (317); triethyl
phosphate (453), below 75°C. However, $(2SO_3)$-dioxane is said to sulfonate benzene at room temperature in one day (398), and $(3SO_3)$-tri-
ethyl phosphate reacts at room temperature to give 20 - 40% of the sulfonate ethyl ester (453). It has long been known that benzene is sulfonated by acetyl sulfate (306), but only recently has this principle been
applied to reduce sulfone formation, as discussed before. n-Butyryl
sulfate also sulfonates benzene (307).

b. Benzene Di- and Trisulfonation

m-Benzenedisulfonic acid is commercially important for producing
resorcinol. Although the monosulfonation of benzene proceeds with
ease, as pointed out in the preceding section, introduction of the second group requires more drastic conditions. It has been studied for
many years (393), recently by the Soviet investigators A. A. Spryskov
and A. P. Shestov and co-workers.

Equilibrium is attained at 66.3% meta and 33.7% para benzenedisulfonic acid isomers at 235°C upon prolonged heating with 87% acid
(379). The meta isomer is practically the sole product on treatment of
the monosulfonic acid with oleum for a short period of time at a moderate temperature (e.g., 85°C for 8 hr.) (143). The para disulfonate can
be prepared as the major product by heating a meta disulfonate salt at
425°C for 6 hr. (153). A kinetic study at 25°C, using 0.7 - 43.6%
oleum for preparing the disulfonic acid (74), is concluded to confirm
the mechanism proposed earlier by Brand, comprising stepwise attach-
ment of SO_3 and H^+ to the substrate, followed by loss of a ring proton.

Several problems are encountered in the commercial production of the meta isomer intermediate to the preparation of resorcinol. If sulfuric acid is used for the monosulfonation step, and 65% oleum is then added to introduce the second group, as has been done commercially (143), much spent sulfuric acid is formed, yielding 6.5 tons equivalent gypsum by lime neutralization per ton of resorcinol produced. In contrast, a theoretically perfect process, using SO_3 for both steps, would require only 1.45 tons of reagent and would give no gypsum. This situation has naturally led to interest in the stronger reagents, which, however, can form much undesired sulfone and its sulfonated derivatives. An increase in strength of the oleum used to introduce the second acid group from 17 to 70% results in an increase in sulfone content of the product from 3 to 31% (354). One procedure used commercially has involved the use of low strength oleum to effect monosulfonation, followed by adding liquid SO_3 to the reaction mixture to introduce the second group (158); this procedure represents a compromise between high formation of sulfone and production of a large quantity of spent sulfuric acid. A somewhat similar approach, which would be more time-consuming and which apparently has not been used commercially, comprises preparation of the monosulfonic acid by partial-pressure distillation, followed by adding 65% oleum (377); this method gives 8% sulfone. There is general agreement that the most effective method of combatting sulfone formation is adding sodium sulfate (353, 354, 403). When using 100% acid in the first step and 65% oleum in the second, the addition of 0.5 mole sodium sulfate per mole benzene reduces sulfone from 24.3 to 1.7% (353). As indicated in the preceding section, adding sodium sulfate also reduces sulfone formation in the monosulfonation of benzene. Here it is desired to eliminate both the sulfone and its sulfonated derivatives. The sulfonated sulfones are concluded to form either by sulfonation of the sulfone or by some mechanism from the monosulfonic acid (353); meta-benzenedisulfonic acid has been concluded not to be a sulfone precursor. One currect commercial approach involves concurrently adding SO_3, benzene and sodium sulfate to the disulfonic reaction product at 140 - 160°C (126, 342). This method gives a 90% yield of a product containing 90% meta-benzenedisulfonic acid, 4% H_2SO_4, and 4% of sulfonated sulfone. A major problem in working with benzene disulfonation has been product analysis. Chromatography, polarography, fusion to resorcinol, conversion to the sulfonyl chlorides (354, 377), or to the amine salts (377), and optical (279) methods have been used.

Benzene-1,3,5-trisulfonic acid has been prepared by heating the meta-disulfonic acid with oleum in the presence of mercury at 275 - 300°C (393). More recently, it has been shown (376) that the trisulfonate forms at a reasonable rate with 60% oleum at 200°C and quite rapidly at 230°C. The para and ortho disulfonate isomers do not trisulfonate at 230°C; they would be expected to react less easily than the meta compound for reasons of steric hindrance and unfavorable orientation.

c. Toluene

As indicated in Table 2-13, toluene undergoes sulfonation much more rapidly than benzene; at 25°C with 82.3% acid, $k_t/k_b = 66.1$ (463). Sulfur trioxide also reacts several times as rapidly with toluene (317). Partial rate factors for the isomers in 82.3% acid were established (463) as para: 258, meta: 5.7; ortho: 63.4. These data differ from that previously available and agree for the first time with Brown's free-energy selectivity relationship for other electrophilic substitution reactions of toluene. However, the extent of agreement at other acid strengths was not investigated. A new rapid and quantitative ultraviolet spectrophotometric analytical procedure for the toluenesulfonate isomers should facilitate further study (75).

Factors influencing orientation with various reagents are summarized in Table 2-14. With sulfuric acid, reagent concentration exercises the major influence, the proportion of ortho showing an increase and that of para decreasing, with meta showing some increase. This is explained (77) on the basis that solvation of the transition state of the sterically more hindered ortho isomer decreases with increasing acid concentration. This fact alone might suggest an even greater conversion to ortho isomer with the stronger reagents ClSO$_3$H and SO$_3$. However, the opposite effect has been noted, as shown in Table 2-14. Drastic conditions (high temperature, and a 14 hr. reaction time) leads by desulfonation-resulfonation (cf., Chapter 8) to fairly rapid disappearance of the least stable ortho isomer and substantial conversion to the most stable meta isomer. This method can even be used to prepare the meta isomer.

The partial-pressure distillation procedure - cited before for benzene - has been studied in some detail for toluene, using 96% acid (122, 308a), since this procedure, even though time-consuming, has in the past been commercially favored (203). As stated below, SO$_3$ in liquid SO$_2$ is now also used.

Toluene not only undergoes monosulfonation many times as fast as benzene with SO$_3$, but it is disulfonated more rapidly (74), a reaction which can be reduced during monosulfonation by adding SO$_3$ to the hydrocarbon, rather than vice versa (7, 334), even though this mode of addition gives more sulfone. Addition of liquid SO$_3$ to liquid toluene in the laboratory (7) gives about 5 wt. -% of disulfonate, but the milder vapor form yields less than 1% (7, 151). Toluene also forms sulfones, but considerably less than benzene under comparable conditions (151, 334). Addition of liquid SO$_3$ gives about 11 wt. -% sulfones in the pilot plant (67), and 14% in the laboratory (151). Vaporized SO$_3$ is reported to give 22% (241). By using liquid SO$_2$ as reaction solvent, and especially by simultaneously adding the two reagents dissolved in SO$_2$ to the reactor (7, 292, 334), sulfone formation can be reduced to 2% or even less, and the product sulfonic acid is richer in para isomer (292) than when sulfuric acid is used (cf., Table 2-14). Several American companies manufacture toluenesulfonic acid with SO$_3$ using this solvent.

TABLE 2-14

Orientation in Toluene Sulfonation with H_2SO_4 and with SO_3

Acid Strength	Temp.	Isomer formed, Mole-%			Reference
		Ortho	Meta	Para	
77.6	25	21.2	2.1	76.7	77
	65	16.4	4.3	79.3	77
85.5	25	38.8	2.6	58.6	77
	65	30.5	4.4	65.1	77
95.8	5	51.6	4.7	43.7	77
	25	50.2	4.9	44.9	77
	65	42.4	7.0	50.6	77
98.8	25	49.3	5.2	45.5	77
74	141	3.2	59.6	37.2	470
94	200	5	54	41	373
SO_3	20	-	-	95	374
SO_3	-80	-	-	60	374

Sulfone formation from toluene and SO_3 can also be reduced, as with benzene, by adding acetic or other acids (141, 293, 334).

Sulfur trioxide-dimethylformamide sulfonates toluene very slowly at room temperature (317).

d. Polymethylated Benzenes

Kinetic studies have been reported for the sulfonation of all of the di-, tri-, and tetramethylbenzenes, and for pentamethylbenzene (226, 227, 229, 247, 249). Mesitylene differs from the other trimethylated benzenes in that it also desulfonates during sulfonation; the 1, 2, 3-isomer sulfonates fastest for steric reasons. The tetramethylbenzenes not only undergo sulfonation, but desulfonation, resulfonation, isomerization, and disproportionation as well, with the result that 1, 2, 3, 4-tetramethylbenzenesulfonic acid, being the only stable isomer, is the final product no matter which of the three hydrocarbons is used (227). Disproportionation was concluded to involve the hydrocarbon, and not the sulfonic acid as was previously thought. Sulfonation of the xylenes with 70 - 90% H_2SO_4 is stated to occur in the acid phase (248); the reaction rate increases with the rate of stirring to a certain point and thereafter remains constant. This conclusion has been questioned (217), since heterogeneous sulfonation of toluene has been observed to occur in both phases.

The addition of liquid SO_3 to p-xylene yields about 8 wt. -% sulfone (141, 151), which is less than that formed from toluene; adding acetic acid reduces the yield of it to about 3%. In liquid SO_2, the respective yields of sulfone are 6 and 1.6% (334). m-Xylene is sulfonated immediately and quantitatively by $(2SO_3)$-dioxane (398), but not by SO_3-quinoline at 60°C in 19 hr. (317); $(3SO_3)$-triethyl phosphate reacts at room temperature (453).

The partial-pressure distillation procedure has been used experimentally (244) and commercially (308a) for sulfonating mixed xylenes. Isomer yields obtained with o-xylene are reported in Table 2-15 (276). It will be noted that, as in the case of toluene, low temperature favor sulfonation ortho to a methyl group.

TABLE 2-15

Isomer Distribution in the Sulfonation of O-Xylene
with Concentrated H_2SO_4

Temp.	Wt. -% 3-Isomer	Wt. -% 4-Isomer
10	18	82
50	7	93
70	1.5	98.5
100	0.2	99.8

e. Other Short-Chain Alkylated Benzenes

The homogeneous sulfonation of ethylbenzene and isopropylbenzene at 25°C in 70 - 89% H_2SO_4 (217), and of tert-butylbenzene at 5, 25, and 35°C with 72.4 - 91.0% acid (76), is first order with respect to the organic compound. At a given acid concentration, the relative rate constants decrease in the order toluene, ethylbenzene, isopropylbenzene, tert-butylbenzene, probably as a consequence of increasing steric hindrance for ortho substitution in that order (76). Dealkylation of tert-butylbenzene occurs under the conditions used. An earlier study of the heterogeneous sulfonation of ethylbenzene at 0 - 115°C in 70 - 90.6% H_2SO_4 (248) gave rate constants based on the assumptions that sulfonation occurs only in the acid phase, and that solubility of the hydrocarbon in that phase is not temperature-dependent. Both of these assumptions have been questioned (217), since heterogeneous sulfonation of toluene has been found to occur in both phases.

Ethylbenzene, sulfonated in liquid SO_2 with SO_3, formed sulfone to about the same extent as toluene (334). The same technique gives smooth sulfonation of the mixed isomers of diisopropylbenzene and of di-sec-amylbenzene (7). Tert-butylbenzene also reacts smoothly, but p-di-tert-butylbenzene at 1:1 molar ratio, gives 0.5 mole of unreacted starting material and sulfonates derived from isobutylene and from mono-tert-butylbenzene (7). This result is attributed to high steric hindrance of the tert-butyl group, combined with its known ease of removal from the benzene ring under acid conditions.

A kinetic study of the sulfonation of the three ethyltoluene isomers showed the same relative rates as the corresponding xylenes: meta > ortho > para (246), but the rates were 2 to 4 times faster than those of the xylenes. This remarkable difference lessened at higher temperatures and acid strengths. The meta and para isomers underwent hydrolysis during sulfonation, but the ortho isomer did not, since the sulfonate derived from it contains no alkyl groups ortho to the sulfonic acid group.

f. Long-Chain Alkylated Benzenes

These sulfonates, commercially important as surface-active agents, are made from benzene alkylated with propylene tetramer or with kerosene-derived, n-alkyl chlorides. This process yields a mixture of alkylates with varying chain length, roughly separable by fractionation. A low-boiling fraction, with average side chain about C9, has been sulfonated with SO_3 vapor (127). The C12 alkylated benzene fraction ("dodecylbenzene detergent alkylate") is of major commercial interest for making sulfonates widely used as surface-active agents. A variety of reagents has been employed commercially (143), including 98% acid, various strengths of oleum, SO_3 vapor, and SO_3 dissolved in SO_2. Sulfur trioxide vapor and oleum have been employed with the high-boiling alkylated benzene fraction ("polydodecylbenzene") (149), with dodecyltoluene (131), and with "keryl benzene" made by alkylating benzene with chlorinated long-chain hydrocarbons isolated from kerosene.

The presence of the long alkyl chain in such compounds leads to different behavior during sulfonation from that noted with benzene or toluene. Dealkylation can occur, forming long-chain olefins, with a tendency which varies inversely with the reagent strength. Although the quantity of olefin formed is small, a noticeable difference in product odor results which can be important in household detergents. Sulfur trioxide vapor thus gives the least dealkylation and the best odor; sulfuric acid behaves oppositely. On the other hand, liquid SO_3 cannot be added directly to undiluted dodecylbenzene without prohibitive dealkylation (149, 151), although excellent results are obtained when liquid SO_2 is employed as reaction solvent. The partial-pressure distillation method cannot be used with these long-chain alkylated benzenes, as a result of their high boiling points, and because dealkylation would occur. The small quantity of dialkylated benzene present in detergent alkylate (356), and the larger amount present in polydodecylbenzene (149), are partially dealkylated when using oleum, but remain unchanged when employing SO_3 vapor.

Unlike benzene or toluene, dodecylbenzene forms sulfones only in small amounts (356), but it does give by-product sulfonic anhydrides, possibly via the same types of intermediates as indicated in Equations 2-24 and 2-25. The reason for this interesting difference is not clear.

Steric factors are also noteworthy with the long-chain alkylated benzenes. Toluene yields considerable ortho sulfonate. This is also true of terminally-substituted long-chain benzenes, such as 1-phenyl-octane, or 1-phenyldodecane, which forms 15% ortho isomer (156). However, with the phenyl group in the 2-position, the ortho isomer drops to 7%, and further decrease occurs as the phenyl group is moved toward the center of the chain. The extreme is reached with the para dialkylated benzenes in polydodecylbenzene; steric blockage is virtually complete and hardly any sulfonation occurs (149).

g. Petroleum Oils

Petroleum lubricant raffinates are important raw materials for in-dustrial sulfonates. Although the exact chemical composition of the derived sulfonates is not known, detailed study of the most important group - the so-called "mahogany" or oil-soluble materials - indicates (61) that they are mixtures generally resembling the long-chain alky-lated benzenesulfonates. Similar processes are applicable (143), in-cluding the use of oleum, SO_3 vapor (148, 222), and SO_3 dissolved in liquid SO_2 (186). All of these methods are used commercially. The SO_2 solvent procedure entails no solvent cost, since it is produced by side-reactions during sulfonation.

Although the reagents and reaction conditions for sulfonating lubri-cating oils are generally similar to those used for dodecylbenzene, there are differences, since the latter is a relatively pure material, while the former is a mixture of hydrocarbons ranging from highly reactive to inert. Much of the art of petroleum sulfonate manufacture is, therefore, concerned with the correct choice of base stock and its method of refining, and with procedures for separation of the product sulfonate from sludge and unreacted oil. Petroleum hydrocarbons dif-fer from dodecylbenzene in not forming anhydrides during SO_3 sulfona-tion.

h. Polystyrene

Two types of sulfonated polystyrene are of commercial interest, one completely water-soluble, prepared from styrene homopolymer, the other entirely insoluble in water and made from styrene-divinylbenzene copolymer (344). Both types are fairly easy to sulfonate, therein resembling the nonpolymeric alkylated benzenes such as toluene or xylene, but their polymeric nature does entail certain unusual problems.

In preparing the water-soluble material from styrene homopolymer, sulfone formation must be avoided, since more than 0.1% gives an insoluble product (331). This can be achieved by employing a large excess of sulfuric acid (57), but separation of the sulfonate from the residual acid, or from the sulfate salt, is difficult. This problem led to consideration of the use of SO_3. It is somewhat surprising that such a strong reagent, which favors sulfone formation, can be used at all. Observance of the following conditions (331) makes this possible, using SO_3 either as vapor or liquid: (1) use of solvents (liquid SO_2 for the SO_3; carbon tetrachloride for the polymer, which is poorly soluble in SO_2); (2) low dilutions (1 - 10%); (3) pure solvents; (4) low reaction temperatures (-20 - 45°C); (5) use of SO_3 free of higher polymers; (6) efficient agitation; (7) concurrent feeding of reagents; (8) low molar excess of sulfonating agent; (9) use of a small reaction vessel; (10) use of vinyl-toluene-containing polymers; and (11) rapid workup of the finished product. Liquid SO_2 has proved especially useful as a reaction solvent for sulfonating styrene or vinyltoluene copolymers with acrylonitrile or maleic anhydride (30). Reaction of the powdered solid polymer with SO_3 gas has also been effected in a fluidized bed (115).

Sulfur trioxide adducts, as with bis-(2-chloroethyl) ether (322), dioxane (359), thioxane (359), or acetone (37) have also been used. The first complex yields (331) a water-soluble sulfonate more easily than the second, but some crosslinking by sulfone formation does occur, and stringent control is necessary. The SO_3-trialkyl phosphate complexes are of special interest (453), since those containing 2 - 4 moles SO_3 per mole phosphate yield entirely water-soluble sulfonates under varied conditions even from high molecular-weight polymers. These complexes are not ordinary sulfonating reagents, however, since as much as 40% of the groups introduced can be alkylsulfonate, rather than free sulfonic acid groups. Apparently, reactions 1-8 and 1-9 occur without accompanying sulfone formation, possibly by a mechanism similar to that shown in reaction 2-23-B. This result suggests consideration of other cheaper reagents for direct introduction of the alkylsulfonate moiety, such as methyl chlorosulfonate, which is known to react with aromatic hydrocarbons as follows (130):

$$RH + CH_3OSO_2Cl \longrightarrow RSO_2OCH_3 + HCl \qquad (2-28)$$

Ion-exchange resins are made by sulfonating styrene-divinyl-benzene copolymers. Since the reaction is entirely heterogeneous, beads of the copolymer are preswollen with an organic solvent to insure smooth and uniform penetration of the sulfonating agent (482); otherwise, straining and cracking occur, yielding a weak and unstable resin. The rate of sulfonation in such a polymer is diffusion-controlled; the higher the degree of crosslinking, the slower the rate. Sulfonation can be accomplished with excess concentrated H_2SO_4 at 100°C (482), resulting in the introduction of one sulfonic group for each benzene ring. Removal of the excess reagent after reaction involves a volume change and the dissipation of the heat of dilution. Since these factors also tend to disrupt the beads, special procedures must be used at this stage to moderate the reaction, e.g., treatment with concentrated aqueous sodium chloride instead of sodium hydroxide. As might be expected, some cracking of the copolymer beads occur when employing SO_3 dissolved in SO_2 (31).

A further advance has comprised conducting the copolymerization in the presence of solvents (268). Depending on the proportion of the solvent and crosslinking agent, a gradation in properties from those of an expanded network to those of a macroporous material is obtained. After sulfonation, these new "disentangled" copolymers take up normally incompatible solvents, which the older, conventional types do not. They also show marked differences from the earlier types in their ion-exchange kinetics and equilibria. Such macroreticulate resins have been sulfonated with SO_3 gas in a fluidized bed operation (325).

Sulfonated polystyrenes can be made either by sulfonating the polymers, as discussed above, or by polymerizing styrenesulfonic acid salts (177), as indicated in Chapter 5. The sulfonated polymers made by the two methods differ somewhat in properties. By taking advantage of the fact that the rate of sulfonation is diffusion-controlled, and therefore dependent upon the degree of crosslinking, and the fact that the rate of desulfonation using concentrated HCl is independent of crosslinking, it is possible to make ion-exchange resins with sulfonic acid groups, the number of which either is, or is not, related to pore size (282).

Styrene-divinylbenzene copolymer membranes are being used increasingly. These can be sulfonated with SO_3 using 1,2-dichloroethane as solvent (80). Such membranes have also been sulfonated industrially with benzoyl sulfate, made from SO_3 and benzoic acid, the latter being recovered and recycled (261).

$$C_6H_5COOH \xrightarrow{SO_3} C_6H_5COOSO_3H \xrightarrow{ArH} ArSO_3H + C_6H_5COOH \quad (2\text{-}29)$$

3. HALOGENATED BENZENES

The sulfonation of halogenated benzenes and alkylbenzenes has been well reviewed by Suter (393) through 1941. As shown in Tables 2-12 and 2-13, the halobenzenes sulfonate more slowly than the parent hydrocarbons, since the halogen atoms are electron-withdrawing. Sulfur trioxide-dioxane sulfonates benzene, but not chlorobenzene (398).

A study of the conversion of chlorobenzene to the 4-sulfonic acid using ClSO$_3$H has been reported (86). The halogens are ortho-para-directing and very little meta isomer is ordinarily formed. However, chlorobenzene, heated in a sealed tube at 185 - 238°C with 94% acid, yields 46% para, 54% meta, and none of the ortho isomers (373), because the second is more stable and accumulates in the reaction mixture under drastic conditions by desulfonation-resulfonation, as discussed in Chapter 8. Earlier work (393) had similarly shown that at 300°C 20% oleum forms the 3,5-disulfonic acid from chlorobenzene, from the 4-sulfonic acid, or from the 2,4-disulfonic acid.

Numerous halogenated benzene mixtures have been separated into their component isomers by differential sulfonation-desulfonation, as discussed in Chapter 8. A series of 24 halogenated benzenes were reacted with oleum forming the sulfonic acid anhydrides directly, as indicated in Section III-A-9. Direct conversion to the sulfonyl halides with ClSO$_3$H is mentioned in Section III-A-10. The sulfonic acid is assumed to be intermediate to the formation of both types of products.

Direct addition of liquid SO$_3$ to the undiluted organic compound over the range 25 - 105°C is practical for sulfonating chloro- (151), bromo-, 1-chloro-4-bromo-, 1,4-dibromo-, and 1,2,4-trichloro-, and -tribromobenzenes (459); sulfones are usually formed as by-products. Bromobenzene (324) and iodobenzene (95) forms 96 and 98% of the para isomers with SO$_3$ in liquid SO$_2$. Hexachlorobenzene does not react with SO$_3$ even at 200°C (10).

4. AMINES

Aniline and its derivatives are sulfonated by two procedures which yield different isomers. Liquid-phase sulfonation at moderate temperatures (e.g., 30 - 80°C) with excess acid or oleum will introduce the sulfonic group meta to the amino group, as with o- or p-anisidine, or 5-aminosalicylic acid, or para to it (as with 2,5-dichloroaniline) (202). Aniline forms a mixture of all three isomers, while dimethylaniline gives the meta and para compounds (5). The "baking process," on the other hand, always yields the para isomer; if the para position is blocked, it yields the ortho compound. This procedure involves heating the amine sulfate at 170 - 280°C, either in solid form, or as a suspension in a solvent such as o-dichlorobenzene (72), or diphenyl sulfone (361). It has been used with aniline (143) and with a variety of substituted anilines, naphthylamines, and aminobiphenyls (72, 361).

The rapid simultaneous formation of substantial amounts of meta and ortho-para isomers observed with aniline and dimethylaniline is apparently unique in aromatic substitution. Mixtures of this kind can be made from phenol (cf., Table 2-16), toluene (Table 2-14), or chlorobenzene, but only by prolonged heating at elevated temperature. (Subjection of aniline to such conditions would be of interest.) This effect has usually been explained by holding that the trialkylammonium group - present in high concentration - is meta-directing and strongly deactivating, whereas

TABLE 2-16

Sulfonation of Phenol and 2-Cresol with H_2SO_4

Hours	Temp.	Ortho,%	Meta,%	Para,%	Reference
		Phenol			
120	20	39	0	61	275
8	40	36	0	64	275
8	100	4	0	96	275
30	120	Low	3.7	96	221
150	160	Low	20.8	79	221
50	180	Low	23.2	76	221
20	209	Low	38.1	61	221
		2-Cresol			
24	-10	0	0	100	405
-	20	47	0	53	275
-	40	35	0	65	275
12	20 - 60	0	25	75	405
-	100	16	0	84	275
1	150	0	87	18	405

the free amino group, because of its ability to enter into conjugative resonance with the aromatic system, is ortho-para-directing and activating, which tends to make up for its low concentration:

$$\text{Meta} \xleftarrow{\quad SO_3 \quad} \underset{2}{ArNR_2^+}(H) \underset{-H^+}{\overset{+H^+}{\rightleftharpoons}} \underset{2}{ArNR_2}(\cdot\cdot) \xrightarrow{\quad SO_3 \quad} \text{Ortho-Para}$$

$$(2\text{-}30)$$

This assumption is apparently rendered unnecessary by the recent proposal that the anilinium ion is para, as well as meta-directing (323). It has been suggested (5) that the ortho-para-directing species for aniline is actually the sulfamic acid, although the free base is concluded to fulfill this function with dimethylaniline. It seems more likely, however, that the sulfamic acid, which is known to be unstable, is present only incidentally (206).

The sulfamation of aromatic amines is discussed in Chapter 7. Sulfanilic acid is a useful sulfoarylating reagent, as indicated in Chapter 5.

5. PHENOLIC COMPOUNDS

Phenols and many of their derivatives sulfonate with unusual ease (393). They undergo reaction on the ring with SO_3 or its hydrates, or with SO_3 adducts at elevated temperature. At moderate temperatures, the adducts form sulfates (cf. , Chapter 6).

As indicated in Table 2-16, the position of the entering sulfonate group is initially ortho-para. With increasing time and/or temperature, the least stable ortho isomer disappears and is gradually replaced by the most stable meta compound, which comprises about 40% at equilibrium (221). This occurs by desulfonation-resulfonation (cf. , Chapter 8). 2-Cresol appears to behave similarly, although the data are less consistent.

Phenol and phenolic ethers react so easily that even comparatively inert reagents, such as sulfamic acid or SO_3-pyridine (393) can be used at 170 - 200°C to form the 4-sulfonate. Phenol has been monosulfonated by direct addition of liquid SO_3 at 50°C, disulfonated at 95°C, and trisulfonated at 120°C (96). 2-Cresol, guaiacol, 2-chlorophenol, 2, 6-xylenol, and resorcinol were likewise monosulfonated above their melting points. Phenol was disulfonated with SO_3 vapor (479). The purity of these sulfonates was not determined. Salicylic acid reacts with liquid SO_3 in tetrachloroethylene suspension (151), and methyl salicylate with SO_3 vapor at 25 - 110°C (176). 3-Hydroxy- (350) and 4-hydroxybenzoic (231) acids were reacted as solids with SO_3 vapor, a rather cumbersome procedure. The same method was employed with 3-(4-hydroxyphenyl)-propionic (phloretic) acid (280). Anisole has been sulfonated with SO_3 vapor (65), and with SO_3-dioxane at room temperature (469). The rate of reaction of 4-nitroanisole with SO_3 is reported in Table 2-12. Diphenyl ether gives 93% of the sulfonic acid with acetyl sulfate (392). Dodecyldiphenyl ether has been disulfonated to a commercial surfactant with SO_3 in methylene chloride (108, 381). Phenyl benzoate was mono- and trisulfonated in a heterogeneous reaction with SO_3 vapor (119); excess SO_3 causes ester cleavage.

Phenolsulfonic acid is used as a sulfoarylating reagent, as discussed in Chapter 5.

6. MONO- AND DICARBOXYLIC ACIDS AND RELATED COMPOUNDS

Benzoic acid forms benzoyl sulfate with SO_3-dioxane (398) or with SO_3 in 1, 2-dichloroethane (261) at room temperature:

$$C_6H_5COOH + SO_3 \longrightarrow C_6H_5COOSO_3H \qquad (2\text{-}31)$$

As noted in Section III-A-2, the sulfate has been used as a sulfonating agent, with recovery and recycle of the benzoic acid (Eq. 2-29). It has also been prepared from benzoyl chloride and sulfuric acid (406).

Aromatic carboxylic acids are comparatively difficult to sulfonate, since the carboxyl group is strongly deactivating (393). Oleum or sulfuric acid forms all three isomers, the stability of which decreases in the order ortho-meta-para. The ortho isomer disappears rapidly in favor of the meta, which comprises about 95% of the product under normal conditions. Prolonged heating at high temperatures results in gradual buildup of the para isomer at the expense of the meta, but in work to date this has not been carried beyond conversion of 15 - 20% of the meta to the para isomers. Practical preparation of the para isomer involves indirect procedures such as oxidation of paratoluene-sulfonic acid, or the diazonium method cited in Chapter 3. Benzoic acid forms the 3,5-disulfonic acid with 35% oleum in 7 hr. at 260°C (1).

Sulfur trioxide, on the other hand, forms only the meta isomer. Molten benzoic acid can be treated with the liquid (151) or the vapor (240). Benzoyl sulfate is presumably the intermediate with SO_3, as well as with its hydrates (240, 318), since the SO_3 does not boil out even though the reaction proceeds much above its boiling point (151). Sulfur trioxide, either as solid, liquid, or gas, has been used to sulfonate the toluic acids (151), 4-n-propyl- and 4-isopropylbenzoic acids (483), the various chloro- (151), and 4-bromobenzoic (41) acids. 3,5-Dimethylbenzoic acid is converted to a mixture of the two possible isomers (321), both of which are abnormally oriented with relation to the carboxyl group. 3-Nitrobenzoic acid may decompose violently upon heating with liquid SO_3 (7).

Aromatic acid chlorides, upon heating with SO_3 for 3 hr. at 110 - 160°C, form the sulfonyl chlorides of the acids:

$$C_6H_5COCl + SO_3 \longrightarrow C_6H_4(1\text{-}COOH)\ (3\text{-}SO_2Cl) \qquad (2\text{-}32)$$

This approach has been used with benzoyl, 2-toluyl, 4-chlorobenzoyl (264), and other (263) acid chlorides. Benzoyl chloride had previously been thought to yield the carboxylic acid chloride of the sulfonic acid. A nitrobenzoyl chloride is reported (118) not to react.

Aromatic dicarboxylic acids are even more difficult to sulfonate than the mono analogues. Phthalic anhydride is 99% monosulfonated with SO_3 at 190 - 210°C in 23 hr. (466). With three equivalents of SO_3, the reaction is largely completed in 6 hr. at 100°C (136), and entirely complete after 10 more hours at 190°C. This sulfonation can also be run in an autoclave (135), although such is not required, since the SO_3 forms an adduct with the anhydride, and is, therefore, retained in the reaction mixture, as with benzoic acid. In the presence of mercuric sulfate, the 3,5-disulfonated anhydride is formed in 93% yield even in 8 hr. (466). Isophthalic acid also is monosulfonated by SO_3 at 250°C

(62, 180). Terephthalic acid does not react with SO_3 under conditions suitable for the other two isomers (7), although it has been monosulfonated with oleum at 260°C under pressure (345). This behavior is expected, since substitution occurs ortho to a carboxyl group, which is both sterically and electronically unfavorable. 2, 6-Disulfoterephthalic acid has been prepared as follows (347):

$$C_6H_4(1\text{-}C_2H_5)\ (4\text{-}COOH) \xrightarrow{\text{Oleum}} C_6H_2(1\text{-}C_2H_5)\ (2, 6\text{-}di\ SO_3H)\ (4\text{-}COOH)$$

$$\downarrow O \qquad\qquad (2\text{-}33)$$

$$C_6H_2(1, 4\text{-}di\ COOH)\ (2, 6\text{-}di\ SO_3H)$$

Aromatic mononitriles form cyclic sulfamates, as discussed in Chapter 7. Amides are dehydrated to the nitriles or undergo sulfamation. Phthalonitrile, treated with H_2SO_4 or $ClSO_3H$ under sulfonating conditions, forms phthalimide, but no sulfonic acid (200).

Several of the compounds mentioned in this section have been employed as sulfoarylating agents, as discussed in Chapter 5.

7. NITRO COMPOUNDS

The sulfonation of nitrobenzene gives almost entirely the meta isomer; the nitration of benzenesulfonic acid, on the other hand, yields a mixture (393). Gradual addition of liquid or vaporized SO_3 to nitrobenzene over the range 100 - 150°C is now used industrially (7), even though some sulfone is formed. Another commercial approach involves 65% oleum in a two-stage continuous process at 80 - 120°C (4). The reaction of nitrobenzene with a mixture of SO_3 and FSO_3H is mentioned in Section III-A-10.

Data for the rates of reaction of nitrobenzene, 4-nitrotoluene, and 4-nitroanisole with SO_3 are presented in Table 2-12. A study of the sulfonation of the nitrotoluene under the conditions used to make TNT (232) has shown that the dinitrotoluenes and the meta mononitro compound do not sulfonate under nitrating conditions. The sulfonation of 4-nitrochlorobenzene or of 2-nitro-6-chlorotoluene with oleum (144), or of 3-nitrobenzoic acid with liquid SO_3 (7) can lead to violent explosions.

8. MISCELLANEOUS BENZENE DERIVATIVES

Benzaldehyde (240) has been reported to yield only the meta sulfonic acid upon treatment with SO_3 vapor at 140°C. Others, however, have found (7, 118) that the reaction gives only a small amount of the desired product, possibly because of the sensitivity of the aldehyde group to oxidation. Oleum gives satisfactory results (7, 467). As shown in Chapter 5, this sulfonate is a sulfoarylating reagent.

Benzoquinone (420) does not react with SO_3-pyridine, but it does react variously with SO_3-dioxane, depending upon the mole ratio used:

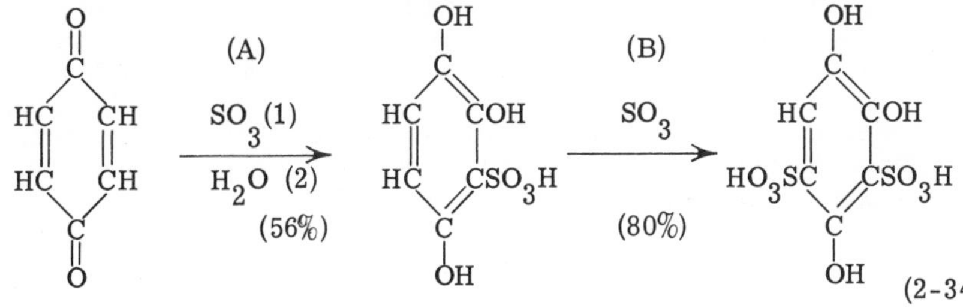

(2-34)

In reaction 2-34-A, the quinone reacts as a typical alkene via a β-sultone or carbyl sulfate-type intermediate, as discussed in Section II-B-1. Reaction 2-34-B is a typical ring sulfonation. Toluquinone and 1,4-naphthoquinone behave similarly. m- and p-Xyloquinone and 1,2-naphthoquinone, on the other hand, form the mono- or disulfonated quinones. These reactions parallel those of mesityl oxide, as shown in Table 2-10; there is some structural resemblance. Duroquinone, as expected, did not react, since it has no ring hydrogen atoms.

Aryltrimethylsilanes react as follows with SO_3 (113):

$$ArSi(CH_3)_3 \xrightarrow{SO_3} ArSO_2OSi(CH_3)_3 \xrightarrow{H_2O} ArSO_3H +$$

$$HOSi(CH_3)_3$$

(2-35)

Cleavage occurs according to the concepts developed in Chapter 6, Section VIII-D. The yields are good, the reaction general, and the conditions mild. This approach has been suggested for preparing aromatic sulfonic acids of abnormal orientation, e.g., 3-toluenesulfonic acid.

9. THE DIRECT PREPARATION OF AROMATIC SULFONIC ANHYDRIDES

Although aromatic sulfonic anhydrides have been prepared in the past by various methods (279), it was recognized only fairly recently that they can be made by simple addition of the aromatic compound to excess strong oleum or SO_3 dissolved in nitromethane. Twenty-four halogenated benzenesulfonic anhydrides were thus prepared from 65% oleum (255, 256). Sulfone formation and disulfonation occurred to only a minor degree, and only with 1,2,3-tribromobenzene was more than one isomer formed. Sulfur trioxide in nitromethane was used at 0°C with 4 aromatic hydrocarbons and 12 halogenated aromatic hydrocarbons (78). Five compounds gave no product in this study (benzene, anthracene, anthraquinone, p-dichlorobenzene, and p-diiodobenzene). The author refers to his reagent as a "solution of SO_3 in nitromethane," but, as indicated in Chapter 1, it seems likely that it comprises a solution of SO_3-nitromethane complex. As expected, yields increases inversely with the sulfuric acid content of the reagent, since 20% oleum gave no anhydride, and SO_3-nitromethane formed more product than 65% oleum. Sulfur trioxide in liquid SO_2 at -10°C yields more toluenesulfonic anhydride (7) than SO_3-nitromethane; this approach has not been explored with other aromatic compounds.

It has been suggested (256) that the anhydrides form via the pyrosulfonic acids, as indicated in Equations 2-20, 2-24, and 2-25.

10. THE DIRECT PREPARATION OF AROMATIC SULFONYL HALIDES

This procedure involves two reactions:

$$RH + ClSO_3H \longrightarrow RSO_3H + HCl \qquad (2\text{-}36)$$

$$RSO_3H + ClSO_3H \rightleftharpoons RSO_2Cl + H_2SO_4 \qquad (2\text{-}37)$$

Reaction 2-36 occurs easily, since hydrogen chloride is evolved, driving the reaction to completion. Reaction 2-37, on the other hand, is an equilibrium, and a considerable excess of reagent is required to insure a fair yield of the desired sulfonyl chloride. Reaction 2-36 is sometimes used in the laboratory, and rarely on a commercial scale, for preparing sulfonic acids. Sulfonyl fluorides are prepared similarly using FSO_3H. Compounds thus converted to their sulfonyl chlorides commercially, include acetanilide (143) (an intermediate for all sulfa drugs), benzene and chlorobenzene (for insecticides), salicylic acid, 2-hydroxy-1-naphthoic acid, and chlorinated nitrobenzene (all as dye intermediates), and toluene (for saccharin). In the case of toluene, a low temperature (about 0°C) is used to promote preferential formation of the desired ortho isomer; in the other cases the range 10 - 60°C is common.

Representative types of compounds thus converted to their sulfonyl chlorides are listed in Table 2-17. The variety of materials amenable to such conversion is of interest, as well as the fact that fairly sensitive functional groups, such as ester, amide or olefinic, can retain their identity during the sulfonation step, as well as in the aqueous working up procedure. The trichlorosilane group, however, is hydrolyzed to siloxane.

The di(chlorosulfonation) of anilines meta-substituted by halogen, methoxy, nitro, amino, trifluoromethyl or methyl groups has become of special interest because of the activity of their derivatives as diuretics (83, 242, 294, 305, 488). The reaction is usually run by heating with excess $ClSO_3H$ for 2 - 4 hr. at 115 - 180°C; yields are improved by adding NaCl or $SOCl_2$. Dichloro- and chloroiodoanilines have likewise been converted to the disulfonyl chlorides (294). Aniline and acetanilide form the trisulfonyl chlorides in preference (294), although N-methylaniline forms the di- compound (83). A commercial plant for converting m-chloroaniline to the disulfonyl chloride has been generally described (238). Fluorobenzene and meta-oriented fluoro-, chloro-, and bromotoluenes, as well as the corresponding chlorofluoro-, chlorobromo-, and dibromobenzenes, were also di(chlorosulfonated) in 20 hr. at 170°C using pentachloroethane as reaction solvent (42).

TABLE 2-17

Direct Preparation of Aromatic Monosulfonyl Chlorides

Compound	Reference
Thirty-five alkylated benzenes	192
Forty-three aromatic ethers	98, 194, 299
Twenty-eight halogenated benzenes	193, 388
Acyl anilides, imides, and ureas; 4-alkyl anilides	298, 299, 365
Octyl-, decyl-, and dodecylbenzenes and toluenes	89, 182
Hydroxy- and chlorobenzoic acids	199, 339, 484
Dianilinoanthraquinones	338
Cinnamic acid and amide	302
4-Nitrotoluene, 2-nitrochlorobenzene	79, 352
Chlorotoluidines	85
4-Methoxybenzenephosphonic acid	175
2-Phenylethyl trichlorosilane	24
Phenoxyacetic esters	56, 380

The evolution of hydrogen chloride in reaction 2-36 can be avoided by using a mixture of SO_3 and $ClSO_3H$, the quantity of SO_3 being equimolar with the organic reactant. Reaction 2-36 now becomes:

$$RH + SO_3 \longrightarrow RSO_3H \qquad (2\text{-}38)$$

This approach has been applied to benzene, chlorobenzene, 1, 2, 4-trichlorobenzene, and to acetanilide, and has been used to prepare the sulfonyl fluoride of nitrobenzene (138, 151). It has also been applied to isophthalic acid (360). Acetanilide forms a more storage-stable sulfonyl chloride by this procedure than when using $ClSO_3H$ alone.

Although reaction 2-36 goes to completion easily, since HCl is evolved, reaction 2-37 is an equilibrium and, just as when using SO_3 hydrates for sulfonation, as discussed in Section III-A-1, special means are required to drive it to maximum completion. Completing reaction by distillative removal of a reaction product - a useful technique when sulfonating with sulfuric acid - cannot be applied here because of the high boiling points. Use of excess sulfonating agent (varying from 1 to as high as 6 moles $ClSO_3H$ per mole of organic compound) does improve the yield, and is standard laboratory and industrial practice, even though complete reaction is still not achieved. For example, in one commercial procedure for preparing the sulfa drug intermediate 4-acetylaminobenzenesulfonyl chloride, 5. 4 moles of $ClSO_3H$ are used per mole of acetanilide (143).

Chemical removal of the H_2SO_4 formed has also been considered as a method for completing reaction 2-37. The yield of benzenesulfonyl chloride was raised from 75 - 90% by the combined use of excess $ClSO_3H$ and NaCl, the latter removing the sulfuric acid by forming sodium acid sulfate and HCl, and at the same time reducing sulfone formation from 5 to 0. 2% (196, 251). (Reduction of sulfone formation from benzene with sodium sulfate was mentioned in Section III-A-2). Further improvement was obtained, in terms of reduced $ClSO_3H$ requirements, by the combined use of NaCl and an inert organic solvent such as carbon tetrachloride, which must be present during the reaction, rather than added later to extract the sulfonyl chloride after drowning the reaction mixture on ice. The data are summarized in Table 2-18.

An ingenious expedient for chemical removal of the H_2SO_4 comprises adding a reagent capable of reconverting it to $ClSO_3H$, thereby not only reducing the required $ClSO_3H$, but also driving the reaction to completion (343). Carbon tetrachloride and sulfur with chlorine have been used; they react in each case with H_2SO_4 as follows:

$$CCl_4 + H_2SO_4 \longrightarrow ClSO_3H + HCl + COCl_2 \qquad (2\text{-}39)$$

$$S + 2\ Cl_2 + 2\ H_2SO_4 \longrightarrow 2\ ClSO_3H + SO_2 + 2\ HCl \qquad (2\text{-}40)$$

Sulfonation with $ClSO_3H$ is thought to involve pyrosulfonate intermediates similar to those proposed for SO_3, as discussed in Section III-A-2 (256). Sulfone formation is noted with both reagents (193).

TABLE 2-18

Benzenesulfonyl Chloride Yield Data

Method	Benzene, moles	$ClSO_3H$, moles	NaCl, moles	Yield, %
Standard (no solvent, no NaCl)	2	6	None	76
NaCl	2	10.7	2.1	90
NaCl plus solvent	2	6	2.1	90

B. Naphthalene and Biphenyl Derivatives

The mono- and polysulfonation of naphthalene, as well as of its hydroxyl and amino derivatives, has been important for many years for the industrial preparation of many dye intermediates. This complex and specialized field has been reviewed in considerable detail by others (117, 279, 304, 393, 461), and will, therefore, be considered here only very briefly and from the standpoint of the general principles involved.

Nearly all of these sulfonations are effected with sulfuric acid or oleum. Mixtures are always formed, but satisfactory yields of the desired isomers are achieved by a careful choice of acid: hydrocarbon ratio, acid concentration, and time-temperature relationship, and the use of correct product workup procedures. In preparing polysulfonic acids in the naphthalene series, including the hydroxyl and amino derivatives, it is often customary to add the reagents in several steps, with gradually increasing temperature and acid concentration. Low temperatures (i.e., below about 100°C) and short reaction times favor sulfonation in the more electron-rich 1- (or α) positions, but the more thermodynamically stable 2-isomers accumulate at the expense of the 1-isomers with the passage of time, especially at elevated temperatures. This occurs intermolecularly by desulfonation-resulfonation, as discussed in Chapter 8, Section III-C. Hydrolytic desulfonation has been employed for the preparation of certain hydroxy- and aminonaphthalene-sulfonic acids, as pointed out in Chapter 8, Section III-D-4. Hydroxy- and aminonaphthalenesulfonic acids are also made by application of the Bucherer reaction, in which an amino group in a sulfonic acid is exchanged for a hydroxyl group, or vice versa. This approach is discussed in Chapter 3, Section III-B.

Naphthalene monosulfonates much more rapidly than benzene, as indicated in Table 2-13. A summary of conditions which can be used for the practical preparation of the two monosulfonic acids is given below:

Spryskov and co-workers have made a lengthy study of the monosulfonation of naphthalene with sulfuric acid in sealed tubes under varying conditions (254, 371); some of their data are cited in Table 2-19. It is noteworthy that nearly all of the acid applied reacts at 100°C, provided a sufficiently long time is employed (1444 hr.). Initial attack forms the 1-isomer, but the more stable 2-isomer accumulates at the expense of the 1-isomer under the influence of time and temperature.

Study of the polysulfonation of naphthalene and its derivatives has led to the formulation of empirical orientation rules to the effect that: (1) a second sulfonic group cannot be introduced ortho, para, or peri to an existing sulfonic group; (2) in disulfonation of a naphthalenemonosulfonic acid, the second group enters the unsulfonated ring. The implication of these rules is that of the ten theoretical disulfonic acids, only six can be obtained by direct sulfonation, and that only three of the fourteen possible trisulfonic acids can be so prepared. Only 1 tetrasulfonic acid (the 1, 3, 5, 7-isomer) has been obtained by direct sulfonation; it can be made in good yields. Sulfone formation, which complicates the disulfonation of benzene, is not a practical problem with naphthalene. The factors involved in the case of naphthalene have been studied, however, by Ito and co-workers (208) in the course of a detailed study of various aspects of naphthalene sulfonation (208a).

Little attention has been given to the use of other reagents for sulfonating naphthalene. Side reactions, including sulfone formation and polysulfonation are apparently extensive with SO_3 vapor (34, 110). With chloroform as solvent, an 88% yield of monosulfonate is obtained below 10°C (88). Sulfur trioxide-dioxane (398) and SO_3-thioxane (283) sulfonate naphthalene at room temperature, and SO_3-pyridine at 170°C forms mostly 1-sulfonate, with a little of the 2-isomer (32).

With more than one molar equivalent of SO_3, naphthalene yields different products depending upon conditions. With dimethyl or diethyl sulfates, or phosphorus oxychloride, as reaction solvents, 1.5 moles of SO_3 vapor at 25°C gives the anhydride of 1-naphthalenesulfonic acid (243):

$$2 \ C_{10}H_8 + 3 \ SO_3 \longrightarrow (C_{10}H_7SO_2)_2O + H_2SO_4 \qquad (2\text{-}41)$$

TABLE 2-19

Sulfonation of Naphthalene

Temp.	Time Hr.	Acid, conc., %	Mole ratio, $C_{10}H_8:H_2SO_4$	Sulfonic acids; 2-[a], 1-[a], Di-[b]			Residual H_2SO_4[c]
100	400	92.8	1.0	80.7	19.3	17.2	15.9
100	600	92.8	1.0	83.9	16.1	14.8	14.1
100	1000	192.8	1.0	87.7	12.3	11.4	12.2
100	1444	100	1.08	97.8	2.2	1.8	0.5
122	100	100	1.0	92.4	7.6	2.9	8.9
122	514	92	1.0	95.4	4.6	4.1	8.2
140	62.5	95.6	0.8	80.8	19.2	6.4	22.4
140	62.5	100	0.9	90.0	10.0	3.4	16.7
140	165	89.2	1.33	94.3	5.7	3.5	5.6
163	4	96.2	0.71	81.6	18.4	4.5	32.4
163	11	100	0.80	88.4	11.6	6.5	24.0
163	4	100	1.00	91.0	9.0	4.8	14.4
163	3.5		1.14	94.0	6.0	3.4	9.9

[a]Per cent of total monosulfonic acids

[b]Per cent of total sulfonic acids.

[c]Per cent of initial.

As noted in Section III-A-2, benzenoid compounds also form anhydrides with excess SO_3, although adding dimethyl sulfate promotes their conversion to sulfones rather than to anhydrides. A 41% yield of 1,5-disulfonate results from the addition of 2 moles of SO_3 at 0 - 10°C to naphthalene dissolved in chloroform (88). With 3 moles, the yield increases to 50%, which goes to 65% upon standing 24 hr. This shows that the disulfonate forms a stable adduct - possibly a pyrosulfonate - with the excess SO_3, and only slowly releases it for conversion of mono- to disulfonate (88). A 75% yield of very pure 1,5-disulfonate is claimed upon treating naphthalene dissolved in tetrachloroethylene with SO_3 at 20°C (279).

1-Methylnaphthalene sulfonates quantitatively in the 4-position with SO_3-dioxane (166).

Dialkylated naphthalenesulfonates are commercial surface-active agents. Diamylnaphthalene has been sulfonated with SO_3 vapor and with sulfuric acid; the products give comparable performance as surface-active agents (151). Di-tert-butylnaphthalene, the sulphonate of which is a useful wetting agent and antitussive drug, has been reacted with SO_3 in liquid SO_2 (297), sulfuric acid (455), and $ClSO_3H$ (265). The last reagent is convenient for laboratory use, and has been employed in several other cases cited below. Dinonylnaphthalene reacted at -15°C with 20 mole-% excess SO_3, using a mixture of liquid SO_2 and CCl_4 as solvent (296).

Tetrahydronaphthalene (tetralin) is sulfonated in the 2-position with SO_3-dioxane (167), as is also 1, 4-endoethylene-1, 2, 3, 4-tetrahydronaphthalene (223). Decahydronapthalene (decalin) is converted to an unidentified sulfonic acid in two hours by treatment with SO_3 vapor at 193°C (81); dehydrogenation apparently precedes or accompanies sulfonation.

Of the four commercially important naptholmonosulfonic acids, only two are produced by direct sulfonation of the naphthol. 2-Naphthol-1-sulfonic acid (Armstrong's acid) is formed by treatment with 97% acid at low temperature with a short reaction time, or with SO_3 vapor at 25°C using tetrachloroethane solvent (442). 2-Naphthol-6-sulfonic acid (Schaeffer's acid) is produced at 125°C with 78% sulfuric acid, or by treatment at room temperature with SO_3-dioxane (166). 1-Naphthol gives a good yield of the 2-sulfonic acid with SO_3-dioxane (166). The two major naphtholdisulfonic acids [2-naphthol-6, 8-disulfonic acid (G acid), and 2-naphthol-3, 6-disulfonic acid (R acid)] are formed together by the direct sulfonation of 2-naphthol, using sulfuric acid followed by oleum and raising the temperature in steps from 15 to 80°C. They are isolated as the potassium and sodium salts, respectively, by differential salting out.

The naphthylaminesulfonic acids are an important group of dye intermediates. The monosulfonates, as well as many of the others, are usually made by indirect procedures, since direct sulfonation of the corresponding amines yields complex mixtures, or an unduly high proportion of unwanted isomers. 1-Naphthylamine-4-sulfonic acid (naphthionic acid) is, however, prepared by the baking process (cf., Section III-A-4) at 180°C for 8 hr. by heating either dry in an oven, or suspended in o-dichlorobenzene solvent. 2-Naphthylamine is converted in 90% yield to the 1-sulfonate by treatment with SO_3 vapor in tetrachloroethane, followed by heating for 5 hr. at 95°C (443), or for 2 hr. at 145°C (277). Two important naphthylaminedisulfonic acids (the 6-amino- and the 7-aminonaphthalene-1, 3-disulfonic acids) are prepared together by direct treatment of 2-naphthylamine with 45% oleum at 95°C. The latter acid is obtained as a direct sulfonation product, but the former is produced by the removal (by hydrolytic desulfonation) of one sulfonic group from a trisulfonic acid formed during the sulfonation.

As indicated in Tables 2-12 and 2-13, 1-nitronaphthalene sulfonates much more rapidly than nitrobenzene, because reaction occurs on the unnitrated ring.

1,4-Naphthoquinone reacts with SO_3-dioxane in the same manner as benzoquinone, as discussed in Section III-A-8, except that the nonquinoid ring also sulfonates (420);

$$(2-42)$$

1,2-Naphthoquinone, on the other hand, resembles the xyloquinones, since it forms a quinonedisulfonate.

Biphenyl and several of its derivatives have been sulfonated with $ClSO_3H$ (346) using chloroform as solvent. This is a convenient laboratory procedure, since the pure sulfonic acid precipitates as formed.

C.   Polycyclic Compounds

The sulfonation of polycyclic hydrocarbons with sulfuric acid usually gives mixtures of several mono- and disulfonic acids, a situation not greatly improved by varying conditions, or even by accepting low total conversion to sulfonate (401). Gore has pointed out (154) that, like naphthalene and benzene derivatives, anthracene and phenanthrene undergo rapid initial sulfonation at the most reactive (i.e., electron-rich) positions, which are also quite sterically hindered. Slow, proton-catalyzed rearrangement by desulfonation-resulfonation occurs next, resulting in essentially irreversible substitution at less reactive positions. These factors are discussed in more detail in Chapter 8. Failure to understand this situation has resulted in past confusion as to the products formed.

Considerably better results have been noted with SO_3 complexes, probably because substitution with these materials, unlike that with sulfuric acid, is irreversible as a result of the much less protonic environment. In the case of anthracene, use of a mixture of sulfuric acid and acetyl sulfate greatly reduces disulfonation; the product comprises 20% disulfonate, 50% 1-monosulfonate, and 30% 2-monosulfonate (27). Acetyl sulfate in the absence of sulfuric acid forms 50% each of the two monosulfonates. However, SO_3-pyridine yields only 1% of the 2-sulfonate at 165 - 175°C (26,27), the rest being the 1-isomer. In this case a paraffin hydrocarbon was employed as the reaction solvent, and a 40% total conversion to sulfonate was obtained. At the same temperature, the use of nitrobenzene as solvent gave only 15 - 20% conversion, but the product was pure 1-sulfonate.

Phenanthrene behaves similarly. With concentrated acid at 60°C, it forms a mixture of 4 mono- and 5 disulfonic acids. In contrast, SO_3-dioxane gives 95% monosulfonation (366). Four sulfonate isomers were isolated with no significant change in yields over the range 0°C (for 30 hr.) to 60°C (for 3 hr.). Indene also reacts with SO_3-dioxane, but the structure of the products were not determined (394).

Limited data suggest that fluorene reacts likewise. Although sulfuric acid gives a mixture, acetyl sulfate (472) forms the 2-sulfonate quantitatively, and SO_3 in chloroform yields 90% of the same sulfonate (87). Pure pyrene-1-sulfonic acid is obtained in 93% yield with sodium pyrosulfate (2); no disulfonation was noted. 1,1-Binaphthyl forms the 4,4-disulfonic acid with $ClSO_3H$ in dry nitrobenzene at 0°C (209).

Anthraquinone, which sulfonates in a much more cleancut manner than anthracene because of the presence of the two electron-withdrawing carbonyl groups, gives favorable results with SO_3 vapor at 150 - 170°C (348), forming the 2-sulfonic acid in 65% yield, with 10% quinone unreacted and 25% going to disulfonates. These results parallel those obtained with oleum, but no spent acid is formed with SO_3. At 130°C no reaction occurs; at 200°C oxidation is excessive. In the presence of mercury compounds of any valence state, anthraquinone forms the 1-sulfonate, as opposed to the 2-isomer which is formed almost exclusively in their absence. Tl_2O_3 likewise catalyzes formation of the 1-sulfonate (102), but $TlNO_3$, on the contrary, has no catalytic effect.

On the other hand, polycyclic mono- and diketones analogous to anthraquinone, but with larger fused-ring systems - namely, benzanthrone, benzonaphthone, dibenzpyrenequinone, isodibenzanthrone, and pyranthrone - are best sulfonated by first making their SO_3 adducts at low temperature, and then warming them to 180°C for 3 hr. (257), to effect rearrangement to the sulfonic acids. Direct reaction with SO_3 at the higher temperature gives poor results. Anthraquinone forms a similar adduct (88), but conversion of it to the sulfonate has not been explored, since direct reaction at 170°C proceeds satisfactorily, as stated before.

IV. SULFONATION OF HETEROCYCLIC COMPOUNDS

Heterocyclic compounds contain electron-rich atoms (O, N, S, Fe, etc.) which easily form complexes with acidic sulfonating agents, as discussed in Chapter 1. The sulfonation of heterocyclic compounds therefore involves reaction not with the free base, but rather with its protonated form, or with its Lewis acid adduct with SO_3. The transitory formation of such complexes is also probable even in the numerous cases where acid-sensitive heterocyclic compounds are sulfonated with reagents such as SO_3-pyridine. The formation of such adducts is always assumed in the ensuing discussion, unless otherwise stated.

A. Oxygen- and Sulfur-Containing Compounds

1. FURAN DERIVATIVES

The sensitivity of furan (Formula 2-43-A) and many of its derivatives to acid conditions makes the choice of a sulfonating agent difficult. Sulfuric acid, free SO_3, SO_3 in acetic anhydride, and SO_3-dioxane give only tar with furan, while H_2SO_4-pyridine and SO_3-trimethylamine do not react (426). Sulfur trioxide-pyridine performs satisfactorily, but not in the presence of excess pyridine; SO_3-picoline likewise gives good results.

Initial study of the sulfonation of furan with SO_3-pyridine at 100°C for 8 - 10 hr. with 1,2-dichloroethane solvent (424) showed that the yield of 2-monosulfonate could be increased from 30 to 90% by increasing the quantity of sulfonating agent. The same conditions gave 80% 3,5-disulfonate from 2-methylfuran, and the 3-sulfonate from 2,5-dimethylfuran; 2-methylfuran formed the 5-sulfonate in one month at room temperature (425). Subsequent repetition of this work by others (349) showed that the reaction products are usually mixtures - not single compounds as originally indicated - and that higher temperatures and proportions of sulfonating agent increase disulfonation. The data are summarized in Table 2-20.

TABLE 2-20

Sulfonation of Furan Derivatives with SO_3-Pyridine

	Percentage yield (under conditions given)							
	8 hr., 100°C Excess furan No solvent		4 days, 35-65°C Excess furan Solvent used		3 days, 25°C Excess furan Solvent used		3 days, 25°C Equiv. furan Solvent used	
	Mono	Di	Mono	Di	Mono	Di	Mono	Di
Furan	12-18	34-75	4	77-85	20-46	15-55	0-20	0-20
2-Methyl-furan	0-20	50-58	48-56	30-33	36-44	36-42	28-64	0
2,5-Di-methyl-furan	60-80	10-24	86-95	0	58-66	0	0-32	0

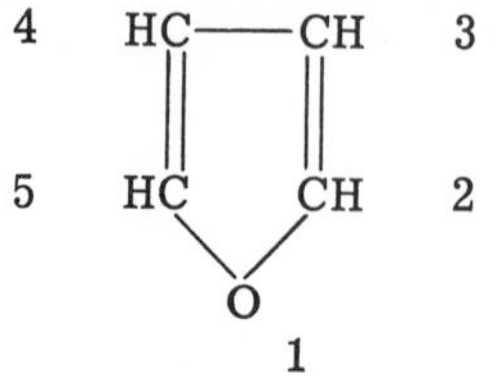

4   HC——CH   3

5   HC   CH   2

O

1

(A)

Furan

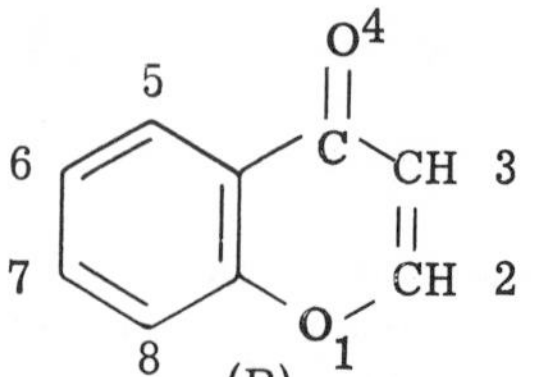

O^4

5

6

7

8   (B)

C—CH 3

CH 2

O

1

(2-43)

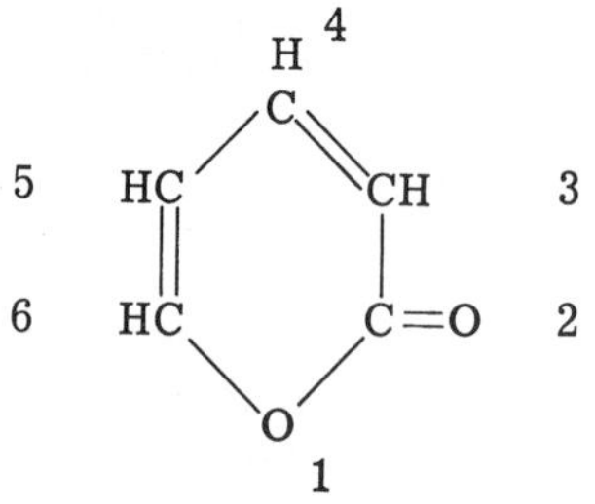

Chromone

H 4

C

5   HC   CH   3

6   HC   C=O   2

O

1

(A)

2-Pyrone

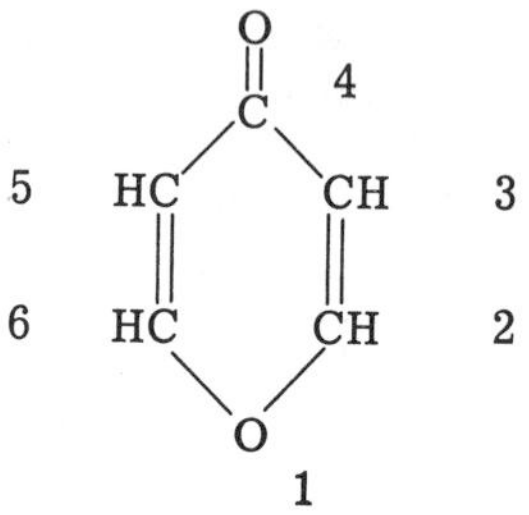

O

4

C

5   HC   CH   3

6   HC   CH   2

O

1

(B)

(2-44)

4-Pyrone

2-Acetylfuran gave 83% of 5-sulfonate in 10 hr. at 140°C (427). Furfural, which has always formed only tars in previous attempts at sulfonation, gave a 20% yield with SO_3-pyridine (215); efforts to obtain a better yield by varying conditions were without success. Furan-2-carboxylic acid (pyromucic acid) is less sensitive to acid reagents, since it could be converted to the 5-sulfonic acid with H_2SO_4 (188), and to the 5-sulfonyl chloride with $ClSO_3H$ (155). With SO_3-pyridine at 100°C, the acid decarboxylated during sulfonation, forming furan-2-sulfonic acid (425). Its acid chloride gave the 5-sulfonic acid with pure SO_3 in methylene chloride solvent below 0°C to minimize decomposition. As indicated in Chapter 5, this compound has been reacted with azo dyes to render them water-soluble. Benzofuran (cumarone) formed 100% 2-sulfonate with SO_3-pyridine in 10 hr. at 100°C (425). As would be expected, dibenzofuran is acid-stable. A 75% yield of the 2-sulfonate was formed with H_2SO_4 at 100°C (481); earlier work on this compound was reviewed and questioned.

2. PYRONE DERIVATIVES

2,6-Dimethyl-4-pyrone (cf., Formula 2-44-B) forms an SO_3 complex (279), but its properties have not been studied; sulfonation in the

3- or 5- position should occur easily. Several disubstituted 2-pyrones (cf. , Formula 2-44-A) were easily converted to the sulfonyl chlorides at 90°C in 2 hr. (357). Substituted chromones (cf. , Formula 2-43-B) were converted to mono-, di-, and trisulfonic acids, and in some cases to the sulfonyl chlorides, with 1 to 15 molar proportions of ClSO₃H at 60 - 140°C in 1 - 6 hr. (214). It is evident that the pyrones are much more stable under acid sulfonating conditions than the furans.

3. THIOPHENE DERIVATIVES

Thiophene (Formula 2-45) and its derivatives are much less sensitive to acidic conditions than the furan analogues, as indicated by the data in Table 2-21. Earlier work - up to about 1949 - has been summarized elsewhere (38). 2-Iodothiophene gave some disproportionation to 2, 5-diiodothiophene and thiophene in both of the examples cited.

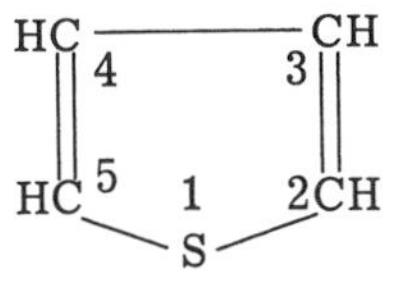

(2-45)

Thiophene

B. Nitrogen Containing Compounds

1. PYRROLE AND INDOLE DERIVATIVES; CARBAZOLE

As shown in Table 2-22 and 2-23, SO_3-pyridine has been the usual reagent for sulfonating these compounds. The relatively unstable sulfamates are formed as primary products; these rearrange at higher temperatures or with a longer reaction time to the more stable sulfonates. As with the furans and thiophenes, the 3-position is less reactive than the 2-position. The fact that 2-phenylindole gives a 95% yield of 3-sulfonate shows that the benzene ring in this position is comparatively unreactive. Carbazole (Formula 2-47-B), expectedly much more acid-stable than the other compounds, can be sulfonated satisfactorily with acid or oleum.

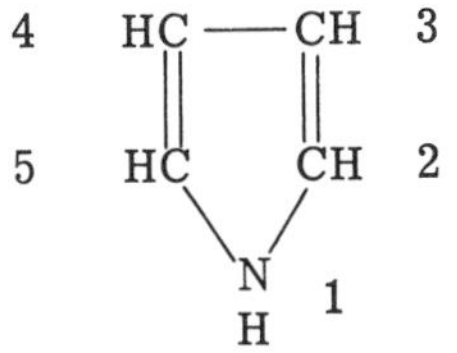

(2-46)

(A)   (B)

Pyrrole   Indole

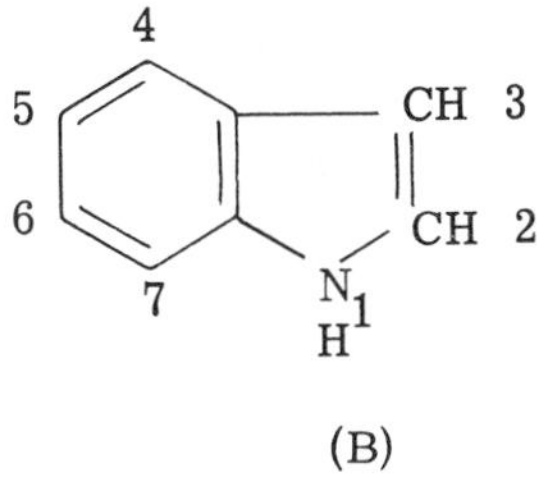

TABLE 2-21

Sulfonation of Thiophene Derivatives

Compound	Reagent	Temp., °C	Product[a]	Yield, %	Reference
Thiophene	Free SO_3	25	2-	50	422
	$(2SO_3)$-pyridine	25	2-	86	422
	As above	100	2, 4-di	-	224, 422
	SO_3-dioxane	-	2-	75	423
	$ClSO_3H$	-15	2-	-	190
	As above	-10	$2\text{-}SO_2Cl$	-	64
	FSO_3H	-	$2\text{-}SO_2F$	-	174
2, 5-Dimethyl-thiophene	SO_3-dioxane	-	3-	95	423
	$(2SO_3)$-pyridine	-	3-	94	423
	SO_3-pyridine	130	3-	75	423
2-Chloro-thiophene	SO_3-pyridine	125	5-	95	421
	$ClSO_3H$	-5	5-SO_2Cl; 3, 5-di SO_2Cl	-	64
2, 4-Dichloro-thiophene	25% oleum	35	5-	-	313
	65% oleum	140	3, 5-di	-	313
2, 5-Dichloro-thiophene	$ClSO_3H$	10	3-	66	448
	As above	-	3-SO_2Cl; 3, 4-di SO_2Cl	-	64
2-Bromo-thiophene	SO_3-pyridine	105	5-	90	421
2, 4-Dibromo-thiophene	$ClSO_3H$	-	3, 5-di SO_2Cl	-	64

continued

TABLE 2-21 (Continued)

Compound	Reagent	Temp., °C	Product[a]	Yield, %	Reference
2-Iodo-thiophene	SO_3-pyridine	100	5-	77	421
	$(2SO_3)$-pyridine	100-130	Mixed di-	-	421
2-Nitro-thiophene	$ClSO_3H$	-	$4-SO_2Cl$	74	64, 252
2-Carbamido-thiophene	As above	-	3, 5-di SO_2Cl	-	64
2-Acetamido-thiophene	As above	25	3, 5-di SO_2Cl	-	252
	H_2SO_4	25	5-	80	341
	As above	100	3, 5-di	89	341
2-Acetamido-methylthiophene	$ClSO_3H$	5-50	$5-SO_2Cl$	37	92
Methyl benzo-thiophenes	Acetyl sulfate	20	2-, or 3-	-	303

[a]Monosulfonic acid isomer formed, unless otherwise indicated.

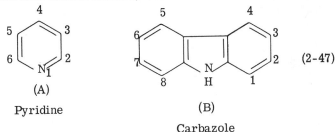

(A)

Pyridine

(B)

Carbazole

(2-47)

2. PYRIDINE AND ALKYL PYRIDINES

Ring sulfonation of pyridine (Formula 2-47-A) below 250°C yields almost exclusively the 3-sulfonate (270), which has been of commercial interest as an intermediate for one method of making nicotinic acid. A study employing oleum (260) showed that free SO_3 in the oleum is the actual reagent; it gave 22 - 71% yields at 230°C in 12 - 24 hr. using mercury sulfate catalyst. The monomethylpyridines reacted similarly, but yields were somewhat lower because of oxidative degradation of the methyl group. 2, 6-Dimethylpyridine also forms the 3-sulfonate (123).

TABLE 2-22

Sulfonation of Carbazole and Indole Derivatives with SO_3-Pyridine

Compound	Time, hr.[a]	Temp.	Product[b]	Yield, %	Reference
Indole	–	Cold;80	Sulfamate[c]	–	417
	10	120	2-	90	417
2-Methyl-indole	10	120	No reaction	–	417
3-Methyl-indole	10	120	2-	55	417
2-Phenyl-indole	8	130	3-	95	439
1-Acetyl-indole	10	130	2-	50	439
3-Indoleacetic acid	10	110	2-	55	439
	2.5	100	Sulfamate[d]	–	320
Acetyl-d,1-tryptophane	2.5	100	Sulfamate[d]	–	320
3-(Dimethyl-aminomethyl) indole	8	130	A sulfonate	Trace	439
1-Acetyl-2,3-dihydroindole	2	60	5-[e]	54	432
Carbazole	–	60	Sulfamate[d]	–	233
	2	15	Sulfamate[e]	–	54
	–	115	1,3,6-tri-[f]	–	55
	–	45-70	3,6-di; 1,3,6-tri-[g]	–	441

[a]A large excess of reagent used for all reactions yielding sulfonates; 1,2-dichloroethane solvent used, except as indicated.

[b]Monosulfonic acid isomer formed, except as indicated.

[c]Water used as solvent.   [d]Pyridine used as solvent.

[e]Chlorobenzene solvent; SO_3-dimethylaniline reagent.

[f]Acid used.   [g]Acid and oleum used.

TABLE 2-23

Sulfonation of Pyrrole Derivatives with SO_3-Pyridine

Compound	Time, hr.[a]	Temp.	Product[b]	Yield	Reference
Pyrrole	10	100	2-	90	435
1-Methylpyrrole	10	100	2-	57	435
2-Methylpyrrole	10	100	5-	54	435
2,4-Dimethyl-pyrrole	10	100	5-	-	435
2,5-Dimethyl-pyrrole	5	100	3-;3,4-di-	47,12	436
1,2,5-Trimethyl-pyrrole	5	100	3-;3,4-di-	40,12	436
2,3,5-Trimethyl-pyrrole	5	100	4-	25	436
1-Phenylpyrrole	8	100	4-	25	435
1-(2-Tolyl)-pyrrole	8	100	2-	45	435
1-Acetylpyrrole	11	100	2,4- and 2,5-di-	-	437
2-Acetylpyrrole	11	100	4-;3,5-di-	-	437
2-Chloropyrrole	4	70	5-	40	438
2-Phenylazo-pyrrole	4	80	5-	50	438

[a]A large excess of reagent and of 1,2-dichloroethane solvent used.

[b]Monosulfonic acid unless otherwise indicated.

The N-oxides of pyridine and of 2,6-dimethylpyridine yield the 3-sulfonates under similar conditions (123, 271), although it had been expected that the former would react more easily. The sulfonation of pyridine, like that of benzene, is reversible and yields the more stable 4-sulfonate under unusually drastic conditions (330°C) (187). Heating SO_3-pyridine with mercury sulfate for 10 hr. at 200°C gave 46% and for 29 hr. at the same temperature 63% of the 3-sulfonate (132); 3-methylpyridine in 12 hr. at 200°C formed 21%. It was then found that 90 - 100%

yields, based on pyridine, resulted at 230°C in 6 hr. in the presence of mercury sulfate, provided 1.7 moles SO_3 are used per mole of pyridine (355). The reaction proceeds even at 170 - 180°C (235a). It is noteworthy that this reaction can be conducted much above the boiling point of SO_3 because of the formation of the complex $(2SO_3)$-pyridine.

2,6-Di-tert-butylpyridine behaves differently because of strong steric shielding of the nitrogen atoms, thereby preventing formation of the SO_3 complex. In marked contrast to pyridine itself, it undergoes sulfonation with SO_3 rapidly in the 3-position - that is, next to a tert-butyl group - even at -10°C in liquid SO_2 (124, 274, 311). It was at first thought that the sulfonate group in this compound was in the 4-position, since sulfonation in other compounds has not been noted in a position next to a group as sterically unfavorable as tert-butyl. This sulfonate is unusual, however, since it is water-insoluble and soluble in liquid SO_2, whereas the analogous dimethylpyridine sulfonic acid behaves oppositely in both respects. 4-Chloro-2,6-di-tert-butylpyridine likewise sulfonates easily in the 3-position (311), as does 2-isopropyl-6-tert-butylpyridine (310). 2,6-Diisopropylpyridine, on the other hand, behaves like pyridine (310). The presence of one methyl group is thus sufficient to block complex formation with a resulting 240°C difference in the sulfonation temperature. Unlike pyridine, 2,6-di-tert-butyl pyridine does not form the 4-sulfonate at high temperature (250°C) (309).

Although 2,6-di-tert-butylpyridine is too sterically hindered to form an SO_3 adduct, it has been shown to protonate. During sulfonation with SO_3, it would, therefore, be expected that the unsulfonated portion of the base would protonate, and that the protonated base would (like pyridine itself) resist sulfonation at -10°C. The maximum conversion of base to sulfonate would then be 50% of theory. Yield data reported in the literature are too indefinite to check this hypothesis.

4,4'-Bipyridyl forms the 3,3',5,5'-tetrasulfonate at 320°C in 6 hr. with sulfuric acid (301).

3. MISCELLANEOUS NITROGEN-CONTAINING HETEROCYCLES

The sulfonation of quinoline (116) and of isoquinoline (133) has been well reviewed. A detailed study of the sulfonation of 1-phenyl-3-methyl-5-pyrazolone (Formula 2-48-A) with oleum (207) has shown that the 4-position reacts most easily, followed by the 1(4)-position on the phenyl group; desulfonation of the less stable 4-sulfonate group also occurs. As noted in Chapter 5, the 1(4)-sulfonate is used commercially and is also prepared indirectly by sulfoarylation. 3-Methyl-1,5-diphenylpyrazole (Formula 2-48-B) reacts in the 4- and 5(4)-positions with oleum, but not at the 1(4)-position (25). Extended studies have been reported on the sulfonation of 5- and 6-nitro and -amino-substituted indazoles (cf., Formula 2-48-C). Reaction always occurs on the benzenoid moiety (94, 308, 391). 6-Nitroindazole forms the 5-sulfonate; sulfonation ortho to a nitro group in this way is unexpected. 2-Amino-

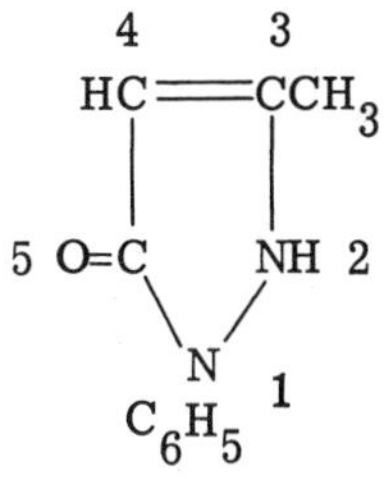

Indazole

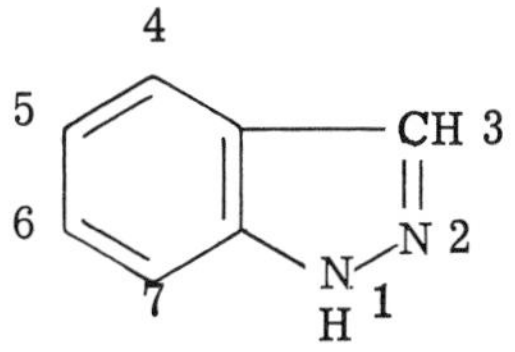

(A) 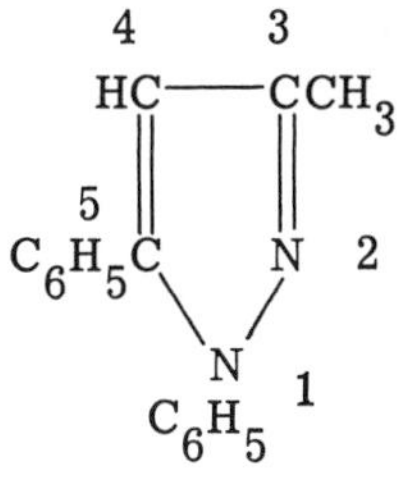   (B)   (C) (2-48)

pyrimidines (cf., Formula 2-49-A), substituted in the 6-position with amino or hydroxyl, are easily converted to the 5-sulfonates with $ClSO_3H$ (225); the presence of the second group in the 6-position notably facilitates reaction.

(2-49)

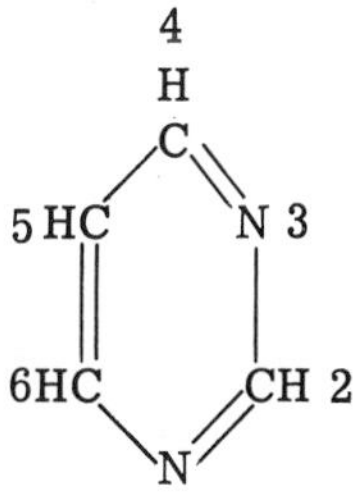

Pyrimidine   Phenazine   1,10-Phenanthroline

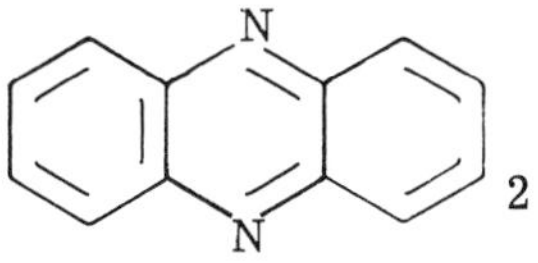

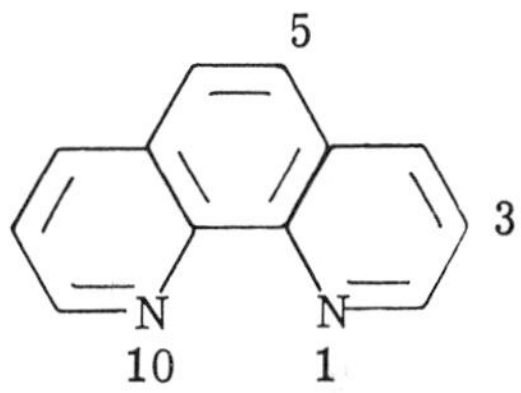

(A)   (B)   (C)

The results of a study of the sulfonation of phenazine (Formula 2-49-B) are summarized in Table 2-25. Not unexpectedly, the formation of disulfonates is a complicating factor in making the 2-sulfonate (259). 1,10-Phenanthroline (Formula 2-49-C) shows extraordinary resistence to sulfonation; it forms 30% of the 5-sulfonate and 4% of the 3-isomer by fusion with NH_4HSO_4 at 365°C (36). Although it has some structural resemblance to pyridine, it is considerably more difficult to sulfonate. 1-Azanthraquinone (Formula 2-50-A) was sulfonated by the four procedures indicated in Table 2-24 (81). Sulfur trioxide gave nearly twice as much 7-isomer as any of the other three approaches. The benzenoid ring expectedly sulfonates more easily than the one containing nitrogen. Sulfur trioxide-pyridine did not react, which is as expected from the low

TABLE 2-24

Sulfonation of 1-azanthraquinone

	Method and per cent yield			
Monosulfonate Isomer Formed	65% oleum; 95°C; Hg catalyst	20% oleum; 150°C; Hg catalyst	20% oleum; 145°C; No catalyst	SO₃; 170°C; No catalyst
8-	33.2	31.2	27.1	21.7
5-	28.7	13.3	0	13.0
7-	12.8	18.7	9.6	34.8

TABLE 2-25

Sulfonation of Phenazine

Strength oleum, %	40	40	45	45	50	70
Oleum: organic wt. ratio	5	10	5	10	10	5
2-Monosulfonate yield	20	25	24	33	41	44
Polysulfonate yield	Trace	3	4	5	10	10

reactivity of both reagent and compound. Attempts to sulfonate 2,3-dimethyl-1-azanthraquinone in an analogous manner gave no identifiable product because of excessive decomposition (82). Sulfonated copper and other analogous metallic phthalocyanines (Formula 2-50-B) are commercially important as dyes. As shown in Table 2-26, one to four sulfonate groups can be introduced with oleum or ClSO3H, the latter forming the sulfonyl chlorides (8, 375, 389). Temperature is

TABLE 2-26

Sulfonation of Copper Phthalocyanines

	Temperature and time (hr.)				Reference
Reagent	Mono-	Di-	Tri-	Tetra-	
40% Oleum	< 20(-)	51(15)	60(-)	-	8
ClSO₃H	-	100(5)	145(5)	150(-)	8, 375

evidently an important factor. Phthalocyanines made by sulfoarylation
(cf. , Chapter 5) have a different color from those made by direct sulfonation, since the former comprise primarily the 4-isomer, while the

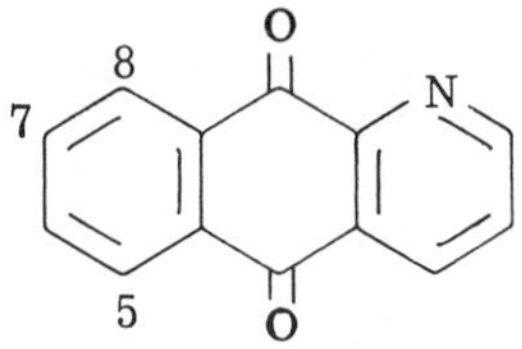

1-Azanthraquinone
(A)

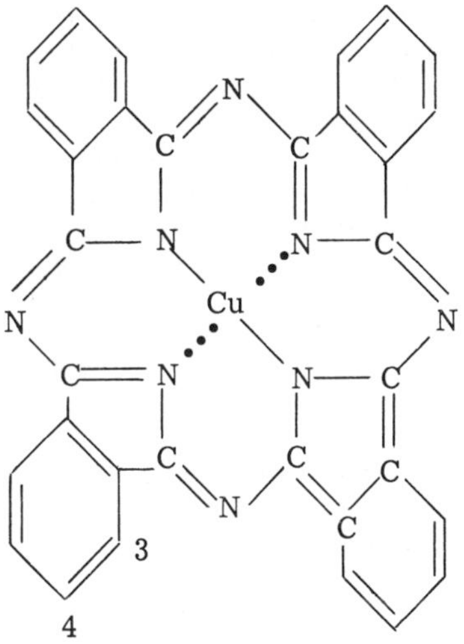

Copper Phthalocyanine
(B)

(2-50)

latter contain much 3-sulfonate (253). Reaction in the sterically unfavorable 3-position may be facilitated by initial complex formation
with the neighboring nitrogen atom. The sulfoarylated products are
derived from 4-sulfophthalic anhydride.

C. Miscellaneous Heterocylic Compounds

   3-Substituted sydnones (Formula 2-51-A) are sulfonated easily in the
4-position with SO_3-dioxane at $40°C$ (458); the substituents include
phenyl, 3-methoxyphenyl, and ethyl. The heterocyclic ring in this case
reacts with exceptional ease - even more easily than the methoxyphenyl
group. A recent study (489) has shown conclusively that 2-acetamido-
thiazoles (cf. , Formula 2-51-B) are sulfonated with $ClSO_3H$ in the 5-

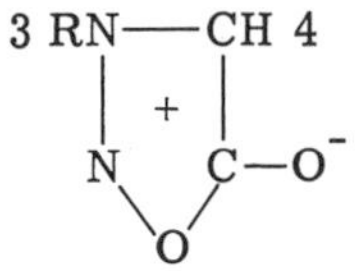

Sydnone   Thiazole   Ferrocene

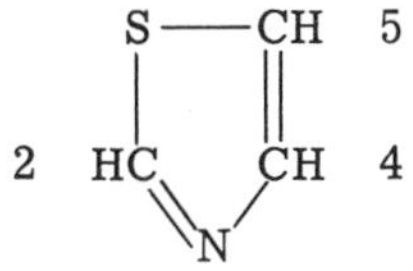

(A)   (B)   (C)

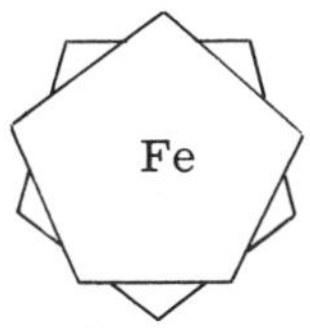

(2-51)

position; previous results were conflicting. Various direct and indirect procedures for sulfonating thiazoles have been well reviewed up to 1957 (370).

Dicyclopentadienyl iron (ferrocene-$(C_5H_5)_2$Fe - Formula 2-51-C), a compound with aromatic properties even more pronounced than those of benzene, can be mono- or disulfonated with acetyl sulfate in the range 25 - 40°C depending upon the quantity of reagent used (480); as expected, the two sulfonic groups are on different rings. The same reagent sulfonates cyclopentadienyl manganese tricarbonyl in excellent yield (66). Ferrocene carboxylic acid, and its methyl ester, were monosulfonated on the ring without the carboxyl group with SO_3-dioxane at 0°C (287). 1,1'-Di-(carbomethoxy) ferrocene reacts with SO_3, but not with SO_3-dioxane (288). 1-Acetylferrocene forms the 1'-sulfonic acid with SO_3, but 1,1'-diacetylferrocene deacetylates to give the 1,1'-disulfonic acid (288). It is interesting that sulfonation of the acetyl groups analogous to that observed with acetophenone and related compounds (cf., Table 2-1) does not occur here. 1,1'-Dibenzoylferrocene did not react with SO_3. Attempts to introduce more than one sulfonic acid or sulfonyl chloride group into each ferrocene ring have so far proved unsuccessful (288).

REFERENCES

1. Abe, K. , S. Yamamoto, and S. Sato, J. Pharm. Soc. Japan, 76, 1094 (1956); Chem. Abstr. , 51, 2636 (1957).
2. Abe, Y. , and Y. Nagai, Kogyo Kagaku Zasshi, 62, 1025 (1959); Chem. Abstr. , 57, 8520 (1962).
3. Adams, C. E. , and C. E. Johnson, U. S. Patent 2, 523, 490; Chem. Abstr. , 45, 6655 (1951).
4. Akiyama, U. , Japanese Patent 10, 323 ('62).
5. Alexander, E. R. , Principles of Ionic Organic Reactions, Wiley, New York, 1950.
6. Allied Chemical Corporation, General Chemical Division, Technical Service Bulletin SO$_3$-B (1959).
7. Allied Chemical Corporation, General Chemical Division, unpublished research data.
8. Andrews, D. B. , P. Kronowitt, F. W. Peck, S. S. Rossander, A. Siegel, O. Stallmann, H. I. Stryker, W. A. Von Schlieben and W. V. Wirth, U. S. Dept. Commerce, FIAT Final Reprt. No. 1313, PB 85, 172
9. Armour Chemical Division, "Alpha-Sulfoalkyl Acids, " Bulletin G-7, 1956.
10. Armstrong, H. E. , Proc. Roy. Soc. (London), 18, 502 (1870).
11. Arnold, R. T. , R. W. Amidon, and R. M. Dodson, J. Am. Chem. Soc. , 72, 2871 (1950).
12. Arnold, R. T. , and J. F. Dowdall, J. Am. Chem. Soc. , 70, 2590 (1948).
13. Asahina, Y. , T. Sano, T. Mayekawa, and H. Kawahata, Ber. , 71B, 312 (1938).
14. Asahina, Y. , and K. Yamaguchi, Ber. , 71B, 318 (1938).
15. Backer, H. J. , Rec Trav. Chim. , 44, 1056 (1925).
16. Backer, H. J. , and J. H. de Boer, Rec. Trav. Chim, 43, 297, (1924).
17. Backer, H. J. , and J. Buining, Rec. Trav. Chim. , 47, 111 (1928).
18. Backer, H. J. , and J. Buining, Rec. Trav. Chim. , 47, 1000 (1928).
19. Backer, H. J. , and W. G. Burgers, J. Chem. Soc. , 1925, 234.
20. Backer, H. J. , and J. V. Dubsky, Proc. Acad. Sci. Amsterdam, 22, 415 (1920).
21. Backer, H. J. , and H. W. Mook, Bull. soc. chim, 43, 542 (1928).
22. Backer, H. J. , and J. M. van der Zanden, Rec. Trav. Chim. , 46, 473 (1927).
23. Backer, H. J. , and J. M. van der Zanden, Rec. Trav. Chim. , 49, 735 (1930).
24. Bailey, D. L. , U. S. Patent 2, 968, 643; Chem. Abstr. , 55, 10387 (1961).
25. Barry, W. J. , J. Chem. Soc. , 1961, 3851.
26. Battegay, M. , and P. Brandt, Bull. soc. chim. , 31, 910 (1922).
27. Battegay, M. , and P. Brandt, Bull. soc. chim. , 33, 1667 (1923).
28. Bauer, K. H. , and J. Stockhausen, J. Prakt. Chem. (2), 130, 35 (1931).

29.   Bauer, K. H. , and J. Stockhausen, Seifensieder-Ztg. , 59, 34
      (1932); Chem. Abstr. , 26, 1897 (1932).
30.   Bauman, W. C. , and H. H. Roth, U. S. Patent 2, 835, 655; Chem.
      Abstr. , 52, 15966 (1958).
31.   Bauman, W. C. , and R. M. Wheaton, U. S. Patent 2, 733, 231; Chem.
      Abstr. , 50, 6711 (1956).
31a. Baumann, H. , W. Stein, and M. Voss, German Patent 1, 159, 430;
      Chem. Abstr. , 60, 7917 (1964).
32.   Baumgarten, P. , Ber. , 59B, 1976 (1926).
33.   Bertsch, H. , U. S. Patent 1, 923, 608; Chem. Abstr. , 27, 5565
      (1933).
34.   Berzelius, J. J. , Ann. Chem. , 28, 1 (1838).
35.   Bistline, R. G. , Jr. , A. J. Stirton, J. K. Weil, and W. S. Port,
      J. Am. Oil Chemists' Soc. , 33, 44 (1956).
36.   Blair, D. , and H. Diehl, Anal. Chem. , 33, 867 (1961).
37.   Blaser, B. , M. Rugenstein, and G. Tischbirek, U. S. Patent
      2, 764, 576; Chem. Abstr. , 51, 6218 (1957).
38.   Blicke, F. F. , "The Chemistry of Thiophene", in Heterocyclic
      Compounds, 1, R. C. Elderfield, ed. , Wiley, New York, 1950.
39.   Bloch, H. S. , U. S. Patent 2, 822, 387; Chem. Abstr. , 52, 11110
      (1958).
40.   Bloch, H. S. , A. E. Hoffman, and H. E. Mammen, U. S. Patent
      2, 677, 702; Chem. Abstr. , 48, 9087 (1954).
41.   Boettinger, C. , Ber. , 7, 1781 (1874).
42.   Boggiano, B. G. , S. E. Condon, M. T. Davies, G. B. Jackman,
      B. G. Overell, V. Petrow, O. Stephenson, and A. M. Wild, J.
      Pharm. Pharmacol. , 12, 419 (1960).
43.   Bordwell, F. G. , R. D. Chapman, and C. E. Osborne, J. Am. Chem.
      Soc. , 81, 2002 (1959).
44.   Bordwell, F. G. , F. B. Colton, and M. Knell, J. Am. Chem. Soc. ,
      76, 3950 (1954).
45.   Bordwell, F. G. , and G. W. Crosby, J. Am. Chem. Soc. , 78, 5367
      (1956).
46.   Bordwell, F. G. , and C. E. Osborne, J. Am. Chem. Soc. , 81, 1995
      (1959).
47.   Bordwell, F. G. , and M. L. Peterson, J. Am. Chem. Soc. , 76,
      3952 (1954).
48.   Bordwell, F. G. , and M. L. Peterson, J. Am. Chem. Soc. , 76,
      3957 (1954).
49.   Bordwell, F. G , and M. L. Peterson, J. Am. Chem. Soc. , 81,
      2000 (1959).
50.   Bordwell, F. G. , M. L. Peterson, and C. S. Rondestvedt, Jr. ,
      J. Am. Chem. Soc. , 76, 3945 (1954).
51.   Bordwell, F. G. , and C. S. Rondestvedt, Jr. , J. Am. Chem. Soc. ,
      70, 2429 (1948).
52.   Bordwell, F. G. , C. M. Suter, J. M. Holbert, and C. S. Rondestvedt,
      Jr. , J. Am. Chem. Soc. , 68, 139 (1946).

53. Bordwell, F. G. , C. M. Suter, and A. J. Webber, J. Am. Chem. Soc. , 67, 827 (1945).

54. Borodkin, V. F. , J. Appl. Chem. (USSR) (English Transl.), 23, 803 (1950); Chem. Abstr. , 46, 8089 (1952).

55. Borodkin, V. F. , and T. V. Mal'kova, J. Appl. Chem. (USSR) (English Transl.), 21, 849 (1948); Chem. Abstr. , 43, 6205 (1949).

56. Botez, G. H. , Bul. Inst. Politech. Iasi, 6, 133 (1960); Chem. Abstr. , 57, 14984 (1962).

57. Boundy, R. H. , R. F. Boyer, and S. M. Stoesser, Styrene-Its Polymers, Copolymers, and Derivatives, Reinhold, New York, 1952.

58. Bradley, J. A. , P. Perkins, and J. J. Polisin, Paper presented at the 138th American Chemical Society Meeting, Sept. , 1960.

59. Breslow, D. S. , and R. R. Hough, J. Am. Chem. Soc. , 79, 5000 (1957).

60. Brooks, R. F. , U. S. Patents 2, 889, 360-1; Chem. Abstr. , 53, 18914 (1959).

61. Brown, A. B. , and J. O. Knoblock, ASTM Bull. , 224, 213 (1958).

62. Burns, H. W. , U. S. Patent 2, 895, 986; Chem. Abstr. , 54, 1447 (1960).

63. Burton, D. , and E. E. Byrne, J. Soc. Leather Trades' Chemists, 36, 309 (1952).

64. Buzas, A. , and J. Teste, Bull. Soc. Chim. France, 1960, 793.

65. Cahours, A. , Annales Chim. Physique (3), 27, 439 (1849).

66. Cais, M. , and J. Kosikowski, J. Am. Chem. Soc. , 82, 5667 (1960).

67. Carlson, E. J. , G. Flint, E. E. Gilbert, and H. R. Nychka, Ind. Eng. Chem. , 50, 276 (1958).

68. Carpenter, S. , PhD, Dissertation, University of Missouri; Dissertation Abstr. , 19, No. 10, 2464 (1959).

69. Carr, J. I. , U. S. Patent 2, 000, 061; Chem. Abstr. , 29, 4027 (1935).

70. Carr, J. I. , and M. A. Dahlen, U. S. Patent 1, 999, 955; Chem. Abstr. , 29, 4029 (1935).

71. Carr, J. I. , M. A. Dahlen, and E. F. Hitch, U. S. Patent 2, 007, 327; Chem. Abstr. , 29, 5864 (1935).

72. Casper and Petzold, U. S. Dept. Commerce, OTS Rept. PB 73, 911 Frames 4648-60.

73. Centre National de la Recherche Scientifique, French Patent 1, 055, 420.

74. Cerfontain, H. , Rec. Trav. Chim. , 80, 296 (1961).

75. Cerfontain, H. , H. G. J. Duin, and L. Vollbracht, Anal. Chem. , 35, 1005 (1963).

76. Cerfontain, H. , A. W. Kaandorp, and F. L. J. Sixma, Rec. Trav. Chim. , 82, 565 (1963).

77. Cerfontain, H. , F. L. J. Sixma, and L. Vollbracht, Rec. Trav. Chim. , 82, 659 (1963).

77a.   Cerfontain, H. , and A. Telder,   Proc. Chem. Soc. , 1964, 14.
78.   Christensen, N. H. ,   Acta Chem. Scand. ,   15, 1507 (1961).
79.   Chrzaszczewska, A. ,   B. Oprzadek, and S. Pizon,   Lodz. Towarz.
       Nauk. Wydzia III Acta Chim. ,   2, 87 (1957);   Chem. Abstr. ,
       52, 4537 (1958).
80.   Clarke, J. T. ,   U. S. Patent 2, 731, 411;   Chem. Abstr. ,   50, 7350
       (1956).
81.   Clemo, G. R. ,   and N. Legg,   J. Chem. Soc. ,   1947, 539.
82.   Clemo, G. R. ,   and N. Legg,   J. Chem. Soc. ,   1947, 545.
83.   Close, W. J. ,   L. R. Swett, L. E. Brady, J. H. Short, and M.
       Vernsten,   J. Am. Chem. Soc. ,   82, 1132 (1960).
84.   Cockerille, F. O. ,   U. S. Patent 2, 333, 701;   Chem. Abstr. ,   38,
       2347 (1944).
85.   Cohen, E. ,   B. Klarberg, and J. R. Vaughan,   J. Am. Chem. Soc. ,
       82, 2731 (1960).
86.   Cook, W. A. and K. H. Cook,   J. Am. Pharm. Assoc. Sci. Ed. ,
       38, 239 (1949).
87.   Courtot, C. ,   Ann. Chim. (10), 14, 17 (1930).
88.   Courtot, C. ,   and J. Bonnet,   Compt. Rend. ,   182, 855 (1926).
89.   Cross, J. M. ,   and M. E. Chiddix, U. S. Patent 2, 694, 727;   Chem.
       Abstr. ,   49, 13290 (1955).
90.   Crowder, J. A. , U. S. Patent 2, 268, 443;   Chem. Abstr. ,   36,
       2564 (1942).
91.   Crowder, J. A. ,   and E. E. Gilbert,   U. S. Patent 2, 842, 589;
       Chem. Abstr. ,   52, 18215 (1958).
92.   Cymerman, J. ,   and D. Faiers,   J. Chem. Soc. ,   1952, 165.
93.   Datin, R. C. ,   U. S. Patent 2, 290, 167;   Chem. Abstr. ,   36, 388
       (1942).
94.   Davies, R. R. ,   J. Chem. Soc. ,   1955, 2412.
95.   Davies, T. G. ,   PhD. Dissertation, Brigham Young University
       1963; Dissertation Abstr. ,   24, No. 4, 1395 (1963).
96.   Davison, B. K. ,   and L. F. Byrne,   British Patent 820, 659;   Chem.
       Abstr. ,   54, 14191 (1960).
97.   Debus,   U. S. Dept. Commerce, OTS Rept. ,   PB 70, 332.
98.   Delacoux, E. ,   G. Tsatsas, and R. Delaby,   Bull. Soc. Chim. ,
       France,1959, 1980; Chem. Abstr. ,   55, 2542 (1961).
99.   Djerassi, C. ,   J. Org. Chem. ,   13, 848 (1948).
100.   Dmitriev, M. A. ,   G. A. Sokol'skii, and I. L. Knunyants,   Khim.
       Nauka i Prom. ,   3, 826 (1958); Chem. Abstr. ,   53,11211 (1959).
101.   Doering, W. von E. ,   and F. M. Beringer,   J. Am. Chem. Soc. ,
       71, 2221 (1949).
102.   Dokunikhin, N. S. ,   and L. A. Gaeva,   Zh. Vses. Khim. Obsh-
       chestva im. D. I. Mendeleeva,   6, 234 (1961);   Chem. Abstr. ,
       55, 19877 (1961).
103.   Dombrovskii, A. V. ,   Ukr. Khim. Zh. ,   16, No. 5, 539 (1950);
       Chem. Abstr. ,   48, 10682 (1954).
104.   Dombrovskii, A. V. ,   Dokl. Akad. Nauk USSR,   81, 411 (1951);
       Chem. Abstr. ,   46, 7998 (1952).

105. Dombrovskii, A. V. , Zh. Obshch Khim. , 22, 2136 (1952); Chem. Abstr. , 48, 1946 (1954).
106. Dombrovskii, A. V. , and G. M. Prilutskii, Zh. Obshch Khim. , 25, 1943 (1955); Chem. Abstr. , 50, 8450 (1956).
107. Dow Chemical Company, British Patent 893, 732.
108. Dow Chemical Company, Dowfax 2A1, 1959.
109. Downing, F. B. , and R. G. Clarkson, U. S. Patents 2, 061, 617-20; Chem. Abstr. , 31, 783 (1937).
110. Downs, C. R. , U. S. Patent 1, 321, 994; Chem. Abstr. , 14, 287 (1920).
111. Dresel, E. , and C. N. Hinshelwood, J. Chem. Soc. , 1944, 649.
112. Dreyfus, H. , U. S. Patent 2, 402, 538; Chem. Abstr. , 40, 5572 (1946).
113. Eaborn, C. , and T. Hashimoto, Chem. Ind. (London), 1961, 1081.
114. Eaborn, C. , and R. Taylor, J. Chem. Soc. , 1960, 1480
115. Eichorn, J. , and J. M. Steinmetz, U. S. Patent 2, 945, 842; Chem. Abstr. , 54, 23426 (1960).
116. Elderfield, R. C. , "Quinoline Derivatives, " in Heterocyclic Compounds, Vol. 4, R. C. Elderfield, ed. , Wiley, New York, 1952.
117. Elsevier's Encyclopaedia of Organic Chemistry, Series III, 12B, Elsevier, New York, 1955, pp. 4841-5686.
118. Engelhardt, A. , Z. Chemie, 1864, p. 42.
119. Engelhardt, A. , and P. Latschinow, Z. Chemie, 1868, p. 75.
120. Engelhardt, A. , and P. Latschinow, Z. Chemie, 1868, p. 266.
121. England, D. C. , M. A. Dietrich, and R. V. Lindsey, Jr. , J. Am. Chem. Soc. , 82, 6181 (1960).
122. Englund, S. W. , R. S. Aries, and D. F. Othmer, Ind. Eng. Chem. , 45, 189 (1953).
123. Evans, R. F. , and H. C. Brown, J. Org. Chem. , 27, 1329 (1962).
124. Evans, R. F. , and H. C. Brown, J. Org. Chem. , 27, 3127 (1962).
125. Farbwerke Hoechst AG, French Patent 1, 307, 710.
126. Farbwerke Hoechst AG, German Patent 1, 063, 151; Chem. Abstr. , 55, 13377 (1961).
127. Feighner, G. C. , U. S. Patent 2, 822, 406; Chem. Abstr. , 52, 14680 (1958).
128. Fincke, J. K. , U. S. Patent 2, 572, 605; Chem. Abstr. , 46, 3077 (1952).
129. Fitzky and Cramer, U. S. Dept. Commerce, OTS Rept. PB 58, 818.
130. Frerejacque, M. , Compt. Rend. , 170, 326 (1920).
131. Furness, R. , and A. D. Scott, British Patent 669, 899; Chem. Abstr. , 46, 8881 (1952).
132. Galat, A. , Canadian Patent 472, 364.
133. Gensler, W. J. , "Isoquinoline, " in Heterocyclic Compounds, 4, R. C. Elderfield, ed. , Wiley, New York, 1952.
134. Gerhards, B. , and W. Dirscherl, Ann. , 642, 71 (1961).

135. Gesellschaft fuer Chemische Industrie in Basel, German Patent 572,962; Chem. Abstr., <u>27</u>, 4250 (1933).
136. Gesellschaft fuer Chemische Industrie in Basel, German Patent 578,724; Chem. Abstr., <u>28</u>, 783 (1934).
137. Gibbs, H. H., and M. I. Bro, J. Org. Chem., <u>26</u>, 4002 (1961).
138. Gilbert, E. E., Canadian Patent 538,297.
139. Gilbert, E. E., U. S. Patent 2,695,308; Chem. Abstr., <u>49</u>, 12528 (1955).
140. Gilbert, E. E., and S. L. Giolito, U. S. Patent 2,647,925; Chem. Abstr., <u>48</u>, 7631 (1954).
141. Gilbert, E. E., and S. L. Giolito, U. S. Patent 2,704,295; Chem. Abstr., <u>49</u>, 7874 (1955).
142. Gilbert, E. E., and S. L. Giolito, U. S. Reissue Patent 24,435; Chem. Abstr., <u>52</u>, 7358 (1958).
143. Gilbert, E. E., and P. H. Groggins, in Unit Processes in Organic Synthesis, P. H. Groggins, ed., McGraw-Hill, New York, 1958.
144. Gilbert, E. E., and E. P. Jones, Ind. Eng. Chem., <u>43</u>, 2034 (1951).
145. Gilbert, E. E., and C. B. Miller, U. S. Patent 2,793,964; Chem. Abstr., <u>51</u>, 13466 (1957).
146. Gilbert, E. E., and J. A. Otto, U. S. Patent 2,506,417; Chem. Abstr., <u>44</u>, 6664 (1950).
147. Gilbert, E. E., J. A. Otto, and C. J. McGough, Ind. Eng. Chem., <u>51</u>, 925 (1959).
148. Gilbert, E. E., and B. Veldhuis, Ind. Eng. Chem., <u>49</u>, 31 (1957).
149. Gilbert, E. E., and B. Veldhuis, Ind. Eng. Chem., <u>50</u>, 997 (1958).
150. Gilbert, E. E., and B. Veldhuis, U. S. Patent 2,872,437; Chem. Abstr., <u>53</u>, 6602 (1959).
151. Gilbert, E. E., B. Veldhuis, E. J. Carlson, and S. L. Giolito, Ind. Eng. Chem., <u>45</u>, 2065 (1953).
152. Gillespie, R. J., and J. A. Leisten, Quart. Rev. (London), <u>8</u>, 40 (1954).
153. Goodman, I., and R. A. Edington, British Patent 834,251; Chem. Abstr., <u>54</u>, 20986 (1961).
154. Gore, P. H., J. Org. Chem., <u>22</u>, 135 (1957).
155. Graenacher, C., A. E. Siegrist, and H. Bruengger, U. S. Patent 2,623,050; Chem. Abstr., <u>48</u>, 2778 (1954).
156. Gray, F. W., and I. J. Krems, J. Org. Chem., <u>26</u>, 209 (1961).
157. Greenhalgh, R., U. S. Patent 1,986,808; Chem. Abstr., <u>29</u>, 1179 (1935).
158. Grillet, N. B., U. S. Patent 1,956,571; Chem. Abstr., <u>28</u>, 4071 (1934).
159. Grob, A. R., and C. C. Adams, U. S. Patent 1,422,564; Chem. Abstr., <u>16</u>, 3094 (1922).
160. Grotowsky, H., U. S. Dept. Commerce, OTS Rept. PB 75,372.
161. Gudriniece, E., E. Dreimanis, and G. Vanags, Dokl. Akad. Nauk USSR, <u>110</u>, 786 (1956); Chem. Abstr., <u>51</u>, 8052 (1957).

162.   Gudriniece, E. , A. Ievins, and G. Vanags,   Nauch. Dokl.
        Vysshei Shkoly Khim. i Khim, Tekhnol. , 1958, 746; Chem.
        Abstr. , 53, 8085 (1959).
163.   Gudriniece, E. , A. Ievins, G. Vanags, V. Bruners, and J.
        Bankovskis, Latvijas PSR Zinatnu Akad. Vestis, 1960, 3,
        103; Chem. Abstr. , 55, 476 (1961).
164.   Gudriniece, E. , A. Ievins, G. Vanags, and D. Kreicberga,
        Latvijas PSR Zinatnu Akad. Vestis, 1961, 2, 111; Chem.
        Abstr. , 55, 25872 (1961).
165.   Gudriniece, E. , A. Ievins, G. Vanags, H. Stipnice, and E.
        Mateus, Latvijas PSR Zinatnu Akad. Vestis, 1960, 8, 95;
        Chem. Abstr. , 55, 11327 (1961).
166.   Gudriniece, E. , and I. Lielbriedis, Latvijas Valsts Univ.
        Kim, Fak. , Zinatniskie Raksti, 15, 5, 291 (1957); Chem.
        Abstr. , 53, 18922 (1959).
167.   Gudriniece, E. , and I. Lielbriedis, Latvijas Valsts. Univ.
        Kim. Fak. Zinatniskie Raksti, 22, 115 (1958); Chem. Abstr.
        53, 15018 (1959).
168.   Gudriniece, E. , G. Vanags, and L. Mazkalke, Zh. Obshch.
        Khim. , 30, 1904 (1960); Chem. Abstr. , 55, 7274 (1961).
169.   Guenther, F. , U. S. Dept. Commerce, OTS Rept. PB 30,081.
170.   Guenther, F. , H. Haussmann, and B. von Reibnitz, U. S.
        Patent 2,267,731; Chem. Abstr. , 36, 2648 (1942).
171.   Guenther, F. , and J. Hetzer, U. S. Patent 1,926,442; Chem.
        Abstr. , 27, 6001 (1933).
172.   Guenther, F. , and H. Holsten, U. S. Patent 2,037,974; Chem.
        Abstr. , 30, 3911 (1936).
173.   Guenther, F. , F. Muenz, and H. Haussmann, U. S. Patent
        1,932,176; Chem. Abstr. , 28, 671 (1934).
173a.   Gulf Oil Corporation, Chem. Eng. News, 42, (10), 31 (1964).
174.   Halbedel, H. S. , and J. C. Heath, U. S. Patent 2,480,465; Chem.
        Abstr. , 44, 1142 (1950).
175.   Hardy, E. M. , U. S. Patent 3,017,321; Chem. Abstr. , 56,
        11622 (1962).
176.   Harris, J. O. , U. S. Patent 2,527,880; Chem. Abstr. , 45,
        1164 (1951).
177.   Hart, R. , and R. Janssen, Makromol. Chem. , 43, 242 (1961).
178.   Haussmann, H. , U. S. Patent 1,931,491; Chem. Abstr. , 28,
        491 (1934).
179.   Heertjes, P. M. , H. C. A. Van Beek, and G. I. Grimmon, Rec.
        Trav. Chim. , 80, 82 (1961).
180.   Heine, K. , Ber. , 13, 491 (1880).
181.   Helferich, B. , and W. Klebert, Ann. , 657, 79 (1962).
182.   Henkel et Cie. GmbH, British Patent 679,185; Chem. Abstr.
        48, 2772 (1954).
183.   Henkel et Cie. GmbH, British Patent 741,770; Chem. Abstr.
        50, 11693 (1956).

184. Henkel et Cie. GmbH, British Patent 787,229; Chem. Abstr.,
      52, 7111 (1958).
185. Henkel et Cie. GmbH, German Patent 1,155,120.
186. Henning, H., W. J. Alvord, and L. E. Hutchings, U. S. Patent
      2,802,026; Chem. Abstr., 51, 18579 (1957).
187. den Hertog, H. J., H. C. van der Plas, and D. J. Buurman,
      Rec. Trav. Chim., 77, 963 (1958).
188. Hill, H. B., and A. W. Palmer, Am. Chem. J., 10, 373 (1888).
189. Hine, J., Physical Organic Chemistry, 2nd ed., McGraw-
      Hill, New York, 1962.
190. Houff, W. H., and R. D. Schuetz, J. Am. Chem. Soc., 75,
      6316 (1953).
191. Howard, E. C., Jr., U. S. Patent 2,623,898: Chem. Abstr.,
      47, 9364 (1953).
192. Huntress, E. H., and J. S. Autenreith, J. Am. Chem. Soc.,
      63, 3446 (1941).
193. Huntress, E. H., and F. H. Carten, J. Am. Chem. Soc., 62,
      511 (1940).
194. Huntress, E. H., and F. H. Carten, J. Am. Chem. Soc., 62,
      603 (1940).
195. Huttenlocher, R., U. S. Patent 1,943,319: Chem. Abstr., 28,
      2210 (1934).
196. I. G. Farbenindustrie AG, U. S. Dept. Commerce, OTS Rept.
      PB 58,835.
197. I. G. Farbenindustrie AG, U. S. Dept. Commerce, OTS Rept.
      PBL 65,802.
198. I. G. Farbenindustrie AG, U. S. Dept. Commerce, OTS Rept.
      PB 65,823.
199. I. G. Farbenindustrie AG, U. S. Dept. Commerce, OTS Rept.
      PB 74,120, Frames 14-17.
200. I. G. Farbenindustrie AG, U. S. Dept. Commerce, OTS Rept.
      PB 75,246.
201. I. G. Farbenindustrie AG, U. S. Dept. Commerce, OTS Rept.
      PB 75,259.
202. I. G. Farbenindustrie AG, U. S. Dept. Commerce, OTS Rept.
      PB 85,687.
203. I. G. Farbenindustrie AG, U. S. Dept. Commerce, OTS Rept.
      PB 91,355.
204. I. G. Farbenindustrie AG, U. S. Dept. Commerce, OTS Rept.
      PB 98,165.
205. I. G. Farbenindustrie AG, U. S. Dept. Commerce, OTS Rept.
      PB 100,055.
206. Illuminati, G., J. Am. Chem. Soc., 78, 2603 (1956).
207. Ioffe, I. S., and Z. Ya. Khavin, J. Gen. Chem. (USSR) (English
      Transl.), 17, 528 (1947); Chem. Abstr., 42, 1933 (1948).
208. Ito, A., Kogyo Kagaku Zasshi, 62, 402 (1959): Chem. Abstr.
      57, 8512 (1962).

208a.   Ito, A. , S. Kitahara, and H. Hiyama, Kogyo Kagaku Zasshi,
        66, No. 11, 1587 (1963); Chem. Abstr. , 60, 13203 (1964).
209.   Janczewski, M. , and H. Szeczeklik, Roczniki Chem. , 35, 369
        (1961); Chem. Abstr. , 55, 21063 (1961).
210.   Jeffery, E. A. , and D. P. N. Satchell, J. Chem. Soc. , 1962,
        1913.
211.   Jiang, S. H. , Hua Hsueh Hsueh Pao, 23, 330 (1957); Chem.
        Abstr. , 52, 15493 (1958).
212.   Joly, R. , R. Bucourt, and J. Mathieu, Rec. Trav. Chim. , 78,
        527 (1959).
213.   Joseph, R. T. , and P. J. Cole, U. S. Patent 2, 697, 117; Chem.
        Abstr. , 49, 15960 (1955).
214.   Joshi, D. V. , J. R. Merchant, and R. C. Shah, J. Org. Chem. ,
        21, 1104 (1956).
215.   Jurasek, A. , and J. Kovac, Sb. Prac Chem. Fak. SVST, 1961,
        41; Chem. Abstr. , 58, 2420 (1963).
216.   Kaandorp, A. W. , H. Cerfontain, and F. L. J. Sixma, Rec. Trav.
        Chim. , 81, No. 11, 969 (1962).
217.   Kaandorp, A. W. , H. Cerfontain, and F. L. J. Sixma, Rec. Trav.
        Chim. , 82, 113 (1963).
218.   Kachurin, O. I. , A. A. Spryskov, and E. V. Kovalenko, Izv.
        Vysshikh Uchebn. Zavedenii, Khim. i Khim. Tekhnol. , 6,
        No. 3, 425 (1963); Chem. Abstr. , 59, 13781 (1963).
219.   Kaji, A. , K. Hashimoto, and S. Kano, J. Chem. Soc. Japan,
        82, 782 (1961).
220.   Kalischer, G. , F. Guenther, K. Keller, and J. Hetzer, U. S.
        Patent 1, 835, 404; Chem. Abstr. , 26, 1146 (1932).
221.   Karavaev, B. I. , and A. A. Spryskov, Zh. Obshch. Khim. , 33,
        No. 6, 1890 (1963); Chem. Abstr. , 59, 11221 (1963).
222.   Kaye, H. E. Forsythe, and A. I. Mills, World Petrol. Congr.
        Proc. 5th, N. Y. , Sect. 3, 1959.
223.   Kazanskii, B. A. , and P. I. Svirskaya, Zh. Obshch. Khim. ,
        29, 2588 (1959); Chem. Abstr. , 54, 10965 (1960).
224.   Kazitsyna, L. A. , Vestnik Moskov. University, 1947, No. 3,
        109; Chem. Abstr. , 42, 3751 (1948).
225.   Khromov-Borisov, N. V. , and R. S. Karlinskaya, Zh. Obshch.
        Khim. , 24, 2212 (1954); Chem. Abstr. , 50, 355 (1956).
226.   Kilpatrick, M. , and M. W. Meyer, J. Phys. Chem. , 65, 530
        (1961).
227.   Kilpatrick, M. , and M. W. Meyer, J. Phys. Chem. , 65, 1312
        (1961).
228.   Kilpatrick, M. , M. W. Meyer, and M. L. Kilpatrick, J. Phys.
        Chem. , 64, 1433 (1960).
229.   Kilpatrick, M. , M. W. Meyer, and M. L. Kilpatrick, J. Phys.
        Chem. , 65, 1189 (1961).
230.   King, J. F. , P. de Mayo, E. Morkved, A. B. M. A. Sattar, and
        A. Stoessl, Can. J. Chem. , 41, 100 (1963).
231.   Koelle, R. , Ann. , 164, 150 (1872).

232. Kovache, A. , and H. Thibon, Mem. Poudres, 36, 47 (1954); Chem. Abstr. , 51, 10409 (1957).
233. Kraenzlein, G. , H. Greune, M. Thiele, and F. Helwert, U. S. Patent 1, 933, 985; Chem. Abstr. , 28, 491 (1934).
234. Kraft, F. , and G. Heizmann, Ber. , 33, 3588 (1900).
235. Krajcinovic, M. , Arhiv. hem. farm. , 5, 2 (1931); Chem. Abstr. , 25, 3955 (1931).
235a. Kretzschmann, W. , and H. Fuerst, Chem. Tech. (Berlin), 15, No. 9, 559 (1963); Chem. Abstr. , 59, 15291 (1963).
236. Krzikalla, H. , and A. Tartter, German Patent 800, 410; Chem. Abstr. , 45, 1619 (1951).
237. Kuusinen, T. , and M. Lampinen, Suomen Kemistilehti, 31B, 381 (1958); Chem. Abstr. , 53, 17167 (1959).
238. Labine, R. A. , Chem. Eng. , 66, 60 (1959).
239. Lasarenko, O. , Ber. , 7, 125 (1874).
240. Lauer, K. , J. Prakt. Chem. , 143, 127 (1935).
241. Lauer, K. , and R. Oda, J. Prakt. Chem. , 143, 139 (1935).
242. Logemann, W. , P. Giraldi, and B. Galimberti, Ann. , 623, 157 (1959).
243. Lecher, H. Z. , and F. H. Adams, U. S. Patent 2, 483, 213; Chem. Abstr. , 44, 2563 (1950).
244. Lee, R. J. , U. S. Patent 2, 556, 429; Chem. Abstr. , 46, 4854 (1952).
245. Leiserson, L. , R. W. Bost. , and R. Le Baron, Ind. Eng. Chem. , 40, 508 (1948).
246. Leitman, Ya. I. , and I. N. Diyarov, Zh. Prikl. Khim. , 34, 376 (1961); Chem. Abstr. , 55, 16453 (1961).
247. Leitman, Ya. I. , and I. N. Diyarov, Zh. Prikl. Khim. , 34, 1920 (1961); Chem. Abstr. , 56, 2355 (1962).
248. Leitman, Ya. I. , and M. S. Pevzner, Zh. Prikl. Khim. , 32, 1842 (1959); Chem. Abstr. , 54, 5530 (1960).
249. Leitman, Ya. I. , V. I. Sorokin, and I. V. Tselinskii, Zh. Prikl. Khim. , 33, 1875 (1960); Chem. Abstr. , 55, 435 (1961).
250. Lepouse, H. , Bull. Soc. Chim. Belges, 34, 133 (1925).
251. Levina, L. I. , S. N. Patrakova, and D. A. Patrushev, Zh. Obshch. Khim. , 28, 2427 (1958); Chem. Abstr. , 53, 3120 (1959).
252. Lew, H. Y. , and C. R. Noller, J. Am. Chem. Soc. , 72, 5715 (1950).
253. Linstead, R. P. , and F. T. Weiss, J. Chem. Soc. , 1950, 2975.
254. Lisk, G. F. , Ind. Eng. Chem. , 41, 1923 (1949).
255. Lukashevich, V. O. , Dokl. Akad. Nauk SSSR, 99, 995 (1954); Chem. Abstr. , 50, 217 (1956).
256. Lukashevich, V. O. , Dokl. Akad. Nauk SSSR, 112, 872 (1957); Chem. Abstr. , 51, 14591 (1957).
257. Lukin, A. M. , J. Soc. Dyers Colourists, 68, 468 (1952).
258. MacMullin, C. W. , and H. A. Bruson, U. S. Patent 2, 301, 561; Chem. Abstr. , 37, 2103 (1943).
259. Maffei, S. , Gazz. Chim. Ital. , 80, 651 (1950).

260.   McElvain, S. M. , and M. A. Goese,   J. Am. Chem. Soc. ,   65,
        2233 (1943).
261.   McRae, W. A. , and S. S. Alexander,   U. S. Patent 2, 962, 454;
        Chem. Abstr. ,   55, 8703 (1961).
262.   Meier, W. , D. Meuche, and G. Heilbronner,   Helv. Chim.
        Acta,   46, 1929 (1963).
263.   Meiser, W. , U. S. Dept. Commerce, OTS Rept.   PB 73, 893,
        FIAT Microfilm Reel N-77, Frame 6402.
264.   Meiser, W. , U. S. Patent 2, 273, 974;   Chem. Abstr. ,   36, 3809
        (1942).
265.   Menard, M. , L. Mitchell, J. Komlossy, A. Wrigley, and
        F. L. Chubb, Can. J. Chem. ,   39, 729 (1961).
266.   Michel, U. S. Dept. Commerce, OTS Rept. PB 73, 911, Frames
        4816-18.
267.   Mikeska, L. A. , and C. A. Cohen, U. S. Patent 2, 716, 088; Chem.
        Abstr. ,   50, 4493 (1956).
268.   Millar, J. R. , D. G. Smith, W. E. Marr, and T. R. E. Kressman,
        J. Chem. Soc. ,   1963, 218.
269.   Miron, S. , and G. H. Richter,   J. Am. Chem. Soc. ,   71, 453
        (1949).
270.   Mosher, H. S. ,   "The Chemistry of the Pyridines, " in Hetero-
        cyclic Compounds, 1, R. C. Edlerfield, ed. , Wiley, New York,
        1950.
271.   Mosher, H. S. , and F. J. Welsh,   J. Am. Chem. Soc. ,   77, 2902
        (1955).
272.   Moyer, W. W. , U. S. Patent 2, 195, 186;   Chem. Abstr. ,   34,
        5208 (1940).
273.   Moyer, W. W. , U. S. Patent 2, 195, 188;   Chem. Abstr. ,   34,
        5208 (1940).
274.   Muller, N. , and W. J. Wallace,   J. Org. Chem. ,   24, 1151
        (1959).
275.   Muramoto, Y. ,   Science Ind. (Japan),   29, 315 (1955); Chem.
        Abstr. ,   50, 9946 (1956).
276.   Muramoto, Y. , Yuki Gosei Kagaku Kyokaishi, 18, 644 (1960);
        Chem. Abstr. ,   54, 24492 (1960).
277.   Murphy, A. R. , and J. B. Oesch, U. S. Patent 1, 794, 861: Chem.
        Abstr. ,   25, 2153 (1931).
278.   Mustafa, A. ,   Chem. Rev. ,   54, 195 (1954).
279.   Muth, F. , in Houben-Weyl, Methoden der Organischen Chemie,
        IX, 4th ed. , Thieme Verlag, Stuttgart, 1955, p. 429.
280.   Nachbaur, C. , J. Prakt. Chem. ,   75, 45 (1858).
281.   Naik, K. G. , and C. M. Desai,   J. Sci. Ind. Res. (India), 7B,
        195 (1948); Chem. Abstr. ,   43, 4031 (1949).
282.   National Chemical Laboratory, Dept. of Scientific and Indus-
        trial Research, Annual Report 1960, London.
283.   Nawiasky, P. , and G. E. Sprenger, U. S. Patent 2, 219, 748;
        Chem. Abstr. ,   35, 1067 (1941).

284. Nawiasky, P. , and G. E. Sprenger, U. S. Patent 2,335,193; Chem. Abstr. , 38, 2666 (1944).

285. Nelson, K. L. , in Friedel-Crafts and Related Reactions, G. A. Olah, ed. , Interscience, New York, 1963.

286. Nelson, K. L. , and H. C. Brown, in The Chemistry of Petroleum Hydrocarbons, 3, Reinhold, New York, 1955, p. 537.

287. Nesmeyanov, A. N. , and O. A. Reutov, Izv. Akad. Nauk SSSR Otdel. Khim. Nauk, 1959, 926; Chem. Abstr. , 54, 469 (1960).

288. Nesmeyanov, A. N. , and B. N. Strunin, Dokl. Akad. Nauk SSSR, 137, 106 (1961); Chem. Abstr. , 55, 19885 (1961).

289. Nesmeyanov, N. A. , S. T. Zhuzhlikova, and O. A. Reutov, Dokl. Akad. Nauk SSSR, 151, No. 4, 856 (1963); Chem. Abstr. , 59, 12838 (1963).

290. Nishikawa, M. , and H. Hagiwara, J. Pharm. Soc. Japan, 74, 76 (1954).

291. Nopco Chemical Co. , British Patent 642,836; Chem. Abstr. , 45, 3624 (1951).

292. Norwood, S. L. , and T. W. Sauls, U. S. Patent 2,828,333; Chem. Abstr. , 52, 13791 (1958).

293. Norwood, S. L. , and T. W. Sauls, U. S. Patent 2,831,020; Chem. Abstr. , 52, 14682 (1958).

294. Novello, F. C. , S. C. Bell, E. L. A. Abrams, C. Ziegler, and J. M. Sprague, J. Org. Chem. , 25, 965 (1960).

295. Nozoe, T. , Y. Kitahara, K. Yamane, and A. Yoshikoshi, Proc. Japan, Acad. , 27, No. 1, 18 (1951); Chem. Abstr. , 47, 4870 (1953).

296. NV de Bataafsche Petroleum Maatschappij, British Patent 764,020.

297. NV de Bataafsche Petroleum Maatschappij, German Patent 947,416; Chem. Abstr. , 53, 11821 (1959).

298. NV Philips Gloeilampenfabrieken, British Patent 822,237; Chem. Abstr. , 54, 3316 (1960).

299. NV Philips Gloeilampenfabrieken, British Patent 829,142; Chem. Abstr. , 54, 18440 (1961).

299a. Olah, G. A. , and M. W. Meyer, in Friedel-Crafts and Related Reactions, 1, G. A. Olah, ed. , Interscience, New York, 1963.

300. Oranienburger Chemische Fabrik AG, French Patent 801,022; Chem. Abstr. , 31, 116 (1937).

301. Otroshchenko, O. S. , A. S. Sadykov, and A. A. Ziyaev, Zh. Obshch. Khim. , 31, 678 (1961); Chem. Abstr. , 55, 23527 (1961).

302. Overberger, C. G. , H. Biletch, and F. W. Orttung, J. Org. Chem. , 24, 289 (1959).

303. Pailer, M. , and E. Romberger, Monatsh. , 92, 677 (1961).

304. Parmelee, H. M. , in The Chemistry of Synthetic Dyes and Pigments, H. A. Lubs, ed. , Reinhold, New York, 1955.

305. Pelayo, C. , J. Iriarte, and H. I. Bingold, J. Org. Chem. , 25, 1067 (1960).

306. van Peski, A. J. ,   Rec. Trav. Chim. ,   40, 103 (1921).
307. van Peski, A. J. ,   Rec. Trav. Chim. ,   40, 736 (1921).
308. Petitcolas, P. , and R. Sureau,   Bull. Soc. Chim. France,
      1950, 466.
308a. Phillips, M. A. , Mfg. Chemist, 34, No. 12, 575 (1963).
309. vander Plas, H. C. , and T. H. Crawford,   J. Org. Chem. , 26,
      2611 (1961).
310. vander Plas, H. C. , and H. J. den Hertog,   Chem. Weekblad,
      53, No. 42, 560 (1957).
311. vander Plas, H. C. , and H. J. den Hertog,   Tetrahedron Letters,
      1960, No. 1, 13.
312. Potapov, V. M. , A. P. Terent'ev, and V. M. Dem'yanovich, Zh.
      Obshch. Khim. , 30, 1043 (1960); Chem. Abstr. , 55, 371
      (1961).
313. Profft, E. , and A. Kubat, Ann. , 634, 185 (1960).
314. Prud'homme, M. , Compt. Rend. , 70, 1137 (1870).
315. Puzitskii, K. V. , Ya. T. Eidus, and A. Yu. Rabinovich, Zh.
      Prikl. Khim. , 32, 1819 (1959); Chem. Abstr. , 53, 23008
      (1959).
316. Quilico, A. , and E. Fleischner, Atti Accad. Lincei, 7, 1050
      (1928); Chem. Abstr. , 23, 1628 (1929).
317. Ratcliff, G. A. , Ph. D. Dissertation, Cornell University;
      Dissertation Abstr. , 14, 2018 (1954).
318. Reese, J. S. , J. Am. Chem. Soc. , 54, 2009(1932).
319. Reichspatentamt, Berlin, U. S. Dept. Commerce, OTS Rept.
      PB 83, 606.
320. Reitz, H. C. , R. E. Ferrel, H. S. Olcott, and H. Fraenkel-
      Conrat,   J. Am. Chem. Soc. , 68, 1031 (1946).
321. Remsen, I. , and P. Brown, Am. Chem. J. , 3, 218 (1881).
322. Reynolds, D. D. , and J. A. Cathcart, U. S. Patent 2, 725, 368;
      Chem. Abstr. , 50, 9786 (1956).
323. Ridd, J. H. , Chem. Eng. News, 41, No. 44, 48 (1963).
324. Robertson, J. C. , Ph. D. Dissertation, Brigham Young Uni-
      veristy, 1962; Dissertation Abstr. , 23, 4117 (1963).
325. Rohm and Haas Co. , French Patent 1, 280, 353.
326. Rondestvedt, C. S. , Jr. : J. Am. Chem. Soc. , 76, 1926 (1954).
327. Rondestvedt, C. S. , Jr. , and F. G. Bordwell, Org. Syn. , 34,
      85 (1954).
328. Rondestvedt, C. S. , Jr. , and J. C. Wygant, J. Am. Chem. Soc. ,
      76, 509 (1954).
329. Ross, J. , U. S. Patent 2, 160, 343; Chem. Abstr. , 33, 7438
      (1939).
330. Ross, J. , U. S. Patent 2, 195, 581; Chem. Abstr. , 34, 5208
      (1940).
331. Roth, H. H. , Ind. Eng. Chem. , 49, 1820 (1957).
332. Rueggeberg, W. H. C. , and T. W. Sauls, U. S. Patent 2, 743, 288;
      Chem. Abstr. , 50, 12511 (1956).

333.   Rueggeberg, W. H. C. , and T. W. Sauls, U. S. Patent 2, 810, 746;
        Chem. Abstr. , 52, 1656 (1958).

334.   Rueggeberg, W. H. C. , T. W. Sauls, and S. L. Norwood, J. Org.
        Chem. , 20, 455 (1955).

335.   Rummelsburg, A. L. , U. S. Patent 2, 344, 833; Chem. Abstr. ,
        38, 3756 (1944).

336.   Salzberg, P. L. U. S. Patent 2, 139, 697; Chem. Abstr. , 33,
        2252 (1939).

337.   Sandeman, I. , J. Chem. Soc. , 1953, 1135.

338.   Sandoz, Ltd. , British Patent 712, 771; Chem. Abstr. , 49, 2083
        (1955).

339.   Sanna, G. , and A. Carta, Rend. Seminario Fac. Scie. Univ.
        Cagliari, 20, 43 (1950); Chem. Abstr. , 47, 2136 (1953).

340.   Sauls, T. W. , and W. H. C. Rueggeberg, J. Am. Oil Chemists'
        Soc. , 33, 383 (1956).

341.   Scheibler, H. , and K. Falk, Chem. Ber. , 87, 1186 (1954).

342.   Scherer, O. , R. Huebner, and G. Otten, German Patent
        1, 104, 500; Chem. Abstr. , 56, 418 (1962).

343.   Schirm, E. , German Patent 757, 503; Chem. Abstr. , 49,
        15972 (1955).

344.   Schneider, P. , in Houben-Weyl, Methoden der Organischen
        Chemie, XIV/2, Thieme Verlag, Stuttgart, 1963.

345.   Schoop, P. , Ber. , 14, 223 (1881).

346.   Schultz, R. G. , J. Org. Chem. , 26, 5195 (1961).

347.   Schulz, J. C. F. , and P. M. Ruoff, J. Org. Chem. , 26, 939
        (1961).

348.   Schwenk, E. , Z. Angew. Chem. , 44, 912 (1931).

349.   Scully, J. F. , and E. V. Brown, J. Org. Chem. , 19, 894 (1954).

350.   Senhofer, C. , Z. Chem. , 1870, 44.

351.   Serchi, G. , and A. R. Poggi, Ann. Chim. (Rome), 41, 723
        (1951); Chem. Abstr. , 47, 10488 (1953).

352.   Seymour, G. W. , V. S. Salvin, and W. D. Jones, U. S. Patent
        2, 511, 547; Chem. Abstr. , 45, 653 (1951).

353.   Shestov, A. P. , and N. A. Osipova, J. Gen. Chem. USSR
        (English Transl.), 29, 595 (1959); Chem. Abstr. , 54, 367
        (1960).

354.   Shestov, A. P. , and N. A. Osipova, Sb. Statei, Nauchn. -Issled.
        Inst. Organ. Poluprod. i Krasitelei, 1961, No. 2, 13: Chem.
        Abstr. , 57, 16511 (1962).

355.   Shive, W. , and R. A. Glenn, U. S. Patent 2, 409, 806; Chem.
        Abstr. , 41, 2088 (1947).

356.   Shoji, H. , and K. Majima, J. Am. Oil Chemists' Soc. , 40,
        179 (1963).

357.   Shusherina, N. P. , N. D. Dmitrieva, and R. Ya. Levina, Dokl.
        Akad. Nauk SSSR, 135, 1406 (1960); Chem. Abstr. , 55, 12396
        (1961).

358.   Sierbin, R. , Przemysl Chem. , 9, 72 (1953); Chem. Abstr. ,
        48, 11366 (1954).

359. Signer, R. , U. S. Patent 2,604,456; Chem. Abstr. , 46, 9891 (1952).

360. Singley, J. E. , W. C. Duckworth, C. E. Feazel, and W. H. C. Rueggeberg, Off. Dig. Federation Paint Varnish Prod. Clubs, 30, 835 (1958).

361. Skrowaczewska, Z. , Trav. Soc. Sci. Lettres Wroclaw, Ser. B, No. 61, 5 (1953); Chem. Abstr. , 48, 7568 (1954).

362. Smith, C. W. , U. S. Patent 2,566,810; Chem. Abstr. , 46, 2576 (1952).

363. Snyder, J. C. , and A. V. Grosse, U. S. Patent 2,493,038; Chem. Abstr. , 44, 4021 (1950).

364. Soc. pour l'ind. chim. a Bale, Swiss Patent 231,254; Chem. Abstr. , 43, 2632 (1949).

365. Solodar, L. S. , and Z. N. Shevchenko, J. Appl. Chem. USSR (English Transl.), 22, 508 (1949); Chem. Abstr. , 44, 2468 (1950).

366. Solomon, M. G. , and D. J. Hennessy, J. Org. Chem. , 22, 1649 (1957).

367. Sperling, R. , J. Chem. Soc. , 1949, 1925.
368. Sperling, R. , J. Chem. Soc. , 1949, 1932.
369. Sperling, R. , J. Chem. Soc. , 1949, 1938.
370. Sprague, J. M. , and A. H. Land, "Thiazoles and Benzothiazoles, " in Heterocyclic Compounds, V, R. C. Elderfield, ed. , Wiley, New York, 1957.

371. Spryskov, A. A. , J. Gen. Chem. USSR (English Transl.), 16, 2126 (1946); Chem. Abstr. , 42, 894 (1948).

372. Spryskov, A. A. , J. Gen. Chem. USSR (English Transl.), 17, 1370 (1947); Chem. Abstr. , 43, 2178 (1949).

373. Spryskov, A. A. , Zh. Obshch. Khim. , 30, 2449 (1960); Chem. Abstr. , 55, 12336 (1961).

374. Spryskov, A. A. , and B. G. Gredin, Zh. Obshch. Khim. , 33, No. 4, 1082 (1963); Chem. Abstr. , 59, 9748 (1963).

375. Spryskov, A. A. , and A. I. Kobenin, Trudy Ivanovsk. Khim. Tekhnol. Inst. , 1956, No. 5, 196; Chem. Abstr. , 53, 13601 (1959).

376. Spryskov, A. A. , and S. P. Starkov, Zh. Obshch. Khim. , 26, 2862 (1956); Chem. Abstr. , 51, 8038 (1957).

377. Spryskov, A. A. , and S. P. Starkov, Zh. Obshch. Khim. , 27, 2780 (1957); Chem. Abstr. , 52, 8071 (1958).

378. Spryskov, S. P. , and A. A. Spryskov, Izv. Vysshikh Uchebn-Zavedenii Khim i Khim. Tekhnol. , 3, 868 (1960); Chem. Abstr. , 55, 8335 (1961).

379. Starkov, S. P. and A. A. Spryskov, Zh. Obshch. Khim. , 27, 3067 (1957); Chem. Abstr. , 52, 8072 (1958).

380. Stavric, B. , and E. Cerkovnikov, Croat. Chem. Acta, 31, 107 (1959); Chem. Abstr. , 54, 20949 (1960).

381. Steinhauer, A. F. , U. S. Patent 2,854,477; Chem. Abstr. , 53, 15605 (1959).

382. Stern, R. , and P. Baumgartner, Compt. Rend. , <u>257</u>, No. 10, 1713 (1963).

383. Stirton, A. J. , J. Am. Oil Chemists' Soc. , <u>39</u>, 490 (1962).

384. Stirton, A. J. , J. K. Weil, and R. G. Bistline, Jr. , J. Am. Oil Chemists' Soc. , <u>31</u>, 13 (1954).

385. Strakov, A. , E. Gudriniece, A. Ievins, and G. Vanags, Zh. Obshch, Khim. , <u>30</u>, 3967 (1960); Chem. Abstr. , <u>55</u>, 22251 (1961).

386. Strakov, A. Ya. , E. Gudriniece, and G. Vanags, Latvijas PSR Zinatnu Akad. Vestis, Kim. Ser. , <u>1962</u>, 427; Chem. Abstr. , <u>59</u>, 12717 (1963).

387. Strakov, A. , O. Neilands, E. Gudriniece, and G. Vanags, Dokl. Akad. Nauk SSSR, <u>141</u>, 374 (1961); Chem. Abstr. , <u>56</u>, 11505 (1962).

388. Strepetov, N. P. , Trudy Voronezhsk. Gos. University, <u>49</u>, 31 (1958); Chem. Abstr. , <u>56</u>, 378 (1962).

389. Struve, W. S. , in The Chemistry of Synthetic Dyes and Pigments, H. A. Lubs, ed. , Reinhold, New York, 1955.

390. Stubbs, F. J. , C. D. Williams, and C. N. Hinshelwood, J. Chem. Soc. , <u>1948</u>, 1065.

391. Sureau, R. , Bull. Soc. Chim. France, <u>1960</u>, 32.

392. Suter, C. M. , J. Am. Chem. Soc. , <u>53</u>, 1114 (1931).

393. Suter, C. M. , The Organic Chemistry of Sulfur, Wiley, New York, 1944.

394. Suter, C. M. , U. S. Patent 2, 098, 114; Chem. Abstr. , <u>32</u>, 191 (1938).

395. Suter, C. M. , U. S. Patent 2, 135, 358; Chem. Abstr. , <u>33</u>, 1064 (1939).

396. Suter, C. M. , U. S. Patent 2, 365, 783; Chem. Abstr. , <u>39</u>, 4508 (1945).

397. Suter, C. M. , and F. G. Bordwell, J. Am. Chem. Soc. , <u>65</u>, 507 (1943).

398. Suter, C. M. , P. B. Evans, and J. M. Kiefer, J. Am. Chem. Soc. , <u>60</u>, 538 (1938).

399. Suter, C. M. , and J. D. Malkemus, J. Am. Chem. Soc. , <u>63</u>, 978 (1941).

400. Suter, C. M. , and W. E. Truce, J. Am. Chem. Soc. , <u>66</u>, 1105 (1944).

401. Suter, C. M. , and A. W. Weston, Organic Reactions, <u>3</u>, Wiley, New York, 1946, p. 141.

402. Sveda, M. , U. S. Patent 2, 383, 752; Chem. Abstr. , <u>40</u>, 21 (1946).

403. Swisher, R. D. , British Patent 679, 827; Chem. Abstr. , <u>48</u>, 4003 (1954).

404. Swisher, R. D. , U. S. Patent 2, 693, 487; Chem. Abstr. , <u>49</u>, 14804 (1955).

405. Tatibouet, F. , and R. Setton, Bull. Soc. Chim. France, <u>1952</u>, 382.

406.   Tauber, S. J. , and N. N. Lowry, J. Org. Chem. , 27, 2659
        (1962).

407.   Tennessee Corporation, Surface Active Sul-fon-ate OA-5,
        1954.

408.   Terent'ev, A. P.., Vestnik Mosk. University, No. 6, 9 (1947);
        Chem. Abstr. , 44, 1480 (1950).

409.   Terent'ev, A. P. , Zh. Obshch. Khim. , 23, 746 (1953); Chem.
        Abstr. , 48, 4430 (1954).

410.   Terent'ev, A. P. , and A. V. Dombrovskii, Dokl. Akad. Nauk
        SSSR, 65, 513 (1949); Chem. Abstr. , 45, 2892 (1951).

411.   Terent'ev, A. P. , and A. V. Dombrovskii, Dokl. Akad. Nauk
        SSSR, 67, 859 (1949); Chem. Abstr. , 44, 1891 (1950).

412.   Terent'ev, A. P. , and A. V. Dombrovskii, J. Gen. Chem.
        USSR (English Transl.), 19, 1467 (1949); Chem. Abstr. ,
        44, 1481 (1950).

413.   Terent'ev, A. P. , and A. V. Dombrovskii, J. Gen. Chem.
        USSR (English Transl.), 20, 1875 (1950); Chem. Abstr. ,
        45, 2892 (1951).

414.   Terent'ev, A. P. , and A. V. Dombrovskii, J. Gen. Chem.
        USSR (English Transl.), 21, 278 (1951); Chem. Abstr. ,
        45, 7025 (1951).

415.   Terent'ev, A. P. , and A. V. Dombrovskii, J. Gen. Chem.
        USSR (English Transl.), 21, 704 (1951); Chem. Abstr. ,
        45, 8969 (1951).

416.   Terent'ev, A. P. , A. V. Dombrovskii, and R. A. Gratscheva,
        Zh. Obshch. Khim. , 23, 1132 (1953); Chem. Abstr. , 47,
        12238 (1953).

417.   Terent'ev, A. P. , S. K. Golubeva, and L. V. Tsymbal, Zh.
        Obshch. Khim. , 19, 781 (1949); Chem. Abstr. , 44, 1095
        (1950).

418.   Terent'ev, A. P. , and R. A. Gratscheva, Zh. Obshch. Khim. ,
        30, 3663 (1960); Chem. Abstr. , 55, 18659 (1961).

419.   Terent'ev, A. P. , R. A. Gratscheva, and S. F. Schtscherbatova,
        Dokl. Akad. Nauk SSSR, 84, 975 (1952); Chem. Abstr. , 47,
        3262 (1953).

420.   Terent'ev, A. P. , and A. N. Grinev, Zh. Obshch. Khim. , 24,
        1049 (1954); Chem. Abstr. , 49, 8850 (1955).

421.   Terent'ev, A. P. , and G. M. Kadatskii, Zh. Obshch. Khim. ,
        21, 1524 (1951); Chem. Abstr. , 46, 2536 (1952).

422.   Terent'ev, A. P. , and G. M. Kadatskii, Zh. Obshch. Khim. ,
        22, 153 (1952); Chem. Abstr. , 46, 11178 (1952).

423.   Terent'ev, A. P. , and G. M. Kadatskii, Zh. Obshch. Khim. ,
        23, 251 (1953); Chem. , Abstr. , 48, 3339 (1954).

424.   Terent'ev, A. P. , and L. A. Kazitsyna, Zh. Obshch, Khim. ,
        18, 723 (1948); Chem. Abstr. , 43, 214 (1949).

425.   Terent'ev, A. P. , and L. A. Kazitsyna, Zh. Obshch, Khim. ,
        19, 531 (1949); Chem. Abstr. , 43, 7015 (1949).

426.   Terent'ev, A. P. , L. A. Kazitsyna, and S. E. Suvorova, Zh. Obshch. Khim. , 19, 1951 (1949); Chem. Abstr. , 44, 1954 (1950).

427.   Terent'ev, A. P. , L. A. Kazitsyna, and A. M. Turovskaya, Zh. Obshch. Khim. , 20, 185 (1950); Chem. Abstr. , 44, 5862 (1950).

428.   Terent'ev, A. P. , A. N. Kost, A. M. Yurkevich, and E. E. Khaskina, Zh. Obshch, Khim. , 23, 746 (1953); Chem. Abstr. , 48, 4430 (1954).

429.   Terent'ev, A. P. , A. N. Kost, A. M. Yurkevich, E. E. Khaskina, and L. I. Obreimova, Vestn. Mosk. University, 8, No. 6, Ser. Fiz. -Mat. i Estestven. Nauk. No. 4, 121 (1953); Chem. Abstr. , 49, 8104 (1955).

430.   Terent'ev, A. P. , V. M. Potopov, and V. M. Dem'yanovich, Zh. Obshch. Khim. , 29, 949 (1959); Chem. Abstr. , 54, 1334 (1960).

431.   Terent'ev, A. P. , V. M. Potapov, and I. Z. Semion, Zh. Obshch. Khim. , 26, 2934 (1956); Chem. Abstr. , 51, 7321 (1957).

432.   Terent'ev, A. P. , and M. N. Preobrazhenskaya, Zh. Obshch. Khim. , 30, 1218 (1960); Chem. Abstr. , 55, 511 (1961).

433.   Terent'ev, A. P. , and N. P. Volynskii, J. Gen. Chem. USSR (English Transl.), 19, 784 (1949); Chem. Abstr. , 44, 1095 (1950).

434.   Terent'ev, A. P. , and L. A. Yanovakaya, Dokl. Akad. Nauk SSSR, 75, 235 (1950); Chem. Abstr. , 45, 8445 (1951).

435.   Terent'ev, A. P. , and L. A. Yanovskaya, Zh. Obshch, Khim. , 19, 538 (1949); Chem. Abstr. , 43, 7015 (1949).

436.   Terent'ev, A. P. , and L. A. Yanovskaya, Zh. Obshch. Khim. , 19, 1365 (1949); Chem. Abstr. , 44, 1095 (1950).

437.   Terent'ev, A. P. , and L. A. Yanovskaya, Zh. Obshch. Khim. , 19, 2118 (1949); Chem. Abstr. , 44, 3973 (1950).

438.   Terent'ev, A. P. , and L. A. Yanovskaya, Zh. Obshch. Khim. , 21, 281 (1951); Chem. Abstr. , 45, 7025 (1951).

439.   Terent'ev, A. P. , and L. A. Yanovskaya, Zh. Obshch. Khim. , 21, 1295 (1951); Chem. Abstr. , 46, 2048 (1952).

440.   Terent'ev, A. P. , L. A. Yanovskaya, A. M. Berlin, and E. A. Borisov, Vestn. Mosk. University, 8, No. 6, Ser. Fiz. -Mat i Estestven. Nauk. , No. 4, 117 (1953); Chem. Abstr. , 49, 8092 (1955).

441.   Thurston, J. T. , U. S. Dept. Commerce, OTS Rept. PB 60, 890, FIAT Final Rept. 949. 949.

442.   Tinker, J. M. , and V. A. Hansen, U. S. Patent 1, 934, 216: Chem. Abstr. , 28, 495 (1934).

443.   Tinker, J. M. , and V. A. Hansen, U. S. Patent 1, 969, 189; Chem. Abstr. , 28, 6160 (1934).

444.   Treibs, W. , and I. Lorenz, Chem. Ber. , 8 2, 400 (1949).

445.   Treibs, W. , and W. Schroth, Ann. , 586, 202 (1954).

446.   Truce, W. E. , and C. C. Alfieri, J. A. Chem. Soc. , 72, 2740 (1950).

447.   Truce, W. E. , and P. F. Gunberg,   J. Am. Chem. Soc. , 72, 2401
        (1950).
448.   Truce, W. E. , and F. J. Lotspeich,   J. Am. Chem. Soc. , 77,
        3410 (1955).
449.   Truce, W. E. , and P. T. Mori,   J. Org. Chem. , 18, 1655 (1953).
450.   Truce, W. E. , and C. E. Olson,   J. Am. Chem. Soc. , 75, 1651
        (1953).
451.   Truce, W. E. , and C. M. Suter,   J. Am. Chem. Soc. , 70, 3851
        (1948).
452.   Truce, W. E. , and C. W. Vriesen,   J. Am. Chem. Soc. , 75, 2525
        (1953).
453.   Turbak, A. F. ,   Ind. Eng. Chem. Prod. Res. Develop. , 1, 275
        (1962).
454.   Turbak, A. F. ,   Paper presented at the 144th American Chemi-
        cal Society Meeting, Los Angeles, Cal. , March 31-April 5,
        1963.
455.   Ueda, M. , and H. Sekiguchi,   Japanese Patent 18, 284('60);
        Chem. Abstr. , 55, 22270 (1961).
456.   Ueyangai, J. ,   J. Pharm. Soc. Japan, 71, 613 (1951); Chem.
        Abstr. , 46, 949 (1952).
457.   Vasil'ev, A. A. , M. B. Gershman, and T. A. Vasil'eva,   J. Appl.
        Chem. USSR (English Transl.), 35, 2288 (1962); Chem. Abstr.,
        58, 6224 (1963).
458.   Vasil'eva, V. F. , and V. G. Yashunskii,   Khim. Nauka i Promy. ,
        3, 282 (1958); Chem. Abstr. , 52, 20013 (1958).
459.   Veldhuis, B. ,   Anal. Chem. , 32, 1681 (1960).
460.   Velluz, L. , R. Joly, and R. Bucourt,   Compt. Rend. , 248, 114
        (1959).
461.   Venkataraman, K. ,   The Chemistry of Synthetic Dyes, Aca-
        demic Press, New York, 1952.
462.   Vicary, D. R. ,   and C. N. Hinshelwood,   J. Chem. Soc. , 1939,
        1372.
463.   Vollbracht, L. , H. Cerfontain, and F. L. J. Sixma,   Rec. Trav.
        Chim. , 80, No. 1, 11 (1961).
464.   Vulcan Chemical Co. , Ltd. ,   British Patent 747, 659; Chem.
        Abstr. , 51, 1265 (1957).
465.   Wadsworth, K. D. , and C. N. Hinshelwood,   J. Chem. Soc. , 1944,
        469.
466.   Waldman, H. , and E. Schwenk,   Ann. , 487, 287 (1931).
467.   Wallach, O. , and M. Wuesten,   Ber. , 16, 149 (1883).
468.   Walles, W. E. ,   U. S. Patent 2, 832, 696; Chem. Abstr. , 52,
        15086 (1958).
469.   Walsh, J. A. , and D. A. Davenport,   Abstracts of papers pre-
        sented at the 134th meeting of the American Chemical Society,
        Chicago, Ill. , Sept. 7-12, 1958.
470.   Wanders, A. C. M. , and H. Cerfontain, ;   Proc. Chem. Soc. ,
        1963, 174.

471.   Wedekind, E., D. Schenk, and R. Stuesser, Ber. , 56, 640
        (1923).
472.   Wedekind, E. , and R. Stuesser, Ber. , 56, 1557 (1923).
473.   Weil, J. K. , R. G. Bistline, Jr. , and A. J. Stirton, J. Am. Chem.
        Soc. , 75, 4859 (1953).
474.   Weil, J. K. , R. G. Bistline, Jr. , and A. J. Stirton, J. Am. Oil
        Chemists' Soc. , 32, 370 (1955).
475.   Weil, J. K. , R. G. Bistline, Jr. , and A. J. Stirton, J. Am. Oil
        Chemists' Soc. , 34, 100 (1957).
476.   Weil, J. K. , A. J. Stirton, and R. G. Bistline, Jr. , J. Am. Oil
        Chemists' Soc. , 37, 295 (1960).
477.   Weil, J. K. , A. J. Stirton, R. G. Bistline, Jr. , and W. C. Ault,
        J. Am. Oil Chemists' Soc. , 37, 679 (1960).
478.   Weiland, H. J. , and M. A. Prahl, U. S. Patent 2, 015, 023; Chem.
        Abstr. , 29, 7678 (1935).
479.   Weinhold, C. , Ann. Chem. , 143, 58 (1867).
480.   Weinmayr, V. , J. Am. Chem. Soc. , 77, 3009 (1955).
481.   Wendland, R. T. , C. H. Smith, and R. Muraca, J. Am. Chem.
        Soc. , 71, 1593 (1949).
482.   Wheaton, R. M. , and D. F. Harrington, Ind. Eng. Chem. , 44,
        1796 (1952).
483.   Widman, O. , Ber. , 22, 2274 (1889).
484.   Widmer, W. , and A. Fasciati, U. S. Patent 2, 615, 913; Chem.
        Abstr. , 47, 7786 (1953).
485.   Windaus, A. , and E. Kuhr, Ann. , 532, 52 (1937).
486.   Windaus, A. , and K. H. Mielke, Ann. , 536, 116 (1938).
487.   Worstall, R. A. , Am. Chem. J. , 20, 664 (1898).
488.   Yale, H. L. , K. Losee, and J. Bernstein, J. Am. Chem. Soc. ,
        82, 2042 (1960).
489.   Ziegler, C. , E. K. Kuhl, and J. M. Sprague, J. Org. Chem. , 25,
        1454 (1960).

CHAPTER 3

SULFONATION WITH COMPOUNDS OF SULFUR DIOXIDE

I. INTRODUCTION

Sulfite ion is the reagent of primary interest in this chapter, although the term "compounds of sulfur dioxide" is used broadly to include sulfuryl chloride and similar systems (sulfuryl chlorofluoride and mixtures of sulfur dioxide and chlorine), and sulfur dioxide with oxygen. Even in cases where bisulfite is used, kinetic studies have shown that the much more nucleophilic sulfite ion is often the effective attacking species, even though present in substantially lower concentration. This has been demonstrated, or considered probable, in the sulfonation of aldehydes and ketones, epoxides, quinones, and open-chain heteroconjugate systems. The high nucleophilic power of the sulfite ion, which is greater than that of alkoxide in some cases (4a), would not be predicted from its basicity ($pK_a \sim 7$), or from the electronic structure as usually given, of which A is one canonical form.

(A)   (B)

A more accurately descriptive structure is B (4a), resulting from sp^3 hybridization, with a considerable amount of pd-π bonding. This structure provides the sulfur atom with a convenient orbital for bond formation, and makes it comparatively highly polarizable. These two factors help to account for much of the behavior of the sulfite ion, including the formation of a carbon-sulfur bond, rather than carbon-oxygen, in reaction with organic halides.

In oxygen-sulfur compounds a double—bond orbital occupies approximately the same amount of space in the valency shell of the sulfur atom as does a lone pair orbital (345a). Thus, a bond order of 1.33 for the sulfite ion is consistent with this idea, which would predict a structure for sulfite ion similar to that established for sulfate ion, with a lone pair in place of one of the double bonds. It appears likely that the sulfite ion and the chlorate ion, which are isoelectronic, have similar structures.

Except for isolated papers, study of the underlying chemistry in almost all areas of this field has been largely neglected. The Strecker reaction (alkyl halides with sulfites) has been used steadily for synthetic purposes over the past century, but the mechanism of this important procedure was considered in only one paper in 1956. The relationship between structure and reactivity of the aliphatic aldehydes and ketones with bisulfite was last seriously studied in 1905, and that of the aromatic aldehydes in 1941. The basic chemistry and theory of the epoxide-bisulfite reaction are also largely undeveloped. Early studies of the sulfochlorination reaction, and of the free-radical catalyzed addition of bisulfite to alkenes, have not been greatly extended since their discovery and early development. The same can be said of sulfoxidation, although a current revival of commercial interest in the process has already resulted in further understanding of this reaction. A heartening exception to this general lack of concerted activity is provided by the papers of Bogdanov and of Rieche, and their respective co-workers, on the course and mechanism of the Bucherer reaction.

The methods described in this chapter have proved especially useful for the synthesis of aliphatic compounds, and of aromatic sulfonates with orientation not attainable by direct sulfonation. Many of the sulfoalkylating agents discussed in Chapter 5 are made by sulfite procedures. Steric factors, associated with the introduction of the bulky sulfonate group, are noted with these procedures, as with those involving direct sulfonation discussed in Chapter 2. Effects of this type are especially pronounced in sulfochlorination, and in the addition of bisulfite to alkenes, epoxides, aldehydes, and ketones. Numerous examples are cited herein of the addition of bisulfite across the carbon-nitrogen double bond; this type of reaction appears to have a hitherto unsuspected degree of generality.

II.   ALIPHATIC AND ALICYCLIC SULFONATES

A.   Preparation from Saturated Compounds

1. SULFOCHLORINATION

a. Sulfochlorination with Sulfur Dioxide and Chlorine

It was observed by Reed in 1936 (335) that a $-SO_2Cl$ group could be placed on an aliphatic carbon atom by using a mixture of sulfur dioxide and chlorine in the presence of a chain - initiating catalyst such as actinic light:

$$Cl_2 \xrightarrow{\text{Catalyst}} 2Cl\cdot \tag{3-1}$$

$$Cl\cdot + RH \longrightarrow R\cdot + HCl \tag{3-2}$$

$$R\cdot + SO_2 \longrightarrow RSO_2\cdot \tag{3-3}$$

$$RSO_2\cdot + Cl_2 \longrightarrow RSO_2Cl + Cl\cdot \tag{3-4}$$

Since this procedure seemed at the time to provide the long-sought method for easy sulfonation of cheap paraffinic petroleum fractions, it was accorded immediate and intensive study by the du Pont Company in the United States and by the I. G. Farbenindustrie in Germany. The raw materials were, respectively, a petroleum white oil and a hydrogenated gas oil obtained by the Fischer—Tropsch process. These yielded sulfonate detergents by alkaline hydrolysis of the sulfonyl chlorides; annual production of the German detergent of this type (Mersolate) reached 80,000 tons by the end of World War II.

The chemical and technological factors involved in the sulfochlorination of pure paraffin hydrocarbons (i. e. , propane, butane, n-dodecane), as well as of industrial mixtures, have been well reviewed by participants in the experimental work, including Eckoldt (124), Lockwood (257), and Asinger (14), with coverage by the last being especially complete. The process has also been reviewed by others (380). The main side reactions noted during sulfochlorination are chlorination and disulfochlorination, the extent of the latter being 10, 30, and 50% at degrees of hydrocarbon conversion of 20, 50, and 70%, respectively, in the typical case of n-dodecane (257). These side reactions can be reduced, but not eliminated, by resorting to partial conversion of the organic compound, and by using a considerable molar excess of SO_2 relative to chlorine. The consequent necessity for raw material recovery and recycle, high raw material cost (i. e. , the consumption of unproductive chlorine), the need for specialized equipment (because of the formation of corrosive hydrogen chloride and the requirement of photochemical activation), and the necessity for a final saponification step, have put this process in an unfavorable position for commercial detergent production compared to the direct sulfonation of dodecylbenzene, which has none of these objections.

These sulfonyl chlorides have, however, achieved commercial acceptance as specialized tanning agents; during tanning, sulfonamides are formed by interaction with amino groups in the leather. Another promising application of sulfochlorination involves the conversion of polyethylene to an elastomer which can be cured by reaction with various inorganic or organic agents to a synthetic rubber of outstanding abrasion resistance and durability on exposure to oxygen, ozone, heat, and weather (399). Chemically, the elastomer is a high molecular weight chlorinated polysulfonyl chloride. It is noteworthy that both of these applications involve reactions of the sulfonyl chloride group other than simple hydrolysis, a concept capable of extension to the preparation of other potentially useful compounds such as the sulfinic acids or the thiols and the formation of esters with alcohols or phenols. A third commercial application comprises production of 2-chloroethansulfonyl chloride by the combined chlorination-sulfochlorination of ethane (109).

Several noteworthy observations have emerged during study of the sulfochlorination of pure paraffin hydrocarbons by Asinger and co-workers (14), and in later studies. The point of introduction of one sulfonyl chloride group into a paraffin hydrocarbon is entirely random, with the relative reaction rates of primary to secondary hydrogen atoms being 1:3.25, which is approximately the ratio observed in chlorination or nitration (13). Tertiary hydrogen atoms are never replaced by sulfonyl chloride groups, although they do react with chlorine; this difference is explained on steric grounds (15, 19). The presence of one sulfonyl chloride group has been concluded to inhibit the nearby introduction of a second. Thus, propane forms only the 1,3-disulfonyl chloride (21), and 2-propanesulfonyl chloride does not react (417). With n-dodecane and n-tetradecane some inhibition was noted in the introduction of a second group, even several carbon atoms distant from the first group (17, 20). Tests with pure 1-hexanesulfonyl chloride gave similar results (16a). On the other hand, inhibition is not directly proportional to the distance from the first group, since n-butane forms a 20:80 mixture of the 1,4-and the 1,3-disulfonyl chlorides (16). It is also of interest that the 1,2-disulfonyl chloride has been made by the sulfochlorination of ethane (15), although the yield was only 1%, and that even methane has been converted to the disulfonyl chloride (168) in very low yield and under forcing conditions.

Comparatively little has been done on the sulfochlorination of substituted paraffins. Toluene, ethylbenzene, and tert-butylbenzene gave 0, 7.5, and 40% yields of sulfonyl chlorides, respectively (418), again suggesting inhibition of sulfochlorination by a neighboring group through other than steric factors. Chlorinated alkanes (C3-6) (185) yield mixtures, with the nearest sulfonyl chloride group on the third carbon atom removed from that holding the chlorine atom. Ethyl chloride, on the other hand, was later shown to give 30-60% of the 2-sulfonyl chloride (452); liquid sulfur dioxide was here employed as a novel sulfochlorination solvent. The authors point out that analogy to chlorination would suggest formation of the 1-isomer; however, they make no mention of its substantially greater steric requirement compared to the 2-isomer. The methylated and ethylated chlorosilanes also show interesting neighboring - group effects in sulfochlorination (87). Tetramethylsilane reacts normally, trimethylchlorosilane gives only a 17% yield, and dimethyldichlorosilane and methyltrichlorosilane do not react. Diethyldichlorosilane and ethyltrichlorosilane, on the other hand, do undergo sulfochlorination:

$$C_2H_5SiCl_3 + SO_2 + Cl_2 \xrightarrow{\text{Light}} Cl_3SiCH_2CH_2SO_2Cl + HCl \qquad (3\text{-}5)$$

The authors conclude that these results are similar to those obtained during photochemical chlorination of the same compounds. A poly (dimethylsiloxane) rubber, $(-Si(CH_3)_2O-)_x$, was sulfochlorinated on every second methyl group using a Co 60 catalyst (122). Steric inhibition may be less pronounced here, but Co 60 is a more effective catalyst for this reaction than light. Other substituted paraffin hydrocarbons subjected to sulfochlorination include di-(tert-butyl) peroxide (354), to the monosulfonyl chloride, and the hydrochlorides of the C4-12 aliphatic amines (136a, 350). In the second case, product composition was found consistent with the principles cited above, in that amines lower than C3 gave little or no yield, while n-butylamine formed a mixture of the 3- and 4-sulfonyl chlorides.

The nitroparaffins (nitromethane, nitroethane, and 2-nitropropane) are stated to give fair yields of products with the sulfonyl chloride group on the same carbon atom as the nitro moiety (101). These results are remarkable in being the only examples known to date where an existing electronegative group actually promotes sulfochlorination on the same carbon atom, rather than inhibiting an attack not only on the geminal carbon atom, but on those surrounding it. Also exceptional is the preferential replacement of a tertiary hydrogen atom in 2-nitropropane. In the chlorination of the nitroparaffins, conditions favoring the existence of the aci form of the nitro compound (179) lead to the formation of gem chlorinated derivatives; a similar explanation seems likely here:

$$R_2CHNO_2 \rightleftharpoons R_2C = \overset{+}{N}\underset{OH}{\overset{O^-}{\diagup}} \xrightarrow[Cl_2]{SO_2} \left[R_2C\underset{SO_2Cl}{\overset{|}{}} \overset{+}{N}\underset{Cl}{\overset{O^-}{\diagup}}OH \right] \longrightarrow$$

$$R_2\underset{SO_2Cl}{\overset{|}{C}}\text{---}NO_2 + HCl \qquad (3\text{-}6)$$

The direction of addition, with the formation of a carbon-sulfur bond, is similar to that noted in the sulfonation of other unsaturated nitrogen compounds in Sections II-B-7 and IV-A.

An interesting effort to exploit the above-mentioned, group - repulsion effect involved the attempted preparation of 1, 3-propanesultone by intramolecular sulfochlorination (264):

$$HOCH_2CH_2CH_3 \xrightarrow{SO_2Cl_2}$$

$$ClSO_2OCH_2CH_2CH_3 \nearrow \overset{\boxed{\quad\quad}}{SO_2(CH_2)_3O}$$

$$\searrow SO_2CH_2\underset{}{CHCH_3}$$

$$\underset{O}{\overset{|}{}} \quad \underset{O}{\overset{|}{}}$$

$$CH_3\underset{}{CHCH_2}\text{-}SO_2$$

$$(3\text{-}7)$$

The compound shown was formed in preference to the desired sultone (265a, 368). Apparently anomalous placement of the sulfonic group in the 1-position and of oxygen in position 2 can be explained by chlorination of the alcohol to 2-chloro-1-propanol, followed by dehydrochlorination to the epoxide and a sequence of reactions generally similar to those involving halohydrins and sulfites discussed in Section II-A-5.

In a discussion of the reaction mechanism of sulfochlorination, Walling has suggested (451) that, contrary to previous proposals, reaction 3-3 is reversible. This view is based on the observations that sulfochlorination does not proceed in the vapor phase, and that SO_2 - olefin polymerizations, which are also held to involve a mechanism of the type indicated by reaction 3-3, have a "ceiling temperature." The failure of toluene to sulfochlorinate under these conditions is thus explained by the stability of the benzyl radical, a situation which reverses reaction 3-3. Isobutane does not sulfochlorinate in the vapor phase because the ceiling temperature has been exceeded. As indicated in Chapter 8, the sulfochlorination reaction has, in fact, been proved reversible more recently by a free-radical chain process under a variety of conditions.

As stated before, polyethylene is sulfochlorinated commercially for the preparation of an elastomer. Polypropylene, more recently available, has been studied toward a similar end, but apparently has not as yet been commercialized. A study of process variables with relation to properties for a stereoblock polypropylene of 60% isotactic structure (209, 430) showed that the products varied from crystalline to rubbery to brittle as the sulfur content rose from 0 to 6%; materials containing over 2% sulfur were chemically unstable. C2-3 copolymers have also been considered (40, 296). One such material of about 40% C3 content gave a sulfochlorinated product with better rubbery properties than that made from high-pressure polyethylene (40).

Technological developments in sulfochlorination include operation under pressure (100 p. s. i.) (63), which insures superior gas-liquid contact with consequent improved heat removal compared to conventional operation at atmospheric pressure. The most important advance is the observation that γ radiation using Co 60 is an excellent sulfochlorination catalyst, as applied to heptane (189), cetane (41), cyclohexane (369), a petroleum white oil (268), ethyl chloride (24), poly (dimethylsiloxane) rubber (122) and polyethylene (468). With cetane, the introduction of oxygen while using Co 60 desirably inhibits chlorination without affecting sulfochlorination. In conventional catalysis by ultraviolet light, on the other hand, the desired reaction is also inhibited. γ-Radiation has been proposed for the catalysis of sulfochlorination in large - scale, continuous, commercial operation (369). As indicated in the next section, this approach is also being seriously considered for commercial sulfoxidation.

b. Sulfochlorination with Sulfuryl Chloride

Kharasch and Read (226) observed that the sulfochlorination of alkanes (n-heptane), cycloalkanes (cyclohexane and methylcyclohexane),
and aralkanes (ethylbenzene, tert-butylbenzene) occurred with sulfuryl
chloride in the presence of light, provided pyridine, quinoline, or other
materials were added in small quantity:

$$RH + SO_2Cl_2 \xrightarrow{\text{Light; catalyst}} RSO_2Cl + HCl \qquad (3\text{-}8)$$

In the absence of added catalyst, chlorination occurred with the total
exclusion of sulfochlorination. However, even with the catalyst added,
considerable chlorination was always noted, the maximum yield of sulfonyl chloride being 55% in the case of cyclohexane. Toluene gave only
the chloride under any conditions. Organic (226) and inorganic (349)
sulfur compounds are also effective catalysts. Light is not required if
a combination catalyst (an azo compound with an amide) is employed
(258).

Aliphatic acids also form mixtures of the chlorides and the sulfonyl
chlorides (223), but the addition of pyridine is not necessary in this
case. As noted before with relation to the sulfochlorination of sulfonyl
chlorides, the acids sulfochlorinate randomly on the aliphatic chain,
but not in the position α to the carboxyl group; acetic acid accordingly
does not react. Under strictly anhydrous conditions, the mixed acid
anhydride can be isolated from propionic acid:

$$CH_3CH_2COOH + SO_2Cl_2 \xrightarrow{\text{Light}} ClSO_2CH_2CH_2COOH \longrightarrow$$

$$\overline{O_2SCH_2CH_2COO} + HCl \qquad (3\text{-}9)$$

Sulfopropionic anhydride is a sulfoacylating reagent, as discussed in
Chapter 5.

Sulfuryl chloride has been employed relatively seldom for synthetic
purposes compared to the use of sulfur dioxide and chlorine, since by-
product chlorination is usually lower by the second procedure, as a result of the use of excess sulfur dioxide. In some cases, as with ethylbenzene or tert-butylbenzene, the two methods give closely similar
yields, but in others the sulfuryl chloride approach gives inferior results. Thus, ethyl chloride (452) gives sulfonyl chloride yields of 5 and
35%, respectively, by the two methods.

2. SULFOXIDATION

It was discovered by Platz of the I. G. Farbenindustrie at Hoechst in
1940 that paraffin hydrocarbons form sulfonic acids upon irradiation

with ultraviolet light in the presence of sulfur dioxide and oxygen, according to the following overall scheme:

$$RH + SO_2 + O_2 \xrightarrow{\text{Light}} RSO_2OOH \xrightarrow[H_2O]{SO_2} RSO_3H + H_2SO_4 \qquad (3\text{-}10)$$

This "sulfoxidation" reaction was immediately studied intensively by the IG as an even cheaper approach than sulfochlorination for the manufacture of sulfonate detergents from the long-chain paraffin hydrocarbons obtained by the Fischer-Tropsch process. All aspects of this work have been reviewed by Orthner (308), and especially by Asinger (14), both of whom participated actively. Like sulfochlorination, discussed in the foregoing section, this is a free-radical chain process forming a mixture of products, but it differs in that it yields the acid rather than the sulfonyl chloride.

It is noteworthy that paraffin hydrocarbons can be sulfonated with sulfur dioxide and oxygen by three procedures: (1) sulfoxidation; (2) light-catalyzed reaction of the paraffin with sulfur dioxide to form the sulfinic acid, subsequently oxidized in a separate step to the sulfonic acid; this procedure is referred to later in this section; and (3) oxidation of the paraffin to the hydroperoxide, followed by treatment with sulfite; this method is discussed in Section II-A-3. None of these procedures has been commercialized. Interest in sulfoxidation for the preparation of detergents abated following development of the dodecylbenzenesulfonate type from tetrapropylene, but has recently revived as a result of interest in biodegradable detergents. Sulfoxidation has become more attractive because of the cheap availability of straight-chain paraffins by new processes directly from kerosene, and the development of Co 60 as a greatly improved catalyst.

The sulfoxidation of several hydrocarbons has been studied in some detail. In contrast to their ease of sulfochlorination, propane and isobutane undergo little or no sulfoxidation (14), but n-butane reacts more easily. However, even methane could be forced to yield 3% of the sulfonic acid (429). n-Dodecane (18) forms an equimolar mixture of all the possible secondary sulfonates. Primary sulfonates were formed to the expected lesser degree as noted for chlorination, nitration, and sulfochlorination. Cyclohexane (166) gives the persulfonic acid as the primary reaction product. Being a powerful and unstable oxidizing agent, it reacts with cyclohexane to form cyclohexene and water as byproducts, and with sulfur dioxide and the water to give sulfuric acid. In another study, heptane (431) gave 67% monosulfonic acid, 6% disulfonic acid, 5-9% alcohol, and 18% sulfuric acid. The authors in this case differ from others who have studied the sulfoxidation reaction in suggesting a sulfinic acid intermediate in preference to a free-radical chain mechanism, possibly following the lead of Dainton and Ivin (96), who had indeed earlier shown that liquid or gaseous paraffin hydrocarbons and SO$_2$ do form sulfinic acids in the presence of ultraviolet light:

$$RH + SO_2 \xrightarrow{\text{Light}} RSO_2H \qquad (3\text{-}11)$$

They concluded that the reactivity ratios of CH$_4$, primary, secondary, and tertiary hydrogen atoms are 2:5:34:48, and that reaction occurs by "direct addition of excited SO$_2$. " (It is noteworthy that sulfoxidation, as noted below, in contrast only occurs with secondary hydrogen atoms.) It is also known that sulfinic acids are easily oxidized to sulfonic acids, as discussed in Chapter 4.

A variety of chain-initiating catalysts has been employed for sulfoxidation, including chlorine [used with cyclohexane, n-heptane, and for other straight-chain paraffins (222), and for a Fischer-Tropsch hydrocarbon mixture (239)], ozone [similarly applied (310)], and hydrogen peroxide [for adamantane (395)]. Of technical interest is a process (456) operating under 18 atm. air pressure at 45°C using chlorine as initiator; sulfur dioxide, present in excess as a separate liquid layer, extracts the soluble sulfonate as it is formed. A similar process, also operating under pressure, and considered well suited for sulfochlorination, was cited in the preceding section.

Black and Baxter (42) have thrown new light on the sulfoxidation reaction by their study of initiation by γ radiation using Co 60. This catalyst was found highly effective, since chain lengths as high as 1000 were noted with normal paraffins (hexane, heptane, octane, and hexadecane) and with cyclohexane. Previous work using photochemical initiation, on the other hand, gave chain lengths of only about 8 at the highest. 1-Hexene, 2,3-dimethylbutane, and 2,2-dimethylbutane did not react, and the addition of 10% or more of the first two compounds to normal paraffins inhibited their sulfoxidation. It was accordingly concluded, contrary to Asinger, that primary hydrogen atoms are not replaced during sulfoxidation. Tertiary hydrogen atoms are too sterically hindered to react. These conclusions are consistent with an earlier observation (14) that isobutane did not sulfoxidize with light catalysis. 2,2-Dimethylbutane, however, contains secondary hydrogen atoms, which reacted easily in the normal paraffins studied. Models of this compound showed that steric hindrance is not a factor unless the —O—S—O— bond angle is increased above normal, which the authors conclude probably does occur for reasons unstated. Propane, also containing only one carbon atom with secondary hydrogen atoms, similarly did not undergo sulfoxidation in the presence of light (14). Black and Baxter also observed that the sulfoxidation reaction, once well started, continued after removal of the γ ray source in the cases of n-hexane and n-heptane, but not with cyclohexane or n-octane. Graf (166) had observed a similar effect using light, but concluded it to be limited to n-heptane, cyclohexane, and methylcyclohexane. Black and Baxter conclude that the following mechanism applies:

$$RH \xrightarrow{\text{Co } 60} R\cdot + H\cdot \qquad (3\text{-}12)$$

$$R\cdot + SO_2 \longrightarrow RSO_2\cdot \qquad (3\text{-}13)$$

$$RSO_2\cdot + O_2 \longrightarrow RSO_2O_2\cdot \qquad (3\text{-}14)$$

$$RSO_2O_2\cdot + RH \longrightarrow RSO_2O_2H + R\cdot \qquad (3\text{-}15)$$

$$RSO_2O_2H \longrightarrow RSO_3\cdot + OH\cdot \qquad (3\text{-}16)$$

$$RSO_3\cdot + RH \longrightarrow RSO_3H + R\cdot \qquad (3\text{-}17)$$

$$OH\cdot + RH \longrightarrow H_2O + R\cdot \qquad (3\text{-}18)$$

$$RSO_2O_2H + H_2O + SO_2 \longrightarrow RSO_3H + H_2SO_4 \qquad (3\text{-}19)$$

This scheme is in essential agreement with that proposed by Graf (166) for the photochemical sulfoxidation of cyclohexane. Black and Baxter's findings suggest that further study of the relation between structure and reactivity in sulfoxidation could yield interesting results. Their process has been developed semicommercially (12); it yields a water-soluble, biodegradable detergent, which is a more effective cleaner than many now on the market.

Others have studied Co 60 - catalyzed sulfoxidation with polyethylene (123), n-hexane (38), and poly (dimethylsiloxane) rubber (122).

Walling (451) considers the mechanism of sulfoxidation to be strongly analogous to aldehyde oxidation. Reaction 3-13, common to both sulfochlorination and sulfoxidation, is (as mentioned in the preceding section) considered by him to be reversible, a postulate which has recently been demonstrated experimentally for sulfochlorination. A similar analysis and study would be of interest for sulfoxidation.

The sulfoxidation of substituted paraffins has been little studied. Acetic, hexanoic, and heptanoic acids undergo sulfoxidation in the presence of a variety of catalysts (130b). The last two acids give good yields, but that from acetic is only 10-15%. This result indicates that sulfoxidation occurs more easily than sulfochlorination on a carbon atom α to a carboxyl group, since acetic acid does not undergo sulfochlorination (cf., Section II-A-1). Patents refer to the sulfoxidation of chlorinated alkanes and cycloalkanes (92, 142), acids and nitriles (93), esters and ethers (94, 143), and alcohols (94).

3. THE HYDROPEROXIDE-BISULFITE REACTION

Long-chain alkyl hydroperoxides, prepared by the air oxidation of paraffinic petroleum fractions, yield sulfonates by reaction with an excess of aqueous metallic bisulfite:

$$ROOH + 2\ NaHSO_3 \longrightarrow RSO_3Na + NaHSO_4 + H_2O \qquad (3\text{-}20)$$

This reaction was studied in the 1950's by two independent industrial groups interested in making cheap sulfonate detergents from petroleum sources (29, 30, 219, 305, 306, 307). It will be noted that the raw materials (hydrocarbon, SO_2, and oxygen) and the products (organic sulfonate and sulfate ion) are the same for this process as for sulfoxidation, but that this method operates in two chemical steps. Although some of the early patents on this process (306, 307) cite the use of alkaryl hydrocarbons, such as nonyltoluene, or of aromatic kerosene fractions, later work (30) showed that paraffinic hydrocarbons are the preferred raw materials, and that the aromatics should in fact be removed as completely as possible prior to oxidation, since their hydroperoxides undergo cleavage to phenols, which strongly inhibit further hydroperoxidation of all hydrocarbon species.

Tetralin hydroperoxide apparently undergoes a similar type of reaction with bisulfite (178), as do the hydroperoxides of cyclic ketones (cyclohexanone, cyclopentanone, 4-methylcyclopentanone) (286); in these cases ring cleavage also occurs:

$$HOOC(CH_2)_5SO_3H \qquad (3\text{-}21)$$

If an excess of alkyl hydroperoxide is used, as opposed to an excess of bisulfite as mentioned above, an organic sulfate is formed instead of the sulfonate (29, 219):

$$ROOH + NaHSO_3 \longrightarrow ROSO_3Na + H_2O \qquad (3\text{-}22)$$

Cumene hydroperoxide reacts with aqueous bisulfite (224), but no sulfur-containing products were isolated.

Olive oil (largely glyceryl trioleate) is stated (29, 219) to form a sulfonate via the hydroperoxide in a similar manner. Other fatty oils and acids (e.g., ricinoleic) containing isolated double bonds undergo sulfonation upon treatment with air and bisulfite (108, 243, 244, 312). These products, being true sulfonates, but otherwise not characterized, are chemically more stable than the usual "sulfonated oils" made with sulfuric acid, which largely comprise sulfates and other relatively unstable compounds, as discussed in Chapter 6. Air hydroperoxidation of an allylic carbon atom is a possible first step in these cases, followed by reaction with bisulfite. Free-radical, catalyzed addition of bisulfite to the double bond, discussed in the next section, may also occur, but this type of reaction proceeds poorly with nonterminal double bonds. Ethyl stearate has been hydroperoxidized and converted with bisulfite to the "sodium salt of sulfated ethyl stearate (275). "

The mechanism of the hydroperoxide-sulfite reaction has been studied in the specific case of tert-butyl hydroperoxide (10b). Two main reaction paths are seen: direct oxidation (yielding tert-butyl alcohol and sulfate ion), and formation of tert-butyl oxonium ion, which then undergoes cleavage in several possible ways, forming methane, methanol, acetone, and polymeric 2-propenesulfonic acid. The sulfur appears primarily as sulfate ion.

4. ORGANOMETALLIC COMPOUNDS WITH SULFURYL CHLORIDE

Sulfonyl chlorides are formed from Grignard reagents with sulfuryl chloride:

$$RMgBr + ClSO_2Cl \longrightarrow RSO_2Cl + MgClBr \qquad (3\text{-}23)$$

$$(R = \text{saturated aliphatic})$$

This procedure gives yields of 20-35% and has been employed relatively little (227). Its use for preparing an acetylenic sulfonate is mentioned in Section II-B-4. A newer and considerably more satisfactory approach involves treatment of the Grignard reagent with SO_2 to form the sulfinate, followed by anhydrous chlorination:

$$RMgBr + SO_2 \longrightarrow RSO_2MgBr \xrightarrow{Cl_2} RSO_2Cl + MgClBr \qquad (3\text{-}24)$$

This technique is reviewed in Chapter 4.

Sulfonyl chlorides can also be prepared from aluminum trialkyls as follows (86):

$$R_3Al + 3 \ ClSO_2Cl \longrightarrow 3 \ RSO_2Cl + AlCl_3 \qquad (3\text{-}25)$$

The yield of n-octanesulfonyl chloride by this method is 75%. This approach may prove of practical preparative interest now that aluminum alkyls are commercially available.

5. ALKYL HALIDES WITH SULFITE (THE STRECKER REACTION)

This widely-applicable and simple procedure for preparing aliphatic sulfonates, involving the reaction of halides with metallic sulfites, has found steady use since its discovery in 1868:

$$RX + Na_2SO_3 \longrightarrow RSO_3Na + NaX \qquad (X = Cl, Br, I) \qquad (3\text{-}26)$$

It has been reviewed (334, 415) with detailed typical examples.   This procedure should not be confused with the Strecker synthesis for the preparation of amino acids.

The Strecker reaction is ordinarily conducted by refluxing the halide with an aqueous inorganic sulfite for periods of time which may vary from 1 hr. to 7 days, depending upon the compound reacted.   Water-miscible cosolvents (e. g. , alcohols, glycols, dimethylformamide) are sometimes added.   This approach gives 85% yields with the C2-12 n-alkyl bromides (198, 251, 346, 463).   Reaction can be expedited by operating under pressure at 160-200°C for 5-10 hr. , a method which has been applied to the C8-18 n-alkyl bromides (99, 106, 336), to 1-chloro-dodecane and -octadecane (155), and to a chlorinated petroleum fraction (333).   1-Bromo-2, 4-diphenylbutane did not react with aqueous sulfite even upon prolonged refluxing, but the addition of sufficient ethylene glycol to raise the reflux temperature to 145°C gave a satisfactory conversion in 10 hr. (435).

A study of the mechanism of the Strecker reaction in the case of methyl iodide (393) has shown that direct alkylation of the sulfur atom occurs, rather than alkylation of an oxygen atom followed by rearrangement, which had previously been considered possible.   It was also found that no reaction occurs under anhydrous conditions using acetone or dioxane as solvents, or even with acetonitrile, which has a fairly high dielectric constant.

The Strecker procedure has been used largely for the preparation of primary sulfonates.   Although secondary halides are stated rarely to give yields above 25% (334), in some cases the conversions are excellent.   Thus, isopropyl bromide froms 85% of sulfonate, compared to 98% for n-propyl bromide under the same conditions (347).   On the other hand, bromocyclohexane gives only a 9% yield (405), since cyclohexene formation predominates.   Alkyl bromides are the preferred halides, since they react more easily than the chlorides, and are more easily accessible and less subject to side reactions during sulfonation compared with iodides.

Side reactions with the Strecker reaction result from the basicity of aqueous metallic sulfites, and from its activity as a reducing agent. Aqueous solutions of normal ammonium, sodium, and potassium sulfites are all alkaline, with the latter two being in the range of pH 8-9. Tertiary halides, therefore, usually form the corresponding alkenes, rather than the desired sulfonates.   1-Phenyl-2-chloroethane likewise yields styrene, and gives none of the expected sulfonate (82).

Since the Strecker reaction is usually conducted in aqueous medium, hydrolysis often also occurs.   1, 2-Dibromo-2-methylpropane thus forms a hydroxysulfonate (247):

$$BrCH_2CBr(CH_3)_2 + 2\ Na_2SO_3 + H_2O \longrightarrow NaO_3SCH_2C(OH)(CH_3)_2 +$$

$$\text{(3-27)}$$

$$2\ NaBr + NaHSO_3$$

Hydrolysis also occurs in the sulfonation of 1,2-dibromoethyl acetate (419), forming the expected aldehydic sulfonate:

$$BrCH_2CHBrOCOCH_3 + 2\ Na_2SO_3 + H_2O \longrightarrow$$

$$\left[NaO_3SCH_2CHOHOCOCH_3\right] \longrightarrow \qquad (3\text{-}28)$$

$$NaO_3SCH_2CHO + CH_3COOH + 2\ NaBr + NaHSO_3$$

Benzhydryl chloride undergoes hydrolysis in complete preference to sulfonate formation (360):

$$2\ (C_6H_5)_2CHCl + 2\ Na_2SO_3 + H_2O \longrightarrow \left[(C_6H_5)_2CH\right]_2O +$$

$$2\ NaCl + 2\ NaHSO_3 \qquad (3\text{-}29)$$

The analogous 4-methylbenzhydryl bromide, on the other hand, sulfonates as expected (320). Hydrolysis may partly explain the low yields noted when alkyl iodides are sulfonated under some conditions, as discussed below. The basic character of the reagent is also evident with 1-bromo-2-aminopropane, which forms an isomeric sulfonate via the ethylenimine, rather than that expected by direct metathesis (351):

$$CH_3CHBrCH_2NH_2 \xrightarrow{-HBr} CH_3\overset{\frown}{CHCH_2NH} \xrightarrow{NaHSO_3}$$

$$CH_3CH(NH_2)CH_2SO_3Na \qquad (3\text{-}30)$$

A similar effect occurs with 2-bromo-1-propanol and with 2-chloro-1-propanol, both of which form the primary sulfonates via the epoxides (368), rather than the expected secondary compounds.

Reduction has been noted as a side reaction with alkyl iodides, as during the preparation of sodium iodomethanesulfonate in 75% yield (253):

$$CHI_3 + 3\ Na_2SO_3 + H_2O \longrightarrow ICH_2SO_3Na + 2\ NaI +$$

$$Na_2SO_4 + NaHSO_3 \qquad (3\text{-}31)$$

Reduction may explain the low yields observed in reacting alkyl mono-iodides, although this has not been proved. Thus, methyl iodide gives 90% sulfonate in 8 days at 15°C, but only 30-60% at 120-150°C (393). Repeated unsuccessful attempts were made to convert hexadecyl and other iodides to sulfonates at elevated temperatures (85, 300); loss by hydrolysis appears likely in these cases. However, fair yields of sulfonate have been noted with ethyl iodide (156), 2-phenyl-1-iodoethanol (363), and mannitol diiodide (213), and, as stated below, benzyl chloride derivatives are advantageously sulfonated via the iodides. Another example of reduction during sulfonation is the following (135):

$$CHCl_2F + 3 Na_2SO_3 + H_2O \longrightarrow FCH_2SO_3Na +$$

$$2 NaCl + Na_2SO_4 + NaHSO_3 \qquad (3\text{-}32)$$

This reaction was run under fairly drastic conditions (20 hr. at $180°C$); the expected sulfonate was also formed.

If appropriate care is taken, halides also containing sensitive groups can be successfully sulfonated with sulfite. With 1-chloro-1-nitrocyclohexane the yield is determined by careful control of pH (120). Epichlorohydrin is said to give a 71% yield of sulfonate if the temperature is kept below $25°C$ and the aqueous sulfite is less than 10% in strength (367):

$$ClCH_2CHCH_2O + Na_2SO_3 \longrightarrow NaO_3SCH_2CHCH_2O + NaCl \quad (3\text{-}33)$$

However, this conclusion can be questioned, since cleavage of the oxirane ring usually proceeds much faster than the Strecker reaction.

Consideration has been given to methods for expediting the Strecker reaction. This can be done by adding a small quantity of alkali iodide (334). Chloromethylated aromatic compounds can be sulfonated more rapidly if they are first completely converted to the iodides by heating with equivalent sodium iodide in acetone for 15 min. ; the crude iodides are then sulfonated directly without purification (69). Although this procedure was demonstrated for only two cases, it should be widely applicable because of the easy accessibility of many types of chloromethylated aromatic compounds (151, 304a). The sulfonation of benzyl chloride (447), of 1, 2-dichloroethane (382), and of methylene chloride (127) is expedited by adding copper ion. Chloromethylated polystyrene does not react with sodium sulfite, but the dimethyl sulfonium derivative converts with facility (114):

$$RCH_2Cl \xrightarrow{(CH_3)_2S} RCH_2S(Cl)(CH_3)_2 + Na_2SO_3 \longrightarrow$$

$$RCH_2SO_3Na + NaCl + (CH_3)_2S \qquad (3\text{-}34)$$

The sulfide can be recovered and recycled. A similar approach involves conversion to the quaternary ammonium compound. Those of structure (RR'R''NCH$_2$R''')Cl, where R and R''' are aromatic, form the sulfonate with particular ease, as with phenyldimethylbenzylammonium chloride (401). R''' and the tertiary amine can both be heterocyclic, as in the case of thiamine (vitamin B$_1$), which forms a sulfonate with especial facility (465). The conversion of long-chain primary bromides is facilitated by adding dianilidophosphate (99).

The behavior of polyhalides with sulfites is of special interest because polysulfonation can occur. By using suitable proportions of reagents, dichloromethane can be converted to the chloromethanesulfonate or to the disulfonate in 4 hr. at 155°C (22,127,398). Sodium sulfite is used to prepare the former, potassium sulfite the latter (398). (Use of the former compound as sulfomethylating agent is discussed in Chapter 5, Section II-A-3.) Dibromomethane yields the bromosulfonate (127). Chloroform, in 5 hr. at 125°C, and chlorodifluoromethane, in 20 hr. at 120°C, give the expected dichloro- and difluoromethanesulfonates (135). Dichlorofluoromethane, in 20 hr. at 180°C, forms the expected fluorochloromethanesulfonate, together with some fluoromethanesulfonate formed by reduction. With 1,2-dichloroethane, the use of methanol as reaction solvent and copper turnings as catalyst represses disulfonate formation and gives a 71% yield of the chlorosulfonate (199, 200). Laboratory preparations employing aqueous ethanol as solvent (427), preferably in the presence of copper turnings (365), give 78-93% yields of the chlorosulfonate. If dilute aqueous sulfite is used (less than 5% concentration), preferably in the absence of air, an 89% yield of it results without using an organic cosolvent (378). Another process gives 80% monosulfonate in 1 hr. without the use of alcohol (129). 1,2-Dibromoethane gives the bromosulfonate in 65% yield (288,313,371, 372), or the disulfonate in 43% (347) to 75% (359) yield. (The use of sodium 2-chloro- and 2-bromoethanesulfonates as sulfoalkylating reagents is discussed in Chapter 5, Sections I-B-3 and -4, respectively). 1,2-Dibromo-1-phenylethane forms the disulfonate (228), as does 1,1-dibromoethane (347), the latter in 82% yield. In the conversion of a series of polymethylene dibromides, from C2-10, to the disulfonates by refluxing with aqueous sodium sulfite, it was noted that the short-chain compounds required only 12 hr., but that the higher molecular weight materials took as long as 7 days (218,347,413,473). 1,2-Dichlorides derived from long-chain alkenes formed the disulfonates in 21 hr. at 200°C (358). 1,1,3-Tribromoethane and 1,2,3-tribromopropane give 95 and 84% yields of the expected trisulfonates (347). 1,4-Dichloro- (338), and 1,4-dibromo-2-butene (220) have been converted only to the disulfonates, but 1,4-dichloro-2-butyne forms the chlorosulfonate (329). 1,3-Bis(bromomethyl) benzene (254) and 3,3-bis(bromomethyl) oxacyclobutane (160) easily form the disulfonates. The second compound was converted to the dihydroxysulfonate and to the disultone, both of which appear interesting as possible starting materials for synthesis (159a):

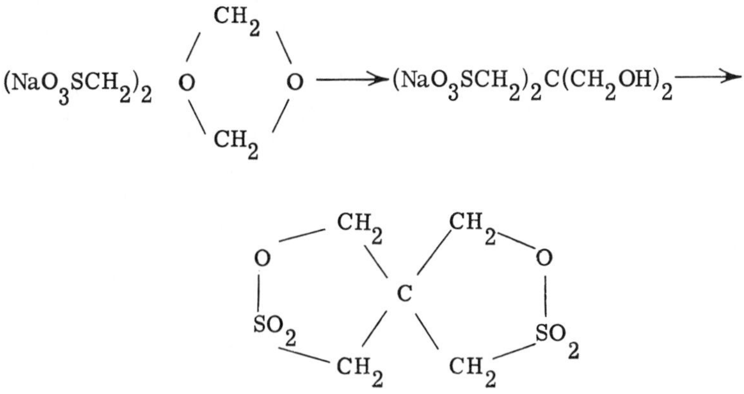

$$(NaO_3SCH_2)_2 \quad O \overset{CH_2}{\underset{CH_2}{\diagup\diagdown}} O \longrightarrow (NaO_3SCH_2)_2C(CH_2OH)_2 \longrightarrow$$

(3-35)

α-Chloro-ω-trichloroalkanes (C5, 7, and 8) were converted to trichlorosulfonates without serious attack of the trichloromethyl group (326). Dibromohydrin gave 40% of monosulfonate (271). Only one of the two halogen atoms in sodium dichloro- and dibromoacetates has been converted to a sulfonate group (202, 249).

The greater reactivity of bromine compared to the chlorine atom has been used to advantage in preparing chloroalkylsulfonates. This approach has been applied to the C1 (103), C2 and C3 terminal chlorobromides (373).

The Strecker reaction, like other sulfonation procedures, has begun to find application in the preparation of polymeric sulfonates. The sulfonation of chloromethylated polystyrene, as stated above, is facilitated by first forming the sulfonium halide (114). Poly(vinyl alcohol haloacetal) was converted to an ion-exchange resin by heating with aqueous sulfite at 150°C for 7 hr. (291):

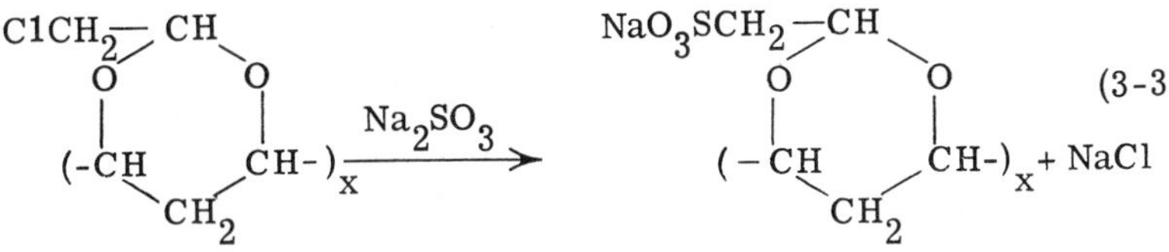

(3-36)

Poly(epichlorohydrin) forms a sulfonate of structure ($-OCH(CH_2SO_3Na)$ $CH_2-)_x$ (432). Polymers made by reacting formaldehyde with long-chain alkylphenolic ethers of the structure $RC_6H_4(OCH_2CH_2)_2Cl$ react with sulfite in 4 hr. at 170°C (45). Poly(vinyl chloride), suspended in an aqueous swelling agent, was sulfonated by refluxing for 72 hr. (315). It is noted that in all cases except the last, reaction involves a primary chloride; in the last case the degree of sulfonation may, therefore, be relatively small.

Recent applications of the Strecker reaction are given in Tables 3-1, 3-2, 3-3, and 3-4. As expected, major industrial interest has centered about the least expensive and most highly reactive primary chloride derivatives, namely those made from chloroacetic acid, ethylene chlorohydrin, allyl chloride, and similar compounds. Derivatives of these types are accordingly listed separately in Tables 3-1, 3-2, and 3-3, respectively. Miscellaneous applications are tabulated in Table 3-4. The prior, extensive industrial study of the preparation of sulfonates via the chloroacetates, including lauryl sulfoacetate and the sulfoacetamide of 2-aminoethyllaurate (125), which are manufactured as specialty surfactants, has been well reviewed (379, 380). Another industrial application has involved preparation of long-chain glycol ether sulfonates of the Triton type (379); more recent examples of this type of product are given in Table 3-2. The Strecker reaction was also used

TABLE 3-1

Sulfonates from Compounds of Structure Cl- or BrCH(R)COR'

Compound	Reference
$BrCH_2COCH_3$, $ClCH_2COCH_3$	35, 113, 317
$BrCH(CH_3)COCH_3$	331
Chlorodiheptyl ketone	203
Bromoacetophenone, -acetothienone, -acetomesitylene, -pinacolone, -propiophenone, -isobutyrophenone	433
$ClCH_2COC_6H_4R$ (R = long-chain)	233, 453, 454
$1,3-(BrCH_2CO)C_6H_4$	438
$ClCH_2COOR$ (R = long-chain)	71, 126, 176, 177, 194, 297
$ClCH_2CONHR$ (R = various aromatic)	68, 285, 357
$ClCH_2CONHR$, $-NR_2$ (R = long-chain)	23, 221
$Cl_2CHCOONa$, $Br_2CHCOONa$	202, 249

TABLE 3-2

Sulfonates from Halogenated Alcohols, Ethers, and Esters

Compound	Reference
$HOCH_2CH_2Cl$, $HOCH(CH_3)CH_2Cl$	232, 410
$C_6H_5CHOHCH_2Br$, $C_6H_5CHOHCH_2I$, $C_6H_5CHICH_2OH$	228, 363
$C_6H_5OCH_2CHOHCH_2Cl$, $C_6H_5OCH_2CHClCH_2OH$	363
$BrCH_2CHOHCH_2Br$	271
$HO(CH_2)_3Cl$, $CH_3CHOH(CH_2)_2Cl$, $HOCH_2C(CH_3)_2CH_2Br$, $Br(CH_2)_2COH(CH_3)_2$	299
$ROCH_2CHOHCH_2Cl$, $ROCH_2CH_2Cl$ (R = long-chain)	153, 356, 389a
Oleic amide chlorohydrin	77
$HOCH_2CHClCHOHCH_2OH$	218
$ClCH_2CH_2OCH_2CH{:}CH_2$	67
$(ClCH_2CH_2)_2O$, $(Cl(CH_2)_4)_2O$	391, 472
$ROCH_2OCH_2CH_2Cl$, $RCONHCH_2CH_2Cl$ (R = long-chain)	309
$RC_6H_4OCH_2CH_2Cl$ (R = H, NO_2, alkyl, alkoxy)	37, 304
$CH_3SCH_2CHClCH_3$	267
Benzal 2-bromopropane-1,3-dithiol	328
$CH_3COO(CH_2)_3Cl$, $CH_3COO(CH_2)_4Cl$	186, 187, 436
3- and 6-Chlorohexyl acetates	186

TABLE 3-3

Sulfonates from Allylic Halides

Compound	Reference
$BrCH_2CH{:}CH_2$	36, 327
$ClCH_2CH{:}CHCH_3$, $ClCH(CH_3)CH{:}CH_2$, $ClCH_2C(CH_3){:}CH_2$	66, 67, 183
$BrCH_2C(CN){:}CH_2$	88
$ClCH_2CH{:}CHCH_2OR$ (R = long-chain)	248
3-Bromocyclohexene	405
$ClCH_2CH{:}CHCH_2Cl$, $BrCH_2CH{:}CHCH_2Br$, $ClCH_2CH{:}CClCH_3$	131, 220, 338
$ClCH_2C{:}CH$, $ClCH_2C{:}CCH_2Cl$	329
4-Chloro-2-hexene, 1-Chloro-2-pentene, etc.	105

for the semicommercial production of detergent sulfonates from the reaction products of long-chain alkenes and nitrosyl chloride (380). In
this case the normal reaction was complicated by extensive side reactions involving reduction and hydrolysis of the nitroso and related
groups.

Several of the sulfoalkylating and sulfoacylating reagents discussed
in Chapter 5 are, or can be, made by the Strecker reaction. These
include the salts of chloromethane-, chloroethane-, bromoethane-,
chloropropane-, bromopropane-, and acetonesulfonic acids, as well as
sulfoacetic and chlorosulfoacetic acids.

TABLE 3-4

Miscellaneous Applications of the Strecker Reaction

Compound	Reference
Benzyl, nonylbenzyl, halobenzyl, nitrobenzyl, hydroxybenzyl, and methoxybenzyl chlorides and bromides	82, 136, 172, 265, 282, 294
2-Phenylethyl chloride and bromide, 2-(4-methoxyphenyl)ethyl bromide	172, 282, 436
2-(4-Nitrophenyl)ethyl, 2-mesitylethyl, and 2-naphthylethyl bromides	70, 100, 102
4-Phenyl-, and 2,4-diphenyl-1-bromobutane	82, 353, 435, 436
1-(α-Naphthyl)chloromethane, 2-bromoethane, 3-bromopropane, 4-bromobutane	282, 439
α-Bromo long-chain nitriles	402
Ethyl 6-bromohexanoate, 5-chloropentanoate	326, 467
$Cl(CH_2)_3COC_2H_5$; $Cl(CH_2)_2COCH_3$	104, 186
4-Chloro-1-aminobutane, 3-bromo-1-aminopropane	137, 384
$R_3N(Br)CH_2CH_2Br$ (R = varied alkyl)	32
$(RCHClCH_2)_2S$ (R = long-chain)	147
Long-chain secondary halides	119
A 5-Bromovaleryl imidazoline	121
6-Iododeoxy glucosides	188

6. ALKYL SULFATES WITH SULFITES

Aliphatic sulfonates can be prepared by reacting alkyl sulfates with metallic sulfites:

$$ROSO_3Na + Na_2SO_3 \longrightarrow RSO_3Na + Na_2SO_4 \tag{3-37}$$

This procedure, which is formally similar to the Strecker reaction, is comparatively seldom used, since sodium sulfate is more difficult to separate from the desired sulfonate than is a metallic halide, and the organic sulfates are usually no more easily accessible than the corresponding halides.

Sodium 2-aminoethanesulfonate (taurate), a useful sulfoethylating reagent discussed in Chapter 5, has been prepared thus in the laboratory (205, 352, 448), although the procedure has not been employed commercially. Taurine derivatives, substituted on nitrogen and on carbon, have also been made in this way for use as dye intermediates (204, 292). As indicated in Chapter 6, the required aminoethyl sulfates are easily prepared by heating with sulfuric acid the corresponding aminoalcohols, available from amines with epoxides:

$$R_2NCH_2CH_2OH \xrightarrow[\text{NaOH}]{H_2SO_4} R_2NCH_2CH_2OSO_3Na \xrightarrow{Na_2SO_3}$$

$$R_2NCH_2CH_2SO_3Na + Na_2SO_4 \tag{3-38}$$

Sodium ethyl sulfate forms the sulfonate quantitatively by heating with sodium sulfite under pressure for 4 hr. at 120°C (272). Sodium methanesulfonate has been made from dimethyl sulfate, but purification proved difficult (266). Reaction of C12-16 long-chain, primary alkyl sulfates, usually conducted under fairly drastic conditions [e. g. , 12 hr. at 200°C (207, 374)], is facilitated by adding amidophosphate catalysts (99). Like the Strecker reaction, this procedure has usually been applied to primary sulfates. It has, however, also been used with the sulfates of C10-16 secondary alcohols (119), and of alcohols of the structure $RCH_2CHOHC_6H_5$ (292).

7. ALCOHOLS WITH BISULFITE

Triphenyl, and tri(paratolyl), carbinols have long been known to form sulfonates on standing at room temperature with aqueous bisulfite (25, 290):

$$R_3COH + NaHSO_3 \longrightarrow R_3CSO_3Na + H_2O \tag{3-39}$$

Subsequent work (192, 377) has shown that this type of reaction also applies to compounds of the general structure

$$R_1 \langle\bigcirc\rangle CHOHR_3$$
$$R_2$$

R_1 or R_2 must be OH or NH_2

R_3 may be H, CH_3, or R_4CH_2

R_4 may be various (NH_2, amido, alkyl)

The reaction does not proceed when both R_1 and R_2 are H, when R_1 is methoxyl, or when the necessary ring hydroxyl group is situated in the meta, rather than in the ortho or para, position. These observations led to the conclusion that the resonance associated with ortho or para position is essential for a reaction to occur (192). A kinetic and mechanistic study (193, 375, 376) has shown that above pH 5, the reaction is simple, S_N2, but that below ph 5 a parallel S_N1 reaction also occurs. An earlier study (388) had shown that mono- and di- ring-methylated o- and p-hydroxybenzyl alcohols react similarly with sulfonate formation.

Most of the preceding studies were made at room temperature. Similar reactions have been run under pressure at 135°C, using conditions simulating those employed commercially for the manufacture of paper pulp from wood. The objective of these experiments was to determine the mechanism of lignin sulfonate formation. Diphenyl carbinol and phenyl ethyl carbinol formed sulfonates under these conditions (241), although benzyl alcohol did not react. Phenyl benzyl carbinol and triphenyl carbinol surprisingly did not react, although earlier work had shown that both formed sulfonates at room temperature. Two p-hydroxybenzyl alcohol derivatives (vanillyl alcohol and apocynol) gave sulfonates (255), which is consistent with the conclusion cited above regarding the requirement of an ortho or a para hydroxyl group. On the other hand, veratryl alcohol, diveratryl ether, and veratryl ethyl ether also underwent sulfonation (255, 256). These compounds contain methoxyl groups in the 3 and 4 positions, but do not have ring hydroxyl groups. Apparently the much higher temperature used in these experiments induced reaction not appreciable at room temperature. This type of reaction is used commercially to convert a 4, 4' -bis(dialkylamino)benzhydrol ("Michler's Hydrol") to a sulfonate dye intermediate (2).

In addition to benzyl alcohol derivatives, a second class of alcohols forms sulfonates upon heating with bisulfite or sulfurous acid. This category comprises compounds of the general structure $RCH_2CH(R')OH$, where R is a strongly electronegative group such as nitro or carbonyl, and R' is hydrogen or alkyl. A series of 2-nitro-1-alkanols thus reacts as follows (161, 162):

$$O_2NCH_2CH(R')OH + SO_2 \longrightarrow O_2NCH_2CH(R')SO_3H \quad (3\text{-}40)$$

The acetate likewise yields the sulfonate (162). Similar results were noted with R = substituted dihydrotriazinyl (269), but no reaction occurred when R was phenyl (241). Sulfonation occurs easily with R as C_6H_5CO-, and with several of its substituted derivatives (241), leading to the suggestion that intermediate dehydration to the carbonyl-conjugated olefin occurs, which then adds bisulfite as discussed in Section II-B-2. This mechanism could also apply to the nitro alcohols and their derived acetates, since these can also form the nitroalkenes. The formation of a polymeric sulfonic acid by heating allyl alcohol with liquid SO_2 in the presence of peroxide (195) can be explained similarly, since others (400) had shown that under such conditions they form a polymeric alcohol of structure $(-CH_2CH(CH_2OH)SO_2-)_x$, a configuration known in analogous cases to undergo easy dehydration and addition of bisulfite. The polymeric sulfonic acid would accordingly be $(-CH_2CH(CH_2SO_3H)SO_2-)_x$.

B. Preparation from Unsaturated Compounds

1. ALKENES AND ALKYNES WITH BISULFITE

a. Alkenes

It was shown in 1938 by Kharasch, May, and Mayo (225, 273, 451) that alkenes add bisulfite by a free-radical chain process:

$$SO_3\cdot^- + CH_2{:}CHR \longrightarrow -SO_3CH_2\dot{C}HR \quad (3\text{-}41)$$

$$-SO_3CH_2\dot{C}HR + HSO_3^- \longrightarrow -SO_3CH_2CH_2R + SO_3\cdot^- \quad (3\text{-}42)$$

This reaction has been applied to numerous noncarbonyl-conjugated alkenes and alkynes, as well as to a number of their derivatives containing chloride, fluoride, hydroxyl, ester, carboxyl, and metallic sulfonate groups. Terminal olefins have most often been used, although nonterminal olefins, such as cyclohexene, pinene, 2-pentene, 3-hexene, trimethylethylene, and 8-pentadecene behave similarly (361, 459), but in poor yield. A diene (isoprene) also reacts (361). The reaction is initiated by an oxidizing agent, such as oxygen, a peroxide, or nitrate ions, and is most often run at room temperature in 20-40% aqueous buffered solutions containing an excess of bisulfite at ph 5-7, with a stream of air or oxygen passing through the reaction mixture (407).

This reaction has not been studied systematically (407, 451). The exact nature of the adding species is not known, and there is little or no information on its scope, or on the stereochemical factors involved. As indicated in Chapter 8, nothing is known about its reversibility.

At atmospheric pressure ethylene yields ethanesulfonic acid salts, but at high pressure both it and propylene form telomeric sulfonates (174, 210), which is not surprising since the oxygen-bisulfite combination is a known polymerization initiator. Similarly, acrylate esters, with sulfur dioxide and a peroxide, form short-chain polymers terminated at both ends with sulfonic groups (337). Vinyl chloride forms sodium 2-chloroethanesulfonate (84, 462), a sulfoalkylating agent discussed in Chapter 5. Vinyl bromide, formerly thought to form a salt of ethenesulfonic acid (236), has more recently been shown to form only the 1, 2-disulfonate (434) by a mechanism held to involve acetylene formation as the first step (as discussed in the following section), but addition-elimination as follows is not excluded:

$$CH_2:CHBr \xrightarrow{\text{NaHSO}_3} NaO_3SCH_2CH_2Br \xrightarrow{\text{-HBr}}$$

$$NaO_3SCH:CH_2 \xrightarrow{\text{NaHSO}_3} NaO_3SCH_2CH_2SO_3Na \qquad (3\text{-}43)$$

Cis-Dichloroethylene forms the 1, 1, 2-trisulfonate salt, also presumably via chloroacetylene per Equation 3-50, but the trans analogue did not react, apparently because it does not form chloroacetylene under the conditions used (434). 1, 1-Dichloroethylene, on the other hand, gave the trisulfonate even in the presence of a free-radical inhibitor (434). This result invites further clarification, since the addition of bisulfite to either a double or a triple bond is thought to be of the free-radical type. Perfluorinated α olefins give the corresponding 2-H-perfluoroalkanesulfonic acid salts (83, 238) at 120°C using peoxide catalyst.

Styrene yields three products as follows (224):

$$C_6H_5CH:CH_2 \xrightarrow{\text{NaHSO}_3} C_6H_5CH_2CH_2SO_3Na +$$

$$(37\%)$$
$$(3\text{-}44)$$

$$C_6H_5CHOHCH_2SO_3Na + C_6H_5CH:CHSO_3Na$$

$$(52\%) \qquad\qquad (5\%)$$

The oxygen used as initiator apparently led to formation of the second product. Long-chain (C10-22) α olefins form detergent sulfonates (80,

81, 138, 175, 303). These materials, of current industrial interest because of the cheap availability of such olefins from petroleum (73, 80), can be prepared in 95-99% yields, provided several process conditions are observed. These include control of the pH between 7 and 9, use of air or peroxide as initiator, presence of an alcoholic solvent (methanol, ethanol, isopropanol), gradual addition of the bisulfite, and efficient mixing. (Short-chain alkenes, being more soluble in aqueous bisulfite, do not require such careful control of conditions to obtain good yields.) γ-Radiation is an effective catalyst for this reaction (412). Nonterminal, long-chain olefins do not react under the conditions given.

Bisulfite addition also occurs to non-hydrocarbon olefinic compounds. 10-Undecenoic acid (345), 3-methylenecyclobutanecarbonitrile and related compounds (460), 4, 4-dimethyl-4-silapentene (423), oleic anilide (117), allylamine (190), N-allylaniline and several of its derivatives (117, 230), and amides of endomethylenetetrahydrophthalic acid (274) have also been similarly sulfonated. Unsaturated fatty oils and esters (108, 243, 244, 312) and Vitamin D_2 (a complex polyolefin (471) also form sulfonates of unknown composition with air and aqueous bisulfite. The hydroperoxide-bisulfite reaction, reviewed in Section II-A-3, may be involved here, as well as the alkene addition type of sulfonation. The sulfonate of allyl alcohol (182) is used commercially to prepare propanesultone, a reactive sulfoalkylating agent discussed in Chapter 5:

$$CH_2:CHCH_2OH \xrightarrow{\quad NaHSO_3 \quad} NaO_3SCH_2CH_2CH_2OH \xrightarrow[\text{(2) } -H_2O]{\text{(1) } H^+}$$

$$\overline{O_2S(CH_2)_3O} \qquad\qquad (3\text{-}45)$$

Methallyl (394) and crotyl (43) alcohols, allyl carbinol (43), and 3-hydroxy-1-nonadecene (464) have similarly been sulfonated, and the first three products were converted to the sultones.

At pH 5. 4, cyclohexene adds ammonium bisulfite normally in the presence of oxygen, forming the monosulfonate (406). However, at pH 3. 9 or lower, the sole product is the 1, 2-disulfonate:

$$-CH:CH- + 2\ NH_4SO_3H \xrightarrow{\quad O_2 \quad} -CH(SO_3NH_4)CH(SO_3NH_4)- \quad (3\text{-}46)$$

A similar unexpected result was noted some years later (182) with allyl alcohol, which, like cyclohexene, forms the normal monosulfonate as the sole product at pH 7, but which yields only the sulfinate-sulfonate at pH 4:

$$CH_2{:}CHCH_2OH + 2\ KHSO_3 \xrightarrow{\ O_2\ }$$

$$KO_3SCH_2CH(SO_2K)CH_2OH + H_2O \qquad (3\text{-}47)$$

Long-chain α olefins likewise form the sulfinate-sulfonates at low pH (80). Propargyl alcohol follows a similar pattern, since, as noted in the next section, it can form either the normal saturated disulfonate, or it can given an unsaturated sulfinate-sulfonate. The initial product formed from cyclohexene could also have been a sulfinate-sulfonate, since sulfinate groups are easily oxidized to sulfonate, and the reaction was run in the presence of oxygen. It, therefore, appears that sulfinate-sulfonate formation may be a general reaction which should be considered in further studies of the free-radical catalyzed addition of bisulfite to alkenes.

b. Alkynes

The addition of bisulfite to n-butylacetylene and to phenylacetylene was shown to be free-radical in character (457), since no reaction occurred in the absence of oxygen:

$$RC{:}CH + NaHSO_3 \longrightarrow RCH{:}CHSO_3Na \xrightarrow{\ NaHSO_3\ }$$

$$RCH(SO_3Na)CH_2SO_3Na \qquad (3\text{-}48)$$

In an independent experiment, $C_6H_5CH{:}CHSO_3Na$ was also shown to form $C_6H_5CH(SO_3Na)CH_2SO_3Na$ only in the presence of oxygen (457). Sodium ethenesulfonate behaved similarly. They, therefore, differ from the corresponding carboxylic acid salts, which react ionically, as discussed in Section II-B-2. Conjugation of the sulfone group with the neighboring unsaturated carbon is accordingly concluded to be small compared with that of the carbonyl group (332). (Addition of bisulfite to α, β-unsaturated sulfones is also discussed in Section II-B-2). Acetylene forms 80% of the unsaturated monosulfonate in the presence of peroxide catalyst (314); others report the formation of a mixture of the mono- and disulfonate (208). Divinylacetylene adds one mole of bisulfite to give a sulfonate of unstated composition (459).

The addition of bisulfite to mono- and diacetylenic alcohols and glycols has also been shown to be free-radical in nature (146, 457). Included in this group are 1, 4-dihydroxy-2-butyne, propargyl alcohol, 3-hydroxy-3-methyl-1-butyne, and the related amines, ethers and esters, all of which add bisulfite upon refluxing with an aqueous solution of it for several hours (146, 182, 208, 234, 338). No catalyst was deliberately added in these experiments, but no effort was apparently made to exclude air during reaction. In most cases, only the disulfonates were prepared, but one report describes isolating the monosulfonate from 1, 4-dihydroxy-2-butyne, and another (338) concluded that the monosulfonates can be made, but gives no supporting evidence. In the cold, in the presence of added oxygen, propargyl alcohol can form either the olefinic sulfonate (47) or the sulfinate-sulfonate (182):

$$HC:CCH_2OH + KHSO_3 \xrightarrow{O_2} KO_3SCH:CHCH_2OH \xrightarrow[KHSO_3]{O_2}$$

$$KO_3SCH:C(SO_2K)CH_2OH \qquad\qquad (3\text{-}49)$$

As stated in the preceding section, alkenes sometimes behave similarly.

The alkyne addition reactions cited before apparently proceed by a free-radical chain reaction. On the other hand, chloroacetylene adds bisulfite even in the presence of the added free-radical inhibitor diphenylamine (434). The only product actually isolated was the 1, 1, 2-ethanetrisulfonate salt, presumably formed by the following sequence:

$$ClC:CH \xrightarrow{KHSO_3} \left[ClCH:CHSO_3K\right] \xrightarrow[+\ KHSO_3]{-\ HCl\ or}$$

$$\left[HC:CSO_3K\ \text{or}\ KO_3SCHClCH_2SO_3K\right] \xrightarrow[+KHSO_3]{-\ HCl\ or}$$

$$\left[KO_3SCH:CHSO_3K\right] + KHSO_3 \longrightarrow KO_3SCH_2CH(SO_3K)_2 \quad (3\text{-}50)$$

Cis-Dichloroethylene is thought to react similarly via the intermediate formation of chloroacetylene, but the trans analogue did not react, since it cannot dehydrohalogenate. 1, 1-Dichloroethylene, on the other hand, does not form chloroacetylene under the conditions used, but it does yield the trisulfonate. Vinyl bromide also formed the disulfonate, presumably via acetylene, although an addition-elimination sequence similar to the preceding one was not ruled out. Further study is evidently required to clarify the factors involved in the alkyne-bisulfite reaction.

2. HETEROCONJUGATED ALKENES WITH BISULFITE

Although the addition of bisulfite to alkenes, as discussed in the preceding section, is a free-radical chain reaction, addition to olefins with conjugated carbonyl, cyano, nitro, or similar groups, involves simple ionic addition of the sulfite ion.

Morton and Landfield (289), and Walling (451) have concluded that 1-4 addition occurs to the conjugated system, via compounds 3-51-C, and 3-51-D:

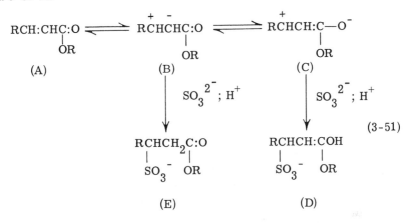

$$(3-51)$$

An increase in pH resulted in a marked increase in the rate of reaction in a manner suggesting that sulfite ion concentration is rate-determining. Methyl acrylate and methacrylate showed much lower activation energies than methacrylonitrile. This observation is consistent with an expected higher resonance polarization of the former as a result of the more electronegative character of the oxygen, as opposed to the nitrogen atom. This line of thought assumes that the resonance effect predominates.

Schenck and Danishevsky (362), on the other hand, were undecided between 1-4 addition to systems of this type, and direct addition to the olefinic bond of species 3-51-B. They also concluded that bisulfite, rather than sulfite, ion is the actual reactive entity with sodium acrylate and crotonate, since the reaction is most rapid in the pH range were bisulfite is at its maximum concentration.

A study of the addition of bisulfite to acrolein (140) led to proposal of the following reaction sequence, based on the observation that aldehyde-bisulfite (compound 3-52-A) formation appeared rapid and reversible, while that of compound 3-52-B was slow and irreversible:

$$CH_2:CHCHO + NaHSO_3 \rightleftharpoons \underset{(A)}{CH_2:CHCHOHSO_3Na} \xrightarrow{NaHSO_3}$$

$$\underset{(B)}{NaO_3SCH_2CH_2CHOHSO_3Na} \qquad (3-52)$$

An earlier study with crotonaldehyde (197) had also led to a similar conclusion. The sulfite ion might be expected to react more easily, however, directly with acrolein in forms 3-51-B or 3-51-C, as shown before, rather than with the nonconjugated olefinic bond of compound

3-52-A. This alternative would involve the sequence:

$$CH_2:CHCHO \xrightarrow{NaHSO_3} NaO_3SCH_2CH_2CHO \xrightarrow{NaHSO_3} 3\text{-}52\text{-}B \qquad (3\text{-}53)$$

In the work cited before, as indicated for the conversion of 3-51-B to 3-51-E and 3-51-C to 3-51-D, the addition of sulfite to heteroconjugate systems has been considered "essentially" irreversible. Actually, this type of reaction appears reversible, with the equilibrium being far toward completion under the conditions used with these particular compounds. A similar system (74), involving a sulfonated naphthoquinone, was shown to be reversible in a mildly basic solution by a mechanism essentially the reverse of that shown before. Likewise, the formation of tetralonesulfonates is easily reversed, as discussed in Section III-B with reference to the mechanism of the Bucherer reaction. The addition of sulfurous acid to tetracyanoethylene, which occurs with extreme facility, is reversed by the mild application of heat (283, 284):

$$(NC)_2C:C(CN)_2 + H_2O + SO_2 \rightleftharpoons (NC)_2CHC(CN)_2SO_3H \qquad (3\text{-}54)$$

The product is a dibasic acid, the hydrogen atom on the carbon atom being loosely attached because of the proximity of the two strongly electron-withdrawing cyano groups.

The general preparative utility of this type of reaction has been reviewed (to 1954) with detailed typical examples (334). Industrial interest in it has involved the preparation of many long-chain, surface-active sulfonates from the amides (and especially the esters) of acrylic, citraconic, itaconic, aconitic, and maleic acids, a subject which has been reviewed to 1958 (379, 380). A series of such sulfonates, made from the long-chain diesters of maleic acid, has been commercialized, and details for the commercial manufacture of a typical one are available (157). Many patents (379, 380) describe similar surface-active materials prepared by adding bisulfite to the monoesters or monoamides, of structure ROCOCH:CHCOOH and RNHCOCH:CHCOOH, made by reacting equimolal quantities of an alcohol or amine with maleic anhydride. The direction of addition across the double bond for such compounds has not been definitely determined. Detergents have also been made by reacting bisulfite with compounds of the structure $RC_6H_4COCH:CHCOC_6H_4R$ (383), $RC_6H_4CH:CHNO_2$ (330), and CH_2: CHCONHR (10a) (R = long-chain in all cases), the second being an extension of the bisulfite-nitroethene reaction discovered earlier (162). The addition of bisulfite to maleate esters is accelerated by ultraviolet light (110), although the reaction proceeds rapidly without a catalyst.

This type of reaction has begun to find use for preparing polymeric sulfonates. Three patents (46, 75, 446) describe the addition of bisulfite to polymaleate esters of the general structure $(\text{-COCH:CHCOORO-})_x$, where R represents various glycols. The addition of bisulfite to one of the double bonds of methylene bis(methacrylamide) leaves the other free for conversion to polymeric sulfonates (97). Poly(vinyl alcohol) fibers have been treated successively with maleic anhydride and bisulfite (450). Natural polymers have been similarly sulfonated. Starch (72) and cellulose acetate (191) have been converted to the half-maleate esters, and these have been reacted with bisulfite. Corn starch, containing one sulfomaleate moiety for every 24 anhydroglucose units, and similar products, have been on the market for some years (295). Cellulose crotonate has similarly been converted to a water-soluble sulfonate with bisulfite (116).

Acrylonitrile adds sodium bisulfite in the expected manner, as discussed in Chapter 5, Section II-C-5. The analogous diene not unexpectedly adds 1-4 (245):

$$CH_2:CHCH:CHCN + NaHSO_3 \longrightarrow NaO_3SCH_2CH:CHCH_2CN \qquad (3-55)$$

2- and 4-Vinylpyridines react normally with bisulfite, but the 3-isomer does not react; the authors regard these results as expected on structural grounds (79, 111). Ketonic steroids containing carbonyl-conjugated double bonds form sulfonates, and are thus separable from steroids with isolated double bonds, which do not react (159).

The addition of bisulfite to the $-COCH:CHCO-$ system in quinones is discussed in Section III-A.

The formation of sulfonates from bisulfite and alcohols containing electron-withdrawing groups on the carbon next to that holding the hydroxyl group may, as discussed in Section II-A-7, proceed via heteroconjugate systems of the types mentioned above.

The preparation of derivatives from the aldehydic and carboxylic sulfonates cited in this section is discussed in Chapter 5, Section II-C.

Although the addition of bisulfite to α, β-unsaturated carbonyl compounds, and to related materials, clearly proceeds by an ionic mechanism as discussed before, addition to other types of possibly similar systems may be free-radical in character, rather than ionic. Sodium ethylenesulfonate and related compounds add bisulfite by a free-radical mechanism, as pointed out in the preceding section. The sulfone group in this and related compounds was accordingly concluded to be only slightly conjugated with the neighboring olefinic bond, as contrasted with the carbonyl-conjugated system. On the other hand, ethylenesulfonates do undergo ionic addition to many electrophiles, as discussed in Chapter 5, Section II-B-7. This appears to leave open the question of the mechanism of the reaction of α, β-unsaturated sulfones, which add bisulfite easily upon refluxing in aqueous medium (339, 442):

$$RSO_2CH:CH_2 + NaHSO_3 \longrightarrow RSO_2CH_2CH_2SO_3Na \qquad (3-56)$$

Vinyl sulfides and sulfoxides react with similar ease (339). Bisulfite addition to vinylphosphonic esters of the structure $(RO)_2P(:O)CH:CH_2$

is apparently free-radical in character when R is long-chain alkyl, and
ionic when it is short-chain (366). Further study of these systems is
evidently required.

3. ALKENES WITH SULFURYL CHLORIDE OR SULFURYL CHLORO-FLUORIDE

Sulfuryl chloride forms a sulfonyl chloride from ethylene in the
presence of pyridine as catalyst (469):

$$CH_2:CH_2 + ClSO_2Cl \longrightarrow ClCH_2CH_2SO_2Cl \qquad (3-57)$$

Propylene and vinyl chloride give analogous products. With sulfur
monochloride as catalyst, chlorosulfites are said to be formed instead.
A conjugated diolefin polymer with terminal unsaturation likewise
yields a sulfonyl chloride with pyridine as catalyst and a metallic sulfite as promoter (62). Vinyl chloride forms 2, 2-dichloroethanesul-
fonyl chloride using stoichiometric aluminum chloride as catalyst
(235). A free-radical mechanism for any of these reactions is considered unlikely (407).

In the presence of peroxides, however, sulfuryl chloride acts
largely as a chlorinating agent. No sulfonyl chlorides have been isolated as such, but chlorinated sulfones, possibly formed via an unstable
chlorosulfonyl radical by a free-radical chain reaction, have been
identified (451):

$$RCH:CH_2 + \cdot SO_2Cl \longrightarrow \left[R\dot{C}HCH_2SO_2Cl \right]$$

$$\xrightarrow[\text{Several steps}]{RCH:CH_2} (RCHClCH_2)_2SO_2 \qquad (3-58)$$

The fluorosulfonyl radical, on the other hand, is more stable, and
therefore reacts in a more clean-cut manner forming sulfonyl fluorides.
With ethylene in the presence of peroxide sulfuryl chlorofluoride
forms a small quantity of 2-chloroethanesulfonyl fluoride and mainly
various telomers, but apparently no sulfone (421, 424):

$$CH_2:CH_2 + ClSO_2F \xrightarrow{\text{Peroxide}} ClCH_2CH_2SO_2F +$$

$$Cl(CH_2CH_2)_xSO_2F \qquad (3-59)$$

Other α olefins (propylene, isobutylene, 1-octene, undecenoyl chloride, allyl chloride, various fluorinated olefins) behave similarly (421,
422, 424). 1, 6-Heptadiene, using an azo catalyst, reacts as follows
(148):

$$CH_2{:}CH(CH_2)_3CH{:}CH_2 \xrightarrow{ClSO_2F} ClCH \begin{array}{c} \diagup CH_2 \diagdown \\ \\ \diagdown CH_2 \diagup \\ CH_2 \end{array} \begin{array}{c} \diagdown CHCH_2SO_2F \\ \\ CH_2 \diagup \end{array} \qquad (3\text{-}60)$$

Diallyl ether can form either a similar type of heterocyclic ring sulfonyl fluoride (148), or the chain di(sulfonyl fluoride) (421). Spiro-di-o-xylylene undergoes telomerization with sulfuryl chlorofluoride (128), but the reaction is not clean-cut, since the product contains no sulfur, and only about 10% of the required fluorine. Sulfuryl chlorofluoride is commercially available in experimental quantities (8).

4. GRIGNARD REAGENTS WITH SULFURYL CHLORIDE

An interesting application of this method, cited in Section II-A-4 for preparing saturated aliphatic sulfonates, is the following (158):

$$HC{:}CMgBr + 2\ ClSO_2Cl \longrightarrow ClC{:}CSO_2Cl +$$

$$MgBrCl + SO_2 + HCl \qquad (3\text{-}61)$$

Although the yield was only 10%, this constitutes a direct synthesis for a type of compound not easily accessible by alternative approaches (348). No other unsaturated sulfonates have been made by this method.

5. ALDEHYDE- AND KETONE-BISULFITES

The α-hydroxysulfonate structure $[R_2C(OH)SO_3Me]$ for aldehyde and ketone bisulfite addition compounds has been established by chemical evidence (392), as well as by Raman (76) and other spectral data (408), and by equilibrium constant studies using S_{34} (390). Consideration of the physicochemical aspects of the reaction has included kinetic studies (411), and determination of activation energies for the forward and reverse reactions (170), of heats of reaction (169), and of equilibrium constants by chemical (169), spectroscopic (403), and isotopic (390) methods. The kinetic studies showed that the mechanism of the reaction is fairly complicated, and appears to involve a sulfite, rather than bisulfite, ion, as had usually been assumed (7).

In Tables 3-5 and 3-6 are shown the relative rates and degrees of reaction of various aldehydes and ketones with equimolar bisulfite, except as indicated. Wide variations are noted, presumably explainable by steric factors for the aliphatic aldehydes and ketones. Steric

TABLE 3-5

Relative Reactivities of Aldehydes with Bisulfite[a]

Aldehyde	Per Cent Reaction 0.5 Hr.	1 Hr.	Reference
Aliphatic			
Formaldehyde	Over 97	100	428
Acetaldehyde	88.0	88.7	409
Isobutyraldehyde	-	71.6[b]	324
Phenylacetaldehyde	-	80.7[b]	324
Phenyldimethylacetaldehyde	-	0	426
Aromatic			
Benzaldehyde	-	77.7[b]	324
2-Methoxybenzaldehyde	-	74.8[b]	324
4-Methoxybenzaldehyde	-	52.3[b]	324
2,4,6-Trimethylbenzaldehyde	46(3 weeks)	-	396
2,3,6-Trimethylbenzaldehyde	82(3 days)	-	396
2,3,5,6-Tetramethylbenzaldehyde	93(3 days)	-	396
2,3,4,6-Tetramethylbenzaldehyde	40(2 weeks)	-	396
Pentamethylbenzaldehyde	0(3 weeks)	-	396
2-Methyl-4-hydroxy-5-isopropyl-benzaldehyde	-	0	154

[a]At equimolar ratios of reagents for data given for 0.5 and 1 hr., the ratios were otherwise unknown.

[b]Aqueous-alcoholic $KHSO_3$ used; aqueous $NaHSO_3$ used otherwise.

TABLE 3-6

Relative Reactivities of Ketones with Bisulfite[a]

Ketone	Per Cent Reaction 0.5 Hr.	1 Hr.	Reference
Acetone	47.0	56.2;22[b]	325, 409
Methyl ethyl ketone	25.1	36.4;14[b]	325, 409
Methyl n-propyl ketone	14.8	23.4;12.4[b]	325, 409
Methyl isopropyl ketone	7.5	12.3; 2.7[b]	325, 409
Methyl cyclopropyl ketone	-	- 0[b]	325
Methyl tert-butyl ketone	5.6	5.6; -	409
Methyl n-hexyl ketone	-	5.7[b]	325
Methyl benzyl ketone	-	15.6[b]	324
Methyl phenyl ketone	-	0.8[b]	324
Diethyl ketone	-	1.8[b]	325
Ethyl n-propyl ketone	-	2.0[b]	325
Di-n-propyl ketone	-	0[b]	325
Cyclopentanone	-	7[b]	325
Cyclohexanone	-	35[b]	325
Cycloheptanone	-	4.8[b]	325

[a]Equimolar rations of bisulfite and ketone used throughout.

[b]Aqueous-alcoholic $KHSO_3$ used; aqueous $NaHSO_3$ used otherwise.

hindrance also presumably accounts for the observation that polyacrolein adds bisulfite, but that polymethacrolein does not (370). With methyl-substituted benzaldehydes, however, the situation is more complicated, since a substituent in the para position of the ring also has an important influence. In a group of tri- and tetramethylated benzaldehydes, all of which contained methyl groups in both ortho positions, the two without para methyl groups reacted slowly, but completely, the two with para methyl groups reacted slowly and half as completely, and the fully methylated compound did not react at all. No explanation has been advanced for these interesting differences. The data in the tables show that the carbonyl-bisulfite reaction is quite sensitive to structural factors, and suggest that a deeper and more systematic study might yield results of broad interest.

A reexamination (428) of the formaldehyde-bisulfite reaction has shown that, contrary to a previous view, it goes to completion in about 30 min. while the reaction of formaldehyde with normal sulfite reaches equilibrium almost immediately:

$$CH_2O + NaHSO_3 \longrightarrow HOCH_2SO_3Na \qquad (3\text{-}62)$$

$$CH_2O + Na_2SO_3 \rightleftharpoons HOCH_2SO_3Na + NaOH \qquad (3\text{-}63)$$

This conclusion is consistent with the known behavior of other aldehyde and ketone bisulfite compounds under alkaline conditions. Reexamination of the benzaldehyde-bisulfite reaction (403, 404) indicated the equilibrium constant to be an order of magnitude smaller than previously thought. The reported existence of an enol form of benzaldehyde-bisulfite, with an implied expanded valence shell of ten electrons for sulfur, was disproved (403). The three isomeric pyridinealdehyde adducts with sulfurous acid (270), being inner salts, are both much more stable and much less soluble in water than the analogous benzaldehyde derivatives. The hydroxyarylglyoxal adducts, unlike others, resist the action of both acids and bases (145). A series of aldehydes and ketones has been converted to the primary (3) and tertiary (4) amine bisulfite compounds.

Increasing study is being made of the reaction of sugars with bisulfite. Many aldoses [e. g. , glucose, galactose, mannose, rhamnose, and arabinose (64, 65, 181, 211, 212)] form adducts, some of which at least are of open-chain structure. A ketose (fructose) reacts under some conditions (181), but not under others (64). Disaccharides vary, since sucrose (217) and maltose (65) react, but lactose and cellobiose (181) do not. A study of the behavior of glucose (5) and of xylose and arabinose (89) under wood-pulping conditions (sulfur dioxide with aqueous bisulfite for 9 hr. at 130° C) shows that mixtures of sulfocarboxylic acids are formed, apparently by decomposition under these fairly drastic conditions of the initially-formed aldehyde-bisulfite adducts. Dialdehyde starch has been converted to its bisulfite compound (278).

The use of aldehyde-bisulfite compounds for sulfomethylation is discussed in Chapter 5.   Methods for their use in the purification of aldehydes have been reviewed with detailed examples (34).

6. EPOXIDES, EPISULFIDES, AND CYCLIC IMINES WITH BISULFITE

These compounds all react with ring cleavage:

$$\overline{OCH_2CH_2} + NaHSO_3 \longrightarrow HOCH_2CH_2SO_3Na \qquad (3\text{-}64)$$

It has been stated (363) that the basic chemistry and the theory of the epoxide-sulfite reaction are largely undeveloped. A kinetic study (363) has shown that the reaction is ionic involving sulfite (rather than bisulfite) ion, and is first order with respect to that ion for epoxides of limited solubility - the reaction rates for highly soluble epoxides, e.g., propylene oxide, being too fast to measure. The direction of ring cleavage is known for only a few unsymmetrical epoxides. Styrene oxide and 1,2-epoxyoctane gave the secondary, rather than the expected primary sulfonates which would be distinctly favored on steric grounds:

$$\overline{RCHCH_2O} + NaHSO_3 \longrightarrow RCH(SO_3Na)CH_2OH \qquad (3\text{-}65)$$

Indene oxide likewise yields the sterically less favored sulfonate (414). Phenyl glycidyl ether, on the other hand, formed only the primary compound. Trimethylene oxide gave sodium 3-hydroxypropanesulfonate with $NaHSO_3$, but formed propionaldehyde bisulfite at high pH. These observations led to the conclusion that the divalent character of the sulfite ion outweighs steric factors and the weak polarization of the epoxide. Subsequent work (301) has shown that below 60°C styrene oxide yields the secondary sulfonate, but above it (e.g., at 80°C) the primary product, an effect apparently not observed previously, but which should be considered in future mechanistic studies of this reaction. Propylene oxide is stated to form the primary sulfonate (247, 410), although others (389) have suggested that it, and the butylene oxides, may yield mixtures. 1,2-Epoxyhexadecane forms the primary sulfonate (441). Rationalization of the observed data on the direction of cleavage of unsymmetrical epoxides, with reagents other than bisulfite, has also given difficulty (466).

Also of possible mechanistic interest is the fact that the process can be conducted stepwise. Ethylene oxide and sulfur dioxide easily form ethylene sulfite (134, 449), which is converted to sodium hydroxyethanesulfonate with sodium bicarbonate (397):

$$\overline{OCH_2CH_2} \xrightarrow{\;SO_2\;} \overline{OS(:O)OCH_2CH_2} \xrightarrow{\;NaHCO_3\;}$$

$$HOCH_2CH_3SO_3Na + CO_2 \qquad (3\text{-}66)$$

Sodium 2-hydroxyethanesulfonate has been manufactured for many years from ethylene oxide and sodium bisulfite (200) for use as a commercial sulfoethylating agent, as discussed in Chapter 5. The reaction can be run continuously (382), and best yields are obtained by careful control of the pH of the reaction mixture between 4.5 and 8 (386).

The epichlorohydrin-sulfite reaction is of special interest, since both the chlorine and epoxide groups can react. The use of dilute (10%) aqueous sodium sulfite at low temperature (15-25°C) is stated to give 71% of the epoxysulfonate (367), although this result can be questioned in view of the much faster rate of epoxide cleavage compared to that of the Strecker reaction:

$$ClCH_2\overset{\frown}{CHCH_2O} + Na_2SO_3 \longrightarrow NaO_3SCH_2\overset{\frown}{CHCH_2O} + NaCl \qquad (3\text{-}67)$$

Both groups undergo attack by concentrated neutral sulfite (149):

$$ClCH_2\overset{\frown}{CHCH_2O} + 2\ Na_2SO_3 + H_2O \longrightarrow (NaO_3SCH_2)_2CHOH +$$

$$NaCl + NaOH \qquad (3\text{-}68)$$

Reaction can be limited to the epoxy group by using sodium bisulfite, thus forming sodium 3-chloro-2-hydroxypropanesulfonate, (440), a useful sulfoalkylating agent discussed in Chapter 5:

$$ClCH_2\overset{\frown}{CHCH_2O} + NaHSO_3 \longrightarrow ClCH_2CHOHCH_2SO_3Na \qquad (3\text{-}69)$$

A variation involves use of the neutral sulfite with methyl formate below 35°C (44):

$$ClCH_2\overset{\frown}{CHCH_2O} + Na_2SO_3 + H_2O + HCOOCH_3 \longrightarrow$$

$$ClCH_2CHOHCH_2SO_3Na + HCOONa + CH_3OH \qquad (3\text{-}70)$$

The epichlorohydrin-bisulfite reaction was at one time erroneously thought to form the sulfite, rather than the sulfonate as shown before (149). Long-chain (C10-20) epihydrin ethers react with bisulfite to form the corresponding hydroxypropanesulfonates, of interest as detergents (153, 242, 461).

Ethylene sulfide forms 85% of the expected mercaptosulfonate at 100°C (443):

$$\overset{\frown}{CH_2CH_2S} + NaHSO_3 \longrightarrow HSCH_2CH_2SO_3Na \qquad (3\text{-}71)$$

Propylene sulfide similarly forms sodium 2-mercaptopropanesulfonate.

Ethylenimine gives taurine (152):

$$\overline{CH_2CH_2NH} + SO_2 + H_2O \longrightarrow \overset{+}{H_3}NCH_2CH_2\overset{-}{SO_3} \qquad (3\text{-}72)$$

7. THE ADDITION OF BISULFITE TO CARBON-NITROGEN DOUBLE BONDS

Diazomethane derivatives form sulfonates with sulfur dioxide or sulfites. Diphenyldiazomethane yields the sulfonic acid with SO_2 and water, or the corresponding sulfonate esters, thioesters, or sulfonamides when using alcohols, thiols, or amines, respectively, instead of water. These reactions are thought to proceed through a "sulfene" intermediate, an interesting hypothetical compound structurally analogous to a ketene (229):

$$(C_6H_5)_2CN_2 \xrightarrow{SO_2} \left[(C_6H_5)_2C{:}SO_2 \right] \xrightarrow{ROH} (C_6H_5)_2CHSO_2OR \quad (3\text{-}73)$$

There is considerable current research interest in reactions possibly involving such sulfene intermediates. Potassium diazomethionate reacts with bisulfite to form a similar type of end product, but in this case an intermediate assigned structure 3-74-A was isolated (133, 319):

$$(KO_3S)_2CN_2 + KHSO_3 \longrightarrow (KO_3S)_2\overset{\overset{\displaystyle NH}{\diagup\diagdown}}{C}{-}NSO_3K \xrightarrow{H_2O} (KO_3S)_2CHSO_3K \quad (3\text{-}74)$$

$$(A) \qquad\qquad\qquad (B)$$

A structure $(KO_3S)_2C{:}NNHSO_3Na$ for 3-74-A seems more probable, however. A more likely precursor for 3-74-B might be the bisulfite adduct of 3-74-A, which would be expected to have the structure $(KO_3S)_3CNHNHSO_3K$. Isolation of such intermediates from reaction 3-73 would be of interest, as would also subjection of the diazomethionate to the conditions used for reaction 3-73.

A fairly recent study of process variables in a long-known method for preparing potassium aminomethionate has shown (31) that a maximum yield of 60% is attainable under optimum conditions:

$$KCN + 2\ KHSO_3 + H_2O \longrightarrow H_2NCH(SO_3K)_2 + KOH \qquad (3\text{-}75)$$

The authors conclude that this reaction may be mechanistically analogous to the aldehyde-bisulfite reaction (Section II-B-5). The aminomethionate forms the diazomethionate, mentioned above, by treatment with nitrous acid.

The addition of bisulfites to azomethines constitutes one procedure for sulfomethylation, and is discussed in Chapter 5:

$$RCH:NR' + NaHSO_3 \longrightarrow RCH(SO_3Na)NHR' \qquad (3-76)$$

Aliphatic and aromatic mono- and diisocyanates and isothiocyanates add bisulfites to give water-soluble unstable "blocked isocyanates" (321):

$$RNCO + NaHSO_3 \rightleftharpoons RNHCOSO_3Na \qquad (3-77)$$

It will be noted that in the examples cited before the overall effect involves formation of carbon-sulfur and nitrogen-hydrogen bonds. This would be expected, since electron withdrawal by the nitrogen atom renders the neighboring carbon atom susceptible to nucleophilic attack. Similar addition of bisulfite occurs across the carbon-nitrogen double bonds of heterocyclic compounds; preparative application is discussed in Section IV-A.

III.   THE PREPARATION OF AROMATIC SULFONATES

A.   Quinones with Bisulfite

Since quinones can react in various ways with bisulfite, depending upon the conditions used, the nature of the products formed has been somewhat controversial. Addition to the carbon-carbon double bond, or to either or both carbonyl groups, can occur singly or together; aromatization can also occur following the first reaction. Work prior to 1942 on the reaction with sulfites of benzoquinone and its methylated and halogenated derivatives has been well reviewed by Suter (415).

A detailed study in the case of benzoquinone (260) has shown that the sulfite, rather than the bisulfite, ion is the actual reactive species, and that it attacks a carbonyl carbon of the semiquinone, or of its dimer, rather than of the quinone itself, forming an addition compound. Rearrangement and internal oxidation-reduction next occur, forming hydroquinone monosulfonate between pH 4 and 7.5, and the disulfonate above pH 7. This mechanism, involving rearrangement, differs from that mentioned later on for 2-methyl-1, 4-naphthoquinone, or that cited in the discussion of the addition of sulfite to similar carbonyl-conjugated, open-chain systems given in Section II-B-2. Both of the latter are thought to involve direct attack by sulfite ion on the carbon atom being sulfonated. At 10°C, benzoquinone is stated (246) to form the hydroxysulfonate by addition of bisulfite to one carbonyl group. sec-Undecylquinone yields the sodium hydroquinone monosulfonate (420).

The 2-methyl-1, 4-naphthoquinone-bisulfite reaction has been studied extensively because the product has vitamin K activity. After considerable controversy, it appears that compounds 3-78-B and 3-78-C are both formed (74, 287):

$$(3-78)$$

In the overall sense, both of these products can be regarded as forming the two possible addition products of bisulfite across the olefinic double bond, with compound 3-78-B resulting from 3-78-A by aromatization, but with compound 3-78-C being incapable of doing the same thing. Compound 3-78-C reverts to the starting quinone in mildly basic solution, possibly by removal of a proton at carbon 3, formation of a resonating enolate ion, and spontaneous detachment of the sulfonate group as sulfite ion (74). The sulfonation step would comprise this process in reverse. 1, 4-Naphthoquinone is reported to form products 3-79-A and 3-79-B in the proportions given (165):

$$(3-79)$$

The pattern here may be basically the same as with 2-methyl-1, 4-naphthoquinone; an initial bisulfite adduct across the olefinic double bond can aromatize to compound 3-79-A, or the initial adduct can add a second mole to the carbonyl group forming compound 3-79-B, which cannot aromatize. It is interesting that 2-methyl-1,4-napthoquinone-2,3-epoxide can add bisulfite to the carbonyl group in the 4-position with the epoxide ring remaining intact (1). 1,4-Anthraquinone behaves similarly to 1,4-naphthoquinone (164), forming 40% of a compound analogous to 3-79-A, and 32% of a material similar to compound 3-79-B; aqueous bisulfite was used at 60°C for 8 hr.

A kinetic study of halide displacement with sulfite from 2-halo-3,5,6-trimethyl-p-benzoquinones showed that 1-4 addition comprises the first step (40a), with elimination of hydrohalide being the second. Both steps are general acid catalyzed, and both are dependent upon sulfite, rather than bisulfite, concentration. Relative rates are in the order I $\gg$ Br $>$ Cl.

B. Hydroxy and Amino Compounds with Bisulfite; the Bucherer Reaction

It has long been known that many aromatic compounds of these types (naphthols, aminonaphthols, naphthol- and naphthylaminesulfonic acid salts, hydrazo- and nitrosonaphthalene derivatives, various azo dyes, polyhydric phenols, etc.) form products of varying stability with bisulfites. In spite of much study, it was concluded (28) as recently as 1951 that no definite structural assignments were possible for these derivatives.

Such bisulfite compounds were known to form as intermediates in the Bucherer reaction, a procedure employed for converting naphthols or hydroxyanthracenes to the corresponding amines, and vice versa. Although this method has been widely used since 1903 for the industrial and laboratory-scale preparation of many compounds of these general types (115), and although its kinetics and mechanism have been the subject of special consideration (91), it was not until 1956 that Bogdanov and co-workers apparently solved the problem of the structure of the intermediates. Until then it had been thought (115) that they were simply bisulfite addition compounds of the keto form of the naphthol, or of the imino form of the naphthylamine, similar to the aldehyde-bisulfite adducts or their amine reaction products as discussed in Chapter 5, although it was recognized that, at least in certain cases, ring sulfonation products were formed. Bogdanov, however, identified 1-oxo-1,2,3,4-tetrahydronaphthalene-3-sulfonate (1-tetralone-3-sulfonate) as the reaction product of 1-naphthol with bisulfite (59):

$$(3-80)$$

Similar 1-tetralone-3-sulfonates were identified from 4-nitroso-1-naphthol (59), 1-hydroxyanthracene (55), and its 4-nitroso derivative. 1-Nitroso-2-hydroxyanthracene (54) was shown to behave likewise, with formation of a similar 2-tetralone-4-sulfonate, as were also phenyl-diazo-substituted 2- and 3-phenanthrols (61a).

These observations were confirmed and extended in a series of papers by Rieche and Seeboth (340, 341, 342, 343, 344), who made a spectroscopic study of the adducts and showed that they had typical ketonic properties, rather than those usually associated with ketone-bisulfite adducts. 1-Naphthylamine and its derivatives were also found to form the 1-tetralone-3-sulfonates, with evolution of ammonia, and a 2-hydroxynaphthalene derivative was shown to yield the 2-tetralone-4-sulfonate (343). Naphthols and naphthylamines substituted with amino-, hydroxyl-, and sulfonate groups gave similar ketosulfonates, except those already containing a sulfonate group in the 2- or 3-position, which did not react. The 1-tetralone-3-sulfonates could be monohalogenated in the 2-position. Subsequent dehydrohalogenation gave the 1-naphthol-3-sulfonates by a new synthetic route, a method which was extended to preparation of the 3,4-, 3,5-, 3,6-, and 3,7-disulfonates (344):

$$\text{(3-81)}$$

These observations led to the proposal of a new mechanism for the Bucherer reaction (342), which can be summarized as follows:

$$\text{(3-82)}$$

The facile conversion of compound 3-82-A to 3-82-C is consistent with the behavior of the similarly-constituted quinonesulfonates discussed in the preceding section. Of further interest is the mechanism by which compound 3-82-A is thought to result from 3-82-C. Attack by the sulfite ion on the carbonyl-conjugated keto (or imino) form of compound 3-82-C (3-83), by a scheme such as that mentioned above in connection with 1, 4-quinones, is rejected in favor of the

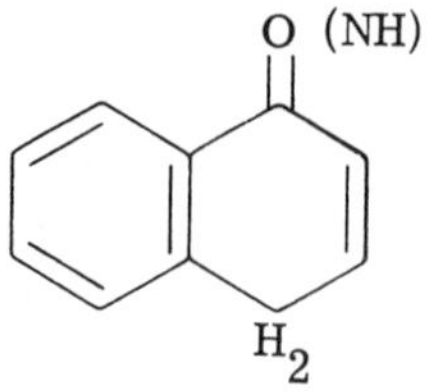

O (NH)

(3-83)

following sequence in which 3-84-A is first formed by the protonization of the naphthol at the electron-rich 4-position:

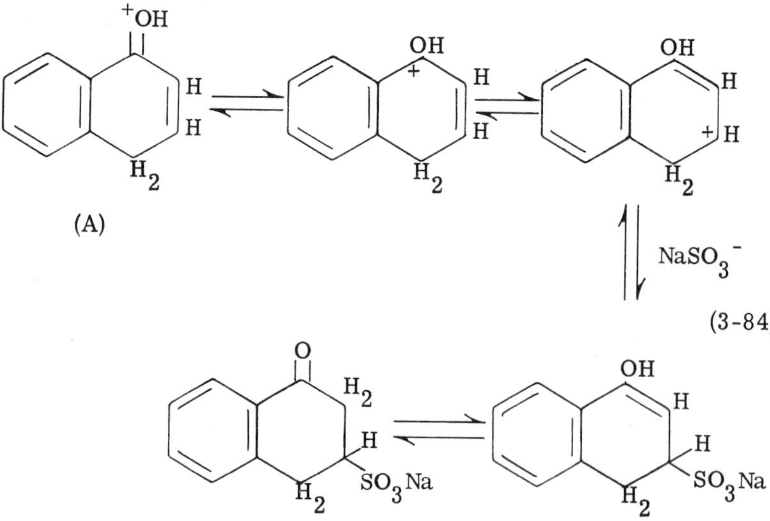

(A)

NaSO$_3^-$

(3-84)

These alternatives differ only slightly, since compound 3-84-A is merely the conjugate acid of 3-83.

The Bucherer reaction has also been applied to heterocyclic compounds, as mentioned in Section IV-B.

Benzene derivatives yield bisulfite adducts in only a few cases, including resorcinol, phloroglucinol, and hydroquinone (115). The resorcinol adduct has been identified as compound 3-85-A (444):

(A)   (3-85)

No mechanism has been proposed for this reaction, but it presumably could involve intermediates of the type shown. These are analogous to those established for the naphthols and the hydroxyanthracenes, as discussed above. Phloroglucinol is known to tautomerize to its triketo form, and since the 3-position is already occupied, the sulfonates in this case are simply the ketone-bisulfite adducts, with one or more hydroxysulfonate groups as in compound 3-85-A (150).

C. Hydroxy and Amino Compounds with Bisulfite and an Oxidizing Agent; the Piria Reaction

A variety of phenolic and amino aromatic compounds undergo sulfonation with sulfite in conjunction with an oxidizing agent. It is convenient to consider the oxidizing agents used under two headings - those which are separate compounds, and those which comprise part of the molecule being sulfonated. The yields in this type of reaction are often poor and mixtures of sulfonates are frequently formed. The sulfonate group enters ortho or para to the hydroxyl or amino group:

The introduction of a hydroxyl group also sometimes occurs during sulfonation, and in some cases more than one sulfonate group is introduced.

The oxidizing agent can be oxygen or ozone. 2-Hydroxy-3-naphthoic acid, bisulfite, and air give a 7% yield of mixed sulfonic acids (52); 1-naphthylamine, with bisulfite and ozone, formed the 1-amino-2-hydroxy-4-sulfonate (26). N, N-dimethyl- (33) and N, N-diethylparaphenylenediamines (280, 281) yielded sulfonates with sodium sulfite in the presence of oxygen, in the second case with a trace of added copper catalyst; their probable structures are mentioned below in connection with the sulfonation of the analogous nitroso compound.

A variety of other oxidizing agents have also been employed. Silver bromide and silver ion (387) induced sulfonation of paraphenylenediamine and its N, N-diethyl derivative, respectively. Lead dioxide, cupric hydroxide, and silver bromide gave the mono- and disulfonates of hydroquinone and catechol (415). Oxides of iron, mercury and lead (53), and sodium nitrite (58) gave the 1-sulfonate from 2-hydroxy-3-naphthoic acid. Manganese dioxide and sodium mercurous sulfite formed a 3% yield of the mixed 2- and 4-sulfonates of 1-naphthol (61), and a 17% yield of the same derivatives of 1-naphthylamine. Various sodium sulfonates of 2-naphthol were further sulfonated with sulfite in the presence of several oxidizing agent, with yields as follows: AgO: 19%: $FeCl_3$: 23-39%; $KMnO_4$: 15-28%; $CuSO_4$: 24-50% (60). Of interest is the fact that no sulfonation occurred with H_2O_2, K_2SO_5, I_2 or $AgNO_3$. Sodium 1, 2-naphthoquinone-4-sulfonate was an effective oxidant. Copper oxide and manganese dioxide had earlier been shown to induce sulfonation of 2-naphthol (56), of 2-hydroxy-3-naphthoic acid, of the 2-naphthol-6-, -4-, -7-mono- and of the 3, 6-disulfonic acids (49, 57), but not of the 1-sulfonic acid (50). Nitro compounds behave similarly, causing sulfonation of 2-naphthol and its derivatives (51), hydroquinone (51), dihydroxy- and tetrahydroxyanthraquinones (27). Nitrobenzene, 4-nitrotoluene, and sodium 3-nitrobenzenesulfonate were used, with the nitro compound undergoing conversion to the sulfamate, as discussed in more detail in Chapter 7.

Of special interest are the numerous cases in which the oxidizing moiety is present in the same molecule which undergoes sulfonation. This can be a quinoid group, as in the case of an indophenol derivative of 1-naphthylamine, which is converted to the hydroxyphenylaminonaphthalenesulfonate (201). The extensive work on the conversion of 1-nitroso-2-naphthol to 1-amino-2-hydroxynaphthalene-4-sulfonate has been well reviewed by Suter (415). The latter (139, 237) and its 6-methoxyl derivative (78) have proved of commercial interest as made by this method. 1-Nitroso-4-naphthol forms the 3-sulfonate, but 2-nitroso-1-naphthol does not react. Bogdanov and co-workers proposed 1-tetralone-3-sulfonate intermediates for this sulfonation (415), as he did many years later for the Bucherer reaction discussed in the preceding section. 1-Nitroso-4-dimethylaminobenzene gives a mixture of the 2- and 3-sulfonates, but the diethylamino analog yields only the 2-

sulfonate, because of greater steric hindrance at the 3-position (33).

The conversion of a nitro compound to aminomono- or disulfonates by heating with sulfite, known as the Piria reaction, has been well reviewed by Suter (415), Muth (293), and others (458). The reaction proceeds as follows:

$$C_6H_5NO_2 + 3 \; NaHSO_3 \longrightarrow 1, 4\text{-}NH_2(SO_3Na)C_6H_4 +$$

$$2 \; NaHSO_4 \tag{3-87}$$

A quantitative analytical study of this reaction mixture for bisulfate ion has been found consistent (163) with earlier views of the course of the reaction. 4-Nitrobiphenyl forms sodium 4-amino-3-biphenylsulfonate, and 4, 4'-dinitrobiphenyl yields the benzidine-3-sulfonate (141), while 3-nitrophenol gives sodium 2-hydroxy-4-aminobenzenesulfonate in 35% yield (6). Nitrobenzene forms no sodium 4-azobenzenesulfonate when heated with aqueous sodium sulfite under the conditions ordinarily used in the Piria reaction (415); however, it does give a good yield of this material when heated with sulfite waste liquor (318). No reaction occurs with dextrose and sulfite. The azo compound is formed, however, by using a mixture of sodium sulfide and sodium thiosulfate, both of which are present in waste liquor (95).

The mechanism of oxidative sulfonation with sulfites has been considered only briefly. With dihydric phenols, such as catechol or hydroquinone, or with a compound such as paraphenylenediamine, the quinone may be formed as intermediate (415). Bogdanov, who has done most of the work in this field (60), has seen a basic similarity of this process to sulfonation with sulfur trioxide, with transformation of sulfite to sulfate or to S_2O_6 probably occurring via metal ion complexes. However, the feasibility of a mechanism of this type in the aqueous medium ordinarily employed in sulfite reactions seems questionable.

D.   Diazonium Compounds with Sulfur Dioxide

The direct preparation of sulfonic acids in poor yield by treating the diazonium salts with sulfur dioxide, preferably in the presence of copper, has been described (293, 415) for those derived from aniline, the three toluidines, 3-aminobenzoic acid, and 1-amino-2-naphthol-4-sulfonic acid. 1-Amino-4-naphthalenesulfonic acid has similarly been converted to the 1, 4-disulfonic acid (216) by an improved procedure.

A more modern approach, developed by Meerwein and co-workers (276, 277) gives 70-90% yields of the sulfonyl chlorides. This procedure involves treatment of the diazonium chloride in concentrated HCl with sulfur dioxide dissolved in acetic acid, preferably using copper ion as catalyst. The method was applied to a series of chloro, bromo-,

nitro-, and carboxy-substituted anilines and naphthylamines. The
three aminobenzenesulfonic acid isomers, and several aminonaphthalenesulfonic acids, gave the disulfonic acids, rather than the expected
sulfonyl chlorides. Anthranilic acid formed the disulfide, and 2-amino-
3-naphthoic acid gave the sulfinic acid. 2-Trifluoromethyl (470) and
4-sulfamylaniline (196, 231) also gave the sulfonyl chlorides, in the
latter case in 80% yield. This method appears entirely practical for
laboratory use.

E. Displacement of Halogen with Sulfite

This technique, which ordinarily proceeds under fairly drastic conditions using a copper catalyst, has been applied to a variety of brominated and chlorinated mono- and polycyclic aromatic compounds,
including those containing hydroxyl, amino, and carbonyl groups. Since
previous reviews of this reaction (293, 415), 1, 4-dichloroanthraquinone
has been converted to a disulfonate (240), and 4-bromolaurophenone to
the monosulfonate in 29% yield (437). Industrial study of the sulfonation of 2-bromo- and 2-chloro-1, 4-diaminoanthraquinones for the preparation of dye intermediates has continued (9, 10, 180).

This reaction proceeds very easily, however, when the halogen is
activated by a nitro group, as recently applied to 1-chloro-2-nitro-4-
naphthalenesulfonate (416). Merely refluxing for 2 hr. in aqueous alcohol with sodium sulfite gave disulfonates by replacement of the 2-
and 4-halogen atoms in 2, 4, 5-trichloronitrobenzenes, 2, 4-dibromo-5-
methylnitrobenzene, and 2, 4-dichloro-1, 5-dinitrobenzene (302).

An interesting kinetic study of the replacement of halide from the
four 1-halogeno-2, 4-dinitrobenzenes with sulfite ion in aqueous ethanol
(4a) has shown (Table 3-7) that the order of reactivity is primarily determined by temperature. Reaction rates decrease as polarity of the
solvent is increased, in accordance with the Hughes-Ingold theory.
Sulfite ion is a more active nucleophile than alkoxide in this type of reaction.

TABLE 3-7

Replacement of Halogen by Sulfite in 1-Halogeno-
2, 4-Dinitrobenzenes

Temp. (°C)	Relative rates
0	F $\gg$ Br > Cl > I
30	F $\gg$ Br ~ Cl > I
100	F $\gg$ Cl > I > Br

The sulfonic group also facilitates removal of ring halogen by sulfite. An interesting comparative study of the preparation of the three benzenedisulfonic acid salts by 10 hr. refluxing of the corresponding halobenzenesulfonic acid salts with aqueous sulfite in the presence of copper gave the yields shown in Table 3-8 (262, 263). It is noteworthy that reactivity decreases in the order chlorine-bromine-iodine, which is the opposite of that observed with the aliphatic halides, and that all three meta compounds showed moderate and similar reactivity. Trisodium 1, 2, 4-benzenetrisulfonate was formed from the 1-bromo- (259) or 1-chloro (261) -2, 4-benzenedisulfonate under similar conditions.

Halide displacement from halogenated benzoquinones is discussed in Section III-A.

TABLE 3-8

Disulfonate Yields from Halobenzenesulfonic Acids

Isomer	Chloro	Bromo	Iodo
Ortho	48. 7	31. 7	32. 1
Meta	21. 7	19. 8	16. 3
Para	68. 2	66. 7	54. 5

F. Displacement of the Nitro Group with Sulfite

Certain compounds containing highly reactive nitro groups undergo replacement of nitro by sulfonate as follows:

$$RNO_2 + Na_2SO_3 \longrightarrow RSO_3Na + NaNO_2 \qquad (3-88)$$

This reaction proceeds easily by simply warming or refluxing a properly constituted nitro compound with aqueous or aqueous-alcoholic sodium sulfite. As shown in previous reviews (293, 415), it has been used for replacing the nitro group in 9-nitroanthracene or 1-nitroanthraquinone, and both nitro groups in 1, 5- and 1, 8-dinitroanthraquinones. Nitro groups vicinal to other electron-withdrawing groups are especially reactive, as in 1-nitroanthraquinone-2-carboxylic acid. This is notably true when the second group is also nitro. 1-Chloro-3, 4-dinitrobenzene yields the 3-sulfonate by replacement of a nitro group, but 1-chloro-2, 4-dinitrobenzene forms the 1-sulfonate by replacement of chlorine, as does also picryl chloride. This type of reaction is of industrial interest for separating 1, 2-dinitrobenzene from the 1,3-isomer, which does not react (139); the 1,4-isomer is also converted to the sulfonate under these mild conditions. The 3-nitro groups in 2,3,4- and 3,4,6-trinitrotoluenes are also easily replaced by sulfonate (173), while the 2,4,6-isomer does not react; this difference provides the basis for the purification of TNT on an industrial scale.

In all the preceding cases, the entering sulfonate group occupies the same position as the leaving nitro group. However, one heterocyclic dinitro compound, as pointed out in Section IV-E, apparently acquires the sulfonate group in a different position.

Nitro compounds can also react with sulfites or bisulfites to form sulfamates (cf., Chapter 7, Section III-A), or aminosulfonates, as discussed in Section III-C.

IV. THE PREPARATION OF HETEROCYCLIC SULFONATES

A. The Addition of Bisulfite to Carbon-Nitrogen Double Bonds

In the earlier discussion of the preparation of aliphatic sulfonates by the addition of bisulfite to unsaturated nitrogen compounds (Section II-B-7), it was pointed out that carbon-sulfur and nitrogen-hydrogen bonds were formed. The same rule applies to the formation of heterocyclic sulfonates. 2-Aminopyrimidine reacts as follows (215):

$$
\begin{array}{c}
HC{=}N \\
HC \quad CNH_2 + NaHSO_3 \longrightarrow HC \quad C{-}NH_2 \\
HC{-}N \qquad\qquad HC{-}NH \; SO_3Na
\end{array}
\tag{3-89}
$$

2,4-Diamino-5-nitropyrimidine forms a triaminodihydropyrimidine-sulfonate (132). The sodium dithionite used may form sodium bisulfite by reduction of the nitro group, followed by addition of the bisulfite to the carbon-nitrogen double bond:

$$
\begin{array}{c}
HC{=}N \\
O_2NC \quad CNH_2 \xrightarrow{Na_2S_2O_4} H_2NC \quad CNH_2 \xrightarrow{NaHSO_3} H_2NC \quad CNH_2 \\
H_2NC{-}N \qquad\qquad H_2NC{-}N \qquad\qquad H_2NC{-}N
\end{array}
\tag{3-90}
$$

Alternatively, a Piria-type reaction may occur (as noted later for nitrouracil), followed by reduction of the double bond by dithionite. 2-Aminothiazoles behave similarly in cases where R is arylsulfonyl and R' hydrogen (214), and where R is hydrogen and R' nitro (316):

$$\underset{\substack{\text{RNHC} \\ \text{S}---\text{CR}'}}{\overset{\text{N}}{\parallel}}\hspace{-0.3cm}\overset{\text{CH}}{\underset{}{}} + \text{NaHSO}_3 \longrightarrow \underset{\substack{\text{RNHC} \\ \text{S}---\text{CR}'}}{\overset{\text{NaO}_3\text{S}}{\overset{\text{NH}}{}}}\hspace{-0.2cm}\overset{\text{CH}}{\underset{}{}} \qquad (3\text{-}91)$$

Tetracyanoethane reacts likewise (283), possibly as follows:

$$\underset{\text{NC}}{\overset{\text{NC}}{\diagup}}\text{CHCH}\underset{\text{CN}}{\overset{\text{CN}}{\diagdown}} \xrightarrow{\text{NaHSO}_3} \left[\underset{\text{NC}}{\overset{\text{NC}}{\diagup}}\text{CHCH}\underset{\underset{\text{HN}}{\overset{\text{CSO}_3\text{Na}}{}}}{\overset{\text{CN}}{\diagdown}} \longrightarrow \right.$$

$$\left. \underset{\text{HN}=\text{C}}{\overset{\text{NC}}{\diagup}}\text{CHCH}\underset{\underset{\text{N}}{\overset{\text{CSO}_3\text{Na}}{}}}{\overset{\text{CN}}{\diagdown}} \right] \longrightarrow \underset{\text{H}_2\text{NC}}{\overset{\text{NC}}{\diagup}}\text{C}\text{—}\text{C}\underset{\underset{\text{NH}}{\overset{\text{CSO}_3\text{Na}}{}}}{\overset{\text{CN}}{\diagdown}} \qquad (3\text{-}92)$$

Pyridine is known to add three moles of bisulfite (364), forming a compound the constitution of which is uncertain, but which is known to yield glutaconic aldehyde and ammonia upon alkaline hydrolysis. A reaction sequence such as the following seems possible:

$$\cdots$$

$$\text{OCHCH}=\text{CHCH}_2\text{CHO} + \text{NH}_3 + \text{NaHSO}_3 \qquad (3\text{-}93)$$

Acridine reacts with bisulfite, by the following proposed scheme (250):

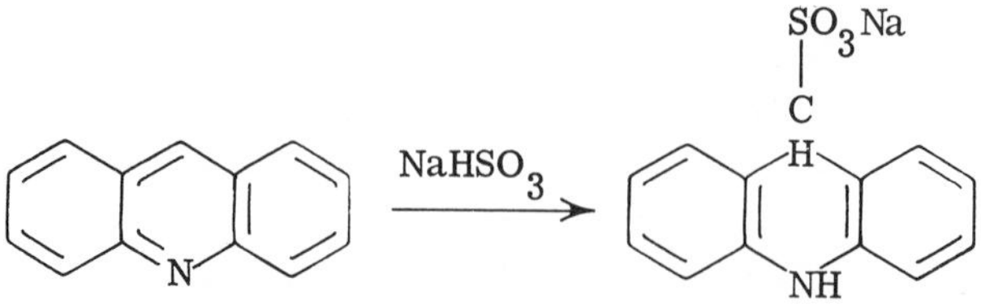

(3-94)

Others, however, in a study of the reaction of acridine, 2-methylacridine and 2-methoxyacridine with bisulfite (118) question the preceding structure and consider the compounds to be merely double salts ("acridinium sulfites"). Indole readily adds bisulfite, forming indolene-2-sulfonate (355):

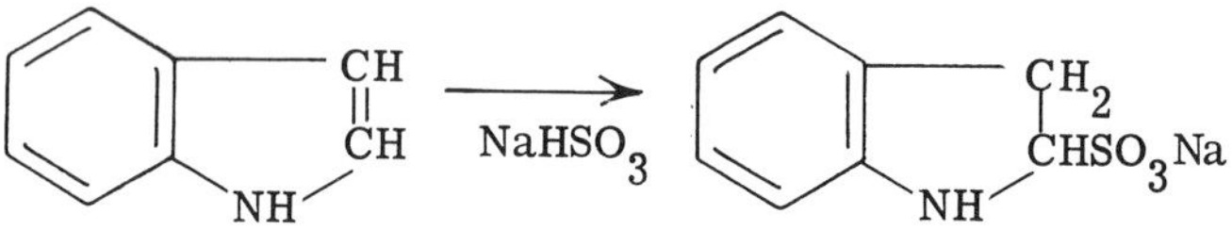

(3-95)

B.   The Addition of Bisulfite to Heteroconjugate Systems

Coumarin, α-naphthapyrone, and their ring-substituted derivatives add bisulfite easily (108, 455):

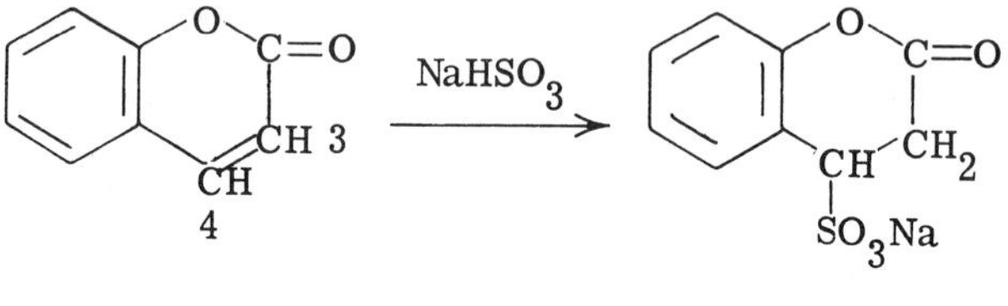

(3-96)

This addition is quite sensitive to steric factors, since the presence of an alkyl or phenyl group in positions 3- or 4- prevents reaction, although it proceeds normally with bromine, chlorine, acetyl or carbethoxy in the 3-position. The sulfonates undergo easy cleavage to the phenolic sulfonate-carboxylates. Coumarin-3-carboxylic acid gives the 4-sulfonate with decarboxylation (98). 3-Pyridizone is stated to undergo the Bucherer reaction (167), which, by analogy to the naphthols, as discussed in Section III-B, would imply formation of the sulfonate intermediate shown below, although such was not isolated or even suggested by the authors:

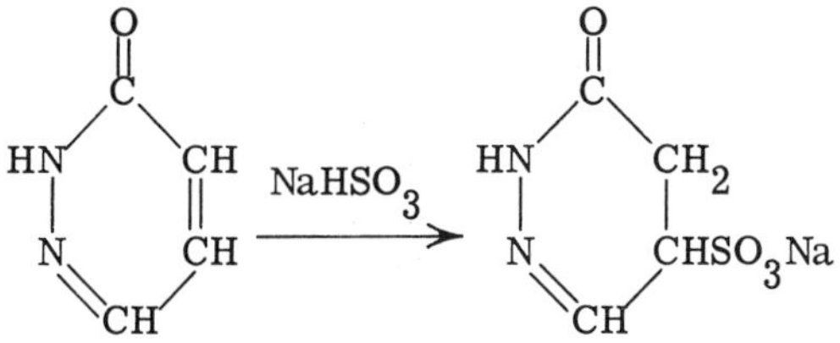

$$\text{(3-97)}$$

5-, 6-, 7-, and 8-Hydroxycinnolines have likewise been subjected to the Bucherer reaction (311), presumably via intermediates of types 3-98-A and 3-98-B:

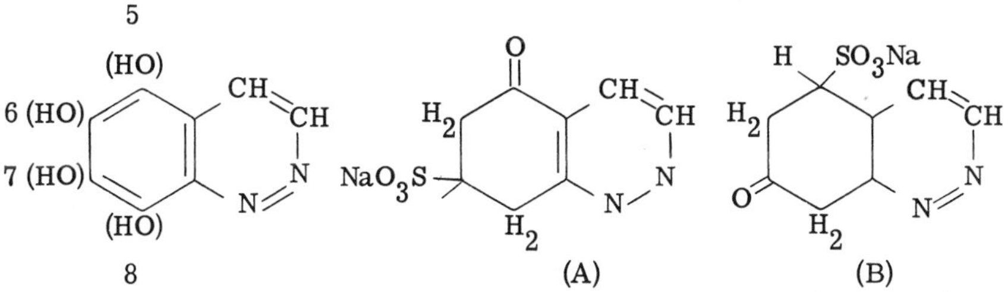

$$\text{(3-98)}$$

As was indicated in the previous discussion of the Bucherer reaction, initial isomerization to the keto form of the phenol may not actually constitute a step in the reaction sequence, although the overall result is the same.

C. Displacement of Halogen with Sulfite

2, 3-Dichlorotetrahydrofuran forms the expected 2-sulfonate upon refluxing for 3 hr. (338):

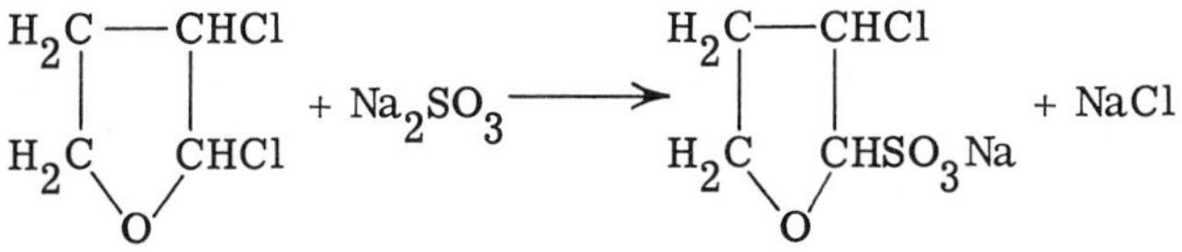

$$\text{(3-99)}$$

The replacement of halogen by sulfite in the 2-, 3-, and 4-positions of pyridine and pyridine oxide has been studied (11, 130). 2-Chloropyridine oxide formed only a 23% yield of sulfonate, but the 2-chloro- and 2-bromopyridines gave even less satisfactory results. 3-Chloropyridine did not react, but its oxide gave a 90% yield of the oxide 3-sulfonate. Replacement of halogen in 4-chloropyridine, its oxide, and in 4-bromo-2,6-lutidine was smooth, but the best preparative procedure for pyridine-4-sulfonates was concluded to be heating N-(4-pyridyl)-pyridinium chloride with sulfite, as mentioned in Section IV-E.

The high reactivity of halogens in the 2- and 4-positions compared to those in the 3- and 5-positions, has allowed analogous preparation of 3,5-dichloro-2- and -4-pyridinesulfonates from the corresponding trichlorides, and the 3,5-dibromo-4-sulfonate from the 3,5-dibromo-4-chloro compound (112). The 2- and 4-chloroquinolines, 4-chloroquinaldine, 2-chlorolepidine (39), 2-chlorobenzothiazole (3-100-A) and 2-chlorobenzoxazole (3-100-B) (206) react similarly.

(A)   (B)   (C)   (3-100)

On the other hand, a 2-brominated anthrapyridine (171) requires more drastic conditions (140°C for 18 hr. under pressure), therein resembling the analogous diaminoanthraquinone derivatives mentioned in Section III-E.

As in the aromatic series, a chlorine atom on the ring next to a nitro group is easily replaced in reaction with sodium sulfite, as in the case of 6-nitro-7-chloroisoindazole (3-100-C) (322).

D.   Sulfonation with Sulfite and an Oxidizing Agent

These types of reactions are quite similar to those discussed under a similar heading for aromatic compounds in Section III-C. The oxidizing moiety in these cases can also be in the compound being sulfonated, or it can comprise a separate compound. 5-Nitrouracil (48,144) undergoes a Piria-type reaction, forming the 5-amino-4-uracilsulfonate, as may also the 2,4-diamino-5-nitropyrimidine mentioned in Section IV-A. 7-Nitroindazole similarly gives a mixture of aminomono- and disulfonates (322). Hemin, and several of its derivatives, upon treatment with aqueous sulfite in the presence of air (298) from water-soluble derivatives of protohemin from which iron is easily removed to give a sulfonated porphyrin. Strychnine and brucine form four isomeric sulfonic acids when reacted with sulfur dioxide in the presence of manganese dioxide. Their properties and reactions have been studied at some length (252).

E.   Miscellaneous Heterocyclic Sulfonations

Alizarin Blue reacts with bisulfite as follows (445):

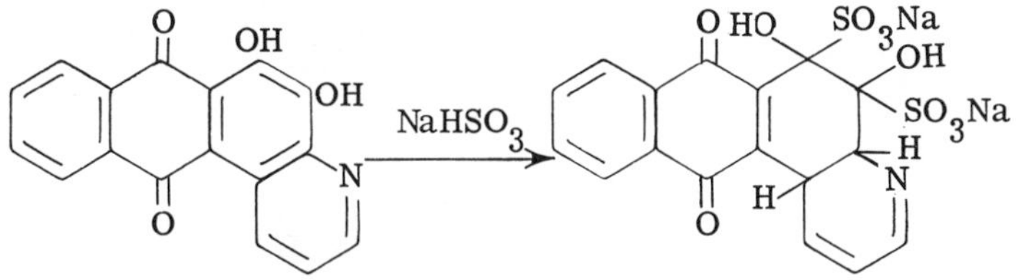

(3-101)

Reaction apparently occurs by simple addition of bisulfite to the diketo
form of the dye, forming a product similar in structure to those derived from resorcinol and phloroglucinol, as discussed in Section III-
B.

Indoxyl red (R = beta-oxindolyl in the formula below) forms a sulfonate, apparently by way of an easily-formed oxidation product (381):

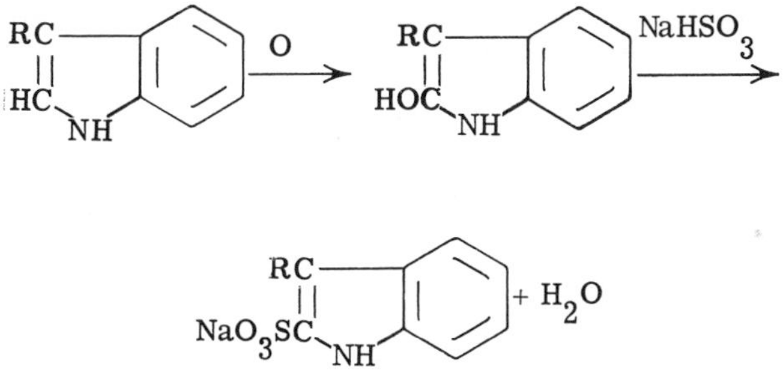

(3-102)

4-Hydroxypyridine likewise forms the 4-sulfonate (130) by overall displacement of the hydroxyl group.   This type of reaction has been noted
with certain alcohols, as pointed out in Section II-A-7, but apparently
has not been observed with aromatic hydroxy compounds.   It is interesting that the reaction proceeds with bisulfite, but not with sulfite.

5, 6-Dinitroindazole is stated to form a mixture of the 5-nitro-7-
sulfonate and the 6-nitro-4-sulfonate (323):

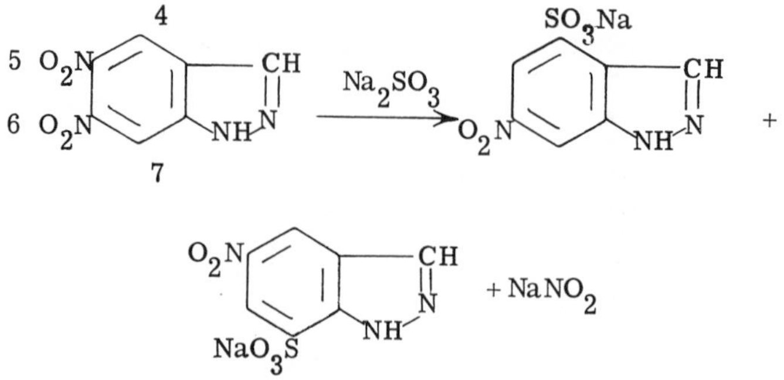

$$(3\text{-}103)$$

As noted in Section III-F, the replacement of an aromatic nitro by a sulfonate group using aqueous sodium sulfite is an established reaction, especially for vicinal dinitro compounds such as 1,2-dinitrobenzene, but this is apparently the only known case where the entering sulfonate group occupies a position other than that already occupied by the leaving nitro group.

Sodium 4-pyridinesulfonate can be prepared (130a, 425) as follows from N-(4'-pyridyl)pyridinium chloride hydrochloride (made by treating pyridine with thionyl chloride):

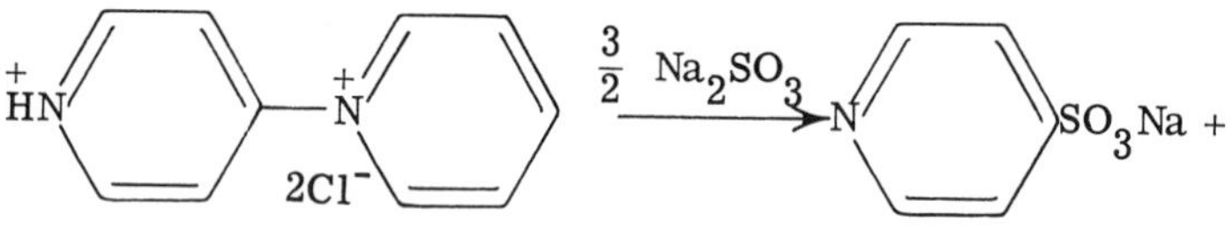

$$2\ NaCl + \frac{1}{2}\ SO_2 + \frac{1}{2}\ H_2O + C_5H_5N \qquad (3\text{-}104)$$

This procedure is regarded as preferred for preparing the 4-sulfonate (130a). The structure of the starting pyridinium compound is not well established.

Thiophene forms the disulfonyl chloride upon refluxing for 1.5 hr. with sulfuryl chloride without added catalyst (90):

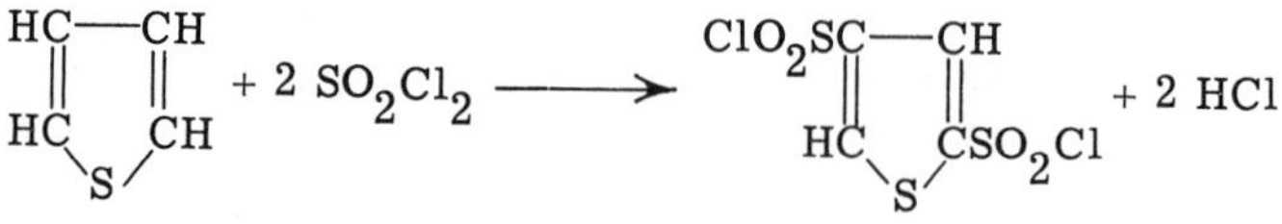

Reaction in this case occurs more easily than that of SO_2Cl_2 with paraffins (Section II-A-1), or with alkenes (Section II-B-3).

REFERENCES

1. Abe, Y. , Japanese Patent 3674 ('51); Chem. Abstr. , 47, 8095 (1953).
2. Adams, D. A. W. , H. Greaves, T. Harrington, P. C. Holmes, and A. Y. Livingstone, BIOS Final Rept. No. 1153, Item No. 22.
3. Adams, R. , and J. D. Garber, J. Am. Chem. Soc. , 71, 522 (1949).
4. Adams, R. , and R. D. Lipscomb, J. Am. Chem. Soc. , 71, 519 (1949).
4a. Adeniran, M. A. , C. W. L. Bevan, and J. Hirst, J. Chem. Soc. , 1963, 5868.
5. Adler, E. , Svensk Papperstid. , 49, 339 (1946); Chem. Abstr. , 40, 7621 (1946).
6. Aguado, L. , M. Lora-Tamayo, A. M. Municio, and J. L. Ruiz, Anales Real Soc. Espan. Fis. Quim. (Madrid), 55B, 523 (1959); Chem. Abstr. , 54, 3292 (1960).
7. Alexander, E. R. , Ionic Organic Reactions, Wiley, New York, 1950.
8. Allied Chemical Corp. , Baker and Adamson Dept. , Morristown, N. J.
9. Allmen, S. V. , and H. Eggenberger, U. S. Patent 2, 517, 613; Chem. Abstr. , 45, 870 (1951).
10. Allmen, S. V. , and H. Eggenberger, U. S. Patent 2, 541, 623; Chem. Abstr. , 45, 8255 (1951).
10a. American Cyanamid Co. , Belgian Patent 638, 678.
10b. Anbar, M. , H. Hefter, and M. L. Kremer, Chem. Ind. (London), 1962 (24), 1055.
11. Angulo, J. , and M. Municio, Anales Real Soc. Espan. Fis. Quim. (Madrid), 55B, 527 (1959); Chem. Abstr. , 54, 3292 (1960).
12. Anon. , Chem. Eng. News, 41, No. 24, 54 (1963).
13. Asinger, F. , Ber. , 77, 191 (1944).
14. Asinger, F. , Chemie und Technologie der Paraffin-Kohlenwasserstoffe, Akademie Verlag, Berlin, 1956.
15. Asinger, F. , and F. Ebender, Ber. , 75, 344 (1942).
16. Asinger, F. , F. Ebender, and E. Boeck, Ber. , 75, 42 (1942).
16a. Asinger, F. , B. Fell, and H. Scherb, Ber. , 96, 2831 (1963).
17. Asinger, F. , and G. Freitag, J. Prakt. Chem. , 7, 320 (1959).
18. Asinger, F. , G. Geiseler, and H. Eckoldt, Ber. , 89, 1037 (1956).
19. Asinger, F. , G. Geiseler, and M. Hoppe, Ber. , 91, 2130 (1958).
20. Asinger, F. , and H. J. Naggatz, J. Prakt. Chem. (4), 2, 37 (1955).
21. Asinger, F. , W. Schmidt, and F. Ebender, Ber. , 75, 34 (1942).
22. Backer, H. J. Rec. Trav. Chim. , 48, 949 (1929).
23. Badische Anilin- und Soda-Fabrik AG, French Patent 1, 045, 154; Chem. Zentr. , 126, 10859 (1955).
24. Badische Anilin- und Soda-Fabrik AG, French Patent 1, 338, 677.
25. Baeyer, A. , and V. Villiger, Ber. , 35, 3013 (1902).
26. Bamann, E. , K. Schriever, and G. Mueller, Arch. Pharmaz. Ber. deut. Pharmaz. Ges. , 287/59, 570 (1954); Chem. Zentr. , 127, 9435 (1956).

27. Bamberger, C. , and J. W. Orelup, U. S. Patent 2, 575, 155; Chem. Abstr. , 46, 6156 (1952).
28. Bamdas, E. M. , D. A. Bochvar, and M. M. Shemyakin, Zh. Obshch. Khim. , 21, 1407 (1951); Chem. Abstr. , 46, 7537 (1952).
29. Baniel, A. , French Patent 1, 071, 071; Chem. Zentr. , 127, 5687 (1956).
30. Baniel, A. , and B. H. Vroman, World Petrol. Congr. Proc. 5th, N. Y. , Sect. 4, 1959.
31. Bannard, R. A. B. , and J. H. Ross, Can. J. Technol. , 33, 317 (1955).
32. Barnhurst, J. D. , J. Org. Chem. , 26, 4520 (1961).
33. Bauer, K. H. , J. Prakt. Chem. (4), 6, 75 (1958).
34. Bayer, O. , in Houben-Weyl, Methoden der Organischen Chemie, Vol. VII/1, Thieme Verlag, Stuttgart, 1954.
35. Bell, R. P. , and G. A. Wright, Trans. Faraday Soc. , 57, 1386 (1961).
36. Belous, M. A. , and I. Ya. Postovskii, Zh. Obshch. Khim. , 20, 1701 (1950); Chem. Abstr. , 45, 2391 (1951).
37. Beringer, F. M. , and R. A. Falk, J. Am. Chem. Soc. , 81, 2997 (1959).
38. Bertram, D. , Dechema Monograph. , 42, Nos. 661-676, 197 (1962); Chem. Abstr. , 59, 3728 (1963).
39. Besthorn, E. , and B. Geisselbrecht, Ber. , 53B, 1017 (1920).
40. Bier, G. , Angew. Chem. , 73, 193 (1961).
40a. Bishop, C. A. , R. F. Porter, and L. K. J. Tong, J. Am. Chem. Soc. , 85, 3991 (1963).
41. Black, J. F. , U. S. Patent 2, 974, 094; Chem. Abstr. , 55, 23344 (1961).
42. Black, J. F. , and E. F. Baxter, Jr. , Soap Chem. Specialties, 34, No. 10, 43 (1958).
43. Blaser, B. , H. Haas, and J. H. Helberger, U. S. Patent 2, 793, 229; Chem. Abstr. , 51, 16519 (1957).
44. Blumenfeld, G. , German Patent 1, 075, 596; Chem. Abstr. , 55, 10316 (1961).
45. Bock, L. H. , and J. L. Rainey, U. S. Patent 2, 454, 543; Chem. Abstr. , 43, 1588 (1949).
46. Bock, L. H. , and J. L. Rainey, U. S. Patent 2, 454, 546; Chem. Abstr. , 43, 1588 (1949).
47. Boehme Fettchemie Gmbh, German Patent 1, 146, 870; Chem. Abstr. , 59, 11259 (1963).
48. Boehringer, A. , E. Boehringer, I. Liebrecht, and E. Liebrecht, British Patent 753, 317; Chem. Abstr. , 51, 7441 (1957).
49. Bogdanov, S. V. , J. Gen. Chem. USSR (English Transl.), 9, 1145 (1939); Chem. Abstr. , 33, 8599 (1939).
50. Bogdanov, S. V. , J. Gen. Chem. USSR (English Transl.), 9, 1846 (1939); Chem. Abstr. , 34, 4067 (1940).
51. Bogdanov, S. V. , J. Gen. Chem. USSR (English Transl.), 13, 584 (1943); Chem. Abstr. , 39, 698 (1945).

52. Bogdanov, S. V. , J. Gen. Chem. USSR (English Transl.), 15, 967 (1945); Chem. Abstr. , 40, 6456 (1946).

53. Bogdanov, S. V. , J. Gen. Chem. USSR (English Transl.), 16, 1535 (1946); Chem. Abstr. , 41, 5482 (1947).

54. Bogdanov, S. V. , and M. V. Gorelik, Khim Nauka i Promy. , 3, 279 (1958); Chem. Abstr. , 52, 20089 (1958).

55. Bogdanov, S. V. , and M. V. Gorelik, Zh. Obshch. Khim. , 29, 136 (1959); Chem. Abstr. , 53, 21899 (1959).

56. Bogdanov, S. V. , and V. A. Ivanova, J. Gen. Chem. USSR (English Transl.), 7, 2884 (1937); Chem. Abstr. , 32, 5393 (1938).

57. Bogdanov, S. V. , and V. A. Ivanova, J. Gen. Chem. USSR (English Transl.), 8, 1071 (1938); Chem. Abstr. , 33, 3782 (1939).

58. Bogdanov, S. V. , and N. N. Karandasheva, J. Gen. Chem. USSR (English Transl.), 16, 1613 (1946); Chem. Abstr. , 41, 6230 (1947).

59. Bogdanov, S. V. , and N. N. Karandasheva, Zh. Obshch. Khim. , 26, 3365 (1956); Chem. Abstr. , 51, 9544 (1957).

60. Bogdanov, S. V. , and I. B. Migacheva, J. Gen. Chem. USSR (English Transl.), 20, 124 (1950); Chem. Abstr. , 44, 5857 (1950).

61. Bogdanov, S. V. , and G. I. Pavlovskaya, J. Gen. Chem. USSR (English Transl.), 19, 1374 (1949); Chem. Abstr. , 44, 1083 (1950).

61a. Bogdanov, S. V. , and L. S. Shibryaeva, Zh. Obsch. Khim. , 33, No. 5, 1529 (1963); Chem. Abstr. , 59, 12729 (1963).

62. Borunsky, J. , U. S. Patent 2, 962, 480; Chem. Abstr. , 55, 16008 (1961).

63. Boynton, H. G. , E. W. Lewis, and A. T. Watson, Ind. Eng. Chem. , 51, 267 (1959).

64. Braverman, J. B. S. , J. Sci. Food Agr. , 4, 540 (1953); Chem. Abstr. , 48, 1718 (1954).

65. Braverman, J. B. S. , and J. Kopelman, J. Food Sci. , 26, 249 (1961); Chem. Abstr. , 55, 25303 (1961).

66. Broderick, E. , U. S. Patent 2, 900, 393; Chem. Abstr. , 54, 296 (1960).

67. Bruson, H. A. , U. S. Patent 2, 601, 256; Chem. Abstr. , 46, 10688 (1952).

68. Bucheler, P. , and A. Peter, U. S. Patent 2, 733, 976; Chem. Abstr. , 50, 9752 (1956).

69. Bunton, C. A. , and E. A. Halevi, J. Chem. Soc. , 1952, 4541.

70. Bunton, C. A. , and G. Stedman, J. Chem. Soc. , 1958, 2420.

71. Cahn, F. J. , and B. R. Harris, U. S. Patent 2, 238, 927; Chem. Abstr. , 35, 4877 (1941).

72. Caldwell, C. G. , and O. B. Wurzburg, U. S. Patent 2, 661, 349; Chem. Abstr. , 48, 1720 (1954).

73. California Chemical Company, Oronite Division, Alpha Olefins Technical Bulletin, San Francisco, Cal. , 1963.

74. Carmack, M. , M. B. Moore, and M. E. Balis, J. Am. Chem. Soc. , 72, 844 (1950).

75. Carnes, J. J. , U. S. Patent 2,761,795; Chem. Abstr. , 51, 4018 (1957).

76. Caughlan, C. N. , and H. V. Tartar, J. Am. Chem. Soc. , 63, 1265 (1941).

77. Chimiotechnie union chimique du nord et du Rhone (Soc. anon.), French Patent 978,996; Chem. Abstr. , 47, 6685 (1953).

78. Ciba AG, Swiss Patent 261,367; Chem. Abstr. , 44, 6138 (1950).

79. Cislak, F. E. , U. S. Patent 2,508,904; Chem. Abstr. , 44, 8380 (1950).

80. Clippinger, E. , Ind. Eng. Chem. Prod. Res. Develop. 3, No. 1, 3 (1964).

81. Clippinger, E. , U. S. Patent 3,084,186; Chem. Abstr. , 56, 7138 (1962) (German analogue).

82. Clutterbuck, P. W. , and J. B. Cohen, J. Chem. Soc. , 123, 2507 (1923).

83. Coffman, D. D. , M. S. Raasch, G. W. Rigby, P. L. Barrick, and W. E. Hanford, J. Org. Chem. , 14, 747 (1949).

84. Colgate Palmolive Co. , French Patent 1,270,616.

85. Collin, G. , T. P. Hilditch, P. Marsh, and A. F. McLeod, J. Soc. Chem. Ind. , 52, 272 T (1933).

86. Continental Oil Co. , British Patent 879,900; Chem. Abstr. 56, 14084 (1962).

87. Cooper, G. D. , J. Org. Chem. , 21, 1214 (1956).

88. Coover, H. W. , and J. B. Dickey, U. S. Patent 2,675,371; Chem. Abstr. , 48, 8589 (1954).

89. Cordingly, R. H. , Tappi, 42, 645 (1959).

90. Cote, R. , French Patent M1082; Chem. Abstr. , 58, 3398 (1963).

91. Cowdrey, W. A. , and C. N. Hinshelwood, J. Chem. Soc. , 1946, 1036.

92. Cramer, G. , and K. Schimmelschmidt, German Patent 903,814; Chem. Abstr. , 49, 3243 (1955).

93. Cramer, G. , and K. Schimmelschmidt, German Patent 907,053; Chem. Abstr. , 49, 4009 (1955).

94. Cramer, G. , and K. Schimmelschmidt, German Patent 907,054; Chem. Abstr. , 49, 3243 (1955).

95. Csellak, W. R. , Tappi, 34, 471 (1951); Chem. Abstr. , 46, 4224 (1952).

96. Dainton, F. S. , and K. J. Ivin, Trans. Faraday Soc. , 46, 374 (1950).

97. Dalton, P. D. , U. S. Patent 2,576,501; Chem. Abstr. , 46, 1809 (1952).

98. Daniewski, W. , Roczniki Chem. , 32, 667 (1958); Chem. Abstr. , 53, 3201 (1959).

99. Davidson, A. , U. S. Patent 2,053,424; Chem. Abstr. , 30, 7125 (1936).

100. Davies, W. , and Q. N. Porter, J. Chem. Soc. , 1956, 2609.

101. Dazzi, J. ,   U. S. Patent 2, 718, 495; Chem. Abstr. , 50, 7122 (1956).

102. De La Mater, G. B. ,   U. S. Patent 2, 913, 451; Chem. Abstr. , 54, 3316 (1960).

103. Demars, R. ,   Bull. sci. pharmacol. , 29, 425 (1922); Chem. Abstr. , 17, 261 (1923).

104. Dermer, O. C. , and J. Newcombe, J. Am. Chem. Soc. , 74, 3417 (1952).

105. De Simo, M. , and J. J. O'Connor, U. S. Patent 2, 243, 331; Chem. Abstr. , 35, 5599 (1941).

106. Desnuelle, P. , R. Massoni, and O. Bernoit-Micaelli, Bull. Soc. Chim. France, 1953, 595.

107. Dey, B. B. , and K. K. Row, J. Chem. Soc. , 125, 554 (1924).

108. Diehl, K. , German Patent 721, 991; Chem. Abstr. , 37, 5081 (1943).

109. Distler, H. , Paper presented at the 19th International Congress for Pure and Applied Chemistry in London, July 10-17, 1963.

110. Divine, R. D. , U. S. Patent 2, 879, 214; Chem. Abstr. , 53, 12715 (1959).

111. Doering, W. E. , and R. A. N. Weil, J. Am. Chem. Soc. , 69, 2461 (1947).

112. Dohrn, M. , and P. Diedrich, German Patent 564, 786; Chem. Abstr. , 27, 1010 (1933).

113. Doser, A. , in Houben-Weyl, Methoden der Organischen Chemie, Vol. IX, IV ed. , Thieme Verlag, Stuttgart, 1955.

114. Dow Chemical Co. , German Patent 1, 075, 833; Chem. Abstr. , 55, 17105 (1961).

115. Drake, N. L. , Organic Reactions, Vol. 1, Wiley, New York, 1942, pp. 105-128.

116. Dreyfus, H. , U. S. Patent 2, 321, 069; Chem. Abstr. , 37, 6893 (1943).

117. Dreyfus, H. , U. S. Patent 2, 402, 538; Chem. Abstr. , 40, 5572 (1946).

118. Drozdov, N. S. , and O. M. Cherntsov, Zh. Obshch. Khim. , 21, 1885 (1951); Chem. Abstr. , 47, 2761 (1953).

119. Du Pont de Nemours and Co. , E. I. , British Patent 522, 840; Chem. Abstr. , 36, 1117 (1942).

120. Du Pont de Nemours and Co. , E. I. , British Patent 814, 494; Chem. Abstr. , 54, 345 (1960).

121. Duschinsky, R. , and S. H. Rubin, J. Am. Chem. Soc. , 70, 2546 (1948).

122. Dzhagatspanyan, R. V. , V. I. Zetkin, V. E. Pospelov, and V. S. Fedchenko, Plasticheskie Massy, 1963, No. 2, 16; Chem. Abstr. , 58, 11554 (1963).

123. Dzhagatspanyan, R. V. , V. I. Zetkin, and N. Zykov, USSR Patent 135, 639; Chem. Abstr. , 55, 14987 (1961).

124. Eckoldt, H. , in Houben-Weyl, Methoden der Organischen Chemie, Vol. IX, Thieme Verlag, Stuttgart, 1955.

125. Emulsol Chemical Corp. , "Sulfocolaurate".
126. Epstein, A. K. , and M. Katzman, U. S. Patent 2, 236, 530; Chem. Abstr. , 35, 4521 (1941).
127. Ernst, O. , and O. Nicodemus, U. S. Patent 1, 888, 794; Chem. Abstr. , 27, 1641 (1933).
128. Errede, L. A. , J. Polymer Sci. , 49, 253 (1961).
129. Etat Francais, British Patent 605, 973; Chem. Abstr. , 43, 660 (1949).
130. Evans, R. F. , and H. C. Brown, J. Org. Chem. , 27, 1329 (1962).
130a. Evans, R. F. , H. C. Brown, and H. C. van der Plas, Org. Syn. , 43, 97 (1963).
130b. Evgen'eva, L. G. , A. V. Topchiev, and G. M. Tsiguro, Tr. Mosk. Inst. Neftekhim. i Gaz. Prom. , No. 44, 114 (1963); Chem. Abstr. , 60, 9137 (1964).
131. Exner, O. , and O. Wichterle, Chem. Listy, 50, 922 (1956); Chem. Abstr. , 50, 16660 (1956).
132. Fahrenbach, M. , and K. H. Collins, U. S. Patent 2, 756, 230; Chem. Abstr. , 51, 2886 (1957).
133. Fantl, P. , and I. Fisch, J. Prakt. Chem. , 124, 159 (1930); Chem. Abstr. , 24, 1841 (1930).
134. Farbwerke Hoechst AG, British Patent 753, 872; Chem. Abstr. , 51, 5821 (1957).
135. Farrar, W. V. , J. Chem. Soc. , 1960, 3058.
136. Farrar, W. V. , J. Chem. Soc. , 1960, 3063.
136a. Feichtinger, H. , Ber. , 96, 3068 (1963).
137. Feichtinger, H. , and S. Puschhof, U. S. Patent 2, 815, 371; Chem. Abstr. , 52, 11890 (1958).
138. Fessler, W. A. , U. S. Patent 2, 653, 970; Chem. Abstr. , 48, 7322 (1954).
139. Fierz-David, H. E. , and L. Blangey, Fundamental Processes of Dye Chemistry, Interscience, New York, 1949.
140. Finch, H. D. , J. Org. Chem. , 27, 649 (1962).
141. Finzi, C. , and G. Leandri, Ann. Chim. (Rome), 40, 334 (1950); Chem. Abstr. , 45, 9009 (1951).
142. Fischer, E. , German Patent 917, 428; Chem. Abstr. , 50, 2652 (1956).
143. Fischer, E. , German Patent 918, 444; Chem. Abstr. , 52, 13782 (1958).
144. Fischer, F. G. , L. Roch, and W. P. Neumann, German Patent 927, 631; Chem. Abstr. , 52, 3874 (1958).
145. Fodor, G. , D. Beke, and O. Kovacs, Acta Chim. Acad. Sci. Hung. , 1, 194 (1951); Chem. Abstr. , 46, 3514 (1952).
146. Foulke, D. G. , O. Kardos, and H. Koretzky, U. S. Patent 3, 002, 903-4; Chem. Abstr. , 56, 1296 (1962).
147. Frazier, D. , U. S. Patent 2, 499, 377; Chem. Abstr. , 44, 4700 (1950).
148. Friedlander, W. S. , and G. van D. Tiers, German Patent 1, 098, 942; Chem. Abstr. , 56, 5810 (1962).

149. Fromm, E. , R. Kapeller, and I. Taubman, Ber. , 61B, 1353 (1928).
150. Fuchs, W. , Ber. , 54, 245 (1921).
151. Fuson, R. C. , and C. H. McKeever, Organic Reactions, Vol. I, Wiley, New York, 1942, p. 63.
152. Gabriel, S. , Ber. , 21, 2667 (1888).
153. Gaertner, V. R. , U. S. Patent 3, 082, 249; Chem. Abstr. , 58, 14323 (1963).
154. Gattermann, L. , and W. Berchelmann, Ber. , 31, 1767 (1898).
155. Geiseler, G. , and F. Asinger, Ber. , 89, 1100 (1956).
156. Ghamrawi, M. A. , and F. Said, J. Pharm. Pharmacol. , 1, 757 (1949).
157. Gilbert, E. E. , and P. H. Groggins, in Unit Processes in Organic Synthesis, P. H. Groggins, ed. , 5th ed. , McGraw-Hill, New York, 1958.
158. Gladshtein, B. M. , and L. Z. Soborovskii, Zh. Obshch. Khim, 30, 1574 (1960); Chem. Abstr. , 55, 1496 (1961).
159. Glaxo Laboratories, Canadian Patent 627, 206.
159a. Goethals, E. , Bull. Soc. Chim. Belges, 72, 11 (1963).
160. Goethals, E. , and L. Josson-Merckaert, Bull. Soc. Chim. Belges, 70, 218 (1961).
161. Gold, M. H. , and L. J. Drucker, U. S. Patent 2, 477, 869; Chem. Abstr. , 43, 9076 (1949).
162. Gold, M. H. , L. J. Drucker, R. Yotter, C. J. B. Thor, and G. Lang, J. Org. Chem. , 16, 1495 (1951).
163. Goldblum, K. B. , and R. E. Montonna, J. Org. Chem. , 13, 179 (1948).
164. Gorelik, M. V. , and S. V. Bogdanov, Zh. Obshch. Khim. , 30, 2954 (1960); Chem. Abstr. , 55, 19911 (1961).
165. Gorelik, M. V. , S. V. Bogdanov, and A. N. Rodionov, Zh. Obshch. Khim. , 30, 2959 (1960); Chem. Abstr. , 55, 23451 (1961).
166. Graf, R. , Ann. , 578, 50 (1952).
167. Gregory, H. , W. G. Overend, and L. F. Wiggins, J. Chem. Soc. , 1948, 2199.
168. Gryaznov, G. V. , A. V. Topchiev, and G. M. Tsiguro, Dokl. Akad. Nauk SSSR, 113, 598 (1957); Chem. Abstr. , 51, 14538 (1957).
169. Gubareva, M. A. , J. Gen. Chem. USSR (English Transl.), 17, 2259 (1947); Chem. Abstr. , 42, 4820 (1948).
170. Gubareva, M. A. , J. Gen. Chem. USSR (English Transl.), 18, 238 (1948); Chem. Abstr. , 42, 8595 (1948).
171. Gunthard, J. , and A. Peter, U. S. Patent 2, 734, 060; Chem. Abstr. , 50, 15595 (1956).
172. Halberstadt, E. S. , E. D. Hughes, and C. K. Ingold, J. Chem. Soc. , 1950, 2441.
173. Halfter, G. , Z. Anal. Chem. , 128, 23 (1947).
174. Hanford, W. E. , U. S. Patent 2, 398, 426; Chem. Abstr. , 40, 3628 (1946).
175. Harman, D. , U. S. Patent 2, 504, 411; Chem. Abstr. , 44, 5897 (1950).

176. Harris, B. R., U. S. Patent 2,221,377; Chem. Abstr., 35, 1549 (1941).
177. Harris, B. R., and F. J. Cahn, U. S. Patent 2,251,932; Chem. Abstr., 35, 7585 (1941).
178. Hartmann, M., and M. Seiberth, Helv. Chim. Acta, 15, 1390 (1932).
179. Hass, H. B., and E. F. Riley, Chem. Rev., 32, 373 (1943).
180. Heinrich, E., U. S. Patent 2,245,780; Chem. Abstr., 35, 6119 (1941).
181. Heiwinkel, H., Svensk Papperstid., 47, 265 (1944); Chem. Abstr., 38, 5082 (1944).
182. Helberger, J. H., Angew. Chem., 73, 69 (1961).
183. Helberger, J. H., and H. Benecke, German Patent 899,939; Chem. Zentr., 125, 10343 (1954).
184. Helberger, J. H., and H. Lanterman, Ann., 586, 158 (1954).
185. Helberger, J. H., G. Manecke, and H. M. Fischer, Ann., 562, 23 (1949).
186. Helferich, B., and V. Bollet, Ber., 94, 505 (1961).
187. Helferich, B., and K. G. Kleb, Ann., 635, 91 (1960).
188. Helferich, B., and W. Ost, Z. Physiol. Chem., 331, 114 (1963); Chem. Abstr., 59, 8851 (1963).
189. Henglein, A., and H. Url, Z. Physik. Chem. (Frankfurt), 9, 285 (1956); Chem. Abstr., 51, 2405 (1957).
190. Henkel et Cie. Gmbh, Belgian Patent 619,161; Chem. Abstr., 59, 11259 (1963).
191. Hiatt, G. D., and J. Emerson, U. S. Patent 2,352,261; Chem. Abstr., 38, 5671 (1944).
192. Higuchi, T., and L. C. Schroeter, J. Am. Pharm. Assoc. Sci. Ed., 48, 535 (1959).
193. Higuchi, T., and L. C. Schroeter, J. Am. Chem. Soc., 82, 1904 (1960).
194. Hoelscher, F., German Patent 801,991; Chem. Abstr., 45, 5176 (1951).
195. Hoelscher, F., German Patent 842,048; Chem. Abstr., 47, 5423 (1953).
196. Holland, G. F., and G. D. Laubach, Paper presented at the Division of Medicinal Chemistry, 137th American Chemical Society Meeting, Cleveland, Ohio, April, 1960.
197. Hori, M., J. Agr. Chem. Soc. Japan, 18, 155 (1942); Chem. Abstr., 45, 4202 (1951).
198. Houlton, H. G., and H. V. Tartar, J. Am. Chem. Soc., 60, 545 (1938).
199. Hoyt, L. F., BIOS Misc. Rept. No. 11, 1945.
200. Hoyt, L. F., U. S. Dept. Commerce, OTS Rept., PB3868.
201. I. G. Farbenindustrie A. G., U. S. Dept. Commerce, PB Rept. 25,630; FIAT Microfilm Reel C190; Frames 806-7, 1935.
202. I. G. Farbenindustrie A. G., U. S. Dept Commerce, OTS Rept. PB 55,102; Frames 4207-8 of FIAT Microfilm Reel Patents 151, PB 20,529, 1944.

203. I. G. Farbenindustrie A. G. , U. S. Dept. Commerce, OTS Rept. PBL65,802, 1938.

204. I. G. Farbenindustrie A. G. , U. S. Dept. Commerce, OTS Rept. PB73,911, Frames 4613-4621, 1932.

205. I. G. Farbenindustrie A. G. , British Patent 406,380; Chem. Abstr. , 28, 4746 (1934).

206. I. G. Farbenindustrie A. G. , British Patent 418,291; Chem. Abstr. , 29, 819 (1935).

207. I. G. Farbenindustrie A. G. , French Patent 716,705; Chem. Abstr. , 26, 2288 (1932).

208. I. G. Farbenindustrie A. G. , French Patent 858,185; Chem. Zentr. , 1941, I, 1738.

209. Il'ina, D. E. , B. A. Krentsel, and A. V. Topchiev, Vysokomolekul. Soedin. , 3, 995 (1961); Chem. Abstr. , 56, 2563 (1962).

210. Imperial Chemical Industries Ltd. , British Patent 583,118; Chem. Abstr. , 41, 3481 (1947).

211. Ingles, D. L. , Australian J. Chem. , 12, 97 (1959); Chem. Abstr. , 53, 12190 (1959).

212. Ingles, D. L. , Australian J. Chem. , 14, 302 (1961); Chem. Abstr. , 55, 22640 (1961).

213. Ingles, D. L. , Chem. Ind. (London), 1959, 1217.

214. Inoue, I. , and M. Kojima, J. Pharm. Soc. Japan, 71, 549 (1951); Chem. Abstr. , 46, 925 (1952).

215. Inoue, I. , and M. Kojima, J. Pharm. Soc. Japan, 71, 939 (1951); Chem. Abstr. , 46, 8039 (1952).

216. Janczewski, M. , and J. Susko, Przemysl. Chem. , 31, No. 8, 234 (1952); Chem. Abstr. , 48, 5840 (1954).

217. Jatkar, S. K. K. , and A. J. Dangre, Proc. Sugar Technol. Assoc. India 1954, Pt. 1, 55; Chem. Abstr. , 50, 17493 (1956).

218. Johnston, T. F. , C. L. Kussner, and L. B. Holum, J. Org. Chem., 25, 399 (1960).

219. Kadimah Chemical Corp. , British Patent 750,609; Chem. Abstr. , 51, 2848 (1957).

220. Kanyaev, N. P. , Zh. Fiz. Khim. , 24, 154 (1950); Chem. Abstr. , 44, 7221 (1950).

221. Katzman, M. U. S. Patent 2,236,541; Chem. Abstr. , 35, 4521 (1941).

222. Kennedy, G. T. , U. S. Patent 2,702,273; Chem. Abstr. , 49, 8330 (1955).

223. Kharasch, M. S. , T. H. Chao, and H. C. Brown, J. Am. Chem. Soc. , 62, 2393 (1940).

224. Kharasch, M. S. , A. Fono, and W. Nudenberg, J. Org. Chem. , 16, 113 (1951).

225. Kharasch, M. S. , E. M. May, and F. R. Mayo, J. Org. Chem. , 3, 175 (1938).

226. Kharasch, M. S. , and A. T. Read, J. Am. Chem. Soc. , 61, 3089 (1939).

227. Kharasch, M. S. , and O. Reinmuth, Grignard Reactions of Non-metallic Substances, Prentice-Hall, Englewood Cliffs, N. J. , 1954.

228. Kharasch, M. S. , R. T. E. Schenck, and F. R. Mayo, J. Am. Chem. Soc. , 61, 3092 (1939).

229. King, J. F. , P. de Mayo, E. Morkved, A. B. M. A. Sattar, and A. Stoessl, Can. J. Chem. , 41, 100 (1963).

230. Kirby, J. E. , and J. H. Werntz, U. S. Patent 2, 323, 714; Chem. Abstr. , 37, 119 (1943).

231. Kirsanov, A. V. , and N. A. Kirsanova, Zh. Obshch. Khim. , 29, 1802 (1959); Chem. Abstr. , 54, 8693 (1960).

232. Klamann, D. , and H. Bertsch, Chem. Ber. , 88, 201 (1955).

233. Kleinholz, M. P. , U. S. Patent 2, 499, 997; Chem. Abstr. , 44, 6176 (1950).

234. Kleinschmidt, R. F. , U. S. Patent 2, 693, 489; Chem. Abstr. , 49, 14022 (1955).

235. Kochetkov, N. K. , Zh. Obshch. Khim. , 23, 744 (1953); Chem. Abstr. , 48, 4429 (1954).

236. Kohler, E. P. , Am. Chem. J. , 19, 728 (1897).

237. Kolev, N. , D. Tsanev, N. Benbasat, and K. Budevska, Godishnik Nauchnoizsledovatel. Inst. Him. Promislenost, 1, 37 (1958); Chem. Abstr. , 55, 19873 (1961).

238. Koshar, R. J. , P. W. Trott, and J. D. La Zerte, J. Am. Chem. Soc. , 75, 4595 (1953).

239. Kowalski, J. , and H. Weghofer, Przemysl Chem. , 9, 138 (1953); Chem. Abstr. , 49, 8092 (1955).

240. Kozlov, V. V. , J. Gen. Chem. USSR (English Transl.), 17, 289 (1947); Chem. Abstr. , 42, 550 (1948).

241. Kratzl, K. , H. Daeubner, and U. Siegens, Monatsh. , 77, 146 (1947); Chem. Abstr. , 42, 4971 (1948).

242. Krumrei, W. C. , U. S. Patent 2, 877, 186; Chem. Abstr. , 53, 9702 (1959).

243. Kuentzel, A. , and L. K. Schwoerzer, Leder, 9, 49 (1958).

244. Kuentzel, A. , and L. K. Schwoerzer, Leder, 11, 60 (1960).

245. Kurtz, P. , Ann. , 572, 23 (1951).

246. Laboratorios del Sr. Esteve SA, Spanish Patent 247, 438; Chem. Abstr. , 55, 2522 (1961).

247. Lambert, A. , and J. D. Rose, J. Chem. Soc. , 1949, 46.

248. Lane, E. W. , and W. D. Niederhauser, U. S. Patent 2, 789, 133; Chem. Abstr. , 51, 12515 (1957).

249. Lech-Chemie Gersthofen, German Patent 853, 442; Chem. Abstr. , 49, 12531 (1955).

250. Lehmstedt, K. , and E. Wirth, Ber. , 61B, 2044 (1928).

251. Lelong, A. L. M. , H. V. Tartar, E. C. Lingafelter, J. K. O'Loane, and R. D. Cadle, J. Am. Chem. Soc. , 73, 5411 (1951).

252. Leuchs, H. , G. Schlempp, and A. Dornow, Ber. , 66B, 743 (1933).

253. Leulier, A. , and G. Nouvel, Bull. Soc. Chim. France, 1947, 699.

254. Lichtenberger, J. , and P. Tritsch, Bull. Soc. Chim. France, 1961, 363.

255. Lindgren, B. O. , Acta Chem. Scand. , 1, 779 (1948); Chem. Abstr. , 42, 6110 (1948).

256. Lindgren, B. O. , Acta Chem. Scand. , 4, 1365 (1950); Chem. Abstr. , 45, 6602 (1951).

257. Lockwood, W. H. ,   Chem. Inds. , 62, 760 (1948).

258. Lockwood, W. H. ,   U. S. Patent 2,503,279; Chem. Abstr. , 44, 5896 (1950).

259. Lundquist, R. , Acta Chem. Scand. , 11, 1421 (1957); Chem. Abstr. , 52, 9002 (1958).

260. Lu Valle, J. E. , J. Am. Chem. Soc. , 74, 2970 (1952).

261. Majda-Grabowska, H. , and K. Okon,   Biul. Wojskowej Akad. Tech. , 10, No. 104, 82 (1961); Chem. Abstr. , 57, 11079 (1962).

262. Majda-Grabowska, H. , and K. Okon,   Bull. Acad. Polon. Sci. Ser. Sci. Chim. , 10, 529 (1962); Chem. Abstr. , 59, 495 (1963).

263. Majda-Grabowska, H. , and K. Okon,   Roczniki Chem. , 37, 367 (1963); Chem. Abstr. , 59, 11313 (1963).

264. Manecke, G. ,   Ber. , 85, 160 (1952).

265. Mark, V. ,   U. S. Patent 2,831,013; Chem. Abstr. , 52, 16296 (1958).

265a. Markgraf, J. H. , B. A. Hess, C. W. Nichols, and R. W. King,   J. Org. Chem. , 29, 1499 (1964).

266. Marvel, C. S. , M. D. Helfrick, and J. P. Belsley,   J. Am. Chem. Soc. , 51, 1272 (1929).

267. Marvel, C. S. , and E. D. Weil,   J. Am. Chem. Soc. , 76, 61 (1954).

268. Mastin, T. W. ,   German Patent 1,070,625; Chem. Abstr. , 55, 19222 (1961).

269. Masuda, K. ,   Yakugaku Zasshi, 81, 533 (1961); Chem. Abstr. , 55, 21131 (1961).

270. Mathes, W. , and W. Sauermilch,   Chem. Ber. , 84, 648 (1951).

271. Matsui, M. , M. Miyano, and Y. Terada,   Nippon Nogeikagaku Kaisha, 31, 233 (1957); Chem. Abstr. , 52, 12759 (1958).

272. Mayer, F. , Ber. , 23, 908 (1890).

273. Mayo, F. R. , and C. Walling,   Chem. Rev. , 27, 351 (1940).

274. McClellan, P. P. , and J. C. Bacon,   U. S. Patent 2,345,539; Chem. Abstr. , 38, 4270 (1944).

275. McLean, A. , M. M. Wirth, and W. J. Oldham,   British Patent 695,547; Chem. Abstr. , 48, 8813 (1954).

276. Meerwein, H. ,   German Patent 859,461; Chem. Abstr. , 50, 2668 (1956).

277. Meerwein, H. , G. Dittmar, R. Goellner, K. Hafner, F. Mensch, and O. Steinfort,   Chem. Ber. , 90, 841 (1957).

278. Mehltretter, C. L. , J. W. VanCleve, and P. R. Watson,   U. S. Patent 2,880,236; Chem. Abstr. , 53, 12720 (1959).

279. Meyer, K. , and W. Brune,   Z. Wiss. Phot. Photophysik Photochem. , 47, 129 (1952); Chem. Zentr. , 124, 3343 (1953).

280. Meyer, K. , and H. Ulbricht,   Zeit. Wiss. Phot. Photophysik Photochem. , 45, 222 (1951); Chem. Abstr. , 46, 45 (1952).

281. Meyer, K. , and B. Wolfgang,   Z. Wiss. Phot. Photophysik Photochem. , 46, 135 (1951).

282. Michel, and Buschmann, U. S. Dept. Commerce, OTS Rept. PB30,176, Frames 214-5 of FIAT Microfilm Reel C 26, PB 12, 272, 1932.

283. Middleton, W. J. , V. A. Engelhardt, and B. S. Fisher, J. Am. Chem. Soc. , 80, 2822 (1958).

284. Middleton, W. J. , R. E. Heckert, E. L. Little, and C. G. Krespan, J. Am. Chem. Soc. , 80, 2783 (1958).

285. Milligan, B. , and J. M. Swan, Textile Res. J. , 31, 18 (1961).

286. Minisci, F. , and U. Pallini, Gazz. Chim. Ital, , 89, 2438 (1959); Chem. Abstr. , 55, 6407 (1961).

287. Moore, M. B. , and W. H. Washburn, J. Am. Chem. Soc. , 77, 6384 (1955).

288. Moriuchi, M. , and S. Nakai, Japanese Patent 3486 ('50); Chem. Abstr. , 46, 10194 (1952).

289. Morton, M. , and H. Landfield, J. Am. Chem. Soc. , 74, 3523 (1952).

290. Mothurf, A. , Ber. , 37, 3153 (1904).

291. Motozato, Y. , H. Egawa, and S. Nojiro, J. Chem. Soc. Japan, Ind. Chem. Sect. 59, 109 (1956); Chem. Abstr. , 50, 15002 (1956).

292. Mueller, U. S. Dept. Commerce, PB Rept. 75, 336, Frames 2268-72 of FIAT Microfilm Reel C 61, PB17, 658, 1935.

293. Muth, F. , in Houben-Weyl, Methoden der Organischen Chemie, Vol. IX, IV ed. , Thieme Verlag, Stuttgart, 1955.

294. Nambury, C. N. V. , J. Sci. Research Banaras Hindu Univ. , 7, 254 (1956); Chem. Abstr. , 52, 10930 (1958).

295. National Starch Products Inc. , Technical Service Bulletin T-23, National X-300, Plainfield, N. J. , 1959.

296. Natta, G. , G. Crespi, and M. Bruzzone, Chim. Ind. (Milan), 42, 463 (1960); Chem. Abstr. , 55, 22888 (1961).

297. Nawiasky, P. , and G. E. Sprenger, U. S. Patent 2, 315, 375; Chem. Abstr. , 37, 5518 (1943).

298. Neilands, J. B. , J. Biol. Chem. , 190, 763 (1951).

299. Nilsson, T. , Thesis, Lund University, 1946; Brit. Abstr. A2, 137 (1948).

300. Norris, M. H. , J. Chem. Soc. , 121, 2161 (1922).

301. Norton, F. H. , U. S. Patent 2, 840, 601; Chem. Abstr. , 52, 20060 (1958).

302. Novello, F. C. , U. S. Patent 2, 965, 655; Chem. Abstr. , 55, 16483 (1961).

303. N. V. de Bataafsche Petroleum Maatschappij, British Patent 682, 207; Chem. Abstr. , 47, 11221 (1953).

304. N. V. Philips' Gloeilampenfabrieken, British Patent 829, 142; Chem. Abstr. , 54, 18440 (1960).

304a. Olah, G. A. , and W. S. Tolgyesi, in Friedel-Crafts and Related Reactions, Vol. 2, Pt 2, G. A. Olah, ed. , Interscience, New York, 1964.

305. Oldham, W. J. , and M. M. Wirth, British Patent 685, 621; Chem. Abstr. , 47, 10876 (1953).

306. Oldham, W. J. , and M. M. Wirth, British Patent 728, 433; Chem. Abstr. , 49, 14354 (1955).

307. Oldham, W. J. , and M. M. Wirth, British Patent 728, 504; Chem. Abstr. , 49, 14354 (1955).

308. Orthner, L. , Angew. Chem. , 62A, 302 (1950).

309. Orthner, L. , and W. Langbein, U. S. Patent 2, 316, 538; Chem. Abstr. , 37, 5807 (1943).

310. Orthner, L. , H. Wagner, and H. Gruschke, German Patent 903, 815; Chem. Abstr. , 49, 4010 (1955).

311. Osburn, A. R. , and K. Schofield, J. Chem. Soc. , 1955, 2100.

312. Ott, K. , and H. Schuessler, U. S. Dept. Commerce, OTS Rept. PB73, 911, FIAT Microfilm Reel N87, Frames 4386-90, 1930.

313. Overberger, C. G. , D. E. Baldwin, and H. P. Gregor, J. Am. Chem. Soc. , 72, 4864 (1950).

314. Park, H. F. , U. S. Patent 2, 727, 057; Chem. Abstr. , 50, 10758 (1956).

315. Park, H. F. , U. S. Patent 2, 750, 358; Chem. Abstr. , 51, 1656 (1957).

316. Parker, R. P. , and W. B. Wright, U. S. Patent 2, 690, 443; Chem. Abstr. , 49, 11721 (1955).

317. Parkes, G. D. , and S. J. M. Fisher, J. Chem. Soc. , 1936, 83.

318. Pearl, I. A. , J. Org. Chem. , 9, 424 (1944).

319. von Pechmann, H. , and P. Manck, Ber. , 28, 2374 (1895).

320. Pederson, E. E. , and K. A. Jensen, Acta Chem. Scand. , 2, 651 (1948).

321. Peterson, S. , Ann. , 562, 216 (1949).

322. Petitcolas, P. , and R. Sureau, Bull. Soc. Chim. France, 1950, 466; Chem. Abstr. , 45, 1583 (1951).

323. Petitcolas, P. , and R. Sureau, French Patent 1, 012, 619; Chem. Zentr. , 125, 7520 (1954).

324. Petrenko-Kritschenko, P. , and T. Dolgopoloff, Ann. , 341, 165 (1905).

325. Petrenko-Kritschenko, P. , and E. Kestner, Ann. , 341, 163 (1905).

326. Petrova, R. G. , and R. Kh. Freidlina, Izvest. Akad. Nauk SSR, Otdel. Khim. Nauk, 1958, 290; Chem. Abstr. , 52, 12750 (1958).

327. Petrun'kin, V. E. , Ukr. Khim. Zhr. , 22, 603 (1956); Chem. Abstr. , 51, 5692 (1957).

328. Petrun'kin, V. E. , and N. M. Lysenko, Zh. Obshch. Khim. , 29, 309 (1959); Chem. Abstr. , 53, 21969 (1959).

329. Pohlemann, H. , German Patent 1, 086, 693; Chem. Abstr. , 55, 15346 (1961).

330. Pollitzer, E. L. , U. S. Patent 2, 824, 891; Chem. Abstr. , 52, 14200 (1958).

331. Potapov, V. M. , A. P. Terent'ev, and V. M. Dem'yanovich, Zh. Obshch. Khim. , 30, 1043 (1960); Chem. Abstr. , 55, 371 (1961).

332. Price, C. C. , and S. Oae, Sulfur Bonding, Ronald Press, New York, 1962.

333. Profft, E. , U. S. Patent 2, 231, 594; Chem. Abstr. , 35, 3460 (1941).

334. Quaedvlieg, M. , in Houben-Weyl, Methoden der Organischen Chemie, Vol. IX, IV ed. , Thieme Verlag, Stuttgart, 1955.

335. Reed, C. F. , U. S. Patent 2, 046, 090; Chem. Abstr. , 30, 5593 (1936).

336. Reed, R. M. , and H. V. Tartar, J. Am. Chem. Soc. , 57, 570 (1935).

337. Rees, R. W. , U. S. Patent 2,883,369; Chem. Abstr. , 54, 12621 (1960).
338. Reppe, W. , et al. , Ann. , 596, 1 (1955).
339. Reppe, W. , et al. , Ann. , 601, 81 (1956).
340. Rieche, A. , and H. Seeboth, Ann. , 638, 43 (1960).
341. Rieche, A. , and H. Seeboth, Ann. , 638, 57 (1960).
342. Rieche, A. , and H. Seeboth, Ann. , 638, 66 (1960).
343. Rieche, A. , and H. Seeboth, Ann. , 638, 76 (1960).
344. Rieche, A. , and H. Seeboth, Ann. , 638, 101 (1960).
345. Rigby, W. , J. Chem. Soc. , 1956, 2560.
345a. Robinson, E. A. , Can. J. Chem. , 42, 1494 (1964).
346. Rogers, A. O. , U. S. Patent 2,934,561; Chem. Abstr. , 54, 17284 (1960).
347. Roll, W. D. , and G. E. Cwalina, J. Am. Pharm. Soc. , 46, 578 (1957).
348. Rondestvedt, C. S. , Jr. , J. Am. Chem. Soc. , 76, 1926 (1954).
349. Ross, J. , D. J. Potter, and S. Yolles, U. S. Patent 2,434,746; Chem. Abstr. , 42, 2790 (1948).
350. Ruhrchemie AG, British Patent 738,527; Chem. Abstr. , 50, 8707 (1956).
351. Rumpf, P. , Bull. Soc. Chim. (5), 5, 871 (1938).
352. Rumpf, P. , Bull. Soc. Chim. France, 1955, 945.
353. Rumpf, P. , and J. Sadet, Bull. Soc. Chim. France, 1958, No. 4, 447.
354. Rust, F. F. , A. R. Stiles, and W. E. Vaughan, U. S. Patent 2,519,403; Chem. Abstr. , 45, 2497 (1951).
355. Rutgerswerke, AG, British Patent 919,864; Chem. Abstr. , 59, 8710 (1963).
356. Sandoz, Ltd. , British Patent 751,244; Chem. Zentr. , 128, 3150 (1957).
357. Sandoz, Ltd. , Swiss Patent 318,825; Chem. Abstr. , 52, 1257 (1958).
358. Sargent, H. , U. S. Patent 2,787,639; Chem. Abstr. , 51, 9190 (1957).
359. Saunders, B. C. , J. Chem. Soc. , 1950, 684.
360. Schenck, D. , Pharm. Ztg. , 54, 725 (1909); Chem. Abstr. , 5, 885 (1911).
361. Schenck, R. T. E. , Ph. D. Dissertation, University of Chicago, 1939.
362. Schenck, R. T. E. , and I. Danishevsky, J. Org. Chem. , 16, 1683 (1951).
363. Schenck, R. T. E. , and S. Kaizerman, J. Am. Chem. Soc. , 75, 1636 (1953).
364. Schenkel, J. , Ber. , 43, 2597 (1911).
365. Schick, J. W. , and E. F. Degering, Ind. Eng. Chem. , 39, 906 (1947).
366. Schimmelschmidt, K. , and W. Denk, German Patent 1,041,045; Chem. Abstr. , 54, 24394 (1960).

367. Schmidt, W. ,   U. S. Patent 2, 265, 200;   Chem. Abstr. , $\underline{36}$, 1955 (1942).

368. Schmitz, H. , H. Grosspietsch, H. Kaltenhaeuser, and H. Wendt, Angew. Chem. Intern. Ed. Engl. , $\underline{2}$, No. 4, 216 (1963).

369. Schneider, A. ,   U. S. Atomic Energy Comm. , Document ANL-5863 (1958).

370. Schneider, P. , in Houben-Weyl, Methoden der Organischen Chemie, Vol. XIV/2, Thieme Verlag, Stuttgart, 1963.

371. Schramm, C. H. ,   U. S. Patent 2, 694, 723; Chem. Abstr. , $\underline{49}$, 13289 (1955).

372. Schramm, C. H. , H. Lemaire, and R. H. Karlson,   J. Am. Chem. Soc. , $\underline{77}$, 6231 (1955).

373. Schramm, C. H. , and C. T. Walling,   U. S. Patent 2, 797, 239; Chem. Abstr. , $\underline{51}$, 12956 (1957).

374. Schrauth, W. , and E. Schirm,   U. S. Patent 2, 171, 117; Chem. Abstr. , $\underline{34}$, 197 (1940).

375. Schroeter, L. C. , and T. Higuchi,   J. Pharm. Sci. , $\underline{50}$, 447 (1961).

376. Schroeter, L. C. , and T. Higuchi,   J. Am. Pharm. Assoc. Sci. Ed. , $\underline{49}$, 331 (1960).

377. Schroeter, L. C. , and T. Higuchi,   J. Pharm. Sci. , $\underline{50}$, 447 (1961).

378. Schwalenberg, A. ,   German (East) Patent 13968; Chem. Abstr. , $\underline{53}$, 11231 (1959).

379. Schwartz, A. M. , and J. W. Perry, Surface Active Agents and Detergents, Vol. 1, Interscience, New York, 1949.

380. Schwartz, A. M. , J. W. Perry, and J. Berch, Surface Active Agents and Detergents, Vol. 2, Interscience, New York, 1958.

381. Seidel, P. ,   Ber. , $\underline{83}$, 20 (1950).

382. Seifert, H. ,   German Patent DDRP 892; Chem. Zentr. , $\underline{124}$, 8986 (1953).

383. Seigle, L. W. ,   U. S. Patent 3, 012, 070; Chem. Abstr. , $\underline{56}$, 10051 (1962).

384. Sen, N. P. ,   Can. J. Chem. , $\underline{40}$, 2189 (1962).

385. Sexton, A. R. , and E. C. Britton,   U. S. Patent 2, 810, 747; Chem. Abstr. , $\underline{52}$, 9197 (1958).

386. Sexton, A. R. , and E. C. Britton,   U. S. Patent 2, 820, 818; Chem. Abstr. , $\underline{52}$, 9195 (1958).

387. Seyewetz, A. ,   14me Congr. Chim. Ind. , Paris, Oct. , 1934; Chem. Abstr. , $\underline{29}$, 6585 (1935).

388. Shearing, E. A. , and S. Smiles,   J. Chem. Soc. , 1937, 1348.

389. Sheetz, D. P. ,   U. S. Patent 2, 914, 499; Chem. Abstr. , $\underline{54}$, 20274 (1960).

389a. Shell Internationale Research Maatschapij N. V. , Belgian Patent 632, 843; Chem. Abstr. , $\underline{60}$, 14388 (1964).

390. Sheppard, W. A. , R. F. W. Bader, and A. N. Bourns,   Can. J. Chem. , $\underline{32}$, 345 (1954).

391. Shoddy, A. O. ,   Org. Syn. , $\underline{37}$, 55 (1957).

392. Shriner, R. L. , and A. H. Land,   J. Org. Chem. , $\underline{6}$, 888 (1941).

393.   Simon, A. , R. Paetzold, and H. Kriegsmann,   Ber. , 89, 883
        (1956).
394.   Smith, C. W. , D. G. Norton, and S. A. Ballard,   J. Am. Chem.
        Soc. , 75, 748 (1953).
395.   Smith, G. W. , and H. D. Williams,   J. Org. Chem. , 26, 2207
        (1961).
396.   Smith, L. I. , and J. Nichols,   J. Org. Chem. , 6, 498 (1941).
397.   Smith, R. M. ,   U. S. Patent 2, 899, 461; Chem. Abstr. , 54, 1301
        (1960).
398.   Smith, T. L. , and J. H. Elliott,   J. Am. Chem. Soc. , 75, 3566
        (1953).
399.   Smook, M. A. , E. T. Pieski, and C. F. Hammer,   Ind. Eng. Chem.,
        45, 2731 (1953).
400.   Snow, R. D. , and F. E. Frey,   Ind. Eng. Chem. , 30, 178 (1938).
401.   Snyder, H. R. , and J. C. Speck,   J. Am. Chem. Soc. , 61, 668
        (1939).
402.   Societe anon. de matieres colorantes et produits chimiques
        Francolor,   French Patent 983, 965; Chem. Abstr. , 49, 14354
        (1955).
403.   Sousa, J. A. , and J. D. Margerum,   J. Am. Chem. Soc. , 82, 3013
        (1960).
404.   Sousa, J. A. , and J. D. Margerum,   J. Org. Chem. , 25, 638
        (1960).
405.   Sperling, R. ,   J. Chem. Soc. , 1949, 1925.
406.   Sperling, R. ,   J. Chem. Soc. , 1949, 1939.
407.   Stacey, F. W. , and J. F. Harris, in Organic Reactions, Vol. 13,
        p. 150, Wiley, New York, 1963.
408.   Stelling, O. ,   Cellulosechemie, 9, 100 (1928); Chem. Abstr. ,
        23, 5465 (1929).
409.   Stewart, A. W. ,   J. Chem. Soc. , 87, 185 (1905).
410.   Stewart, J. M. , and H. P. Cordts,   J. Am. Chem. Soc. , 74, 5880
        (1952).
411.   Stewart, T. D. , and L. H. Donnally,   J. Am. Chem. Soc. , 54,
        3559 (1932).
412.   Stogryn, E. L. , and P. A. Argabright,   German Patent 1, 090, 198;
        Chem. Abstr. , 55, 19788 (1961).
413.   Stone, G. C. H. ,   J. Am. Chem. Soc. , 58, 488 (1936).
414.   Suter, C. M. ,   J. Am. Chem. Soc. , 65, 582 (1943).
415.   Suter, C. M. , The Organic Chemistry of Sulfur, Wiley, New
        York, 1944.
416.   Tabachinikova, N. I. , and N. N. Karandasheva,   Zhr. Obshch.
        Khim. , 31, 1916 (1961); Chem. Abstr. , 55, 27224 (1961).
417.   Terent'ev, A. P. , and A. I. Gershenovich,   Zh. Obshch. Khim. ,
        23, 204 (1953); Chem. Abstr. , 48, 2569 (1954).
418.   Terent'ev, A. P. , and A. I. Gershenovich,   Sbornik Statei Obshch.
        Khim. , Akad. Nauk SSSR, 1, 555 (1953); Chem. Abstr. , 49,
        916 (1955).

419.   Terent'ev, A. P. , A. N. Kost, A. M. Yurkevich, and E. E. Khaskina, Zh. Obshch. Khim. , 23, 746 (1953); Chem. Abstr. , 48, 4430 (1954).
420.   Thirtle, J. R. , and F. C. Duennebier,   U. S. Patent 2, 701, 197; Chem. Abstr. , 49, 10777 (1955).
421.   Tiers, G. V. D. ,   U. S. Patent 2, 846, 472; Chem. Abstr. , 53, 12175 (1959).
422.   Tiers, G. V. D. ,   U. S. Patent 3, 050, 555-6; Chem. Abstr. , 58, 6696 (1963).
423.   Tiers, G. V. D. , and R. I. Coon,   J. Org. Chem. , 26, 2097 (1961).
424.   Tiers, G. V. D. , and R. J. Koshar,   U. S. Patent 2, 877, 267; Chem. Abstr. , 53, 14002 (1959).
425.   Tiesler, A. E. ,   U. S. Patent 2, 330, 641; Chem. Abstr. , 38, 1249 (1944).
426.   Tiffeneau, M. , and H. Dorlencourt,   Ann. Chim. et phys. (8), 16, 248 (1909).
427.   Timell, T. ,   Svensk Papperstid. , 51, 254 (1948); Chem. Abstr., 43, 396 (1949).
428.   Tishchenko, D. , and A. Kislitsyn,   Zh. Prikl. Khim. , 34, 1612 (1961); Chem. Abstr. , 55, 27045 (1961).
429.   Topchiev, A. V. , G. V. Gryaznov, and G. M. Tsiguro,   Dokl. Akad. Nauk SSSR, 113, 839 (1957); Chem. Abstr. , 51, 14538 (1957).
430.   Topchiev, A. V. , B. A. Krentsel, and D. E. Il'ina,   Angew. Chem. , 72, 116 (1960).
431.   Topchiev, A. V. , G. M. Tsiguro, and G. V. Gryaznov,   Dokl. Akad. Nauk SSSR, 113, 1302 (1957); Chem. Abstr. , 51, 16111 (1957).
432.   Tousignant, W. F. , and T. Houtman,   U. S. Patent 2, 861, 101; Chem. Abstr. , 53, 3769 (1959).
433.   Truce, W. E. , and C. C. Alfieri,   J. Am. Chem. Soc. , 72, 2740 (1950).
434.   Truce, W. E. , and M. M. Boudakian,   J. Am. Chem. Soc. , 78, 2752 (1956).
435.   Truce, W. E. , D. D. Emrick, and R. E. Miller,   J. Am. Chem. Soc. , 75, 3359 (1953).
436.   Truce, W. E. , and F. D. Hoerger,   J. Am. Chem. Soc. , 76, 5357 (1954).
437.   Truce, W. E. , and J. F. Lyons,   J. Am. Chem. Soc. , 73, 126 (1951).
438.   Truce, W. E. , and P. T. Mori,   J. Org. Chem. , 18, 1755 (1953).
439.   Truce, W. E. , and G. A. Toren,   J. Am. Chem. Soc. , 76, 695 (1954).
440.   Tsunoo, S. ,   Ber. , 68B, 1334 (1935).
441.   Turbak, A. F. ,   Paper presented at the 144th American Chemical Society Meeting, Los Angeles, Cal. , April 4, 1963.
442.   Ufer, H. ,   U. S. Patent 2, 103, 879-80; Chem. Abstr. , 32, 1813 (1938).
443.   Ufer, H. , and A. Freytag,   German Patent 696, 773; Chem. Abstr. , 35, 5909 (1941).

444. Ufimtsev, V. N. , J. Appl. Chem. USSR (English Transl.), 20, 1199 (1947); Chem. Abstr. , 43, 2595 (1949).
445. Ufimtsev, V. N. , Zh. Obshch. Khim. , 22, 723 (1952); Chem. Abstr. , 48, 2676 (1954).
446. United States Rubber Co. , British Patent 652,128.
447. Uota, H. , Japanese Patent 21('51); Chem. Abstr. , 47, 3876 (1953).
448. Vakilwalla, M. V. , and D. M. Trivedi, J. Indian Chem. Soc. , Ind. News Ed. , 13, 150 (1950).
449. Viard, M. J. , U. S. Patent 2,798,877; Chem. Abstr. , 52, 1249 (1958).
450. Vol'f, L. A. , A. I. Meos, and S. A. Inkina, Zhr. Prikl. Khim. , 35, 2047 (1962).
451. Walling, C. , Free Radicals in Solution, Wiley, New York, 1957.
452. Walling, C. , and W. F. Pease, J. Org. Chem. , 23, 478 (1958).
453. Watkins, F. M. , U. S. Patent 2,529,523-4; Chem. Abstr. , 45, 1763 (1951).
454. Watkins, F. M. , U. S. Patent 2,554,434; Chem. Abstr. , 45, 7348 (1951).
455. Wawzonek, S. , in Heterocyclic Compounds, Vol. 2, R. Elderfield, ed. , p. 173, Wiley, New York, 1951.
456. Weghofer, A. , German Patent 831,095; Chem. Abstr. , 49, 15950 (1955).
457. Wenisch, W. J. , Dissertation Abstr. , 18, 808 (1958).
458. Werner, J. , and P. H. Groggins, in Unit Processes in Organic Synthesis, P. H. Groggins, ed. , 5th ed. , McGraw-Hill, New York, 1958.
459. Werntz, J. H. , U. S. Patent 2,318,036; Chem. Abstr. , 37, 6060 (1943).
460. Werntz, J. H. , U. S. Patent 3,005,014; Chem. Abstr. , 56, 4639 (1962).
461. Whyte, D. D. , U. S. Patent 2,989,547; Chem. Abstr. , 55, 25299 (1961).
462. Wicklatz, J. E. , U. S. Patent 2,600,287; Chem. Abstr. , 47, 1726 (1953).
463. Wilcox, L. A. , and E. C. Lingafelter, J. Am. Chem. Soc. , 75, 5761 (1953).
464. Willems, J. , Bull. Soc. Chim. Belges, 64, 409 (1955).
465. Williams, R. R. , R. E. Waterman, J. C. Keresztesy, and E. R. Buchman, J. Am. Chem. Soc. , 57, 536 (1935).
466. Winstein, S. , and R. B. Henderson, in Heterocyclic Compounds, Vol. 1, R. Elderfield, ed. , p. 48, Wiley, New York, 1950.
467. Woolley, D. W. , J. Biol. Chem. , 183, 495 (1950).
468. Wuckel, L. , L. Savchenko, and A. Seidel, Z. Chem. , 2, 371 (1962); Chem. Abstr. , 58, 10379 (1963).
469. Yakubovich, A. Y. , and Y. M. Zinov'ev, J. Gen. Chem. USSR (English Transl.), 17, 2028 (1947); Chem. Abstr. , 43, 1248 (1949).

470. Yale, H. L. , and F. Sowinski,   J. Org. Chem. , $\underline{25}$, 1824 (1960).
471. Yoder, L. , and B. H. Thomas,   Arch. Biochem. Biophys. , $\underline{60}$, 392 (1956).
472. Young, H. A. , and H. Spitzmueller,   U. S. Patent 2, 394, 834; Chem. Abstr. , $\underline{40}$, 2658 (1946).
473. Zuffanti, S. , and R. Hendrickson,   J. Am. Chem. Soc. , $\underline{63}$, 2999 (1941).

CHAPTER 4

SULFONATION BY THE OXIDATION
OF ORGANIC SULFUR COMPOUNDS

I. INTRODUCTION

As with the procedures discussed in Chapter 3, the techniques described in this chapter are most useful for the preparation of aliphatic
and cycloaliphatic sulfonates, since the aromatic and heterocyclic
compounds, except for those of abnormal orientation, can usually be
made by direct sulfonation. If a sulfonic acid salt is required, and
one is starting from a halide, an alcohol, or an alkene, an oxidative
procedure may seem inefficient, since two steps are required compared to methods employing sulfites, which may involve only one.
However, if the sulfonyl halide or the sulfonic acid is desired, as is
often the case, an oxidative method can be the most direct approach.

Since its recognition in 1936 as a generally useful method, the
aqueous halogenation technique has seen steady application and has
undergone a number of improvements and modifications. Its use with
heterocyclic sulfur compounds in the presence of fluoride ion for the
preparation of the stable sulfonyl fluorides shows promise of helping to
overcome the problems associated with the instability of the chlorides
and the free acids, numerous examples of which are cited in this chapter.

The sulfinic acids (RSO_2H), and their salts, have proved of increasing interest as intermediates in sulfonate preparation, and it appears that this trend may continue. They are of theoretical importance, as being probable reaction intermediates in several methods involving the oxidation of sulfur compounds in a lower valence state.
From a practical viewpoint, they appear fairly easy to prepare by several approaches, and they are easily converted to either a sulfonyl
halide or a sulfonic acid. The sulfonyl halides, including the iodides,
can thus be prepared without using an oxygen donor, which is usually
required for sulfur compounds in a lower valence state.

The halogenation procedure, and the other relatively new oxidative
approaches involving the use of hydrogen peroxide, ozone, or nitrogen
tetroxide should see increasing future use, since the tetroxide is now
commercially available, and ozonization has become a standard laboratory operation.

Oxidative sulfonation methods are, with few exceptions, limited to
laboratory, rather than commercial, use, for the reason that preparation of the sulfur compound to be oxidized is the major problem, rather
than the oxidation step proper. However, this method can be extremely practical when the sulfur compound is available, as exemplified by the preparation of methane- and ethanesulfonic acids from the

201

thiols, which are available as by-products from petroleum cracking.

II. SULFONYL HALIDES BY HALOGENATION IN THE PRESENCE OF AN OXYGEN DONOR

A. Aliphatic and Cycloaliphatic Compounds

Although the aqueous halogenation of thiol derivatives to the sulfonyl halides had been observed in individual instances many years earlier, it was in 1936-38 that Johnson and co-workers (57,117) established the generality of this approach with varied types of sulfur compounds:

$$RSR' \xrightarrow[H_2O]{Cl_2} RSO_2Cl + 4\ HCl + R'Cl \qquad (4\text{-}1)$$

This method has become, with the possible exception of the Strecker synthesis cited in Chapter 3, the most widely applied laboratory procedure for preparing aliphatic sulfonates, not only because of its generality, simplicity, and convenience, but because it yields the sulfonyl chloride directly. The halide is often needed in any case for subsequent preparation of functional derivatives, rather than the sulfonic acid or its salt, which cannot be used without an additional chemical step. The method is also applicable to the preparation of the sulfonyl bromides, fluorides and iodides. If the sulfonic acid is desired, the sulfonyl chloride can be hydrolyzed to it by simply heating the aqueous reaction mixture after completing the chlorination step (90).

Under different conditions, acid or alkaline hypohalites form the sulfonic acids or their salts. This type of reaction is discussed separately in Section IV.

The main types of aliphatic and cycloaliphatic sulfur compounds which have been converted to the sulfonyl chlorides or bromides by aqueous halogenation are listed in Tables 4-1 through 4-8. From Table 4-1 it is evident that isothiouronium salts - the first group of compounds studied by Johnson and Sprague (117) - are still employed, although their use has been somewhat discredited by the serious explosions which have occurred when overchlorination led to the formation of nitrogen trichloride (73). The salts are easily converted to the corresponding thiols, however; and these are smoothly and safely chlorinated to the sulfonyl chlorides (241), as shown by the examples cited in Table 4-3.

$$RSC(:NH)NH_2 \cdot HCl + NaOH \longrightarrow RSH + NaCl + NH_2CONH_2 \quad (4\text{-}2)$$

The isothiouronium salts are prepared by simply heating an alkyl halide, sulfonate, or sulfate with thiourea:

$$RBr + NH_2C(:S)NH_2 \longrightarrow RSC(:NH)NH_2 \cdot HBr \qquad (4\text{-}3)$$

Alcohols are converted to these salts in one step by heating with aqueous HBr and thiourea:

$$ROH + HBr + NH_2C(:S)NH_2 \longrightarrow RSC(:NH)NH_2 \cdot HBr \qquad (4\text{-}4)$$

It thus appears that alkyl halides and alcohols are conveniently converted to sulfonates via the isothiouronium salts, although these salts should not be chlorinated directly, but via the derived thiols.

Kwart (134a) has shown that benzyl isothiouronium salts can cleave in different directions, depending upon chemical structure. The yields of sulfonyl chlorides from the benzyl isothiouronium chlorides are 91, 40, and 0%, respectively, with nitro, hydrogen, or methyl groups as para substituents. It thus appears that sulfonyl chloride formation from this type of compound is favored by the electron-withdrawing nitro moiety, and inhibited by the electron-releasing methyl group, which respectively tend to destabilize and to stabilize the corresponding benzyl carbonium ions. Sulfides can also cleave in two directions, as indicated later in this section.

Thiosulfates (Bunte Salts) are also suitable intermediates for converting alkyl halides to sulfonyl halides (241), as shown in Table 4-2. The thiosulfates are easily prepared (149) by refluxing equimolar amounts of an alkyl halide and sodium thiosulfate in 50% aqueous ethanol for 1 or 2 hr.:

$$RX + NaSSO_3Na \longrightarrow RSSO_3Na + NaX \qquad (4\text{-}5)$$

The thiosulfate approach is not quite as general as the isothiouronium method, since some alkyl chlorides, for example 1-chloropentane, which do not form thiosulfates, do yield isothiouronium salts (241). Primary alkyl bromides, however, form the thiosulfates easily. Secondary bromides in some cases undergo hydrohalide elimination to olefins rather than forming the desired thiosulfates.

Unsymmetrical sulfides (RSR') can form different sulfonyl halides, depending upon the direction of cleavage of the carbon-sulfur bond (cf., Table 4-6). Kwart (134a) has made a detailed study of the direction and mechanism of cleavage of several types of sulfides. In the series C_6H_5SR, where R is tert-butyl, isopropyl, ethyl, or methyl, only the first two compounds undergo cleavage (forming $C_6H_5SO_2Cl$), since only they are capable of yielding stable carbonium ions. Similarly, 4-nitrobenzyl benzyl sulfide forms only 4-nitrobenzylsulfonyl chloride, and 2,4-dinitrophenyl benzyl sulfide yields only 2,4-dinitrobenzenesulfonyl chloride. These reactions are concluded to be of a nonclassical S_N1 type. On the other hand, 4-benzylthio-7-chloroquinoline forms 78% benzylsulfonyl chloride under alkaline conditions, but the yield progressively approaches 0 as the acidity of the reaction medium is increased. 4-Phenylthio-7-chloroquinoline likewise forms benzenesulfonyl chloride by chlorination in aqueous acetic acid, but undergoes no cleavage in a medium of higher acidity. This "abnormal" type of cleavage is concluded to have S_Ni character.   4-Benzylthiopyridine oxide gives only sulfate ion upon aqueous chlorination, and therefore reacts only "normally." As indicated before, benzyl isothiouronium salts can cleave either normally or abnormally, but this depends upon chemical structure as determining the stability of the carbonium ion involved.

Bordwell and Hewett added a new dimension to the chlorination procedure for preparing sulfonyl chlorides by calling attention to the neglected possibilities of using thioacetates.   It had been shown earlier (46) that thioacetic acid easily undergoes anti-Markownikoff, free-radical addition to varied types of alkenes, including cycloalkenes, dienes, and even polyenes such as natural rubber:

$$RCH{=}CH_2 + CH_3COSH \longrightarrow RCH_2CH_2SCOCH_3 \qquad (4\text{-}6)$$

It had also been demonstrated previously (57) (cf. , Table 4-7) that such primary thioacetates form the sulfonyl chlorides by aqueous chlorination.   Bordwell and Hewett extended the thioacetic addition procedure to fourteen additional olefins, including aliphatic (e. g. , 2-methyl-1-butene), alicyclic (camphene), and halogenated (2-chloro-2-butene) types (31), and broadened the scope of the chlorination step to include secondary thioacetates (32).   Others have shown that thioacetic acid adds to C5-18 terminal olefins, undecylenic acid, and methyl oleate (193), but these thioacetates were not chlorinated.   Acrylic and crotonic acids react similarly, various functional derivatives of the thioesters were prepared via the original carboxyl group, and the products were then chlorinated to the sulfonyl chlorides (47).   Thiobenzoic acid also undergoes addition to alkenes (47), and the resulting thiobenzoates can be converted to the sulfonyl chlorides (47, 57); but no reason is evident for preferring these esters to the thioacetates.   Thioacetates have also been made from halides, but this method for converting halides to sulfonyl chlorides has no obvious advantage over the isothiouronium salt approach.   As indicated in Section VI, the thioacetates are also useful for preparing sulfonic acids by peroxide oxidation, but, as shown in Section VIII, they have not been converted to the sulfonic acids by ozonization.

Aliphatic sulfoxides also undergo aqueous chlorination to the sulfonyl chlorides (26a, 135) (cf. , Table 4-8), but the corresponding sulfones are inert to chlorine.

Methanesulfonyl iodide was prepared by treating the sodium sulfinate with iodine in aqueous KI (68a).   Alkanesulfonyl iodides were previously unknown.

Some limitations of the chlorination procedure for making sulfonyl chlorides have become apparent.   Tertiary alkyl and gem. -disulfonyl chlorides cannot be thus prepared, since total cleavage to sulfate ion occurs (67, 201).   Partial cleavage was noted in the chlorination of the isopropyl, isobutyl, sec-butyl, and cyclohexyl isothiouronium salts (202).   Total conversion to sulfate ion was observed with several compounds of structure RCH_2OCH_2SR' (202), doubtless because of easy chlorination of the $-OCH_2-$ moiety. 2-Furylmethyl (202) and 2-thienylmethyl (241) thiol derivatives did not yield the desired sulfonyl chlorides, which is explainable by the high sensitivity of such heterocyclic rings to acid conditions. 4-Methoxybenzyl disulfide did not form the sulfonyl chloride (241), although benzyl and 4-chlorobenzyl disulfides behaved normally, as noted in Table 4-4. 1-Naphthylmethylsulfonyl chloride was formed in very low yield (201). The sulfonic acid, rather than the desired sulfonyl chloride, resulted from chlorination of the thiouronium salt from chloroacetic acid (73).

On the other hand, the chlorination procedure is applicable to various compounds containing amino, olefinic, and activated methylene groups, several of which are listed in Tables 4-1, 4-4, 4-5, and 4-7. Such compounds might rather have been expected to undergo undesired chlorination.

The chlorination technique usually involves (241) the use of aqueous acetic acid as the reaction solvent. In cases where both the starting material and the product are solids, such a system is preferable to the use of water alone, since solubility of the product in the solvent insures smoother chlorination and indicates the completion of reaction (150). Even glacial acetic acid can function as the oxygen donor (56a). The reaction can also be run heterogeneously with water alone as the suspending medium, provided agitation is efficient (57). This procedure is especially satisfactory when both the starting material and product are liquids, as in the chlorination of various thiocyanates (see Table 4-5). The rate of reaction in heterogeneous systems is strongly dependent upon the degree of agitation (150); at high rates the chlorination can often be completed in fifteen minutes. The writer and others (81, 110, 217) have found concentrated hydrochloric acid a suitable reaction medium. Its use greatly reduces the cooling requirements, since the substantial quantity of hydrogen chloride formed is evolved as a gas rather than dissolving exothermically in the water, and the product sulfonyl halide, being insoluble, is easily separated from the reaction mixture. The sulfonyl chloride group is often susceptible to easy hydrolysis, which has suggested the use of a hydrophobic reaction solvent such as carbon tetrachloride (188), use of the theoretical quantity of water (217), employing methanol instead of water as the oxygen donor (188), and conducting the reaction at a low temperature (i. e., 0-$20°C$). Stoichiometric hydrochloric acid with potassium chlorate was applied where it was desired to avoid the presence of excess gaseous chlorine (47, 49, 75). The technique has been used with thioacetates, n-butylisothiouronium bromide, dibenzyldisulfide, and with aromatic and heterocyclic thiols and disulfides.

The following sequence has been suggested by Douglass (56) as corresponding to the course of the reaction for disulfides:

$$\text{RSSR} \xrightarrow{\text{Cl}_2} \text{RSCl} \xrightarrow{\text{Cl}_2} \text{RSCl}_3 \xrightarrow{\text{H}_2\text{O}} \text{RSOCl} \xrightarrow{\text{H}_2\text{O}} \text{RSO}_2\text{H} \xrightarrow{\text{Cl}_2} \text{RSO}_2\text{Cl}$$

$$\quad\quad\quad\ \ \text{I}\quad\quad\quad\quad\quad\quad\quad\quad\text{III}\quad\quad\quad\quad\text{II}\quad\quad\quad\quad\quad(4\text{-}7)$$

Partial chlorination of disulfides had been shown by others (20, 57, 135) to form thiosulfonate esters, RSO_2SR, or mixtures of them with the desired sulfonyl chlorides. This observation led to the proposal that the following reactions may also occur concurrently (56, 135):

$$I + II \longrightarrow RSO_2SR \xrightarrow{Cl_2} RSO_2Cl + I \qquad (4\text{-}8)$$

Sulfoxides presumably are converted via compounds of type III (26a). A somewhat similar reaction scheme has been proposed for hypohalite oxidation to the sulfonic acid, as discussed in Section IV.

TABLE 4-1

Alkanesulfonyl Chlorides from Isothiouronium Salts
$(RSC(:NH \cdot HX)NH_2)$

Identity of R	Reference
Methane, ethane, 2-propane, 2-methyl-1-propane, 1- and 2-butane, 1-hexane, 1-heptane, 1- and 2-octane, 1-dodecane, 1-hexadecane	117, 123, 127a, 201
Cyclopentane, cyclohexane, cyclohexylmethane	14, 201
Phenylmethane, 4-nitrophenylmethane, 2-phenylethane	117, 127a, 134a, 201, 202
C2-10 polymethylene	86, 117, 127a, 136
C4-5 ω-phthalimidoalkyl	86
C4-6 ω-cyanoalkyl	58
2-Acetoxyethane	202
2-Chloro-2-carbomethoxyethane	26
2-Chloroethane	127a
2,2'-Oxydiethyl (from bis(2-chloroethyl) ether)	114, 202
Tetrahydrofurfuryl	202
Long-chain alkyl (from chlorinated paraffin wax)	137
Long-chain alkyl (from poly(vinyl chloride), chlorinated polyethylene)	196
ω-(2-Piperidyl)ethane, -propane, -butane	232

TABLE 4-2

Alkanesulfonyl Chlorides from Thiosulfates
(Bunte Salts)(RSSO$_3$Na)

Identity of R	Reference
Methane (to the bromide)	57, 80
Ethane, 1-propane	57, 200, 241
1-Butane, 2-methyl-1-propane	241
1-Pentane	200, 241
2-Methyl-1-butane, 3-methyl-1-butane	241
1-Hexane, 1-heptane, 2-ethyl-1-butane	241
2-Cyclohexylethane	241
2-Ethoxy-1-ethane	241
Phenylmethane	55, 57, 241
3- and 4-Nitrophenylmethane	241
2- and 4-Chloro-, 2,4-, and 3,4-Dichloro-phenylmethane	200, 241
2-Phenylethane	241
2-(4-Nitrophenyl)ethane	241

TABLE 4-3

Alkanesulfonyl Chlorides from Thiols (RSH)

Identity of R	Reference
Ethane	57
1-Butane	106
1-, 2-, 3-Pentanes	57, 241
2-Methyl-, 2-ethyl-1-butanes; 4-methyl-2-pentane	241
1-, 2-Hexanes; 2-, 4-heptanes; 1-, 2-octanes	241
Cyclopentane, cyclohexane, cyclohexylmethane	147, 241
2-Cyclohexylethane	241
2-Ethoxy-1-ethane	241
Phenylmethane	57
1, 5-Diphenyl-2-pentane	219
1, 1, 5-Trihydrooctafluoro-1-pentane	90
2-Aminoethane(hydrochloride)	159a

TABLE 4-4

Alkanesulfonyl Chlorides from Disulfides $[(RS-)_2]$

Identity of R	Reference
Methane, ethane	135, 217
1-Butane, 1-pentane	57, 135
Cyclopentane, cyclohexane	198, 222
Phenylmethane, 4-chlorophenylmethane	106, 135
3-Phenyl-1-propane, 4-phenyl-1-butane, 5-phenyl-1-pentane	221
Dodecane, C8-22	94, 106
Vinyl	165
1-Chloro-2-propane	210
2-Chloroethane, 2,2,2-trichloroethane	110
2,2,2-Trifluoroethane	222a
3-Carboxybutane	181
4-Aminobutane, 6-aminohexane	52, 160
(Hydantoyl)methane, 2-(hydantoyl)ethane	150
N,N'-Diacetylcystine dimethyl ester	96
N,N'-Dicarbobenzoxycystine dibenzyl ester	185
Polymeric 1,2-ethylenedisulfide	206
Polymeric 1,6-hexamethylenedisulfide	188

TABLE 4-5

Alkanesulfonyl Chlorides from Thiocyanates (RSCN)

Identity of R	Reference
Methane, ethane	115
2-Propane, 2-methyl-1-propane, 1-butane, 1-octane, 2-octane	8, 79, 95, 215
Phenylmethane	115, 131
2-Phenylethane	215
C3 - 10 dithiocyanates	10a, 79, 136
2-Chloroethane, 3-chloro-2-methyl-1-propane	12, 132
C2 - 6 ω-Fluoroalkyl	166, 186
2-(N, N-Dimethylcarbamato)ethane	82

TABLE 4-6

Alkanesulfonyl Chlorides from Cyclic and
Open-Chain Monosulfides

Sulfide used	Sulfonyl chloride formed	Reference
Dimethyl	Methane-	26a, 45a
Bis(2-chloroethyl)	2-Chloroethane-	81, 110
C_2H_5SR' (R' = pyrimidine moiety)	Ethane	118
Di(n-butyl)	1-Butane-	135
Propylene	1-Chloro-2-propane-	210
Trimethylene	3-Chloro-1-propane-	209
Tetramethylene	4-Chloro-1-butane-	231
Phenylethylene	2-Chloro-2-phenylethane-	208
Dibenzyl	Phenylmethane-	135
4-Nitrobenzyl benzyl	4-Nitrophenylmethane-	134a

TABLE 4-7

Alkanesulfonyl Chlorides from Thioacetates($RSCOCH_3$)

Identity of R	Reference
Ethane	57
4-Methyl-1-pentane; 2-methyl-3-pentane	32
2-Phenyl-1-propane	32
Cyclohexane	32
3-Chloropropane	27a
5,7-Dichloro-1-heptane	218
Phenylmethane	57
4-Phthalimido-3-oxo-1-butane; 5-phthalimido-4-oxo-2-pentane	47
2-Norbornane	49
2-Phenylethane	102

TABLE 4-8

Alkanesulfonyl Chlorides from Miscellaneous
Sulfur Compounds

Compounds used	Sulfonyl chloride formed	Reference
Thioformals (ethyl, n-amyl, benzyl)	Ethane-; 1-pentane-; phenylmethane-	135
Thioaldehydes (C1-4)	$ClCH(R)SO_2Cl$	63, 116 119, 135
Sulfoxides (ethyl, butyl)	Ethane-; 1-butane-	135
Xanthates (ethyl, benzyl)	Ethane-; phenylmethane-	57
Trichloro- and trifluoro-methanesulfenyl chlorides	Trichloro- and trifluoro-methane-	93, 216
$(CH_2)_x(SC(:NH)OC_2H_5)_2$ (x = C3, 4)	$(CH_2)_x(SO_2Cl)_2$	136
$C_6H_5CONHC(:S)SC_2H_5)$	Ethane-	57

B. Aromatic Compounds

The oxygen-donor chlorination technique, so extensively employed in the aliphatic series, has been used comparatively little for aromatic compounds, largely because many of the desired sulfonyl halides are easily accessible by direct chlorosulfonation. In addition, it appears that in some cases, notably with phenyl thiocyanate (115) and with 2, 4-dinitrophenyl isothiouronium chloride (202), the reaction proceeds sluggishly to give a low yield of impure product using the normal conditions for obtaining good results with aliphatic compounds. However, thiophenol (57), pentachlorothiophenol (58a), 4-nitrothiophenol (226), 4-thiocresol, dithiohydroquinone, and its dimethyl ether tetraiodide (242), all form the sulfonyl chlorides or bromides smoothly and in fair yields.

Several aromatic disulfides have been thus converted to the sulfonyl chlorides. These include 4-nitrophenyl- (235), 2-(trifluoromethyl) phenyl- (236), 2-carboalkoxyphenyl- (192), several 4-substituted 2-nitrophenyl- (37, 126, 157), 4-acetylaminophenyl- (151), and 2-nitro-5-acylaminophenyl- (91) disulfides. 2-Nitrophenyldisulfide itself has been converted to the sulfonyl chloride on an industrial scale intermediate to the preparation of 2-aminobenzene-sulfonic acid (2). 3-Chloro- and 4-acetylaminophenylthioacetates likewise form the sulfonyl chlorides (151).

As indicated in the preceding section, some aryl alkyl monosulfides undergo cleavage to the arylsulfonyl chlorides.

2, 4-Dinitrophenyl thiobenzoate was chlorinated at first in concentrated H_2SO_4, with aqueous acetic being added later (139). 4-Acetylaminophenyl thiocyanate undergoes ring bromination or chlorination rather than conversion to the sulfonyl halide (151). However, if the thiocyanate is refluxed for 8 hr. with aqueous acetic acid before chlorination, ring halogenation does not occur and sulfonyl halide formation proceeds normally. This difference is explained by conversion of the —SCN moiety to —SCONH2 or to —SS—, both of which were shown in independent experiments to yield the sulfonyl halides.

The preceding compounds were made by the usual method with gaseous chlorine. 4-Nitrophenyldisulfide is advantageously converted to the sulfonyl chloride with a mixture of nitric and hydrochloric acids in the presence of an inert organic solvent (233, 234), while compounds of structure $RSC(C_6H_5)_3$, where R is phenyl, 2-, 3-, or 4-tolyl, yield the sulfonyl bromides by bromide-bromate titration (84). Thiophenol and phenyldisulfide (75) give the sulfonyl chloride using hydrochloric acid with chlorate (75).

Aromatic sulfinic acids are easily prepared from the amines by the Gattermann Reaction. 2-Methoxyphenyl-, 3-chlorophenyl-, and 3-bromophenylsulfinic acids have been converted to the sulfonyl chlorides by aqueous chlorination (111). An interesting variation is conversion of ammonium-2-toluene-sulfinate to the sulfonamide (146):

$$RSO_2NH_4 \xrightarrow{Cl_2} RSO_2NH_2 + HCl \tag{4-9}$$

It will be noted that most of the preceding sulfonyl chlorides have orientations different from those which would result from direct chlorosulfonation.

C. Heterocyclic Compounds

The Johnson and Sprague procedure for preparing aliphatic and aromatic sulfonyl chlorides by aqueous chlorination of thiol derivatives was later extended to heterocyclic thiols by Roblin and Clapp (184). They established the method as generally applicable by using it with four imidazoles, two tetrazoles, six thiazoles, three pyridines, one pyrazine, three thiadiazoles, and four triazoles, but observed that free amino groups or partially saturated ring systems led to undesired side reactions. Thiazoline rings are especially sensitive to ring cleavage, as shown in Section IV. They also noted that thiouracils and thiotriazines give the chlorides in preference to any sulfonyl chloride, and that many of the sulfonyl chlorides decomposed rapidly on standing with the loss of sulfur dioxide, a problem overcome by immediate conversion to the stable sulfonamides. In several cases [(e. g. , with benzothiazole-2-(I), 4, 6-dimethylpyrimidine-2-(II), 1-methyltetrazole-5-(184), and benzimidazole-2-sulfonyl chlorides(128)], decomposition of the sulfonyl chlorides cleanly formed the corresponding chlorides.

(I)　　　　　(II)　　　　　(III)　　　　　(IV)

The method was extended by others to 4-mercaptopyridine oxide (6), and to several mercaptonitroimidazoles (71). With 4-pyridinethiol, the chlorination was effected in nitric acid, or a mixture of nitric and hydrochloric acids was used (7). The addition of $FeCl_3$ or $SnCl_2$ was found to facilitate chlorination of mercaptothiazoles, -imidazoles, -pyridines, and -pyrimidines (161). A mixture of hydrochloric acid and chlorate was employed with 2-acetamido-5-mercapto-1, 3, 4-thiadiazole (75) (III). The benzylthioethers of thiadiazoles, thiazoles, and triazoles similarly gave the sulfonyl chlorides (240). This chlorination, like that of the thiols, was catalyzed by adding $FeCl_3$ or $SnCl_2$ (162). An acylthiothiadiazole likewise formed the sulfonyl chloride (42). It will be seen that except for more pronounced product instability, the same general factors apply as in the preparation of the aliphatic analogues. Acetic, or concentrated hydrochloric, acid is preferred for solubility reasons over water as a chlorination solvent with heterocyclic compounds.

An important advance was made by Beaman and Robins (24) who observed that, although purine thiols as a class are desulfurized to form the chlorides rather than the desired sulfonyl chlorides, chlorination in the presence of a mixture of aqueous hydrofluoric acid, potassium fluoride, and methanol gives the sulfonyl fluorides, which are stable and are equally useful for conversion to amides, esters, and other functional derivatives. The stage (or stages) at which fluorine becomes attached to sulfur is not known; the following reactions seem possible:

$$RSCl + HF \longrightarrow RSF + HCl \qquad (4\text{-}10)$$

$$RSOCl + HF \longrightarrow RSOF + HCl \qquad (4\text{-}11)$$

$$RSO_2Cl + HF \longrightarrow RSO_2F + HCl \qquad (4\text{-}12)$$

This method gives excellent yields of sulfonyl fluorides from 6-, and 2-purinethiols, and from 6-amino- and 6-hydroxypurinethiols. Purine-2,6-dithiol (IV) could be converted to either 6-chloropurine-2-sulfonyl fluoride, or (by adding more potassium fluoride to the reaction mixture) to the 2,6-di(sulfonyl fluoride). Application of this concept to hitherto unsuccessful nonheterocyclic chlorinations (e. g. , the attempted preparation of tert-butanesulfonyl chloride) would be of interest.

One example was noted (22) of the conversion of a heterocyclic sulfinate salt (a pyrazolophenanthridine derivative) to the sulfonyl chloride. Surprisingly, the reaction was conducted under aqueous alkaline conditions using 10% sodium hypochlorite, rather than gaseous chlorine in an acidic medium.

III.   SULFONYL HALIDES BY ANHYDROUS HALOGENATION OF SULFINATE SALTS OR ESTERS

As noted in the preceding section, the chlorination of sulfinic acids to form sulfonyl chlorides is thought to constitute the final step in preparation of the latter from thiol derivatives. This reaction has also been exploited in its own right, employing Grignard Reagents for preparation of the sulfinates:

$$RMgBr + SO_2 \longrightarrow RSO_2MgBr \xrightarrow{\;Cl_2\;} RSO_2Cl + MgBrCl \qquad (4\text{-}13)$$

Since no oxygen donor is required, the chlorination is effected under anhydrous conditions, using either chlorine gas or sulfuryl chloride. On the basis of results from two cases (phenylmethane- and 2,3-dimethylbutanesulfonyl chlorides), the procedure is judged rapid and simple, and to give good yields of exceptionally pure products (191). It is, therefore, considered superior to the older method comprising treatment of the Grignard Reagent with sulfuryl chloride discussed in Chapter 3. The procedure has been extended to preparation of ethanesulfonyl bromide (80). Since the Grignard approach for making sulfinate salts has been established as fairly widely applicable and as giving fair yields (124), this new procedure for preparing sulfonyl halides should be capable of considerable extension. When considered as a method for converting alkyl halides to sulfonates, this technique may be preferable to the isothiouronium salt (or the thiosulfate) procedures, only in cases where the maintenance of anhydrous conditions is essential.

2-Ethylhexylsulfonyl iodide was prepared in good yield by adding the sodium sulfinate to iodine dissolved in benzene-ether (68a). This compound, a representative of the previously unknown species of alkanesulfonyl iodides, could not be prepared in aqueous medium, even though such was suitable for preparing methanesulfonyl iodide.

Methyl methanesulfinate is easily converted to methanesulfonyl chloride or bromide by treatment with the corresponding halogen (57a); preparation of the sulfonyl iodide was not attempted. Alkane- and arenesulfinate esters are easily accessible (57a) from the corresponding thiols or disulfides. Preparation of the sulfonyl halide via the sulfinate ester might be of interest in cases where direct halogenation of the thiol or disulfide is not feasible.

IV. OXIDATION WITH HYPOHALITES

Chlorine and bromine hypohalites have occasionally been employed as oxidizing agents for preparing sulfonic acids and sulfonate salts. Bromine water has been used with the methyl- and ethylsulfinate salts made by the Grignard reaction (28), for ethanethiol and disulfide (238, 239), and for polymethylene dixanthates (211). Sodium hypobromite in alkaline solution has been employed with sodium 2-mercaptopalmitate (229) and 2-[di(carboxymethyl)amino]ethylthiosulfate (99). 3,5-Disubstituted thiohydantoin-2-sulfonic acids are formed from the disulfides (108). 2,6,8-Purinetrithiol forms 6-chloro-8-hydroxypurine-2-sulfonic acid with chlorine and anhydrous methanol (183), but 2,3,6-trichloropurine results when concentrated hydrochloric acid is present during reaction. 8-Hydroxy-2,6-purinedithiol forms the disulfonic acid. N-Methyl-γ-thiolutidone forms the sulfonic acid with chlorine water (148):

$$(4-14)$$

Two cases were noted where, somewhat surprisingly, aqueous alkaline hypohalites formed sulfonyl chlorides rather than sulfonate salts.
Trichloromethanesulfenyl chloride gave the sulfonyl chloride with calcium hypochlorite (216), suitably employing a hydrophobic reaction
solvent (chloroform) to inhibit hydrolysis. A heterocyclic sodium sulfinate formed the sulfonyl chloride in 70% yield using 10% aqueous
sodium hypochlorite (22).

Hypohalites also form sulfonates with carbon-sulfur bond cleavage.
This was observed with n-heptyl sulfoxide and chlorine water (203),
and with methyl, ethyl, n-amyl, and methylene thiocyanates using
bleaching powder solution (159). Ring cleavage of thiazolines to taurines seems a general reaction, since several of them which are car-
bon-substituted with alkyl, aryl, amino, and sulfur-containing groups
react thus with aqueous chlorine or bromine (13, 30, 76, 77, 78):

$$
\begin{array}{c}
CH_2-S \\
| \quad\quad >CH \xrightarrow{\text{HOCl}} H_2NCH_2CH_2SO_3H \\
CH_2-N
\end{array}
\qquad (4\text{-}15)
$$

On the other hand, 2-mercapto-4-methoxybenzothiazone, which contains a similar moiety, forms the sulfonate without bond cleavage
using 15% sodium hypochlorite (60). An interesting bond cleavage
occurs with benzo-1,4-dithiadiene with potassium hypochlorite at 90° C
(164):

$$
\begin{array}{c}
S \\
\text{CH} \\
\| \quad \xrightarrow{\text{KOCl}} \quad
\begin{array}{c} SO_3K \\ SO_3K \end{array} \\
\text{CH} \\
S
\end{array}
\qquad (4\text{-}16)
$$

The 2-acetyl analogue reacts similarly; yields are 70-80%.

The behavior pattern of the hypohalites thus appears generally similar to that observed in preparing sulfonyl chlorides by chlorination,
and, in fact, a kinetic and mechanistic study of the oxidation of ethyl
disulfide to the sulfonic acid with bromine water (238, 239) led to the
suggestion that the sulfonyl bromide might be an intermediate. The
initial, rate-determining step was thought to be cleavage of the disulfide by bromine or hypobromite. This concept appears in general
agreement with that mentioned before for the formation of sulfonyl
chlorides, although the specific intermediates suggested, namely
$RSBr_2$ and RSO, are different, and are, in fact, of unknown types.

V. OXIDATION WITH NITRIC ACID OR OXIDES OF NITROGEN

A. Aliphatic and Cycloaliphatic Compounds

Nitric acid was in the past a favored reagent for converting thiols to sulfonic acids, as evidenced by the many references to its use cited by Suter (213) and by Reid (180). The overall reaction involved is

$$2RSH + 4\ HNO_3 \longrightarrow 2RSO_3H + 4NO + 2H_2O \qquad (4\text{-}17)$$

Reid regards this approach as "an excellent method when the required mercaptans are available," but warns that it is necessary to avoid an excess of either reagent, or the reaction may become violent. Interest in this procedure has diminished in recent years in favor of other methods, especially chlorination to the sulfonyl chloride and oxidation with hydrogen peroxide. Recent examples are cited in Table 4-9. One

TABLE 4-9

Sulfonic Acids Via Nitric Acid Oxidation of
Aliphatic Thiols and Disulfides

Thiol or disulfide oxidized	Reference
Fifteen C5-11 straight- and branched-chain thiols	225
C9-14 thiols (as Pb salts)	156
1-Butanethiol; C5-8 thiols	5, 224, 227
8-Pentadecanethiol; 3, 9-diethyl-6-tridecanethiol	62
2-Dodecanethiol; 1-hexadecanethiol	51, 155
1-Dodecanethiol; 8-pentadecanethiol	3
RSH (R from petroleum)	175
2-(2-) and 2-(4-Pyridinium)ethanethiol chloride	23
Di-(8-pentadecyl)- and -(9-heptadecyl) disulfides	62
Diisoamyl disulfide	107

investigator, however, who prepared a series of straight- and branched-chain sulfonic acids by nitric acid oxidation, preferred this procedure to the chlorination approach for reasons unstated (225).

An interesting variation in the usual procedure is the use of commercially available nitrogen tetroxide, N_2O_4, which obviates the formation of water. It has been used with 1-dodecanethiol and 5-ethylnonane-2-thiol (25):

$$2RSH + 3N_2O_4 \longrightarrow 2RSO_3H + 6NO \qquad (4\text{-}18)$$

Proell and co-workers have carried this concept to its logical conclusion by taking advantage of the fact that nitric oxide is re-oxidized to N_2O_4 by oxygen:

$$2NO + O_2 \longrightarrow N_2O_4 \qquad (4\text{-}19)$$

They, and others, oxidized the C 1-3 thiols from petroleum using air in the presence of a small quantity of nitrogen oxides (112, 113, 167, 169, 170, 173, 174):

$$2RSH + 3O_2 \xrightarrow{\ N_2O_4\ } 2RSO_3H \qquad (4\text{-}20)$$

A disulfide similarly gives the sulfonic acid anhydride (168):

$$2(RS\text{-})_2 + 5O_2 \xrightarrow{\ N_2O_4\ } 2(RSO_2)_2O \qquad (4\text{-}21)$$

Methyl- and ethyl disulfides yielded 80% of the anhydrides in the laboratory (170); these compounds can also be made with ozone, as discussed subsequently. Sulfenyl chlorides form the sulfonyl chlorides (1, 171, 172):

$$RSCl + O_2 \xrightarrow{\ N_2O_4\ } RSO_2Cl \qquad (4\text{-}22)$$

Sulfenyl chlorides can also be converted to the sulfonyl chlorides with nitric acid (35). This approach to the sulfonyl chlorides is basically cheaper than aqueous chlorination, since air is employed as the oxidizing agent instead of chlorine, but it is less convenient for laboratory use.

Nitric acid also yields sulfonic acids with cleavage of a sulfur-carbon bond. Ethylene sulfide is stated to react as follows (50):

$$\overline{SCH_2CH_2} + HNO_3 \longrightarrow HO_3SCH_2COOH +$$

$$HO_3SCH_2CH_2SCH_2COOH \qquad (4\text{-}23)$$

The identity of the second compound seems doubtful, since the sulfide sulfur should undergo oxidation under these conditions. Bis(2-chloroethyl)sulfide forms 2-chloroethanesulfonic acid (74). Oxidation of compounds of structure $RSCH_2CH_2OH$ (R = C8-18) is said to yield purer products than are formed by direct oxidation of the parent thiols (69):

$$RSCH_2CH_2OH + 6\ HNO_3 \longrightarrow RSO_3H + 6\ NO_2 + 2\ CO_2 \quad (4\text{-}24)$$

A similar claim is made for oxidation of the formals $(RS)_2CH_2$ (70). A dithiolane ring cleaves as follows (230):

$$\overline{SCH(C_4H_9)CH_2SC{:}S} \xrightarrow{\ HNO_3\ } C_4H_9CH(SO_3H)CH_2SO_3H \quad (4\text{-}25)$$

Methyl-, ethyl-, and n-butylthiocyanates give 90, 80, and 70% yields of the sulfonic acids (107) using nitric acid; n-heptylthiocyanate reacts in unstated yield (29). 1, 2-Di(thiocyano)cyclohexane (199) and 1, 2-di(thiocyano)ethane (151a) form the disulfonic acids.

B. Aromatic Compounds

Several aromatic xanthates, made from the diazonium compounds, have been oxidized to the sulfonic acids with nitric acid:

$$RSC({:}S)OC_2H_5 \xrightarrow{\ HNO_3\ } RSO_3H \qquad (4\text{-}26)$$

Compounds so prepared include 2-methyl-4-nitrobenzene-(228). 2, 3-, 2, 5-, and 3, 4-dinitrobenzene-(126), pentachlorobenzenesulfonic (64), and 1, 2-benzenedisulfonic (144) acids. 1, 4-Benzenedisulfonic acid was similarly made by diazotizing sulfanilamide, converting to the thiocyanate or disulfide, and finally oxidizing with nitric acid (4, 127). These sulfonates could probably have been prepared more directly by reacting the diazonium compound with sulfur dioxide in the presence of copper chloride by the Meerwein procedure discussed in Chapter 3, since the oxidation step would thus have been obviated.

Nitric acid was also used for oxidizing 4-nitrobenzenethiol (126), 2-nitro-4-(trifluoromethyl)-(126) and 4-nitro-2-(trifluoromethyl)-phenyl-disulfides (39), and 4-tolyl trityl sulfide (85).

It will be noted that all of the preceding sulfonates have an orientation not attainable by direct sulfonation.

C. Heterocyclic Compounds

Mercapto derivatives of thiazole, thiazoline, thiazine, and quinazoline were smoothly oxidized to the sulfonic acids in good yield with nitrogen tetroxide in chloroform at $0°C$ (145, 207) in less than 1 hr. This appears an excellent laboratory procedure for making the acids, but aqueous chlorination is probably preferable if the sulfonyl chlorides are desired. Nitric acid was used for converting pyridine oxide 4-thiol, 2, 6-ditert-butylpyridine-4-thiol (223), pyridine-2, 6-dithiol-4-carboxylic acid (27), and 6, 6'-dinitro-di-(5-indazyl)disulfide (212) to the sulfonic acids.

VI. OXIDATION WITH HYDROGEN PEROXIDE OR PERACIDS

A. Aliphatic and Cycloaliphatic Compounds

Hydrogen peroxide in glacial acetic or formic acid has seen increasing use as a convenient laboratory procedure for converting varied aliphatic sulfur compounds to the sulfonic acids.

Showell, in a useful discussion of the chemistry of such oxidations (193), shows that at 60°C, 1-hexadecanethiol gives essentially only the disulfide when using hydrogen peroxide alone; at 90°C, the sulfonic acid is formed. However, the sulfonic acid is obtained at 60°C, with equimolar hydrogen peroxide and acetic acid from either the thiol or the disulfide. It is concluded that peracetic acid is the more active oxidizing agent, and that its formation from hydrogen peroxide and acetic acid is catalyzed by a small quantity of the product sulfonic acid. (Use of commercial peracetic acid may be undesirable, since it can contain sulfuric acid which leads to product discoloration.) The reaction is strongly exothermic and requires carefully controlled addition of 90% hydrogen peroxide. It is added at 60°C, with the result that it is rapidly consumed and does not accumulate for subsequent uncontrolled reaction.

Mono- and dithiols oxidized by this procedure are listed in Table 4-10. It is interesting that tert-butanethiol forms the sulfonic acid smoothly with hydrogen peroxide, but that total cleavage to sulfate ion

TABLE 4-10

Aliphatic Sulfonic Acids by Oxidation of Thiols
with Hydrogen Peroxide or Peracids

Thiol oxidized	Reference
Tert-Butane-	8
1,1-Dimethyl-1-propane-	16
2-Hydroxy-3-chloro-1-propane-	194
1-Hexadecane-	193
Pentamethylenedi-	120
2,2'-Di(mercaptoethyl)ether	15
4,4'-Di(mercaptobutyl)ether	133
2-Acetamidoethane-	68
2-Aminoethane-; 2-(diethylamino)ethane-	176
3-Hydroxy-1-propane-	154
ω-Aminoethyl-β-thiopropionic acid lactam	129
Thiolactic acid	189
Benzyl-	40

occurs on attempted chlorination of the thiol to the sulfonyl chloride (8), as noted in Section II-A.

Thioacetates, as pointed out in Section II-A, are easily prepared by reacting various types of alkenes or alkyl halides with thioacetic acid. They are easily converted to the sulfonic acids with hydrogen peroxide, either with or without acetic acid:

$$\text{RSCOCH}_3 \xrightarrow{\text{H}_2\text{O}_2} \text{RSO}_3\text{H} + \text{CH}_3\text{COOH} \qquad (4\text{-}27)$$

Examples are cited in Table 4-11. Although this method for converting alkenes or halides to sulfonic acids is not new, the first systematic study of the procedure was made recently by Showell (193). Its simplicity, taken with the increasing availability of a wide variety of olefinic compounds, suggests that this method will see considerably extended future use.

TABLE 4-11

Aliphatic Sulfonic Acids by Oxidation of Thioacetates
with Hydrogen Peroxide or Peracids

Thioacetate oxidized	Reference
4-Hydroxy-1-pentane-, 4-hydroxy-2-butane-	154
2-Methyl-3-bromo-1-propane-	154
3-Oxo-4-phthalimido-1-butane, 4-oxo-5-phthalimido-2-pentane-	48
Benzyl-	40
10-Carboxy-1-decane-	130, 193, 214
17-Carboxy-8(or 9)-heptadecane-	193, 214
Cyclopentane-, cyclohexane-	193
C5-18 terminal alkyl	193

The reaction was concluded to proceed by the following path (193):

$$\text{RSCOCH}_3 \xrightarrow{\text{O}} \overset{\text{O}}{\text{RSCOCH}_3} \xrightarrow{\text{H}_2\text{O}} \overset{\text{O}}{\text{RSH}} \xrightarrow{\text{O}} \text{RSO}_2\text{OH} \qquad (4\text{-}28)$$

Other routes, involving formation of an acyl sulfone before hydrolysis, or hydrolysis to the thiol before oxidation occurs, are considered possible, but less likely. Experimental attempts to detect intermediate oxidation stages were unsuccessful. Earlier consideration of the per-acetate oxidation of benzyl thioacetate (40) also led to the conclusion that formation of the acyl sulfoxide or sulfone is an intermediate step, but disproportionation to the thiosulfonate ester, rather than hydrolytic cleavage, was envisaged as the next stage.

Other types of sulfur compounds form sulfonic acids with hydrogen peroxide or with peracids. Propylene sulfide undergoes ring cleavage to 2-hydroxy-1-propanesulfonic acid (210). DL-Lipoic acid, a cyclic disulfide, forms the corresponding disulfonic acid (153). Aliphatic disulfides, on the other hand, can stop at intermediate stages (195):

$$(RS-)_2 \xrightarrow{\text{CH}_3\text{COO}_2\text{H}} R\overset{\text{O}}{\underset{\uparrow}{S}}SR \xrightarrow{\text{CH}_3\text{COO}_2\text{H}} R\overset{\text{O}}{\underset{\underset{\text{O}}{\downarrow}}{\overset{\uparrow}{S}}}SR \qquad (4\text{-}29)$$

2-Methyl-4-amino-5-pyrimidylmethyldisulfide forms the sulfonic acid (187), as do polymers and copolymers of ethylenethiocyanate (109). Polymers and copolymers of methoxymethylethylenesulfide undergo cleavage to the polymeric sulfonic acids (109), as follows:

$$(\text{CH}_3\text{OCH}_2 \mid S\overset{|}{C}HCH_2-)_x \xrightarrow{\text{H}_2\text{O}_2} (\text{HO}_3S\overset{|}{C}HCH_2-)_x \qquad (4\text{-}30)$$

As noted in Section II-A, cleavage similarly occurred upon attempted aqueous chlorination of such ethers to the sulfonyl chlorides. Sulfenyl chlorides form the sulfonyl chlorides:

$$\text{RSCl} \xrightarrow{\text{H}_2\text{O}_2} \text{RSO}_2\text{Cl} \qquad (4\text{-}31)$$

This type of oxidation has been conducted with hydrogen peroxide in ether (36). Trichloromethanesulfenyl chloride is oxidized by adding 30% hydrogen peroxide to the compound in boiling glacial acetic acid (197). Several aromatic thiosemicarbazones form the sulfonic acids (100, 101):

$$\text{RCH:NNHC(:S)NH}_2 \xrightarrow{\text{H}_2\text{O}_2} \text{RCH:NN:C(SO}_3\text{H)NH}_2 \qquad (4\text{-}32)$$

Trifluoromethanesulfonic acid, a very strong acid of high stability and low boiling point, can be made by oxidizing the mercury compound $(\text{F}_3\text{CS})_2\text{Hg}$ with hydrogen peroxide (92). It could not be prepared by nitric acid oxidation of the disulfide, or by the Strecker reaction. The corresponding difluoro analogue was made by the Strecker reaction, however, as noted in Chapter 3.

B. Aromatic Compounds

Peroxide oxidation, as applied to the preparation of aromatic sulfonic acids has, in most cases, involved oxidation of the sulfinic acids with hydrogen peroxide:

$$RSO_2H \xrightarrow{\text{H}_2\text{O}_2} RSO_3H + H_2O \qquad (4\text{-}33)$$

There are several methods for making the sulfinic acids, including treating diazonium compounds with sulfur dioxide. 1,7-Naphthionic acid was thus converted to the 1-sulfonic-7-sulfinic acid, which was then oxidized to the 1,7-disulfonic acid (138). This approach to the disulfonic acid was concluded to be the best available, and was operated commercially on a pilot plant scale. The sulfinate of fluorobenzene, made from fluorobenzene and sulfur dioxide in the presence of aluminum chloride, was similarly oxidized (88), as was also 2-(α-naphthyl)-benzenesulfinic acid (33).   Truce and Lyons (220), in preparing the three toluene- and dodecylbenzenesulfonic acids by this method, found that lithiation of the bromo- or chloro compounds, followed by treatment of the lithium aryls with sulfur dioxide, was superior to the Grignard method for making the sulfinates.   They also noted that in some cases oxidation with sodium permanganate was better than using hydrogen peroxide, since the latter gave excessive foaming.

Other aromatic sulfur compounds converted to the sulfonic acids by peroxide oxidation include tetra-(4-thiocresyl) orthocarbonate (17) and cholesteryl isothiouronium chloride (237). The second oxidation, run with performic acid (hydrogen peroxide in formic acid), is stated to comprise the first cleancut synthesis of a sterolsulfonic acid. Bis(2-aminophenyl)disulfide, and several of its ring-substituted derivatives, were oxidized with hydrogen peroxide in 75% H_2SO_4 (89).   These acids are hard to prepare by other methods; one approach is cited in Section II-B.

C. Heterocyclic Compounds

Heterocyclic sulfonic acids have been prepared in relatively few cases by peroxide oxidation. 4-Pyridinethiol was oxidized with peracetic acid (45), or by hydrogen peroxide in the presence of aqueous barium hydroxide (61). 2,4-Dimethyl-6-pyrimidinesulfonic acid was made by treating the disulfide with performic acid for 3 hr. at room temperature (83).   The disulfide was likewise employed for preparing several 3,5-disubstituted thiohydantoin-2-sulfonic acids (108). 2-Pyridyldisulfide was converted to the sulfonic acid in 25% yield with hydrogen peroxide in dilute hydrochloric acid (67a). 2-Mercapto-4-methylthiazole (158) formed the sulfonic acid in alkaline solution, but in neutral solution gave only sulfate ion and 4-methylthiazole. 2-Mercaptobenzimidazole, on the other hand, formed the sulfonate in either acid or alkaline medium (128).

VII. OXIDATION WITH PERMANGANATES

A. Aliphatic and Cycloaliphatic Compounds

Long-chain alkanethiols (C16,18) and their disulfides can be smoothly converted to the sulfonates with dry powdered potassium permanganate in acetone (44), although aftertreatment with concentrated hydrochloric acid is required to remove inorganic salts. Chromic oxide in acetic acid also gave good results. Others (72, 182) found aqueous permanganate best, since use of acetone gave little sulfonate and much acetone mercaptal, and acetic acid yielded mostly disulfide and potassium sulfonate contaminated with manganese. Two thiol analogues of oxybiotin were oxidized with barium permanganate in aqueous acetone at $0°C$ (97, 98). Aqueous 15% potassium permanganate was employed for a long-chain thiol derived from petroleum (175). Dipotassium 1,1-ethanedisulfonate resulted from the permanganate oxidation of thialdine (87).

Several cycloparaffinic sulfinates made by the Grignard reaction have been oxidized with potassium permanganate, including those derived from cyclopentane, cyclohexane, 3-methylcyclohexane (34, 43), and 3,3-dimethylcyclohexylmethane (53).

B. Aromatic Compounds

A standard procedure for preparing aromatic disulfonic acids has comprised diazotizing the aminosulfonic acids and converting them to the disulfides with sodium disulfide, followed by permanganate oxidation to the desired disulfonates. This approach has been employed with 2-amino (122), 4-amino (177), and 3-methyl-4-aminobenzenesulfonic (205) acids, with 1-aminobenzene-2,4- and 2,5-disulfonic acids (141), and with 1-aminonaphthalene-7- (204) and -8- sulfonic acids (121). The Meerwein procedure, discussed in Chapter 3, comprises a more direct method of converting diazonium compounds to sulfonates.

Benzothiophene forms 2-sulfobenzoic acid with aqueous permanganate (59):

$$(4-34)$$

6-Nitrobenzothiophene sulfone behaves similarly (41).

C. Heterocyclic Compounds

Permanganate oxidation has been seldom used for preparing heterocyclic sulfonates. 4-Mercapto-3,5-dichloropyridine (54), 10-thiaxanthenone-2-thiol (134)(I), 2-mercaptobenzothiazole, and its 6-ethoxy- and 6-benzoyl-amino derivatives (190) have been thus converted to the sulfonates. The last three compounds easily lost sulfur dioxide on standing in acid medium, therein resembling the corresponding sulfonyl chlorides cited earlier.

(I)

VIII.   OXIDATION WITH OZONE OR OXYGEN

Ozonization has become established as a convenient, direct and rapid laboratory procedure for oxidizing thiols to sulfonic acids and disulfides to sulfonic anhydrides. As shown in Table 4-12, yields can be excellent, although varying amounts of thiosulfonates are generally formed as by-products, and in one case (dibenzyl disulfide), thiosulfonate was the only product. Its use should increase, since ozonization has become a standard laboratory technique, and information is available on its generation and handling (18). The oxidation is effected by bubbling a stream of ozonized oxygen through a solution of the sulfur compound in chloroform, carbon tetrachloride, ethyl chloride, or a mixture of nitromethane and carbon tetrachloride (19,21). Thiols can be reacted at room temperature, but a temperature of -25 to 60°C is preferred for disulfides (19).

Although this approach appears promising, it has already become evident that there may be limitations. Reaction conditions and stoichiometry may be fairly critical, since widely differing results have been obtained by different investigators with the same compounds. Such discrepancies were noted with n-butyl- and benzyl disulfides, and with thiophenol. Attack of the ring may occur during ozonization of aromatic sulfur compounds. Such has been noted with thiophenol, and in the ozonization of aromatic sulfides and sulfoxides (140). Some types of sulfur compounds appear resistant to oxidation by ozone. These include thiosulfonates (RSO_2SR), disulfones (RSO_2SO_2R), and thioacetates ($RSCOCH_3$) (19). This constitutes a limitation of the ozonization procedure compared to the aqueous chlorination and the peroxide

TABLE 4-12

Sulfonic Acids and Anhydrides by Ozonization of Sulfur Compounds

Compound ozonized	Product and per cent yield	Reference
Thiols		
Ethanethiol	RSO_3H(mostly);R_2S_2 and RSO_2SR(small)	142
Long-chain primary and secondary alkyl	RSO_3H (high)	10,11
1,12-Octadecanedithiol	Disulfonic acid (90)	9
Thiophenol	RSO_3H(100;0);R_2S_2, RSO_2SR, $(RSO_2)_2$	19,142
Disulfides		
Methyl	$(RSO_2)_2O$(39); RSO_2SR(50)	19
n-Butyl	$(RSO_2)_2O$(80); RSO_2SR(10); no product	19,104
Benzyl	RSO_2SR(82); complete degradation	104,142
Phenyl	$(RSO_2)_2O$(90); RSO_2SR(6;23)	19,104
4-Chlorophenyl	$(RSO_2)_2O$(84); RSO_2SR(10)	19
Tetrasulfides		
Diisopropyl	$(RSO_2)_2O$(83)	19
Di(4-chlorophenyl)	$(RSO_2)_2O$(75)	19
Thiosulfinates		
$C_6H_5S(:O)SC_6H_5$	$(RSO_2)_2O$(85)	19
$RS(:O)SR$(R=2,4-dinitrophenyl)	$(RSO_2)_2O$(100)	19

approaches, since these methods are known to convert the first and third types of compounds to the sulfonates and they are probably operative with the second. On the other hand, ozone converted 1,3-bis (ethanesulfonyl)-2-butene to ethanesulfonic acid (178). Carbon-sulfur bond cleavage of this type would not be expected with the other reagents under normal conditions. Apparently, the oxidation of sulfinic acids with ozone has not been attempted. If practicable, this reaction could be useful, since both aliphatic and aromatic sulfinates are easily accessible by various methods. Ozonization has not been applied in the preparation of heterocyclic sulfonates.

Barnard (18, 21) has considered the course and mechanism of the ozonization of disulfides to sulfonic anhydrides. The rate-determining step is the initial electrophilic attack of the disulfide by ozone. This is followed by heterolysis of the disulfide, rearrangement to the sulfenic-sulfonic anhydride, and the oxidation to the final sulfonic anhydride, as follows:

$$\text{(4-35)}$$

Thus, all of the first molecule of ozone reacts, but only one-third of each of the other two molecules appears in the final product. Thiosulfonates were found to be resistant to further attack by ozone, and cannot, therefore, be reaction intermediates in the disulfide oxidation; the mechanism of their formation has not been explained. It may be pertinent that sulfinic acid disproportionation, also thought to involve a sulfenic-sulfonic anhydride intermediate via Equations 4-38 and 4-39, forms the thiosulfonate as one product.

The direct use of pure oxygen for the oxidation of sulfur compounds to sulfonic acids has been almost completely neglected, except in the case of the autoxidation of sulfinates discussed in Section X. [Oxygen has been employed for the oxidation of thiols or disulfides in the presence of NO as oxygen carrier (Section V-A), but N_2O_4 is the effective reagent in these cases.] Benzyl mercaptan (or disulfide) is converted to the sulfonate with oxygen in the presence of potassium hydroxide (227a), although potassium tert-butoxide or sodium methoxide gives only benzoic acid. This different behavior of potassium hydroxide is thought to result from the decreased basicity and increased sulfur nucleophilicity of the hydroxide ion. The mercaptide ion is first formed and is then converted to sulfenate (RSO^-) ion. The latter is then either oxidized directly to sulfonate, or disproportionates to sulfonate and disulfide; the disulfide then repeats the cycle.

IX. ELECTROLYTIC OXIDATION

Electrolytic oxidation has been little studied. Aliphatic thiocyanates (methyl-, ethyl-, and methylenedi-), in an electrolyte comprising a mixture of acetic and hydrochloric acids, gave the sulfonic acids (65, 66), as did acetone ethylmercaptal. Phenyl- and 2-nitrophenylthiocyanates, on the other hand, formed only tars. Diphenyldisulfide and phenylethylsulfide both yielded benzenesulfonic acid. C1-4 aliphatic disulfides also form the sulfonic acids by electrolytic oxidation (38); the electrolyte in this case was the product, sulfonic acid, diluted with water.

Electrolytic oxidation appears to have no particular advantages, either for laboratory or commercial use.

X. DISPROPORTIONATION AND AUTOXIDATION OF SULFINATES

Sulfinates are inherently unstable compounds which can easily disproportionate to the sulfonates and other compounds:

$$5RSO_2H \longrightarrow 3RSO_3H + RSSR + H_2O \qquad (4\text{-}36)$$

$$3RSO_2H \longrightarrow RSO_3H + RSO_2SR + H_2O \qquad (4\text{-}37)$$

These reactions proceed easily under various conditions, as has been reviewed by Muth for aromatic sulfinates (152). Sodium 4-toluenesulfinate behaves similarly by route (4-37). Aliphatic sulfinates also disproportionate (143).

Kinetic and mechanistic studies of the disproportionation of 1-dodecane- and 4-toluenesulfinic acids (179) in solution indicate that the reaction is ionic, rather than free radical. Others (125) have concluded that the following sequence occurs:

$$2ArSO_2H \rightleftharpoons Ar\overset{O}{\underset{O}{S}}-SAr + H_2O \qquad (4\text{-}38)$$

$$Ar\overset{O}{\underset{O}{S}}-SAr \xrightarrow[\text{detg.}]{\text{Rate}} (Ar\overset{O}{\underset{O}{S}}-O-SAr) \xrightarrow{ArSO_2H}$$

$$ArSO_2SAr + ArSO_3H \qquad (4\text{-}39)$$

It had been previously thought that the sulfinic acid reacted directly with the product of reaction (4-38), rather than with its derived sulfenic-anhydride, as shown in Equation 4-39. A similar anhydride is thought to be involved in the ozonization of disulfides (Eq. 4-35).

The sulfinates also easily autoxidize to the sulfonates. An interesting kinetic and mechanistic study, employing 40 different solvents with benzenesulfinic acid, shows that this reaction is of the chain type, with initiation and termination being bimolecular (103):

$$C_6H_5SO_2^{\cdot} + O_2 \longrightarrow C_6H_5SO_2OO\cdot \qquad (4\text{-}40)$$
$$\text{(I)} \qquad\qquad\qquad \text{(II)}$$

$$\text{II} + C_6H_5SO_2H \longrightarrow C_6H_5SO_2OOH + I \qquad (4\text{-}41)$$
$$\text{(III)}$$

$$\text{III} + C_6H_5SO_2H \longrightarrow 2\ C_6H_5SO_3H \qquad (4\text{-}42)$$

$$2\ \text{III} \longrightarrow C_6H_5SO_3\cdot + \text{II} + H_2O \qquad (4\text{-}43)$$

It is noteworthy that the key intermediate here is the persulfonic acid (III). Similar intermediates occur in the sulfoxidation of alkanes, as noted in Chapter 3.

These reactions occur so easily that the sulfonate is sometimes isolated when the sulfinate is the intended product. This was noted in attempting to prepare the sulfinate from poly(styryl lithium) (105). Sulfinic acids are thought to be intermediates in the oxidation of thioacetates with hydrogen peroxide (Section VI-A), and in the preparation of sulfonyl chlorides by aqueous chlorination of thiol derivatives (Section II-A).

As pointed out in Chapter 3, long-chain alkanesulfinic acids are reported to be easily accessible by the direct, light-catalyzed reaction of SO_2 with paraffin hydrocarbons. Subsequent oxidation or halogenation of the acids should make the corresponding sulfonic acids and sulfonyl halides easily available.

REFERENCES

1. Adams, C. E. , and W. A. Proell, U. S. Patent 2, 573, 674; Chem. Abstr. , 46, 4026 (1952).
2. Adams, D. A. W. , U. S. Dept. Commerce, OTS Rept. , PB85, 687, 1946.
3. Adams, R. , and C. S. Marvel, U. S. Dept. Commerce, OTS Rept. PB117, 872.
4. Aiello, T. , and G. Pappalardo, Farmaco (Pavia) Ed. Sci. , 3, 145 (1948); Chem. Abstr. , 43, 1738 (1949).
5. Alvaredo, E. M. , W. A. Lazier, and J. H. Werntz, U. S. Patent 2, 402, 587; Chem. Abstr. , 40, 5587 (1946).
6. Angulo, J. , and A. M. Municio, Anales Real Soc. Espan. Fis. Quim. (Madrid), 56B, 395 (1960); Chem. Abstr. , 55, 7409 (1961).
7. Angulo, J. , and A. M. Municio, Chem. Ind. (London), 1958, 1175.
8. Asinger, F. , and F. Ebender, Ber. , 75, 344 (1942).
9. Asinger, F. , F. Ebender, and G. Richter, J. Prakt. Chem. (4), 2, 203 (1955).
10. Asinger, F. , H. Eckoldt, and G. Richter, J. Prakt. Chem. 4, 2, 233 (1955).
10a. Asinger, F. , B. Fell, and H. Scherb, Ber. , 96, 2831 (1963).
11. Asinger, F. , G. Geiseler, and H. Eckoldt, Chem. Ber. , 89, 1233 (1956).
12. Asinger, F. , G. Geiseler, and M. Hoppe, Chem. Ber. , 91, 2130 (1958).
13. Avenarius, C. , Ber. , 24, 260 (1891).
14. Azatyan, V. D. , G. T. Esayan, and G. A. Galoyan, Izv. Akad. Nauk Arm. SSR, Khim. Nauk, 14, No. 1, 57 (1961); Chem. Abstr. , 55, 27190 (1961).
15. Backer, H. J. , Rec. Trav. Chim. , 54, 205 (1935).
16. Backer, H. J. , Rec. Trav. Chim. , 54, 215 (1935).
17. Backer, H. J. , Rec. Trav. Chim. , 70, 254 (1951).
18. Bailey, P. S. , Chem. Rev. , 58, 925 (1958).
19. Barnard, D. , J. Chem. Soc. , 1957, 4547.
20. Barnard, D. , J. Chem. Soc. , 1957, 4673.
21. Barnard, D. , L. Bateman, and J. I. Cunneen, in Organic Sulfur Compounds, N. Kharasch, ed. , Pergamon Press, New York, 1961.
22. Barry, W. J. , I. L. Finar, and A. B. Simonds, J. Chem. Soc. , 1956, 4974.
23. Bauer, L. , and L. A. Gardella, J. Org. Chem. , 26, 82 (1961).
24. Beaman, A. G. , and R. K. Robins, J. Am. Chem. Soc. , 83, 4038 (1961).
25. Beck, L. W. , A. R. Gilbert, and J. K. Wolfe, U. S. Patent 2, 559, 585; Chem. Abstr. , 46, 3065 (1952).
26. Behringer, H. , and P. Zillikens, Ann. , 574, 140 (1951).
26a. Bennett, C. F. , D. W. Goheen, and W. S. MacGregor, J. Org. Chem. , 28, 2485 (1963).
27. Bittner, K. , Ber. , 35, 2933 (1902).

27a.   Bliss, A. D. , W. K. Cline, C. E. Hamilton, and O. J. Sweeting, J. Org. Chem. , $\underline{28}$, 3537 (1963).

28.   Boeseken, J. , and H. W. van Ockenburg, Rec. Trav. Chim. , $\underline{33}$, 319 (1914).

29.   Bogert, M. T. , J. Am. Chem. Soc. , $\underline{25}$, 289 (1903).

30.   Bookman, S. , Ber. , $\underline{28}$, 3117 (1895).

31.   Bordwell, F. G. , and W. A. Hewett, Div. of Organic Chemistry, 126th Meeting, American Chemical Society, New York, N. Y. , Sept. , 1954.

32.   Bordwell, F. G. , and W. A. Hewett, J. Org. Chem. , $\underline{22}$, 980 (1957).

33.   Bordwell, F. G. , W. H. McKellin, and D. Babcock, J. Am. Chem. Soc. , $\underline{73}$, 5566 (1951).

34.   Borsche, W. , and W. Lange, Ber. , $\underline{40}$, 2220 (1907).

35.   Brintzinger, H. , and M. Langheck, Chem. Ber. , $\underline{86}$, 557 (1953).

36.   Brintzinger, H. , and H. Schmahl, Chem. Ber. , $\underline{87}$, 314 (1954).

37.   Bristol-Myers Co. , British Patent 899, 584; Chem. Abstr. , $\underline{58}$, 1406 (1963).

38.   Brown, B. K. , U. S. Patent 2, 521, 147; Chem. Abstr. , $\underline{44}$, 10556 (1950).

39.   Caldwell, W. T. , and A. N. Sayin, J. Am. Chem. Soc. , $\underline{73}$, 5125 (1951).

40.   Cavallito, C. J. , and D. M. Fruehauf, J. Am. Chem. Soc. , $\underline{71}$, 2248 (1949).

41.   Challenger, F. , and P. H. Clapham, J. Chem. Soc. , $\underline{1948}$, 1615.

42.   Chinoin Gyogyszer es Vegyeszeti Termekek Gyara R. T. , British Patent 789, 583; Chem. Abstr. , 53, 16157 (1959).

43.   Clutterbuck, P. W. , and J. B. Cohen, J. Chem. Soc. , $\underline{123}$, 2507 (1923).

44.   Collin, G. , T. P. Hilditch, P. Marsh, and A. F. McLeod, J. Soc. Chem. Ind. , $\underline{52}$, 272T (1933).

45.   Comrie, A. M. , and J. B. Stenlake, J. Chem. Soc. , $\underline{1958}$, 1853.

45a.   Crown Zellerbach Corp. , Technical Information on Dimethyl Sulfide, Camas, Wash. , 1961.

46.   Cunneen, J. I. , J. Chem. Soc. , $\underline{1947}$, 134.

47.   Daeniker, H. V. , and J. Druey, Helv. Chim. Acta, $\underline{40}$, 2148 (1957).

48.   Daeniker, H. V. , and J. Druey, Helv. Chim. Acta, $\underline{40}$, 2154 (1957).

49.   Daeniker, H. V. , and J. Druey, Helv. Chim. Acta, $\underline{45}$, 1972 (1962).

50.   Delepine, M. , and S. Eschenbrenner, Bl. soc. Chim. (4), $\underline{33}$, 705 (1923).

51.   De Simo, M. , and J. J. O'Connor, U. S. Patent 2, 374, 983; Chem. Abstr. , $\underline{40}$, 1864 (1946).

52.   Dirscherl, W. , and K. Otto, Chem. Ber. , $\underline{89}$, 393 (1956).

53.   Doering, W. von E. , and F. M. Beringer, J. Am. Chem. Soc. , $\underline{71}$, 2221 (1949).

54.   Dohrn, M. , and P. Diedrich, German Patent 564, 786; Chem. Abstr. , $\underline{27}$, 1010 (1933).

55. Dougherty, G. , and R. H. Barth, U. S. Patent 2, 293, 971; Chem. Abstr. , 37, 889 (1943).

56. Douglass, I. B. , in Organic Sulfur Compounds, N. Kharasch, ed. , Pergamon Press, New York, 1961.

56a. Douglass, I. B. , B. S. Farah, and E. G. Thomas, J. Org. Chem. , 26, 1996 (1961).

57. Douglass, I. B. , and T. B. Johnson, J. Am. Chem. Soc. , 60, 1486 (1938).

57a. Douglass, I. B. , J. A. Stearns, and D. A. Koop, Abstracts of papers presented at the 147th meeting of the American Chemical Society, Philadelphia, Pa. , April 6-10, 1964, p. 26N.

58. Dreyfus, H. , U. S. Patent 2, 316, 847; Chem. Abstr. , 37, 5736 (1943).

58a. El-Hewehi, Z. , J. Prakt. Chem. , 23, 38 (1964).

59. Erickson, F. B. , U. S. Patent 2, 642, 458; Chem. Abstr. , 48, 5219 (1954).

60. Erlenmeyer, H. , H. Ueberwasser, and H. M. Weber, Helv. Chim. Acta, 21, 709 (1938).

61. Evans, R. F. , and H. C. Brown, Chem. Ind. (London), 1958, 1559.

62. Farlow, M. W. , U. S. Patent 2, 204, 210; Chem. Abstr. , 34, 6947 (1940).

63. Farrar, W. V. , J. Chem. Soc. , 1960, 3058.

64. Farrar, W. V. , J. Chem. Soc. , 1960, 3063.

65. Fichter, F. , and R. Schonlau, Ber. , 48, 1150 (1915).

66. Fichter, F. , and W. Wenk, Ber. , 45, 1373 (1912).

67. Field, L. , and F. A. Grunwald, J. Am. Chem. Soc. , 75, 934 (1953).

67a. Field, L. , H. Haerle, T. C. Owen, and A. Ferretti, J. Org. Chem. , 29, 1632 (1964).

68. Field, L. , T. C. Owen, R. R. Crenshaw, and A. W. Bryan, J. Am. Chem. Soc. , 83, 4414 (1961).

68a. Field, L. , T. F. Parsons, and R. R. Crenshaw, J. Org. Chem. , 29, 918 (1964).

69. Fincke, J. K. , U. S. Patent 2, 547, 906; Chem. Abstr. , 46, 130 (1952).

70. Fincke, J. K. , U. S. Patent 2, 594, 411; Chem. Abstr. , 47, 1181 (1953).

71. Fisher, M. H. , W. H. Nicholson, and R. S. Stuart, Can. J. Chem. , 39, 501 (1961).

72. Flaschentraeger, B. , and G. Wannschaff, Ber. , 67, 1121 (1934).

73. Folkers, K. , A. Russell, and R. W. Bost, J. Am. Chem. Soc. , 63, 3530 (1941).

74. Fournier, P. , French Patent 885, 661; Chem. Abstr. , 48, 1411 (1954).

75. Fusco, R. , and G. Bianchetti, British Patent 801, 037; Chem. Abstr. , 53, 7968 (1959).

76. Gabriel, S. , Ber. , 22, 1142, 1153 (1889).

77. Gabriel, S. , and P. Heymann, Ber. , 23, 158 (1890).

78. Gabriel, S. , and C. von Hirsch, Ber. , 29, 2611 (1896).
79. Geiseler, G. , and F. Asinger, Chem. Ber. , 89, 1100 (1956).
80. Geiseler, G. , and R. Kuschmiers, Chem. Ber. , 93, 2041 (1960).
81. Gladshtein, B. M. , I. P. Kuliulin, and L. Z. Soborovskii, Zh. Obshch.
     Khim. , 28, 2417 (1958); Chem. Abstr. , 53, 3034 (1959).
82. Gladshtein, B. M. , and L. Z. Soborovskii, Zh. Obshch. Khim. , 30,
     1950 (1960); Chem. Abstr. , 55, 6372 (1951).
83. Greenbaum, S. B. , and W. L. Holmes, J. Am. Chem. Soc. , 76,
     2899 (1954).
84. Gregg, D. C. , and C. A. Blood, Jr. , J. Org. Chem. , 16, 1255
     (1951).
85. Gregg, D. C. , K. Hazleton, and T. F. McKeon, Jr. , J. Org. Chem. ,
     18, 36 (1953).
86. Griffin, J. W. , and D. H. Hey, J. Chem. Soc. , 1952, 3334.
87. Guareschi, J. , Ann. , 222, 302 (1884).
88. Hann, R. M. , J. Am. Chem. Soc. , 57, 2166 (1935).
89. Hardy, W. B. , and T. H. Chao, U. S. Patent 3, 038, 932; Chem.
     Abstr. , 57, 16497 (1962).
90. Harris, J. F. , and W. A. Sheppard, J. Org. Chem. , 26, 354 (1961).
91. Hartmann, E. , U. S. Dept. Commerce, OTS Rept. , PB75, 421,
     Enlargement Print of Frames 2713-4 of FIAT Microfilm Reel
     C 61, PB17, 658.
92. Haszeldine, R. N. , and J. M. Kidd, J. Chem. Soc. , 1954, 4228.
93. Haszeldine, R. N. , and J. M. Kidd, J. Chem. Soc. , 1955, 2901.
94. Hentrich, W. , and W. J. Kaiser, German Patent 854, 515; Chem.
     Abstr. , 50, 2194 (1956).
95. Herbrandson, H. F. , W. S. Kelly, and J. Versnel, J. Am. Chem.
     Soc. , 80, 3301 (1958).
96. Heymann, H. , T. Ginsberg, Z. R. Gulick, E. A. Konopka, and R. L.
     Mayer, J. Am. Chem. Soc. , 81, 5125 (1959).
97. Hofmann, K. , U. S. Patent 2, 506, 594; Chem. Abstr. , 44, 7885
     (1950).
98. Hofmann, K. , A. Bridgwater, and A. E. Axelrod, J. Am. Chem.
     Soc. , 71, 1253 (1949).
99. Hoffmann, H. , K. Schimmelschmidt, and E. Mundlos, Chem. Ber. ,
     96, 38 (1963).
100. Hoggarth, E. , J. Chem. Soc. , 1951, 2202.
101. Hoggarth, E. , U. S. Patent 2, 623, 899; Chem. Abstr. , 47, 12419
     (1953).
102. Holmberg, B. , Arkiv Kemi, 12B, No. 47, 3 (1938); Chem.
     Abstr. , 32, 4151 (1938).
103. Horner, L. , and O. H. Basedow, Ann. , 612, 108 (1958).
104. Horner, L. , H. Schaefer, and W. Ludwig, Chem. Ber. , 91, 75
     (1958).
105. Houel, B. , Compt. Rend. , 250, 3839 (1960).
106. Hueter, R. , U. S. Patent 2, 277, 325; Chem. Abstr. , 36, 4831
     (1942).

107. Hunter, W. H., and B. E. Sorenson, J. Am. Chem. Soc., 54, 3365 (1932).
108. Huppert, O., U. S. Patent 2, 384, 837; Chem. Abstr., 40, 7671 (1946).
109. Huva, J. C. H., J. Am. Chem. Soc., 81, 3604 (1959).
110. I. G. Farbenindustrie AG, U. S. Dept. Commerce, OTS Rept., PB96, 587.
111. Jenkins, F. E., and A. N. Hambly, Australian J. Chem., 6, 318 (1953).
112. Johnson, C. E., and W. F. Wolff, U. S. Patent 2, 697, 722; Chem. Abstr., 50, 1892 (1956).
113. Johnson, C. E., and W. F. Wolff, U. S. Patent 2, 727, 920; Chem. Abstr., 52, 6392 (1958).
114. Johnson, T. B., U. S. Patent 2, 275, 378; Chem. Abstr., 36, 4135 (1942).
115. Johnson, T. B., and I. B. Douglass, J. Am. Chem. Soc., 61, 2548 (1939).
116. Johnson, T. B., and I. B. Douglass, J. Am. Chem. Soc., 63, 1571 (1941).
117. Johnson, T. B., and J. M. Sprague, J. Am. Chem. Soc., 58, 1348 (1936).
118. Johnson, T. B., and J. M. Sprague, J. Am. Chem. Soc., 61, 176 (1939).
119. Jonas, H., German Patent 836, 492; Chem. Abstr., 47, 4896 (1953).
120. Jones, W. D., and S. B. McFarlane, U. S. Patent 2, 667, 507; Chem. Abstr., 48, 5553 (1954).
121. Karavaev, B. I., and A. A. Spryskov, Zh. Obshch. Khim., 26, 501 (1956); Chem. Abstr., 50, 13835 (1956).
122. Karavaev, B. I., and S. P. Starkov, Zh. Obshch. Khim., 27, 788 (1957); Chem. Abstr., 51, 16336 (1957).
123. Kharasch, M. S., and R. A. Mosher, J. Org. Chem., 17, 453 (1952).
124. Kharasch, M. S., and O. Reinmuth, Grignard Reactions of Non-metallic Substances, Prentice-Hall, Englewood Cliffs, N. J., 1954.
125. Kice, J. L., and N. E. Pawlowski, J. Org. Chem., 28, 1163 (1963).
126. Kiprianov, A. I., and A. I. Tolmachev, Zh. Obshch. Khim., 27, 486 (1957); Chem. Abstr., 51, 15446 (1957).
127. Kirsanov, A. V., and N. A. Kirsanova, Zh. Obshch. Khim., 29, 1802 (1959); Chem. Abstr., 54, 8693 (1960).
127a. Klamann, D., and F. Drahowzal, Monatsh., 83, 463 (1952).
128. Knobloch, W., and K. Rintelen, Arch. Pharm., 291, 180 (1958); Chem. Abstr., 53, 3197 (1959).
129. Knunyants, I. L., M. A. Dmitriev, and G. A. Sokol'skii, Russian Patent 116, 577; Chem. Abstr., 53, 17909 (1959).
130. Koenig, N. H., and D. Swern, U. S. Patent 2, 892, 852; Chem. Abstr., 54, 1317 (1960).

131. Kostsova, A. G. , Zh. Obshch. Khim. , 23, 949 (1953); Chem. Abstr. , 48, 7570 (1954).
132. Kostsova, A. G. , L. S. Shvetsova, and I. I. Kalganova, Zh. Obshch. Khim. , 24, 1397 (1954); Chem. Abstr. , 49, 10871 (1955).
133. Krasnec, L. , L. Szucs, and J. Durinda, Chem. Zvesti, 14, 464 (1961); Chem. Abstr. , 55, 16395 (1961).
134. Kurihara, T. , and H. Niwa, J. Pharm. Soc. Japan, 73, 1378 (1953); Chem. Abstr. , 49, 313 (1955).
134a. Kwart, H. , Paper presented at the annual meeting of the American Association for the Advancement of Science, December 27, 1962.
135. Lee, S. W. , and G. Dougherty, J. Org. Chem. , 5, 81 (1942).
136. Lichtenberger, J. , and P. Tritsch, Bull. Soc. Chim. France, 1961, 363.
137. Lieber, E. , and A. F. Cashman, U. S. Patent 2, 459, 440; Chem. Abstr. , 43, 3193 (1949).
138. Lisowski, W. , Przemysl Chem. , 12, 697 (1956); Chem. Abstr. , 52, 12815 (1958).
139. Loudon, J. D. , and N. Shulman, J. Chem. Soc. , 1938, 1618.
140. Maggiolo, A. , and E. A. Blair, in Ozone Chemistry and Technology, Adv. Chem. Ser. No. 21, American Chemical Society, Washington, 1959.
141. Majda, H. , and K. Okon, Bull. Acad. Polon. Sci. Ser. Sci. Chim. Geol. Geograph. , 7, 79 (1959); Chem. Abstr. , 54, 17304 (1960).
142. Maneck, M. , Braunkohlenarch. , 40, 53 (1933); Chem. Abstr. , 27, 4907 (1933).
143. Marvel, C. S. , and R. S. Johnson, J. Org. Chem. , 13, 822 (1948).
144. Masuda, J. Y. , and G. H. Hamor, J. Am. Pharm. Assoc. , 46, 61 (1957).
145. Mathes, R. A. , and F. D. Stewart, U. S. Patent 2, 656, 354; Chem. Abstr. , 48, 10777 (1954).
146. Matsumoto, A. , Japanese Patent 177, 918; Chem. Abstr. , 45, 7592 (1951).
147. Merck & Co. , British Patent 902, 881; Chem. Abstr. , 58, 1410 (1963).
148. Michaelis, A. , and A. Hoelken, Ann. , 331, 245 (1904).
149. Milligan, B. , and J. M. Swan, Rev. Pure Appl. Chem. , 12, 72 (1962).
150. Mosher, C. W. , R. M. Silverstein, O. P. Crews, Jr. , and B. R. Baker, J. Org. Chem. , 23, 1257 (1958).
151. Murakami, M. , and S. Oae, J. Pharm. Soc. Japan, 68, 278 (1948); Chem. Abstr. , 45, 9498 (1951).
151a. Murav'eva, K. M. , and M. N. Shchukina, Med. Prom. SSSR, 17, No. 6, 40 (1963); Chem. Abstr. , 59, 9773 (1963).
152. Muth, F. , in Houben-Weyl, Methoden der Organischen Chemie, Vol. IX, IV. ed. , Thieme Verlag, Stuttgart, 1955.
153. Nawa, H. , W. T. Brady, M. Koike, and L. J. Reed, J. Am. Chem. Soc. , 82, 896 (1960).

154.   Nilsson, T. , Thesis, Lund University, 1946; Brit. Abstr. , A II, 137 (1948).
155.   Nishizawa, K. , and I. Ikeda, J. Soc. Chem. Ind. Japan, 46, 1237 (1943); Chem. Abstr. , 42, 6553 (1948).
156.   Noller, C. R. , and J. J. Gordon, J. Am. Chem. Soc. , 55, 1090 (1933).
157.   Novello, F. C. , U. S. Patent 2,965,656; Chem. Abstr. , 55, 22242 (1961).
158.   Ochiai, E. , and F. Nagasawa, Ber. , 72, 1470 (1939).
159.   Oechsner de Coninck, M. , Compt. Rend. , 126, 838 (1898).
159a. Ostapchuk, N. M. , and D. N. Khokhlov, Zh. Prikl. Khim. , 36, No. 7, 1625 (1963); Chem. Abstr. , 59, 15168 (1963).
160.   Otto, K. , and W. Dirscherl, Chem. Ber. , 89, 2566 (1956).
161.   Pala, G. , Farmaco (Pavia) Ed. Sci. , 13, 461 (1958); Chem. Abstr. , 53, 5267 (1959).
162.   Pala, G. , Farmaco (Pavia) Ed. Sci. , 13, 650 (1958); Chem. Abstr. , 53, 18947 (1959).
163.   Panizzi, L. , and R. A. Nicolaus, Gazz. Chim. Ital. , 80, 431 (1950).
164.   Parham, W. E. , H. Wynberg, W. R. Hasek, P. A. Howell, R. M. Curtis, and W. N. Lipscomb, J. Am. Chem. Soc. , 76, 4957 (1954).
165.   Park, H. F. , U. S. Patent 2,772,307; Chem. Abstr. , 51, 5815 (1957).
166.   Pattison, F. L. M. , Nature, 174, 737 (1954).
167.   Proell, W. A. , U. S. Patent 2,433,396; Chem. Abstr. , 42, 2270 (1948).
168.   Proell, W. A. , U. S. Patent 2,489,316; Chem. Abstr. , 44, 1527 (1950).
169.   Proell, W. A. , U. S. Patent 2,489,318; Chem. Abstr. , 44, 1528 (1950).
170.   Proell, W. A. , C. E. Adams, and B. H. Shoemaker, Ind. Eng. Chem. , 40, 1129 (1948).
171.   Proell, W. A. , and W. B. Chilcote, U. S. Patent 2,598,013; Chem. Abstr. , 47, 3332 (1953).
172.   Proell, W. A. , W. B. Chilcote, and B. H. Shoemaker, U. S. Patent 2,598,014; Chem. Abstr. , 47, 3332 (1953).
173.   Proell, W. A. , and B. H. Shoemaker, U. S. Patent 2,433,395; Chem. Abstr. , 42, 2613 (1948).
174.   Proell, W. A. , and B. H. Shoemaker, U. S. Patent 2,505,910; Chem. Abstr. , 44, 7342 (1950).
175.   Profft, E. , U. S. Patent 2,231,594; Chem. Abstr. , 35, 3460 (1941).
176.   Rachinskii, F. Yu. , N. M. Slavachevskaia, and D. V. Ioffe, Zh. Obshch. Khim. , 28, 2998 (1958); Chem. Abstr. , 53, 9045 (1959).
177.   Raghavan, M. , B. H. Iyer, and P. C. Guha, J. Indian Inst. Sci. , 34, 87 (1952); Chem. Abstr. , 47, 6889 (1953).
178.   Raper, A. H. , and E. Rothstein, J. Chem. Soc. , 1963, 1027.

179. Reich, L. , Dissertation Abstr. , 23, No. 8, 2704 (1963).
180. Reid, E. E. , Organic Chemistry of Bivalent Sulfur, Chemical
      Publishing Co. , New York, 1958.
181. Reppe, W. , and others, Ann. Chem. , 596, 1, (1955).
182. Reychler, A. , Bull. Soc. Chim. Belges, 27, 110; Chem. Abstr. ,
      8, 1105 (1914).
183. Robins, R. K. , J. Org. Chem. 26, 447 (1961).
184. Roblin, R. O. , Jr. , and J. W. Clapp, J. Am. Chem. Soc. , 72, 4890
      (1950).
185. Ross, D. L. , C. G. Skinner, and W. Shive, J. Org. Chem. , 24,
      1372 (1959).
186. Saunders, B. C. , G. J. Stacey, and I. G. E. Wilding, J. Chem. Soc. ,
      1949, 773.
187. Sawa, Y. , and S. Horiuchi, Japanese Patent 12, 081 ('60); Chem.
      Abstr. , 55, 1668 (1961).
188. Schlack, P. , and W. Werniger, German Patent 885, 847; Chem.
      Abstr. , 52, 16296 (1958).
189. Schoeberl, A. , and M. Wiesner, Ber. , 65, 1224 (1932).
190. Schubert, M. , and E. Herdieckerhoff, U. S. Patent 2, 018, 813;
      Chem. Abstr. , 30, 299 (1936).
191. Scott, R. B. , J. B. Gayle, M. S. Heller, and R. E. Lutz, J. Org.
      Chem. , 20, 1165 (1955).
192. Senn, O. F. , U. S. Patent 2, 667, 503; Chem. Abstr., 49, 3257
      (1955).
193. Showell, J. S. , J. R. Russell, and D. Swern, J. Org. Chem. , 27,
      2853 (1962).
194. Sjoberg, B. , Svensk Kem. Tidskr. , 50, 250 (1938); Chem.
      Abstr. , 33, 2106 (1939).
195. Small, L. D. , J. H. Bailey, and C. J. Cavallito, J. Am. Chem. Soc. ,
      71, 3565 (1949).
196. Solvay et Cie. , Belgian Patent 593, 523; Chem. Abstr. , 55,
      13906 (1961).
197. Sosnovsky, G. , J. Org. Chem. , 26, 3506 (1961).
198. Sperling, R. , J. Chem. Soc. , 1949, 1932.
199. Sperling, R. , J. Chem. Soc. , 1949, 1939.
200. Sprague, J. M. , U. S. Patent 2, 531, 367; Chem. Abstr. , 45,
      3418 (1951).
201. Sprague, J. M. , and T. B. Johnson, J. Am. Chem. Soc. , 59, 1837
      (1937).
202. Sprague, J. M. , and T. B. Johnson, J. Am. Chem. Soc. , 59, 2439
      (1937).
203. Spring, W. , and C. Winssinger, Bull. Soc. Chim. (2), 49, 72
      (1888).
204. Spryskov, A. A. , and O. S. Ivanova, Zh. Obshch. Khim. , 27, 784
      (1957); Chem. Abstr. , 51, 16375 (1957).
205. Spryskov, A. A. , and T. I. Yokovleva, Zh. Obshch. Khim. , 27,
      239 (1957); Chem. Abstr. , 51, 12847 (1957).
206. Stamicarbon N. V. , Dutch Patent 77, 908; Chem. Abstr. , 50,
      7842 (1956).

207. Stewart, F. D. , and R. A. Mathes, J. Org. Chem. , 14, 1111 (1949).
208. Stewart, J. M. , J. Org. Chem. , 28, 596 (1963).
209. Stewart, J. M. , and C. H. Burnside, J. Am. Chem. Soc. , 75, 243 (1953).
210. Stewart, J. M. , and H. P. Cordts, J. Am. Chem. Soc. , 74, 5880 (1952).
211. Stone, G. C. H. , J. Am. Chem. Soc. , 62, 571 (1940).
212. Sureau, R. , Bull. Soc. Chim. France, 1956, 101.
213. Suter, C. M. , The Organic Chemistry of Sulfur, Wiley, New York, 1944.
214. Swern, D. , Rev. Franc. Corps Gras, 8, 7 (1961); Chem. Abstr. , 55, 12285 (1961).
215. Terent'ev, A. P. , and A. I. Gershenovich, Zh. Obshch. Khim. , 23, 204 (1953); Chem. Abstr. , 48, 2568 (1954).
216. Ter Horst, W. P. , and W. K. Cline, U. S. Patent 2, 664, 443; Chem. Abstr. , 49, 1773 (1955).
217. Teuffert, U. S. Dept. Commerce, OTS Rept. , PB725, Rept. 179.
218. Thomas, R. C. , and L. J. Reed, J. Am. Chem. Soc. , 78, 6150 (1956).
219. Truce, W. E. , D. D. Emrick, and R. E. Miller, J. Am. Chem. Soc. , 75, 3359 (1953).
220. Truce, W. E. , and J. F. Lyons, J. Am. Chem. Soc. , 73, 126 (1951).
221. Truce, W. E. , and J. P. Milionis, J. Am. Chem. Soc. , 74, 974 (1952).
222. Truce, W. E. , and J. P. Milionis, J. Org. Chem. , 17, 1529 (1952).
222a. Truce, W. E. , and J. R. Norell, J. Am. Chem. Soc. , 85, 3231 (1963).
223. vander Plas, H. C. , and H. J. den Hertog, Tetrahedron Letters, 1960, No. 1, 13.
224. Vivian, D. L. , and E. E. Reid, J. Am. Chem. Soc. , 57, 2559 (1935).
225. Vol'fson, L. G. , and N. H. Mel'nikov, J. Gen. Chem. USSR (English Transl.), 20, 2089 (1950); Chem. Abstr. , 45, 5608 (1951).
226. Vries, H. de, and T. A. Zuidhof, Rec. Trav. Chim. , 70, 696 (1951).
227. Wagner, F. C. , and E. E. Reid, J. Am. Chem. Soc. , 53, 3407 (1931).
227a. Wallace, T. J. , H. Pobiner, and A. Schriesheim, J. Org. Chem. , 29, 888 (1964).
228. Warren, A. , and G. H. Hamor, J. Pharm. Sci. , 50 No. 7, 625 (1961).
229. Weil, J. K. , L. P. Witnauer, and A. J. Stirton, J. Am. Chem. Soc. , 75, 2526 (1953).
230. Wenisch, W. J. , Dissertation Abstr. , 18, 808 (1958).

231. Wilkes, J. B. ,   U. S. Patent 2, 623, 069; Chem. Abstr. , <u>48</u>, 1412 (1954).
232. Winterfield, K. , and W. Haering,   Arch. Pharm. , <u>295</u>, 615 (1962).
233. Witte, M. ,   U. S. Patent 2, 465, 951; Chem. Abstr. , <u>43</u>, 6232 (1949).
234. Witte, M. , and M. Welge,   U. S. Patent 2, 465, 952; Chem. Abstr., <u>43</u>, 6232 (1949).
235. Wojahn, H. , and H. Wuckel,   Pharm. Zentralhalle, 87, 97 (1948); Chem. Abstr. , <u>44</u>, 7258 (1950).
236. Yale, H. L. , and F. Sowinski,   J. Org. Chem. , <u>25</u>, 1824 (1960).
237. Yoder, L. ,   J. Org. Chem. , <u>20</u>, 1317 (1955).
238. Young, H. A. ,   J. Am. Chem. Soc. , <u>59</u>, 811, 812 (1937).
239. Young, H. A. , and M. B. Young,   J. Am. Chem. Soc. , <u>61</u>, 1955 (1939).
240. Young, R. W. ,   U. S. Patent 2, 744, 907; Chem. Abstr. , <u>51</u>, 2874 (1957).
241. Ziegler, C. , and J. M. Sprague,   J. Org. Chem. , <u>16</u>, 621 (1951).
242. Zincke, T. , and W. Frohneberg,   Ber. , <u>42</u>, 272 (1909).

CHAPTER 5

SULFOALKYLATION, SULFOARYLATION AND SIMILAR PROCEDURES FOR INDIRECT SULFONATION

I. INTRODUCTION

This chapter is concerned with methods for preparing sulfonates by reacting an organic molecule already containing a sulfonic acid (or the corresponding salt) group with another organic compound to form a final sulfonate with the desired new structure or properties. The organic sulfonates employed have been collectively termed organic sulfonating agents. The agents are classified, depending on their chemical structure, into those used for sulfoalkylation, sulfoarylation, and heterocyclic sulfonation. Sulfoalkylating reagents are further subdivided into those employed for sulfomethylation, sulfoethylation, etc., depending upon the alkyl group involved. Sulfatoalkylation and sulfamalkylation analogously involve introduction of sulfated and sulfamated moieties, respectively.

Each of these reagents contains a functional group, other than sulfonate, sulfate, or sulfamate, which enables it to react with other organic compounds to form the desired product. This group may be carboxyl, or a derivative thereof such as acid chloride, anhydride, or ester. These compounds are termed sulfoacylating reagents. In other reagents it may be hydroxyl, amino, halogen, olefinic unsaturation, carbonyl, Grignard, or, in fact, any of the large number of functional groups ordinarily employed to join two organic molecules. The sulfonation process with these materials therefore involves the standard reactions of organic synthesis, rather than direct treatment with an inorganic sulfonating reagent. It is accordingly referred to as "indirect" sulfonation.

This approach to the preparation of sulfonates can yield products of types or of a degree of purity possibly not attainable by other more conventional but more drastic sulfonation methods involving the use of sulfuric acid or similar strong reagents. A number of these organic sulfonating agents have been employed for many years as "building blocks" for enhancing the water solubility or surface activity of dyes, detergents, and pharmaceuticals. More recently, they have been used for preparing sulfonated polymers. Natural polymers, such as starch or cellulose, can thus be modified to render them water-soluble. Polymerization of unsaturated sulfonates may form water-soluble polymeric sulfonates, and copolymerization of them with appropriate water-insoluble monomers can yield ion-exchange resins or fibers of enhanced due receptivity. Sulfonated polymers and copolymers have also been made from sulfonates containing carboxyl, carbonyl, or phenolic hydroxyl groups.

An attempt is made in this chapter to delineate the special areas in which established reagents of this type, such as 1,3-propanesultone, 2-hydroxyethanesulfonic acid, or phenolsulfonic acid, have already found application. A second objective is to call attention to other such reagents which have so far seen quite limited use, but which now appear fairly cheaply accessible, and, in the opinion of the writer, deserve further consideration. Compounds in this category include styrenesulfonic acid, 2-cyanoethanesulfonic acid, sulfobutyrolactone, and acetonesulfonic acid.

It should be noted that the aliphatic compounds discussed in this chapter are classified according to how many carbon atoms separate the sulfonate group from the reactive functional group. Thus, sulfomethylating reagents include not only $HOCH_2SO_3Na$ itself, but also aldehyde-bisulfite compounds ($HOCHRSO_3Na$) in general. Sodium acetonesulfonate ($CH_3COCH_2SO_3Na$) is thus considered under reagents employed to introduce the sulfoethyl and sulfoethylidene groups, and the α-sulfo long-chain fatty acids ($RCH(COOH)SO_3Na$) are regarded as sulfoacetylating reagents. For convenience, the compounds are usually referred to as "acids"; this designation should be understood to include the various salts as well.

II. SULFOALKYLATION

A. Sulfomethylation

1. ALDEHYDE-BISULFITE COMPOUNDS

a. General Discussion

Aldehyde-bisulfite compounds, especially the one made from formaldehyde, are perhaps the cheapest and most commonly used sulfoalkylating reagents. Formaldehyde-sodium bisulfite (410), and acetaldehyde-potassium bisulfite (585), have been shown to have the hydroxymethanesulfonate structure given in Equation 5-3. There is extensive physiocochemical evidence for this structure, as discussed in Chapter 3, Section II-B-5. The overall reaction involved in sulfomethylating organic compounds with formaldehyde-bisulfite is conveniently represented by Equation 5-9, although the actual course of the reaction may be different, as is discussed more fully later. Other aldehyde-bisulfite compounds similarly yield sulfomethylated derivatives substituted on the methylene carbon. Ketone-bisulfites may react likewise, but the few scattered references to their use permit no definite conclusion.

Sulfomethylation with aldehyde-bisulfite is usually effected by simply mixing the aldehyde, aqueous bisulfite, and the organic compound, and then allowing the mixture to react for several hours at neutral or slightly alkaline pH at room temperature or above. Formaldehyde-sodium bisulfite can be purchased (358, 453), or it can easily be prepared and isolated as a solid (181). When sulfomethylating amines (181), this compound can be used as such, but when it is employed to sulfomethylate other materials, it is necessary to raise the pH of its aqueous solution by adding alkali to insure a satisfactory rate of reaction. For easily sulfoalkylated materials, such as acetoacetic ester (523, 695), no more than 0.1 mole alkali per mole bisulfite is needed. For other more difficult reactions, one mole of alkali per mole of bisulfite is added, which is equivalent to using the neutral sulfite directly, as shown in Equation 5-4. Formaldehyde - sodium bisulfite is by a large margin the sulfomethylating reagent of major interest, although the bisulfites of acetaldehyde, benzaldehyde, furfural, and sugars are occasionally used. Cinnamic aldehyde forms a disulfonated sulfomethylating agent, capable of reacting for example as follows with an amine:

$$RNH_2 + C_6H_5CH(SO_3Na)CH_2CHOHSO_3Na \longrightarrow$$

$$RNHCH(SO_3Na)CH_2CH(SO_3Na)C_6H_5 + H_2O \qquad (5-1)$$

Crotonaldehyde behaves similarly. Acetone - bisulfite has been employed rarely.

Various alternative procedures for sulfomethylation have proved advantageous in special cases. These are: (1) use of sulfur dioxide and water instead of a metallic bisulfite; (2) addition of a metallic bisulfite to an azomethine:

$$RN:CHR' + HSO_3Na \longrightarrow RNHCH(R')SO_3Na \qquad (5-2)$$

(3) reaction of the metallic bisulfite with a preformed methylol compound, as shown in Equation 5-6; (4) reaction of the metallic bisulfite or sulfite with a Mannich base (Eq. 5-12); and (5) addition of a metallic bisulfite to an olefinic bond, by reaction 5-8. Specific examples of these procedures are cited below.

Aldehyde - bisulfites are employed to sulfomethylate nitrogen atoms, as in amines, hydrazines, amides, and sulfonamides. Amines react easily, and aromatic amides with difficulty; aliphatic amides, including carbamates and ureas, and aliphatic and aromatic sulfonamides, are intermediate in ease of reaction. Sulfomethylation of aliphatic compounds containing activated methylene groups, and of phenols, is easy, but heterocyclic rings react only with difficulty. They have not been used to sulfomethylate hydroxy compounds on the oxygen atom, phenolic esthers, or aromatic hydrocarbons. Sulfomethylation on oxygen or sulfur is usually effected with $ClCH_2SO_3Na$, as discussed in Section II-A-3. Acrylonitrile reacts with formaldehyde-bisulfite, forming $NCCH_2CH_2OCH_2SO_3Na$ (334a). This approach may be capable of considerable extension as a novel and simple method for preparing certain compounds sulfomethylated on oxygen.

A study of the reaction of aqueous formaldehyde with sodium sulfite and bisulfite (643) has shown that, contrary to previous belief, reaction 5-3 is irreversible and requires time (i.e., about 1 hr.) to reach completion at room temperature, but that reaction 5-4 reaches equilibrium almost immediately with about 54% of the formaldehyde combined. (This experiment was run at a formaldehyde:sulfite molar ratio of 1:1.25.) It was also shown that formaldehyde-bisulfite is quite stable and gives up its formaldehyde to dimedone only upon prolonged boiling. It is known that sulfomethylation reactions with aldehyde-bisulfites are accelerated by high ph, i.e., the conditions of reaction 5-4. However, formaldehyde and alkali are irreversibly consumed by the Cannizzaro reaction at high pH. For this reason it is preferred to effect sulfomethylation in neutral, or only weakly alkaline solution, even though the reaction is slower (643, 695). Benzaldehyde- (606) and acetaldehyde - bisulfite (643) formation are also alkali - reversible.

$$CH_2O + NaHSO_3 \longrightarrow HOCH_2SO_3Na \qquad (5\text{-}3)$$

$$CH_2O + Na_2SO_3 + H_2O \rightleftharpoons HOCH_2SO_3Na + NaOH \qquad (5\text{-}4)$$

The probable course of the sulfomethylation reaction has been considered briefly. Two routes have been suggested:
Route A:

$$RH + CH_2O \longrightarrow RCH_2OH \qquad (5\text{-}5)$$

$$RCH_2OH + NaHSO_3 \longrightarrow RCH_2SO_3Na + H_2O \qquad (5\text{-}6)$$

The following reactions may occur instead of reaction 5-6, where R= R'R''CH-:

$$R'R''CHCH_2OH \longrightarrow R'R''C{:}CH_2 + H_2O \qquad (5\text{-}7)$$

$$R'R''C{:}CH_2 + NaHSO_3 \longrightarrow R'R''CHCH_2SO_3Na \qquad (5\text{-}8)$$

Route B:

$$RH + HOCH_2SO_3Na \longrightarrow RCH_2SO_3Na + H_2O \qquad (5\text{-}9)$$

Raschig and Prahl (523), in a study of the sulfomethylation of ethyl acetoacetate, favored Route B over Route A (sequence 5-5; 5-7; 5-8) because they found reaction 5-8 inoperable. This objection was later removed by Willems (695), who showed that reaction 5-8 can proceed quantitatively. He preferred Route A (5-5; 5-7; 5-8). Others (414) have more recently agreed with this view as applied to the sulfomethylation of amines via an assumed azomethine intermediate. This proposal may receive support from the observation that ethyl 2-(n-butyl) acetoacetate and 2-nitropropane, which are incapable of undergoing reaction 5-7, do not sulfomethylate. On the other hand, secondary amines and phenols can easily be sulfomethylated, although they are incapable of dehydration by a reaction of type 5-7. Different mechanisms may of course apply depending upon the structure of the compound being sulfomethylated and other factors.

Suter, Bair, and Bordwell (619), in a study of the sulfomethylation of phenols and of activated methylene compounds, preferred Route B, where RH represents "some active form" of the organic compound. They cite as evidence against sequence 5-5; 5-6 the facts that 2-hydroxy-1-naphthylmethanol does not react with sodium sulfite under the conditions by which it can be sulfomethylated, and that ethyl acetoacetate forms only the dimethylol compound with formaldehyde, whereas it can be easily monosulfomethylated. They admit, however, that 2-hydroxybenzyl alcohol reacts with bisulfite by Equation 5-6.

Schiller and Suen (561), in a study of the sulfomethylation of poly (acrylamide), prefer Route A (sequence 5-5; 5-6) to Route B, since their reaction is inoperative at the low pH values which favor reaction 5-3, but does proceed rapidly at pH 10 - 12, which liberates formaldehyde via reaction 5-4. The aldehyde then undergoes reaction 5-5, which was shown by them to proceed more rapidly than reaction 5-6. Falk, Gerecht, and Krems (181), working with the sulfomethylation of ammonia and amines, do not discuss the course of the reaction, but they did employ preformed formaldehyde - sodium bisulfite, and imply by an equation their agreement with Route B. However, aqueous ammonia, with a pH of about 10, would favor reaction 5-4, thereby making possible sulfomethylation by Route A (5-5; 5-6) under their conditions.

Suter, Bair, and Bordwell have made the interesting suggestion (619) that the Mannich and sulfomethylation reactions may have similar mechanisms. The Mannich reaction involves overall aminomethylation as follows:

$$RH + CH_2O + HN(R')(R'') \longrightarrow RCH_2N(R')(R'') + H_2O \qquad (5-10)$$

A review of the various theories proposed for the course of the Mannich reaction (527) indicates that, as in the case of sulfomethylation, more than one explanation may be required to cover all known cases. For both reactions, it appears that the aldehyde reacts first with the sulfite ion in some cases, and with the organic compound in others.

Beside being promoted by alkaline pH, sulfomethylation is strongly accelerated by a rise in temperature (561).

b. Sulfomethylation on a Carbon Atom

(1) ALIPHATIC COMPOUNDS. Primary nitroparaffins (nitroethane, 1-nitropropane) sulfomethylate readily at above pH 6 (241, 242). Formaldehyde and butyraldehyde were used, forming compounds of the

structure $RCH(NO_2)CH(R')SO_3Na$. 2-Nitropropane did not react (619).

Ethyl acetoacetate monosulfomethylates in 87% yield using formal-dehyde - bisulfite with 0.1 mole added base per mole bisulfite (695). Acetaldehyde - , n-butyraldehyde -, and n-heptaldehyde - bisulfites gave yields of 72, 75, and 0%, respectively. However, the alternative approach involving addition of sodium bisulfite to the corresponding preformed methylene derivatives of ethyl acetoacetate (Eq. 5-8) yielded 90, 100, 92, and 90%. Acetone - bisulfite did not react. At higher pH, i.e., using 1.0 mole added base per mole bisulfite, equivalent to using the neutral sulfite by reaction 5-4, both disulfomethylation and ketone cleavage occur, forming sodium 2-acetyl-1, 3-propanedisulfo-nate $(CH_3COCH(CH_2SO_3Na)_2$ (619). Diethyl malonate could be similarly disulfomethylated with neutral sulfite (619), but it was not found pos-sible to monosulfomethylate it at lower pH in a manner analogous to ethyl acetoacetate. Malonic acid does undergo monosulfomethylation with the adduct of acrolein with two moles of potassium bisulfite, fol-lowed by decarboxylation (490):

$$KO_3SCH(OH)CH_2CH_2SO_3K + CH_2(COOH)_2 \longrightarrow$$

$$KO_3SCH(CH_2COOH)CH_2CH_2SO_3K + CO_2 \qquad (5\text{-}11)$$

Similar products are formed from the diadducts of crotonaldehyde and of glyoxal (56). The sulfomethylation of N-arylacetoacetanilides is catalyzed by a trace of KCN (448).

Several ketones (methyl n-propyl, acetophenone, 3-nitroacetophe-none, cyclohexanone, and dimedone) underwent only disulfomethyla-tion (619); efforts to mono- and trisulfomethylate acetophenone were unsuccessful. Propiophenone gave only the monosulfonate and 1, 8-dibenzoyloctane did not react. Combined sulfomethylation and resini-fication yielded tanning agents from acetone and from methyl ethyl ketone (690).

Acetone, cyclohexanone, and acetophenone have, however, been monosulfomethylated indirectly via the corresponding Mannich bases (546):

$$RCH_2N(CH_3)_2 + Na_2SO_3 \longrightarrow RCH_2SO_3Na +$$

$$(CH_3)_2NH + NaOH \qquad (5\text{-}12)$$

This approach has also been used for sulfomethylating phenols and in-dole, as shown in following sections.

(2) AROMATIC COMPOUNDS. Phenolic compounds undergo nu-clear sulfomethylation in positions ortho or para to the hydroxyl group forming sulfonates of the structure $HOC_6H_4CH_2SO_3Na$. The course of

the reaction has not been studied, but, as stated before, both Route A (Eqs. 5-5 and 5-6) and Route B have been suggested as possibilities. Phenols are apparently the only type of aromatic compound to be sulfomethylated on the nucleus with formaldehyde - bisulfite. Aromatic amines might be expected to react similarly, but no example has been noted. (As shown in Section II-A-1, indole does sulfomethylate on a ring carbon.) A practical method for sulfomethylating aromatic nuclei, such as hydrocarbons or phenolic ethers, involves chloromethylation, followed by iodination and sulfonation as follows (89):

$$RH + CH_2O + HCl \longrightarrow RCH_2Cl + H_2O \xrightarrow{NaI}$$

$$RCH_2I \xrightarrow{Na_2SO_3} RCH_2SO_3Na + NaI \qquad (5\text{-}13)$$

This approach to the preparation of sulfomethylated aromatic compounds should be capable of fruitful extension, since chloromethylation is a widely applicable reaction (217).

Aldehyde - bisulfite sulfomethylation has been applied to phenol, 4-cresol, 2, 4-dimethylphenol, 4-tert-butylphenol, 1-naphthol (in 5% yield), 2-naphthol, 2-naphthol-3-carboxylic acid, sodium 2-naphthol-6-sulfonate, and 6-bromo-2-naphthol (386, 619). Sulfomethylated products from 3-pentadecylphenol, diamylphenol, diisobutylphenol, and menthylphenol (278) were not characterized.

The reaction appears fairly sensitive to reaction conditions and to structural factors. 4-Hydroxybiphenyl, 2, 4-dibromophenol, and phenolic ethers do not sulfomethylate (619). 2-Naphthol sulfomethylates with formaldehyde in 75% yield, but does not react when using acetaldehyde, acetone, or benzaldehyde (619). Phenol itself is apparently the only such compound which has been di-, as well as mono-, sulfomethylated (619). Sulfomethylation of phenols is best conducted at neutral or slightly alkaline pH, even though the reaction is slow under this condition (643). Reaction at higher pH may result in yield loss; at lower pH the reaction may not occur.

Although only a limited number of pure sulfomethylated phenols has been prepared and characterized, the reaction has been empirically combined with phenol - formaldehyde resin formation to yield water - soluble polymeric products of technical interest as tanning agents, and water - insoluble materials useful as ion - exchange resins (440). The patent literature on the preparation of such materials is extensive. Typical examples will be cited.

Sulfomethylation of a preformed water - soluble phenol -formaldehyde novolak (molecular weight 800 - 1300) for 3 hr. at 95°C gave tanning agents (65, 476). In most cases, however, resinification and sulfomethylation have been conducted simultaneously, with the correct ratio of reagents for optimum tanning being determined empirically. One such study (394) found the optimum phenol: formaldehyde: NaHSO3 molar ratio to be 1.0:0.4:0.7. Another procedure (476) employs a ratio of 1.0:1.0:0.2 under initial alkaline conditions, but completes the reaction at below pH 1.5. Other phenolic compounds used in this study included 4-ethyl-, 4-octyl, 4-dodecyl-, and 4-chlorophenols, and 2,2-bis(4-hydroxyphenyl)propane. When using the less reactive bis-(4-hydroxyphenyl)sulfone as the phenolic component, the reaction was conducted at 160°C for 30 hr. under pressure, and optimum tanning was noted at a ratio of 1.0:1.25:0.75 (59, 60). Similar products have been made at 100°C and atmospheric pressure (526). Other reports relate chemical structure to tanning power (393, 644). Patents describe the use of polyhydric phenol mixtures (13, 599), or the addition of a supplementary non-phenolic component capable of undergoing sulfomethylation, such as m-benzenedisulfonamide (562). Details have been published for the manufacture of tanning agents from cresol, 2,2-bis(4-hydroxyphenyl)propane, bis-(4-hydroxyphenol)sulfone, and the analogous sulfone derived from cresols (180, 665). Water-insoluble phenolic natural products, such as lignin (366) or yacca gum (522) also yield water-soluble tanning agents by sulfomethylation. Similar products result from phenols with sugar - sulfite mixtures (12).

Excess formaldehyde gives water-insoluble sulfomethylated polymers useful as ion-exchange resins (400). A phenol: formaldehyde: $NaHSO_3$ molar ratio of 1.0: 2.5: 0.5 has been used (491), sometimes with a final curing temperature of 125 to 175°C (134). A molar ratio of 0.5: 2.5: 0.5, with final curing at 150°C, has been employed with bis-(4-hydroxyphenyl)sulfone (135). 2,2-Bis-(4-hydroxyphenyl)propane has also been used (136). Manufacturing details for such resins from technical phenol-cresol mixtures are available (646). More stable resins result from the addition of "catalysts," such as ferric sulfate (666).

Sulfomethylation of phenols has also been effected by two indirect methods. The first procedure involves the reaction of a preformed hydroxymethylated phenol (i.e., a hydroxybenzyl alcohol) with bisulfite via reaction 5-6. This approach is fairly general, but structural factors and reaction conditions appear quite critical, as discussed in Chapter 3, Section II-A-7. The second approach comprises reaction of a Mannich base with bisulfite by reaction 5-12. This technique has been applied to 4-cresol (171), and to 2-naphthol for sulfomethylation in the 1-position (546). Since a variety of Mannich bases are available (66, 527), this method may be capable of considerable extension.

(3) HETEROCYCLIC COMPOUNDS. The only known case of sulfomethylation on a heterocyclic carbon atom involves indole (122):

$$(5\text{-}14)$$

Like other sulfomethylation reactions, this one is pH - responsive, since no reaction occurred with formaldehyde - bisulfite. The same sulfonate was prepared via reaction 5-12 using the Mannich base 3-dimethylaminomethylindole (gramine) (172, 668, 692).

c. Sulfomethylation on a Nitrogen Atom

(1) AMINES, HYDRAZINES, AND HYDRAZIDES. Amino groups react overall as follows with aldehyde - bisulfites:

$$R'R''NH + RCHO + NaHSO_3 \longrightarrow R'R''NCH(R)SO_3Na + H_2O \quad (5\text{-}15)$$

As shown in Table 5-1, the amines can be ammonia, aliphatic, aromatic, or heterocyclic primary or secondary amines. The aldehyde - bisulfite has usually been that made from formaldehyde, although other aldehydes, which usually give lower yields (513), have been used to a minor extent. Ketone - bisulfites have not been employed, except for that from acetone (168, 552) - mentioned in only two cases. Primary amines can form disulfonates:

$$RNH_2 + 2\ HOCH_2SO_3Na \longrightarrow RN(CH_2SO_3Na)_2 + H_2O \quad (5\text{-}16)$$

Ammonia similarly can yield a trisulfonate. The sulfomethylation of amines has been briefly reviewed up to 1957 (513). Hydrazines and hydrazides react like amines, as shown in Table 5-2. The aminomethanesulfonic acids themselves are useful sulfomethylating agents, and are discussed separately in Section II-A-2.

The sulfomethylation of amines is usually effected simply by mixing and heating the amine, aldehyde and the metallic bisulfite for 3 hr. or less in the range 30 - 100°C (513). The reaction is ordinarily conducted in aqueous solution; aqueous alcohol has also been used (88, 427). Non-aqueous organic solvents such as phenol (547) have also been suggested. The amine may be applied as the free base, a salt, as the azomethine of the aldehyde (167, 371, 411, 427, 512, 513), or as the hydroxymethyl derivative of the amine (94). The metallic bisulfite should be freshly prepared before use (512). The addition of gaseous SO_2 to a mixture of the amine and the aqueous aldehyde has been found preferable to the use of a metallic bisulfite, since this procedure minimizes side reactions and loss of sulfite by air oxidation (405). However, this technique at room temperature with various primary amines and benzaldehyde, three aliphatic aldehydes (except formaldehyde), and three ketones, yielded the salts, $RCHOHSO_3H \cdot H_2NR'$, rather than sulfomethylated products (8).

The fact that sulfonamides, $RCH(NHR')SO_2NHR'$, are often formed as coproducts with the sulfonate salts was first observed in 1901 by Eibner, but was apparently neglected until recently, when it was employed for synthesis (479). The equilibrium nature of the process is well illustrated by the fact that a mixture of all four possible sulfon-

TABLE 5-1

Sulfomethylation of Amines with Aldehyde - Bisulfite

Amine	Aldehyde	Remarks	Reference
Ammonia, Aliphatic, and Substituted Aliphatic Amines			
Ammonia	F[a]	Optimized yield; products acylated	181
Ammonia	Five C2 - 6 alde- hydes; benzalde- hyde; phenylace- taldehyde	Amino acid analo- gues; iminodisul- fonate formed in one case	209, 446, 479
Ammonia	Acetaldehyde, citronellal; 3 benzaldehyde de- rivatives	-	37
Ammonia	F	Di- and trisulfo- nates	101
Ammonia, methylamine	F, propionaldehyde, 3-methylhexanal	Used SO_2 gas	145, 277, 306, 468
Hydroxylamine	F	Mono- and disul- fonates	523
Methylamine	F, 4-hydroxyphen- ylglyoxal	Product acylated	36, 181 205, 479
Tert-Butylamine	F	-	36
n-Dodecyl-, cyclohexyla- mine	F	Products unstable; acylated	181
Benzylamine	Seven C1 - 8 alde- hydes; benzal- dehyde	Amino acid analogues	209
Cyclohexylamine	F	Cis- and trans- hydroxycyclohexyl- amines also used	206
2-Hydroxy- ethylamine	F	Mono- and disulfonate	120, 405
Dimethylamine	F	-	36

(continued)

TABLE 5-1 (CONTINUED)

Amine	Aldehyde	Remarks	Reference
Ammonia, Aliphatic, and Substituted Aliphatic Amines			
Diethylamine	F	Yield 81%	373, 479
Bis-(2-hydroxy-ethylamine)	F	-	120
Bis-(2-chloro-ethylamine)	F, acetaldehyde, propionaldehyde	Drug intermediates	339
Ethylene di-amine	F	Tetrasulfonate	405
N, N'-Diethyl-ethylenedi-amine	F	Disulfonate	405
N-(n-Long-chain) poly-amines	F	Trisulfonates	168
N-(n-Dodecyl) trimethyl-enediamine	Acetone	Disulfonate	168
Hexamethyl-enediamine	F	Disulfonate	387
Glycine	F	50% yield of mono-sulfonate	521
Glycine	F	Disulfonate	405
Glycine ester	F, acetaldehyde, acetone, benzal-dehyde, piperonal	-	552, 553
Esters of ala-nine, tyrosine	F	-	553
3-Aminobutyric acid ester	Benzaldehyde	-	553
Amino acid mixture	F	Tanning agent	307
Dicyandiamide	F	Diazo stabilizer	588
Sodium amino-ethanesulfonate	F	Trisulfonate	405

(continued)

TABLE 5-1 (CONTINUED)

Amine	Aldehyde	Remarks	Reference
Ammonia, Aliphatic, and Substituted Aliphatic Amines			
2-Thenylamine	F	-	277
Di-(beta-pyridyl-methyl) amine	F	30% yield	667
Kanamycin, neo-mycin, colimy-cin, colistin, monomycin, paromomycin	F	Di-, tetra-, penta-, hexasulfonates	255, 503, 584, 596, 625
4-Aminomethyl-benzenesulfo-namide	Cinnamic	Disulfonate	53, 182
Alkyl norephe-drines	F	Drugs formed	449
Aromatic Amines			
Aniline	F, C3 - 4, benzal-dehyde, 3-phen-ylpropionalde-hyde	Improved yields	479
Aniline	F, glucose, benz-aldehyde, anti-pyrine aldehyde, 4-hydroxyphen-ylglyoxal	Intermediates for drugs, dyes	36, 88, 166, 205, 235, 411, 417, 638
2-, and 4-Tolu-idines	F, benzaldehyde	Bactericide, dye intermediate	88, 178, 235, 417, 479
2-, and 4-Anis-idines	F, benzaldehyde	Dye intermediate	88, 166, 325, 417
4-Phenetidine	F	-	418
2-, and 4-Chloro-anilines	F, benzaldehyde	-	417, 479
N-Methyl- and N-ethyl-anilines	F	Benzaldehyde did not react	88, 513

(continued)

TABLE 5-1 (CONTINUED)

Amine	Aldehyde	Remarks	Reference
Aromatic Amines			
2-, and 4-Amino-phenols	F	Antitubercular	166, 213
2-Amino-4-nitro-phenol, 2-amino-4-carbometh-oxyphenol	F	Disulfonates	166
3-, and 4-Nitro-anilines	F	Mono- and disul-fonates	88, 166
4-Amino-2-hydro-phenylarsonic acid	F	-	166
3,3'-Diamino-4,4'-dihydroxy-arsenobenzene	F	Trisulfonate	166
3-Trifluoro-methylaniline	F	-	624
Aminoazoben-zenes	F	Bactericide; dye intermediate	178, 179, 417, 669
Paraphenylene-diamine, N, N'-dimethylpara-phenylenedi-amine	F, glucose	Mono- and disulfo-nates	9, 88, 155, 178, 501, 638
N, N'-Diaryl-ethylenedi-amines	F	Disulfonates	403
Monoacetylpara-phenylenedi-amine	F	-	417
Pararosaniline	F	Trisulfonate	478
Benzidine	F	Mono- and disulfo-nates	88
Anthranilic acid	F, benzaldehyde	Mono- and disulfo-nates	61, 88, 386, 405

(continued)

TABLE 5-1 (CONTINUED)

Amine	Aldehyde	Remarks	Reference
Aromatic Amines			
4-Aminobenzoic acid	Benzaldehyde	Sulfonamide also formed	479
Sodium sulfanilate	F	Sulfonamide also formed	88, 479
4-Aminosalicylic acid; its Hg derivatives	F, benzaldehyde, furfural	Antibacterials	506
4-Aminobenzene-sulfonamides	F, benzaldehyde, acrolein, glucose, crotonaldehyde	Amino group only reacts	73, 142, 253, 411, 451, 454
4-Aminobenzene-sulfonamido-thiazole	F, cinnamic	Mono- and disulfo-nates	312, 627
4-Aminobenzene-sulfonamido-pyridines, -pyrimidines, and -thiadi-azoles	Acrolein, acet-aldehyde, cinnamic	Amino group only reacts	10, 53 54, 182, 354, 427
4, 4'-Diaminodi-phenylsulfone	Acetaldehyde, glucose, vanillin	Mono-, di-, and tetrasulfonates	49, 55, 308, 533, 638
4-Amino-4'-(ace-tylamino)diph-enylsulfone	F, cinnamic	Amino group only reacts	517
4, 4'-Diaminodi-phenylsulfoxide	Acetaldehyde, glucose	Di- and tetrasulfo-nates	157
Aminophenyl-thiazoles	F, benzaldehyde	Optical bleaches	2, 493
Aminostilbenes	F, furfural	Optical bleaches	3, 493
2, 4-Diamino-6, 7-bis-(4-aminophenyl) pteridin	F	Disulfonate	94
Aminonaphth-alenes	F, benzaldehyde	Optical bleaches	88, 417, 493

(continued)

TABLE 5-1 (CONTINUED)

Amine	Aldehyde	Remarks	Reference
Aromatic Amines			
Sodium 1-amino-4-naphthalesulfonate	F	-	88, 386
Aminoanthraquinones	F	Vat dyes	365, 508, 547, 669
Heterocyclic Amines			
Pyrrolidine	F	-	159
Piperidine	Benzaldehyde	Sulfonamide also formed	479
2-Phenylazetidine	F	-	634
2-Alkoxy-9-aminopyridines	F, acetaldehyde	Bacteriostats	77, 210, 211
Arylamino(aminopyrimidines)	F	Arylamino group only reacts	97
1-Phenyl-2,3-dimethyl-4-methyl-amino-5-pyrazolone	F	Improved procedure	68, 194, 688
Indole	F	Carbon atom reacts	122
7-Aminocoumarins	F, benzaldehyde	Optical bleaches	4, 5
Azaguanine	F	100°C for 5 hr.	1
Melamine	F	Disulfonate	542, 621
Melamine-formaldehyde resin	F	Water-soluble resin formed	32, 198
N,N,N,Triphenylmelamine	F	Water-soluble resin formed	462

[a]"F" designates formaldehyde.

TABLE 5-2

Sulfomethylation of Hydrazine Derivatives

Hydrazine used	Aldehyde	Remarks	Reference
Hydrazine	F[a]	Mono- and disulfonates	37, 427, 455, 523, 703
1, 2-Dimethylhydrazine	F	Disulfonate	427, 523
Phenylhydrazine	F	Monosulfonate	37
Isopropylhydrazine	F	Gave zwitterion	426
Mono- and dihydrazino-phthalazines	F	Mono- and disulfonates	538
Isonicotinic hydrazide	Glucose	Product drug	583
Isonicotinic hydrazide	F	Disulfonate	427, 703
Isonicotinic hydrazide	F	Monosulfonate	424, 425
Isonicotinic hydrazide	Cinnamic	Disulfonate	592
C8 - 16 fatty acid hydrazides	F	Tuberculostats	623
Gallic acid hydrazide	F	100°C for 0.5 hr.	396

[a] "F" designates formaldehyde.

amides is formed from one aldehyde by reaction with a mixture of two amines, and that the same mixture results by heating one amine with the sulfomethylated derivative of the other.

The sulfomethylation of amino compounds has been studied extensively for increasing the water solubility and compatibility, and lowering the toxicity of drugs (427, 488, 512), including arsenicals, sulfa drugs, hydrazides, and antipyrine derivatives. It has been found that the choice of the aldehyde used can affect the activity of the drug (427). Acetaldehyde, cinnamic aldehyde, or glucose have been found preferable in some cases to formaldehyde. Sulfomethylation of azo or anthraquinone dyes containing amino groups has been employed to enhance their water solubility. Several of these "Ionamine" dyes were formerly marketed (669).

(2) AMIDES, CARBAMATES, AND UREAS.   Aliphatic amido groups easily undergo sulfomethylation forming sulfonates of structure $RCONHCH_2SO_3Na$.   Current thought favors a course involving Route A (reactions 5-5; 5-6).

Benzamide does not react under the mild conditions applicable to aliphatic amides (619).   At 200°C in a sealed tube it does sulfomethylate in poor yield (372); anisamide, however, gives a 60% yield at this temperature.   Sulfomethylation of other aromatic amides has not been reported.

The sulfomethylation of long-chain aliphatic (C12 - 19) amides has been studied toward obtaining detergents.   This type of product was manufactured in Germany (78), but was soon discontinued, because the reaction was difficult to carry to completion and the detergent was unstable to chlorine bleach.   The stearamide derivative has excellent detergency, while that of the C14 amide is poor (705).   Detergency of the C16 compound is strikingly improved by adding sodium hydroxide or carbonate, but not other materials (706).   The reaction can preferably be conducted under anhydrous conditions for 6 hours at 185°C using excess formaldehyde - bisulfite, or in aqueous medium in 3 hr. with a 1:5:10 molar ratio of amide:bisulfite:water (704).   It can also be run in xylene suspension in 13 hr. at 155°C.   The reaction time can be greatly reduced by adding secondary amine catalysts, such as piperidine or dicyclohexylamine (333,432).   The addition of free fatty acid and its soap satisfactorily reduces the high viscosity of the mixture in the final stages of reaction (18).   This reaction mixture can be used as such in detergent formulations, or it can be purified (279).   In the cases cited before, formaldehyde-bisulfite was used. The bisulfites of acetaldehyde (333,700), of acetone (333,700), and of benzaldehyde (333) have also been employed, but the yields are lower (333) than with formaldehyde.   Disulfonates have been made from amides using the bisulfites of crotonaldehyde, cinnamic aldehyde, and sodium 2-benzaldehydesulfonate (543).

Long-chain carbamates $(ROCONH_2)$ have likewise been sulfomethylated to surface-active agents using piperidine to accelerate the reaction (514).   The C18 compound has been disulfonated with crotonaldehyde - bisulfite (543).   Long-chain alkyl ureas $(RNHCONH_2)$ have been sulfomethylated stepwise (173).   Three to 4 hours at 70°C effects monosulfomethylation; 2 and 3 groups can be introduced in 10 - 20 hr. at 100 to 130°C, respectively.   This reaction has also been run at 150°C in an amide solvent (375a).

Poly(acrylamide) has been sulfomethylated to yield soil conditioners and drilling mud additives (561,614).   All the amide groups could be hydroxymethylated, but only half of these could be converted to sulfomethyl groups, presumably because of steric hindrance.   The reaction rate is very sensitive to pH and to temperature.   Sulfomethylation of urea-formaldehyde resins, at a ratio of one sulfomethyl group for about every 12 urea units, has been employed for rendering such resins substantive to the fibers in making wet-strength paper (30, 32,

84, 443, 444, 612). Temperature and pH control are important in preparing such resins (612). Although at one time considered well suited
to commercial use, they have been largely replaced by other materials (84). Such resins have also been made from acetaldehyde - bisulfite (32). Melamine - formaldehyde resins have been similarly sulfomethylated (32).

(3) SULFONAMIDES.   Sulfonamides form sulfomethylated derivatives of structure $RSO_2NHCH_2SO_3Na$. As in the sulfomethylation of
other types of compounds, the rate of reaction is greatly accelerated
by using neutral sulfite with the resulting high pH per Equation 5-4,
rather than using bisulfite (141, 530). Specific examples include preparation of the sulfomethylated derivatives of methanesulfonamide
(336), benzenemono- and -disulfonamides, 4-toluenesulfonamide (372,
530), and long-chain aliphatic sulfonamides, including straight-chain
compounds (530), as well as those made by the sulfochlorination of
petroleum fractions (29, 334).   The last materials are tanning agents
(507) and detergents (29).   4-Aminobenzenesulfonamides sulfomethylate preferentially on the amino group, as indicated in Table 5-1.   4-
Acetylaminobenzenesulfonamide sulfomethylates rapidly and quantitatively on the sulfonamide group under strongly alkaline conditions,
but much more slowly at lower pH (141); heating the product with
aqueous HCl results in cleavage of the acetyl group, leaving the sulfomethyl group intact.

Sulfonamides are ordinarily sulfomethylated under fairly mild conditions, e. g. , in aqueous solution at 50°C (530), or as an anhydrous
melt at 120°C (334). Benzenemono- and -disulfonamides were sulfomethylated in good yields at 200°C in a sealed tube (372).

2. AMINOMETHANESULFONIC ACID AND ITS N-ALKYL
    DERIVATIVES

The preparation of this material, and of several of its N- and C-
substituted analogues, was described before under Sulfomethylation of
Amines. Because of their ease of preparation, these materials are of
interest as sulfoalkylating agents in their own right. Aminomethanesulfonic acid, and its N-methyl derivative, are commercially available in laboratory quantities (99).

Acylation of aminomethanesulfonic acid salts, and 3 of its N-alkyl
derivatives, with acetic anhydride, benzoyl chloride, and with long-
chain acid chlorides, is best conducted at 0°C and at a definite pH,
because of the instability of the starting aminosulfonic acid salts (181).
Yields vary from 30 to 90%. The acylated products are stable and effective as detergents (181, 262). Acylation has also been effected with
carbobenzoxy- and hippuryl chlorides, with phthalimidopropionic
acid, and with carbobenzoxyglycine, in the last two cases via an "anhydride procedure" (209). Amino acid analogues were thus prepared.
Aminomethanesulfonic acid salts react with benzenesulfonyl chloride,

but not with 4-acetylaminobenzenesulfonyl chloride (209).

Aminomethanesulfonic acid has been employed as the amino component in a Mannich - type condensation with thiophene and several substituted thiophenes (277):

$$C_4H_4S + CH_2O + NH_2CH_2SO_3H \longrightarrow$$

$$C_4H_3SCH_2NHCH_2SO_3H + H_2O \qquad (5\text{-}16\text{-}A)$$

A similar type of reaction with sodium N-methyltaurate and with sodium sulfanilate are cited in Sections II-B-2 and V-B, respectively.

3. CHLOROMETHANESULFONIC ACID

Sodium chloromethanesulfonate is usually prepared from methylene chloride and sodium sulfite (175, 202, 349, 405, 518, 519, 589):

$$CH_2Cl_2 + Na_2SO_3 \longrightarrow ClCH_2SO_3Na + NaCl \qquad (5\text{-}17)$$

Other approaches involve a similar reaction with methylene chlorobromide (618), or oxidation of chloromethanethiol derivatives (345, 618, 695). Salts of bromo- and iodomethanesulfonic acids have also been used for sulfomethylation (46, 410), but they have shown no advantages over the chloro compound (46).

Sodium chloromethanesulfonate is uniquely suited to the sulfomethylation of phenols, thiols, and of alcohols (i. e. , cellulose) on the oxygen or sulfur atoms. It has not shown promise for sulfomethylating aliphatic amines (405), which in any case can be done more efficiently with formaldehyde - bisulfite, as discussed earlier in this chapter.

The chlorine atom in sodium chloromethanesulfonate is fairly inert (345, 695), and high reaction temperatures are therefore required in many cases to insure reaction. Salts of 31 mono- and dihydric phenols and of 3 naphthols were reacted as melts at 180 - 200°C in yields of 70% or better (45, 46):

$$C_6H_5ONa + ClCH_2SO_3Na \longrightarrow C_6H_5OCH_2SO_3Na + NaCl \qquad (5\text{-}18)$$

The phenoxymethanesulfonic acid group thus formed is chemically stable, since it remains unchanged during chlorination (47), nitration, or during reduction and diazotization of the nitro compound. Sodium oleate, and other soaps, have also been reacted at 200°C (604):

$$RCOONa + ClCH_2SO_3Na \longrightarrow RCOOCH_2SO_3Na + NaCl \qquad (5\text{-}19)$$

In other cases, sulfomethylation occurs more easily. A series of 7 thiophenols gave good yields by simply refluxing in aqueous medium

(46). Sulfadiazine reacted in 2 hr. at 100°C (477). Cellulose has
been sulfomethylated in the presence of base at 95°C for 15 hr. to a
water-insoluble product (518, 519), or to a water-soluble product at
the same temperature in 40 hr. In the presence of isopropanol, water-
soluble materials were formed from cellulose in 1 hr. at 140°C, or
in 2 hr. at 125°C (202).

4. MISCELLANEOUS SULFOMETHYLATING REAGENTS

Sodium benzylsulfonate has been converted to its Grignard reagent
as follows:

$$C_6H_5CH_2SO_3Na + iso\text{-}C_3H_7MgCl \longrightarrow$$

$$C_6H_5CH(MgCl)SO_3Na + C_3H_8 \qquad (5\text{-}20)$$

This compound displays typical Grignard properties, since it forms
secondary alcoholic sulfonates with acetaldehyde and benzaldehyde
(435), tertiary alcoholic sulfonates with acetone (435), cyclohexanone
and benzophenone (338), and ketonic sulfonates with acetyl and benzoyl
chlorides (436). The versatility of the Grignard reaction could make
this compound a widely useful sulfomethylating reagent.

The analogous lithium compound has been made (437) and found to
react with azomethines as follows:

$$C_6H_5CH(Li)SO_3Na + RCH{:}NR' \xrightarrow{H_2O}$$

$$R'NHCH(R)CH(C_6H_5)SO_3Na + LiOH \qquad (5\text{-}21)$$

The reactions and derivatives of potassium diazomethionate, prepared as described in Chapter 3, Section II-B-7, have been little studied, although many of these should be possible via the reactive diazo
group. "Activated" olefins, such as acrylonitrile, form pyrazolines
(384a):

$$(KO_3S)_2C\overset{\oplus}{=}N\overset{\ominus}{=}N + CH_2{=}CXY \longrightarrow$$

$$\begin{array}{c} CH_2 \!-\! CXY \\ | \qquad\quad | \\ (KO_3S)_2C \diagdown \quad N \\ N \diagup \end{array} \qquad (5\text{-}21A)$$

B. Introduction of Sulfoethyl, Sulfoethylidene, and Sulfoacetyl Groups

1. 2-HYDROXYETHANESULFONIC ACID AND ITS ALKYL DERIVATIVES

a. Preparation

This compound, also known as isethionic acid, has - in the form of its sodium salt - been a commercially interesting sulfoethylating re- agent for many years because of its availability, low cost, low mole- cular weight, and versatility in forming derivatives (25). It is pre- pared in excellent yield and purity from ethylene oxide and sodium bi- sulfite (326):

$$\overline{OCH_2CH_2} + NaSO_3H \longrightarrow HOCH_2CH_2SO_3Na \qquad (5\text{-}22)$$

The reaction can be run continuously (575), and careful control of pH is necessary for optimum yields (576). A less satisfactory alternative commercial preparative procedure involves treatment of ethanol with sulfur trioxide, followed by hydrolysis (326). Numerous other reac- tions yield isethionic acid as one of several products formed (130, 243, 618). The commercial sodium salt is a white powder of 96% purity melting at 180° C (25). A 70% aqueous solution of the free acid is also available (162).

Substituted isethionates can be made similarly from various other available epoxides. However, all of these would be less chemically stable than sodium isethionate, since they are secondary alcohols. They would also be without apparent advantages as sulfoalkylating agents, except possibly the one derived from epichlorohydrin, as dis- cussed in Section C-2. In addition, it appears that the hydroxysulfo- nates derived from propylene oxide, the butylene oxides (579), and styrene oxide (489) may comprise mixtures of the two possible hydro- xysulfonates, while ethylene oxide yields only one product. Propylene oxide apparently gives pure 2-hydroxypropanesulfonate under some conditions (406, 605). This subject is discussed in more detail in Chapter 3, Section II-B-6.

b. Esterification

Esterification with acid chlorides proceeds quantitatively upon heat- ing the reagents in the range 50 to 150° C:

$$RCOCl + HOCH_2CH_2SO_3Na \longrightarrow RCOOCH_2CH_2SO_3Na + HCl \qquad (5\text{-}23)$$

Xylene (243) and chlorobenzene (579) have been used as reaction sol- vents, but none is required. Acid chlorides so reacted include chloro-acetyl (380), phenylacetyl, 2-phenylpropionyl, and acetylmandelyl (243). Herbicides were thus prepared from 2,2-dichloropropionyl (380), 2,4-dichlorophenoxyacetyl, and 2,4,5-trichlorophenoxyacetyl (318) chlorides. Benzoyl chloride yields a fungicide (383); acrylyl and methacryllyl chlorides form monomers (412, 579). The substituted isethionates made from propylene oxide and epoxybutene-1 react similarly with acid chlorides (318, 579, 637). Reaction of oleoyl and other long-chain acid chlorides with sodium isethionate is important industrially for making detergents (131). Details of this commercial process, operated batchwise, are available (326). The procedure can also be run continuously (637), in vacuo (85), or in a thin film. Long-chain acid anhydrides have also been used (224, 231). Amine salts of isethionic acid, and its methyl and ethyl derivatives, react similarly with long-chain acid chlorides (578).

The commercial importance of detergents of this type has prompted efforts to prepare the esters directly from the acids, rather than from the more expensive acid chlorides:

$$RCOOH + HOCH_2CH_2SO_3Na \longrightarrow RCOOCH_2CH_2SO_3Na + H_2O \quad (5\text{-}24)$$

Reaction is impeded by only partial miscibility of the reagents even at 200°C (273), but a 90% yield results in 1 hr. at 220 - 260°C using a vacuum to facilitate removal of water, an inert gas to prevent darkening from oxidation, and an excess of one reagent to drive the reaction to completion (169, 273, 320, 460). This process is used commercially (273). Attempts to facilitate reaction with certain acid catalysts caused excessive product darkening (320), but other catalysts, such as AlCl$_3$, Al$_2$(SO$_4$)$_3$, aluminum isethionate, SnCl$_2$, SnCl$_4$, or ZnSO$_4$, are stated to give yields of 90% or better at 200 - 240°C, compared to only 21% under the same conditions without a catalyst (661). Use of these catalysts with lower-melting mixtures of sodium and potassium isethionates allows reduction of the reaction temperature to 160 - 195°C (17, 659). The esterification is also catalyzed by hypophosphorous acid or its salts (556), phosphorous or phosphoric acids (20), or boric acid (615). Use of a mixed anhydride of the acid and boric acid permits a reaction temperature as low as 140°C (554).

Free isethionic acid, on the other hand, esterifies the long-chain acids even at 100°C when the product is used as reaction solvent (273). The reaction can be operated continuously, and is complete in 90 sec. at 175°C at a 20-mm. vacuum with 10 mole-% excess fatty acid. Isethionic acid, must, however, be made from the sodium salt in a separate operation.

α-Sulfo fatty acids (from palmitic, stearic, and behenic acids) esterify easily on refluxing 6 - 12 hr. in toluene or xylene (685). The resulting isethionate esters are more stable to hydrolysis than the corresponding esters made from the unsulfonated fatty acids; even greater stability results from the use of sodium 2-hydroxypropanesulfonate. Acrylic and methacrylic acids esterify with either sodium isethionate or 2-hydroxypropanesulfonate upon refluxing 6 hours in benzene even without a catalyst (413, 580). Such mild conditions appear exceptional, however. Thus, 1-naphthaleneacetic and 2-naphthoxyacetic (384), 2-chlorobenzoic (383), and chloroacetic acids (380) were reacted in 2 - 5 hr. at 165 - 250°C with no catalyst or solvent. Esterification of 2,4-dichlorophenoxyacetic acid at 200 - 250°C was facilitated by using trichlorobenzene as solvent or by operating in vacuo (382). These sulfonates were of interest as herbicides. The long-chain fatty acids from wax oxidation are reported to esterify at 30 - 40°C in the presence of a stream of anhydrous HCl (131). Castor oil reacts under similar conditions by ester interchange. The same catalyst at 175°C for 2 hr. effected esterification of long-chain fatty acids with sodium isethionate (193) and with sodium 2-hydroxypropanesulfonate (185).

c. Amination

Sodium isethionate reacts with ammonia, or with primary or secondary aliphatic amines to form sodium taurates, as follows (25):

$$RR'NH + HOCH_2CH_2SO_3Na \longrightarrow RR'NCH_2CH_2SO_3Na + H_2O \qquad (5\text{-}25)$$

(R and, or R', is H or alkyl)

This reaction proceeds at 270 - 290°C in aqueous medium in an autoclave (320, 332, 337, 483). Sodium hydroxide or inorganic salts function as catalysts (337, 484). Sodium 2-hydroxypropanesulfonate behaves similarly (483, 574). Primary amines can also yield $RN(CH_2CH_2SO_3-Na)_2$ as by-product. High-boiling long-chain amines can be sulfoethylated at atmospheric pressure (379). Aromatic and heterocyclic amines (aniline, carbazole, 2-heptadecylbenzimidazole) likewise sulfoethylate on nitrogen (492, 628). 2-Heptadecylindole, however, sulfoethylates on carbon in the reactive 3-position. The taurates themselves are important sulfoethylating agents, and are discussed separately in the next section.

d. Amidation

Amides likewise sulfoethylate on nitrogen (492, 628):

$$RCONH_2 + HOCH_2CH_2SO_3Na \longrightarrow RCONHCH_2CH_2SO_3Na + H_2O \quad (5\text{-}26)$$

Aromatic (benzamide, phthalimide) and long-chain aliphatic amides (oleamide, N-methyl oleamide) react at 220°C in 13 hr. The distearic amide of ethylenediamine thus forms a disulfonate. The yields are poor, however (17 - 50%), and reaction of the taurate with an acid chloride, as discussed in the next section, appears a preferable synthetic approach.

e. Etherification

Compounds containing hydroxyl groups react as follows:

$$ROH + HOCH_2CH_2SO_3Na \longrightarrow ROCH_2CH_2SO_3Na + H_2O \quad (5\text{-}27)$$

This reaction has been applied to N-hydroxymethyl, long-chain amides (111), long-chain aliphatic alcohols and glycols, glycol ethers, amino alcohols, phenols, and ethoxylated phenols (44, 315, 376); sodium hydroxide is sometimes added as catalyst. Similar products result from hydroxyethylation (239):

$$x\overline{OCH_2CH_2} + HOCH_2CH_2SO_3Na \longrightarrow HO(CH_2CH_2O)_xCH_2CH_2SO_3Na \, (5\text{-}28)$$

This material can also be made directly from ethylene oxide and sodium bisulfite. Ether sulfonates likewise result from condensation with reactive halides, such as propargyl bromide or 1, 4-dichlorobutyne-2 (87):

$$RBr + HOCH_2CH_2SO_3Na \longrightarrow ROCH_2CH_2SO_3Na + HBr \quad (5\text{-}29)$$

Thiols behave similarly:

$$RSH + HOCH_2CH_2SO_3Na \longrightarrow RSCH_2CH_2SO_3Na + H_2O \quad (5\text{-}30)$$

The thiols used include long-chain thiols (C8 - 18) (222, 314), and aromatic thiols (220, 314).

f. Miscellaneous Reactions

Compounds with active methylene groups (diethyl malonate, ethyl acetoacetate, acetophenone) sulfoethylate on the reactive carbon atoms in 23 - 41% yield (492), forming materials of structure $RR'CHCH2CH2^-$ SO3Na. Dehydration of 2-hydroxyethanesulfonic acid salts and their 2-alkyl derivatives to the corresponding ethenesulfonic acid salts is discussed in Section B-7.

2. 2-AMINOETHANESULFONIC ACID AND ITS ALKYL DERIVATIVES

a. Preparation

Salts of this compound, also called taurine, and of several of its mono-N-alkylated derivatives, are important sulfoethylating reagents. The preferred industrial preparative procedure involves the reaction of sodium isethionate with the corresponding amine, as discussed in the preceding section (Eq. 5-25). An alternative, but less satisfactory commercial approach comprises reaction of the amine with sodium 2-

chloroethanesulfonate (328, 560, 571). Taurines have also been prepared by various other methods (243, 330, 441, 494, 622). Sodium taurate, sodium and potassium N-methyltaurates, sodium N-(n-butyl)
taurate, and sodium N-cyclohexyltaurate are commercially available
(24). The various N-alkylated taurines are stated to display similar
chemical behavior (24). The taurines are versatile sulfoethylating reagents, since they have the high reactivity characteristic of aliphatic
amines (24).

b. Amide Formation

    Long-chain acid chlorides (34, 143, 263, 264), and long-chain acid
chlorides terminally substituted by aromatic groups (151), form surface - active compounds:

$$CH_3NHCH_2CH_2SO_3Na + RCOCl + NaOH \longrightarrow$$

$$RCON(CH_3)CH_2CH_2SO_3Na + NaCl + H_2O \qquad (5\text{-}31)$$

Oleoyl chloride thus yields "Igepon T" (34, 320), which is commercially
important. This reaction is desirably conducted above pH 7 by the
steady addition of base (322). It can be run continuously (681a). The
rate is increased by adding a surface-active agent other than the product itself (322). The reaction can be run in acetone, dioxide and, or
similar solvents (555). Acrylyl chloride forms N-acrylyl taurine, a
comonomer (163). Colored acid chlorides, for example 4-chlorocar-
bonylphenylazo-2-naphthol (469), and other similar compounds (24)
yield dyestuffs. Dyes have also been made from anthraquinone carbonyl chlorides (398). Acid chlorides of iodinated benzoic (245), phenylacetic, cyclopentylacetic, and similar acids have been likewise converted.
    The amides can also be prepared directly from the fatty acids:

$$CH_3NHCH_2CH_2SO_3Na + RCOOH \longrightarrow$$
$$RCON(CH_3)CH_2CH_2SO_3Na + H_2O \qquad (5\text{-}32)$$

Commercial importance of the long-chain acyl taurate surface-active
agents (34) has led to study of this reaction as a cheaper approach to
their preparation compared to the use of the acid chlorides. An early
attempt to do this (320) by heating the reagents in vacuo to 220 - 260°C
for 1 hr. with vigorous agitation gave the desired reaction, but in poor
yield - apparently, at least in part, because of decomposition of the
taurate to the ditaurate (24):

$$2\ CH_3NHCH_2CH_2SO_3Na \longrightarrow CH_3N(CH_2CH_2SO_3Na)_2 + CH_3NH_2 \qquad (5\text{-}33)$$

Further study of the acylation under the same conditions (91, 92) showed that use of 1. 5 - 2. 0 moles of acid per mole of taurate overcame this difficulty and gave complete conversion of the latter to the desired product in 10 hrs. The excess fatty acid in the product is acceptable in detergent bars, and the process is operated commercially for this use (92). The mixture is, however, unacceptable for other applications, where the product made by the acid chloride method can be used. The 10 hr. reaction time can be reduced to a 2 hr. by employing a boric oxide catalyst (615). Other expedients suggested for shortening the time or reducing the reaction temperature include the use of a mixed anhydride of the fatty acid and boric acid (569), use of the acid anhydride (429), or of the acid with an alkali metal phosphite catalyst (660). Some of these approaches were also suggested for facilitating the esterification of sodium isethionate, as mentioned in the preceding section.

Amide formation can also occur by ammonolysis, as with dithiooxamide (682):

$$2H_2NCH_2CH_2SO_3Na + NH_2\overset{\overset{S}{\|}\overset{S}{\|}}{C}CNH_2 \longrightarrow$$

$$(NaO_3SCH_2CH_2NH\overset{\overset{S}{\|}}{C}-)_2 + 2NH_3 \qquad (5\text{-}34)$$

c. Urea and Carbamate Formation

Long-chain chlorocarbonates react in a manner similar to that of the acid chlorides, forming surface-active carbamates of the structure $ROCON(R')CH_2CH_2SO_3Na$ (497, 498). Benzyl chlorocarbonate behaves likewise (446). Di (2-ethylhexyl) carbamyl chloride (78) yields the substituted urea $R_2NCON(R')CH_2CH_2SO_3Na$; it is a good wetting agent, but a poor detergent. Ureas (24) and thioureas (545) also result from reaction with long-chain isocyanates and isothiocyanates. Sodium dicyanimide forms sulfoethyl cyanoguanidine (524).

d. Sulfonamide Formation

Sulfonyl chlorides form sulfonamides $RSO_2N(R')CH_2CH_2SO_3Na$ (24). Surface-active agents result when R is C10 - 20 long-chain alkyl (319) or long-chain alkylphenyl (129). 4-Acetylaminobenzenesulfonyl chloride forms a drug (656), and anthraquinonesulfonyl chlorides yield dyes (398).

e. Alkylation and Arylation

Diazomethane easily converts taurine to the betaine (397):

$$H_2NCH_2CH_2SO_3H + 3\ CH_2N_2 \longrightarrow (CH_3)_3\overset{+}{N}CH_2CH_2SO_3^- \quad (5\text{-}35)$$

Long-chain alkylbenzyl chlorides can also form betaines with N-methyl-taurate in alkaline solution (603). A trichlorobenzyl chloride converts sodium taurate to the tertiary amine, which is stated to be a good detergent (331). Tertiary amines are also formed from reactive aromatic halogen compounds, such as 2-chloro-5-nitrobenzene-2-sulfonic acid salts (24), or salts of chloroacetic acid (313). Surface-active compounds are likewise formed by alkylation with long-chain ethers of 2-chloroethanol (208), or with long-chain epoxides (377, 616, 662):

$$R\overline{CHCH_2}O + CH_3NHCH_2CH_2SO_3Na \longrightarrow$$

$$RCHOHCH_2N(CH_3)CH_2CH_2SO_3Na \quad (5\text{-}36)$$

Short-chain epoxides react similarly (577). Ethylenimine forms a textile auxiliary (516):

$$x\ \overline{CH_2CH_2}NH + H_2NCH_2CH_2SO_3Na \longrightarrow$$

$$H(NHCH_2CH_2)_xNHCH_2CH_2SO_3Na \quad (5\text{-}37)$$

Reductive alkylation with 2-ethylhexaldehyde proceeds as follows (332):

$$RCHO + H_2NCH_2CH_2SO_3Na \longrightarrow RCH_2NHCH_2CH_2SO_3Na \quad (5\text{-}38)$$

Alkylation can also be effected with sodium isethionate (24):

$$HOCH_2CH_2SO_3Na + CH_3NHCH_2CH_2SO_3Na \longrightarrow$$

$$CH_3N(CH_2CH_2SO_3Na)_2 + H_2O \quad (5\text{-}39)$$

As mentioned before, the ditaurate also results from self-alkylation by heating the N-methyltaurate alone. Vinyl octadecyl sulfoxide easily forms surface-active agents of structure $C_{18}H_{37}SOCH_2CH_2NHCH_2CH_2SO_3Na$ (529).

Alkylated derivatives of N-methyltaurine salts can be prepared by using it as the base in Mannich-type condensations with formaldehyde. Long-chain amides thus form surface-active agents of structure $RCONHCH_2N(R')CH_2CH_2SO_3Na$ (24). Water repellents have been made similarly, but with the addition of urea or melamine (541). Long-chain sulfonamides react likewise (24, 496). Melamine thus forms a tanning agent (133). A similar reaction occurs with long-chain alkylated phenols (218), the ring undergoing substitution by the $-CH_2N(CH_3)CH_2-CH_2SO_3Na$ moiety. The products are effective dispersants of lime soaps, but poor detergents. Thymol was rendered water-soluble without loss of antiseptic activity by the same type of reaction (240). Long-chain alkenes with formaldehyde undergo a Prins - type reaction (188), as follows:

$$RCH{:}CH_2 + CH_2O + CH_3NHCH_2CH_2SO_3Na \longrightarrow$$

$$RCHOH(CH)_2N(CH_3)CH_2CH_2SO_3Na \qquad\qquad (5\text{-}40)$$

Formaldehyde, or other low molecular-weight aldehydes alone, form compounds of the structure $RCH[N(R')CH_2CH_2SO_3Na]_2$ (24).

f. Miscellaneous Reactions

Hydrogen sulfide forms an unstable salt with sodium N-methyltaurate (24). Coupling with aryl diazonium salts gives stable diazo compounds (24) of the structure $RN{:}NN(CH_3)CH_2CH_2SO_3Na$. The reaction product with cyanuric chloride (549):

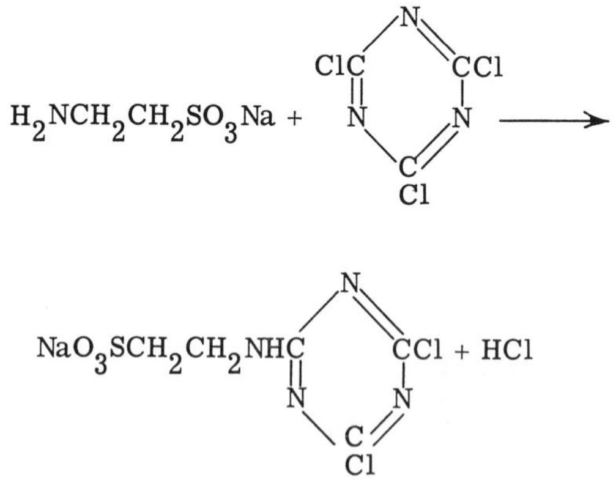

$$(5\text{-}41)$$

has been used to improve the affinity of dyes applied subsequently to rayon. This type of compound could prove interesting in the preparation of fiber-reactive dyes in a manner similar to the analogous derivative of sulfanilic acid discussed in Section V-B. Surface-active compounds result from the reaction of long-chain alkyl taurates with cyanuric chloride at 3:1 molar ratio (309).

3. 2-CHLOROETHANESULFONIC ACID AND SULFONYL CHLORIDE

a. Preparation

This compound has been prepared industrially as the sodium salt by the following reaction:

$$ClCH_2CH_2Cl + Na_2SO_3 \longrightarrow ClCH_2CH_2SO_3Na + NaCl \quad (5\text{-}42)$$

The various expedients employed to insure a good yield in this procedure are summarized in Chapter 3, Section II-A-5. The addition of
sodium bisulfite to vinyl chloride in the presence of an oxidizing agent
(124, 691), the reaction of sodium chloride with carbyl sulfate (cf.,
Section B-5) (98), the use of chlorobromoethane (566), and other approaches (618) have also been considered. Sodium 2-chloroethanesul-
fonate is commercially available for laboratory use (14, 100).

b. Chemical Reactions

Sodium 2-chloroethanesulfonate has been a favored reagent for sulfoethylating cellulose or starch in the presence of alkali. Reaction at
40 - 60°C for 10 - 15 hr. results in a degree of substitution ("DS") of
0.17 - 0.41 sulfoethyl groups per anhydroglucose unit, depending upon
the amount of reagent used (641). Products with a DS of 0.1 are alkali-
soluble, but those of DS 0.2 or higher are water-soluble (640). One of
DS 0.38 had a fibrous structure and dissolved in water to give a clear,
viscous solution (639). The reaction is preferably run in a nitrogen
atmosphere to suppress the formation of carboxyl groups from air oxidation (525, 639). Cation-exchange fabrics can be made by sulfoethylating cotton cloth at 70 - 100°C in 4 - 30 min. in the presence of aqueous alkali of mercerizing strength (267, 268). Simultaneous sulfoethylation and carboxymethylation yields water-soluble products (647); the
reaction is run in the solid phase at 60°C for 4 hr. A sulfoethylated
cellulose ion-exchanger, useful in biochemical separations (518), is
available in laboratory quantities (226). Starch has also been converted to water-soluble products. The reaction is preferably conducted in the presence of an alcoholic solvent (214). Isopropanol and
tert-butanol can be used alone, but ethanol works best in the presence
of toluene. Casein has been sulfoethylated with this reagent (161).

Ammonia, either in the presence or absence of water, forms sodium taurate (560). Methylamine similarly forms the N-methyltaurate
(143, 560, 571). This procedure gives a 96% yield on a commercial
scale (328), and has been used somewhat as a less desirable industrial
alternative to the standard isethionate method cited in Section B-2.
Ethyl-, n-butyl- (143), 2-ethylhexyl-, and n-octylamines (332) similarly form taurates, as do also long-chain acylated 2-hydroxyethyl-
ethylenediamines (341). A series of 29 aniline derivatives was sulfoethylated likewise, with di (sulfoethylation) occurring in 6 cases; 10
primary and secondary naphthylamines reacted in the same way (327).
Nitroanilines behave in a similar manner (147).

Ar-tetrahydro-β-naphthol (385), and a long-chain sulfonamide (507),
formed tanning agents by sulfoethylation in alkaline medium. Heating
with sodium ricinoleate gave the ester (131):

$$RCOONa + ClCH_2CH_2SO_3Na \longrightarrow$$

$$RCOOCH_2CH_2SO_3Na + NaCl \tag{5-43}$$

The isethionate is the usual precursor for this type of product, as discussed in Section B-1.

2-Chloroethanesulfonyl chloride ($ClCH_2CH_2SO_2Cl$), made by the sulfochlorination of ethyl chloride (cf. , Chapter 3), or by chlorination of ethanesulfonyl chloride, has become commercially available (149). It is easily converted to many derivatives via the esters and amides of ethenesulfonic acid (cf. , Section B-7).

4. 2-BROMOETHANESULFONIC ACID

This sulfoethylating agent ($BrCH_2CH_2SO_3Na$) is commercially available in laboratory quantities (148). It can be prepared by gradual addition of sodium sulfite to excess 1, 2-dibromoethane in hot 95% ethanol (442, 499). Others have used this procedure with 50% ethanol (421). The sulfite need not be added gradually, and the crude product can be used without purification (565, 566).

This compound, although similar to the chlorine analogue in general chemical behavior, is more reactive and inherently more expensive. It has proven of special interest for sulfoethylating sulfur compounds. Thiourea forms the isothiouronium salt (511, 565), which was converted to the thiol. Sodium hydrosulfide yields the thiol directly (421). The thiol has also been made via the easily prepared xanthates (564). The N, N-diethyldithiocarbamate (258) and the trisulfonate from trimercaptocyanuric acid (261, 698) are electroplating additives. Heavy metal salts of this thiol have been of interest in chemotherapy (421). Benzal trithioglycerol has been sulfoethylated with this reagent (431).

Aqueous ammonia forms sodium taurate in 50% yield (441). Potassium iodide catalyzes this type of reaction with long-chain amines (540). Potassium phthalimide yields the sulfoethylated imide, which has been saponified stepwise to the phthalamate and to sodium taurate (494). 2-Imidazolines, long-chain alkylated in the 2-position, also sulfoethylate on nitrogen to form surface-active agents (679). 4-Methyl-7-aminocoumarin gives an optical bleach (105).

Starch is converted to a water-soluble product in the presence of alcoholic alkali (214). A hydrolyzed cellulose triacetate film was sulfoethylated to an ion-exchange membrane (683). Surface-active agents are formed from 11- or 13-docosen-1-ol (375), and from N-long-chain alkyl diethanolamines (376). Propargyl alcohol was sulfoethylated to an electroplating additive (87). 4-Iodophenol reacts in aqueous alkali (58).

5. CARBYL SULFATE

a. Preparation

Carbyl sulfate is easily prepared in excellent yield by the direct reaction of ethylene with SO_3 (80):

$$CH_2:CH_2 + 2\ SO_3 \longrightarrow \overline{OCH_2CH_2SO_2OSO_2} \qquad (5\text{-}44)$$

The corresponding 1:1 reaction product, 1,2-ethanesultone, is unknown. Efforts to prepare it by reacting equimolar quantities of ethylene and SO_3 (192) have so far proved unsuccessful, even though numerous fluorinated ethylenes do yield such sultones, as shown in Chapter 2. Reaction of ethylene with carbyl sulfate is stated to give a "polymeric ethanesultone," which is said to behave chemically like the hypothetical parent sultone (192):

$$x\ (\overline{OCH_2CH_2SO_2OSO_2}) + x\ (CH_2:CH_2) \longrightarrow$$

$$(-OCH_2CH_2SO_2-)_{2x} \qquad (5\text{-}45)$$

b. Chemical Reactions

Aromatic (39) and aliphatic (187) amines are sulfatoalkylated by carbyl sulfate under anhydrous conditions, as follows:

$$2RNH_2 + \overline{OCH_2CH_2SO_2OSO_2} \longrightarrow RNHSO_2CH_2CH_2OSO_3{}^- H_3\overset{+}{N}R \quad (5\text{-}46)$$

After treatment with aqueous alkali yields the unsaturated compound:

$$RNHSO_2CH_2CH_2OSO_3{}^- H_3\overset{+}{N}R + 2\ NaOH \longrightarrow RNHSO_2CH:CH_2 +$$

$$Na_2SO_4 + RNH_2 + 2H_2O \qquad (5\text{-}47)$$

Both reactions can be performed in one operation (408). Phenols have similarly been converted to esters of structure $ROSO_2CH:CH_2$ (41), using carefully controlled conditions. These types of compounds can be used to prepare fiber-reactive dyes, as indicated in Section III.

Cellulose, on the other hand, is sulfoethylated to a water-soluble product with carbyl sulfate (146). The reaction is conducted in excess pyridine, followed by treatment with aqueous base. The overall reaction, resulting in the introduction of one sulfoethyl moiety per anhydroglucose unit, is as follows:

$$\text{ROH} + \overline{\text{OCH}_2\text{CH}_2\text{SO}_2\text{OSO}_2} + 3 \text{ NaOH} \longrightarrow \text{ROCH}_2\text{CH}_2\text{SO}_3\text{Na} +$$

$$\text{Na}_2\text{SO}_4 + 2 \text{ H}_2\text{O} \qquad\qquad (5\text{-}48)$$

Lack of past interest in using carbyl sulfate can be explained by the inconvenience of its preparation in the laboratory, its chemical instability, the possible formation of several reaction products from it, and the production of sodium sulfate as a secondary product. Other sulfoethylating agents which, as cited elsewhere herein, can easily be made from carbyl sulfate - i. e. , the salts of ethenesulfonic, ethionic, isethionic, and 2-chloroethanesulfonic acids - are free of some or all of these objections. Consideration of carbyl sulfate may, however, increase now that both raw materials are cheaply available, especially if interest continues to develop in the types of compounds produced by reaction 5-46. 2-Chloroethanesulfonyl chloride, which gives better yields of several of the same derivatives as carbyl sulfate, is commercially available (149).

6. ETHIONIC ACID

Sodium ethionate can be made in good yield by the careful hydrolysis of carbyl sulfate (80):

$$\overline{\text{OCH}_2\text{CH}_2\text{SO}_2\text{OSO}_2} + 2 \text{ NaOH} \longrightarrow \text{NaO}_3\text{SOCH}_2\text{CH}_2\text{SO}_3\text{Na} \qquad (5\text{-}49)$$

Ethionic acid has also been made from ethanol and sulfur trioxide (81):

$$\text{CH}_3\text{CH}_2\text{OH} + 2 \text{ SO}_3 \longrightarrow \text{HO}_3\text{SOCH}_2\text{CH}_2\text{SO}_3\text{H} \qquad (5\text{-}50)$$

Ethionic acid and its salts are therefore available from inexpensive raw materials.

Sodium ethionate, like carbyl sulfate and possibly for the same reasons, has been little studied as a sulfoethylating reagent. Since the sulfate moiety is a powerful leaving group, the reactions of this compound should generally resemble those of sodium 2-chloro- and -bromoethanesulfonates, discussed above. It sulfoethylates cellulose and ethyl cellulose at 150°C in one hour in alkaline medium (146) to form a water-soluble product. A water-soluble material also resulted when using it in the combined sulfoethylation - carboxymethylation of cellulose (647). A cation - exchange fabric resulted from treating cotton cloth with sodium ethionate for 10 min. at 100°C in the presence of alkali (268).

Free ethionic acid is reported to react with stearic acid at 45°C in 10 hr. as follows (131):

$$C_{17}H_{35}COOH + HO_3SOCH_2CH_2SO_3H \longrightarrow$$

$$C_{17}H_{35}COOCH_2CH_2SO_3H + H_2SO_4 \qquad (5\text{-}51)$$

Coconut oil is stated to undergo the following type of reaction at $35°C$ (131):

$$RCOOR' + HO_3SOCH_2CH_2SO_3H \longrightarrow$$

$$RCOOCH_2CH_2SO_3H + R'OSO_3H \qquad (5\text{-}52)$$

Poor yields appear probable in both these reactions.

7. ETHENESULFONIC ACID AND ITS 2-ALKYL DERIVATIVES

a. Preparation

Salts of ethenesulfonic, also known as ethylenesulfonic or vinylsulfonic acid, are easily accessible by several preparative routes. One reviewer of these (362), especially recommends dehydrohalogenation of sodium 2-chloroethanesulfonate with aqueous alkali (407). Others have treated the corresponding sulfonyl chloride (150, 395), sodium ethionate (80, 81), or sodium 2-bromoethanesulfonate (657) with aqueous base. It has also been made from acetylene and sodium bisulfite (502):

$$HC\colon CH + HSO_3Na \longrightarrow CH_2\colon CHSO_3Na \qquad (5\text{-}53)$$

Most of these starting materials are readily available, as indicated elsewhere herein. Sodium ethenesulfonate itself is commercially available in laboratory quantities (125, 184). It is supplied as an aqueous solution, since the solid form is unstable (81).

2-Alkylethenesulfonic acid salts have been made by heating the corresponding hydroxy compounds to $180 - 220°C$ under alkaline conditions (557):

$$CH_3CHOHCH_2SO_3Na \longrightarrow CH_3CH\colon CHSO_3Na + H_2O \qquad (5\text{-}54)$$

Free ethenesulfonic acid has been prepared by acidifying an aqueous solution of the sodium salt, followed by distillation (82), or by distilling sodium isethionate with pyrophosphoric or related acids (26). Preparation from the disulfonyl chloride (399) has been especially recommended:

$$ClSO_2CH_2CH_2SO_2Cl + H_2O \longrightarrow CH_2\colon CHSO_3H + 2\ HCl + SO_2 \qquad (5\text{-}55)$$

b. Chemical Reactions

Unlike other sulfoethylating agents, salts of ethenesulfonic acid desirably form no secondary inorganic products during sulfoalkylation. They undergo various nucleophilic addition reactions with ease (81, 618). Alkali cellulose reacts in 4 hours at 50°C in the solid phase in a dough mixer (481); hydroxyethyl cellulose and methyl cellulose behave similarly. This approach has also been employed (647) for the simultaneous sulfoethylation and carboxymethylation of cellulose. However, the most efficient method of sulfoethylating cellulose is said to involve the use of sodium ethenesulfonate at 65 - 75°C with an organic solvent (isopropanol, tert-butanol, or dioxane) (251, 252) in the presence of aqueous alkali. A similar technique has been employed with ethenesulfonamide (251). These products are all either alkali-soluble or water-soluble. Cotton fabric has been sulfoethylated in 10 min. at 100°C under alkaline conditions (268) with retention of the fibrous structure. A similar type of material has also been prepared from cellulose by stepwise grafting with acrylonitrile and sodium ethenesulfonate (356). Sodium ethenesulfonate forms the taurates with ammonia and methylamine (342).

Salts of 2-alkylethenesulfonic acids, such as the methyl, ethyl, or butyl derivatives (557) easily add alcohols or phenols, forming compounds of the type $ROCH(R')CH_2SO_3Na$. Sodium 2-methylethenesulfonate adds ammonia or piperidine forming substituted taurines, but it does not react with aniline (406).

Other sulfoethylation reactions of ethenesulfonate salts proper have not been reported, possibly because of their limited availability in the past. Addition reactions with ethenesulfonate derivatives other than the salts have been observed, however. Aliphatic and aromatic ethenesulfonate esters react with many compounds containing active hydrogen (149), including amines (139), alcohols (201, 467), phenols (687), thiols (139, 201), nitroalkanes (406), sulfonamides, thiourea, urea, sulfinic acids, oxymethanesulfinic acids, sodium bisulfite, dichloroacetonitrile and methyl dichloroacetate (642), diethyl malonate (at 1:1 and 2:1 molar ratio), and olefins with allylic hydrogen atoms. They also yield Diels-Alder adducts with cyclopentadiene, and form homopolymers and copolymers. Ethenesulfonyl fluoride reacts extremely vigorously with amines (238, 559a); it is noteworthy that addition to the double bond occurs more easily in this case than interaction with the sulfonyl fluoride group. Ethanethiol also reacts, but heat is required. Ethanol did not react, even with prolonged heating. Ethenesulfonamides add diazomethane and phenyl azide, forming pyrazoline - and triazolinesulfonic acid derivatives, respectively (532).

Ethenesulfonic acid, its esters, amide derivatives, salts, and acid chloride and fluoride have been polymerized and copolymerized with various other monomers (362, 399, 486) to form water-soluble and -insoluble polymers of types not accessible by other preparative methods.

The high reactivity of the ethenesulfonate moiety, taken with its ease of preparation, low molecular weight, and lack of formation of secondary products in reactions with other materials, suggests that its uses may be extended considerably in the future.

8. ACETALDEHYDEMONOSULFONIC ACID

This compound ($OCHCH_2SO_3H$), also known as formylmethanesulfonic acid, has been prepared as the barium salt by treating various vinyl ethers (629), acetylene (154), vinyl acetate (630), or acetaldehyde (632, 633) with SO_3-dioxane. Vinyl acetate gives an 85% yield, but acetaldehyde forms only 39%, the disulfonate being the major product.

Acetaldehydemonosulfonic acid is a relatively new compound, and no reactions or derivatives have as yet been reported. Presumably it would behave like the acetonesulfonic acid salts discussed in Section B-10. If so, it could form a variety of derivatives by reaction with either the carbonyl or the activated methylene group, or with both simultaneously. It should be noted that acetaldehydedisulfonic acid, discussed in the following section, undergoes sulfonate cleavage during some of its reactions, thus in effect forming derivatives of the monosulfonic compound. Therefore, the latter might actually be a more efficient source of such derivatives than the disulfonate.

9. ACETALDEHYDEDISULFONIC ACID

This material, also known as formylmethanedisulfonic acid, can be prepared as the barium salt in 80 - 100% yield by the direct sulfonation of acetaldehyde with SO_3 - dioxane (632, 633):

$$CH_3CHO + 2 SO_3 \longrightarrow OCHCH(SO_3H)_2 \qquad (5\text{-}56)$$

Details are available (236) for preparing the monohydrated dipotassium salt in good yield starting from acetylene and oleum. The reaction is conveniently operated continuously, even on a laboratory scale. This salt is commercially available in laboratory quantities (14). The crude acetylene - oleum reaction mixture can sometimes be used instead of the salt for preparing derivatives (236, 464).

A study of the behavior of acetaldehydedisulfonic acid (236) has shown that the aldehyde group has the expected high degree of reactivity, since it can be reduced to the alcohol, removed by basic cleavage, converted to azomethines, an oxime, a phenylhydrazone, and mercaptals, and that it promotes easy halogenation of the adjacent carbon atom. It condenses with various phenols and with alkylated benzenes, forming, respectively, water-soluble and -insoluble resins (464), and materials with surface activity. In all the aromatic condensations, cleavage of one of the sulfonate groups occurs, yielding in effect derivatives of acetaldehydemonosulfonic acid with the structure $R_2CHCH_2SO_3H$. The monosulfonic acid, reviewed in the preceding section, may therefore be a more efficient starting material for such derivatives. Other types of derivatives, in which both sulfonate groups are retained, have reduced solubility in water compared to the analogous monosulfonates.

10. ACETONESULFONIC ACID

This compound ($CH_3COCH_2SO_3H$), also designated 2-oxo-1-propanesulfonic acid, has been prepared in 50 - 96% yield by the direct sulfonation of acetone (631, 633, 650) or of isopropenyl acetate (630) with SO_3 - dioxane, or by reacting bromo- (504) or chloroacetone (15, 57, 156) with metallic sulfites. It does not appear to be commercially available.

The carbonyl group reacts typically by formation of an oxime, a semicarbazone, an acetylhydrazone, and a phenylhydrazone (631). The long-chain acyl hydrazones are wetting agents (112). Reduction of such long-chain acyl hydrazones with sodium amalgam also yields surface-active compounds of the general structure $RCONHNCH(CH_3)-CH_2SO_3Na$ (113). The phenylhydrazone undergoes ring closure as follows (445, 631):

$$C_6H_5NHN{:}C(CH_3)CH_2SO_3Na \xrightarrow{PCl_5} CH_3C \underset{CH_2SO_2}{\overset{N—NC_6H_5}{\Big|}} \qquad (5\text{-}57)$$

Reductive amination with long-chain alkylamines, such as heptyl-, 2-ethylhexyl-, or dodecyl-, has also been studied (330):

$$RNH_2 + CH_3COCH_2SO_3Na \xrightarrow{H} RNHCH(CH_3)CH_2SO_3Na \qquad (5\text{-}58)$$

The aminosulfonates were then further acylated with long-chain acids, or reacted with long-chain isocyanates, forming surface-active agents.

The methylene group is also reactive. It condenses with aromatic diazonium compounds to form $RNHN{:}C(SO_3Na)COCH_3$ (504), and with excess formaldehyde yielding polyolsulfonates (15). 2-Aminobenzaldehyde reacts through both groups (62):

$$1,2\text{-}NH_2C_6H_4CHO + CH_3COCH_2SO_3Na \longrightarrow$$

$$\overset{H}{\underset{N}{\overset{C}{\diagdown}}}{CSO_3Na} + 2\ H_2O \qquad (5\text{-}59)$$

Acetonesulfonic acid salts are easily accessible, reactive, poly-functional materials, which appear to offer wide opportunity for the preparation of varied derivatives.

11. SULFOACETIC ACID, ACID CHLORIDE, AND ANHYDRIDE

Sulfoacetic acid has been prepared by several methods (618), but the best approach is apparently still the following (311, 492, 589):

$$ClCH_2COONa + Na_2SO_3 \longrightarrow NaO_3SCH_2COONa + NaCl \qquad (5\text{-}60)$$

The free acid has been isolated via the barium salt; it can be prepared directly by reacting acetic anhydride with sulfuric acid (434).   The acid is commercially available in laboratory quantities as the mono-hydrate (148).

Alcohols (methyl, ethyl, n-propyl, phenylethyl) easily form the esters upon refluxing with the acid in benzene, preferably in a current of dry HCl (311, 670).   The ester salts are equally well made directly from sodium sulfite and the chloroacetate ester (618).   The long-chain ester salts are surfactants used commercially in cosmetic and phar-maceutical formulations (16, 618).   Cellulose forms an acetate - sulfo-acetate when treated with acetic anhydride and sulfoacetic acid at 100°C using dimethylformamide as solvent (648); the anhydride thus "impels" reaction of the cellulose with the sulfo acid.

Aniline undergoes acylation at 200°C (69, 607) forming $C_6H_5NHCO-CH_2SO_3H$, isolated as the aniline salt.

Sulfoacetic acid derivatives have also been prepared indirectly via an acid chloride.   The diacid chloride is easily made by reacting the acid with $POCl_3$ (311), and careful hydrolysis of it is reported to yield only the expected acid sulfonyl chloride, $HOOCCH_2SO_2Cl$ (311).   This sulfonyl chloride unexpectedly forms the acyl, rather than the sulfonyl, derivatives from aniline and from urea, which had earlier led to the conclusion that the compound was $ClCOCH_2SO_3H$ (69).   It is now known in other cases that sulfonyl chlorides also containing carboxyl groups form the acyl, rather than the expected sulfonyl, derivatives - e. g., the chlorides of 3-sulfobenzoic acid (Section V-H), and furan-2-car-boxylic-5-sulfonic acid (Section VI).   A compound stated to be $ClCO-CH_2SO_3H$ was used to render diethylstilbestrol water-soluble by acyla-tion of both phenolic groups in the presence of pyridine (663).   The diacid chloride forms similar products with sterols (310), since only the acyl chloride group reacts under the conditions used.

A second possible indirect approach to the preparation of sulfo-acetic acid derivatives involves the use of sulfoacetic anhydride, stated to result by reacting ketene with SO_3 - dioxane (586):

$$CH_2:C:O + SO_3 \longrightarrow \begin{array}{c} CH_2 - CO \\ | \qquad | \\ SO_2 - O \end{array}$$

(5-61)

This interesting compound was not isolated, but was shown to react as expected with aniline, forming $C_6H_5NHCOCH_2SO_3H$ (isolated as the aniline salt). It deserves further consideration as a possible direct and inexpensive approach to sulfoacetic acid derivatives having the same structures as those made with the acid - sulfonyl chloride cited before.

12. SULFOCHLOROACETIC ACID

Unlike acetic acid, chloroacetic acid reacts smoothly with SO_3 (35, 589, 595):

$$ClCH_2COOH + SO_3 \longrightarrow HO_3SCHClCOOH$$

(5-62)

Sulfochloroacetic acid is, therefore, more directly accessible than the unchlorinated analogue mentioned in the preceding section. It is available commercially in experimental quantities (14). The disodium salt has been prepared from sodium dichloroacetate and sodium sulfite (282). Other less practical methods have also been used to make the acid and its salts (618).

The acid has been esterified by refluxing with N-(2-hydroxyethyl)-N-ethylaniline (594). Treatment with phosgene in the presence of pyridine, or with benzenesulfonyl chloride in the presence of an aliphatic tertiary amine, yields the acid chloride $ClCOCHClSO_3H$ (106, 107), which has been studied extensively for sulfoacylating phenolic hydroxyl or amino groups to render azo dyes water-soluble.

13. α-SULFONATED LONG-CHAIN FATTY ACIDS

Although acetic, propionic, and butyric acids form the α-sulfonated acids in poor yield by direct sulfonation with SO_3, the higher fatty acids (C9 and above) resemble chloroacetic acid in giving good yields (608). α-Sulfopalmitic and -stearic acids are commercially available (11, 28, 355).

The preparation and derivatization of the long-chain α-sulfo fatty acids, especially those made from palmitic and stearic, have been studied extensively by A. J. Stirton and co-workers. Being α-substituted derivatives of sulfoacetic acid, they generally resemble it in reactivity. A review of the extensive work on these compounds (608) shows that they can be esterified with C1 - 10 alcohols, allyl alcohol, and sodium isethionate. The acid chloride sulfonic acids, easily prepared by treating the acids with thionyl chloride, have been converted to various amide sulfonic acid salts with surface activity. The analogous amides from 6-aminoindazolone are of interest as photographic chemicals (374). It has been truly pointed out (608) that the α-sulfo fatty acids have economic advantages, and that they are versatile intermediates for the formation of surfactants, both monomeric and polymeric, and other types of useful products.

14. SULFOBUTYROLACTONE

γ-Butyrolactone is easily and directly converted to this compound with SO_3 (390, 528):

$$\overline{OCH_2CH_2CH_2CO} + SO_3 \longrightarrow \overline{OCH_2CH_2CH(SO_3H)CO} \qquad (5\text{-}63)$$

The free acid separates in crystalline form from the chloroform used as reaction solvent, or it can be converted to salts. Two moles of SO_3 give the disulfonic acid. The monosulfonate salt can also be made from bromobutyrolactone and sodium sulfite (391, 528).

Primary amines (aniline, cyclohexyl-, oleyl-, or stearylamines) react as follows upon heating at 200° C (392):

$$RNH_2 + \overline{OCH_2CH_2CH(SO_3Na)CO} \longrightarrow$$

$$\overline{RNCH_2CH_2CH(SO_3Na)CO} + H_2O \qquad (5\text{-}64)$$

Secondary amines [e. g. , dicyclohexyl- or N-(2-ethylhexyl)-N-methylamine] can form two types of products (392) depending upon reagent ratios and conditions:

$$R_2NH + \overline{OCH_2CH_2CH(SO_3Na)CO} \longrightarrow$$

$$HO(CH_2)_2CH(SO_3Na)CONR_2 \xrightarrow{R_2NH}$$

$$R_2N(CH_2)_2CH(SO_3Na)CONR_2 + H_2O \qquad (5\text{-}65)$$

The amine derivatives have surface activity.

No other derivatives of sulfobutyrolactone have been reported, although many should be possible if the sulfo compound resembles the highly reactive parent lactone (23, 528), which - being commercially available - allows easy access to derivatives.

15. MISCELLANEOUS SULFOETHYLATING REAGENTS

Sulfoethylated silicon (677) and phosphorus (191) compounds, $R_3 -$ $SiCH_2CH_2SO_3Na$ and $(ClCH_2CH_2O)_2P(:O)CH_2CH_2SO_3Na$, have been prepared but not studied. Compounds of the former type are easily approached by sulfochlorination (126):

$$Cl_3SiCH_2CH_3 + SO_2 + Cl_2 \xrightarrow{\text{Cat.}} Cl_3SiCH_2CH_2SO_2Cl + HCl \qquad (5\text{-}66)$$

C. Introduction of Sulfopropyl, Sulfopropylidene, and Sulfopropionyl Groups

1. 1,3-PROPANESULTONE AND ITS ALKYL DERIVATIVES

The preparation and chemical reactions of the known types of sultones have been outlined through 1959 (472, 473). The present discussion will be limited to consideration of only those sultones which have proved of prime interest for sulfoalkylation, namely, 1,3-propanesultone, 1,4-butanesultone, and their alkyl derivatives. A general review on 1,3-propanesultone (203a) discusses its preparation, properties, and reactions, and gives useful practical information on its handling and use.

a. Preparation

1,3-Propanesultone is commercially available (11,148,304,581). It is prepared by vacuum distilling 3-hydroxypropanesulfonic acid (203, 284):

$$HOCH_2CH_2CH_2SO_3H \longrightarrow \overline{OCH_2CH_2CH_2SO_2} + H_2O \qquad (5\text{-}67)$$

$$\underset{3}{} \quad \underset{2}{} \quad \underset{1}{}$$

$$(A)$$

The parent acid salt can be prepared by the peroxide-catalyzed addition of sodium bisulfite to allyl alcohol under fairly specific conditions (283,284,288,695), or by catalytic reduction of the acrolein-bisulfite adduct (203,695):

$$CH_2:CHCH_2OH + NaHSO_3$$
$$\searrow$$
$$NaO_3SCH_2CH_2CH_2OH \qquad (5\text{-}68)$$
$$\nearrow$$
$$NaO_3SCH_2CH_2CHO + H_2$$

Conversion of the salt to the acid can be effected with mineral acid (284), or with an ion-exchange resin (203). Vacuum distillation of the corresponding 3-chloropropanesulfonic acid (299) or its salts (228, 305) also gives the sultone:

$$ClCH_2CH_2CH_2SO_3H \longrightarrow \overline{O(CH_2)_3SO_2} + HCl \qquad (5\text{-}69)$$

This approach is theoretically inexpensive, since the sulfonic acid is available via sulfochlorination of 1-chloropropane (299), but the yield is low (203a):

$$ClCH_2CH_2CH_3 \xrightarrow{\;SO_2 + Cl_2\;} ClCH_2CH_2CH_2SO_2Cl \xrightarrow{\;H_2O\;}$$

$$ClCH_2CH_2CH_2SO_3H + HCl \qquad (5\text{-}70)$$

The allyl alcohol route has, therefore, been preferred commercially.

Willems (696) has made an extended study of the preparation of propanesultone, six monoalkyl, four dialkyl, three trialkyl and one of its arylalkyl derivatives, using three variations of the thermal dehydration method - one involving no solvent, the second a hydrophilic solvent (ethylene glycol mono-n-butyl ether), and the third a hydrophobic solvent (xylene). All three methods gave 40 - 60% yields of propanesultone, but in some of the other cases no product could be obtained by the first two approaches. However, the third gave fair to good yields in all instances.

As indicated in Chapter 2, a series of six tertiary 1, 3-sultones was made in 50 - 80% yields by direct reaction of SO_3-dioxane with the appropriate γ-branched olefin. This procedure seems simple, but obtaining the desired olefin may be more difficult.

1-Methyl-1, 3-propanesultone has similarly been prepared in 67% yield by sulfochlorination of 1-chlorobutane (299), followed by conversion to the sulfonic acid and distillation; the other 33% comprised 1, 4-butanesultone. These sultones behave similarly, but the second reacts more slowly than the first. Since their separation is laborious, the mixture was used in the early exploratory work on sultone reactions by Helberger and co-workers as described below.

b. Chemical Reactions

The five- and six-membered ring alkane sultones, and their alkyl derivatives are highly reactive and versatile sulfoalkylating agents. As a class they are much more reactive than the similarly-constituted open-chain sulfonic acid esters (696). [The four-membered ring sultones, now thought to be the primary products in the reaction of SO_3 with alkenes (cf., Chapter 2), are even more reactive and unstable, and were, therefore, largely unknown until recently.] They react readily with many nucleophiles; fission of the carbon-oxygen bond occurs, forming a 3-substituted propanesulfonate or a 4-substituted butanesulfonate. Propanesultone, with a five-membered ring, as expected reacts more rapidly than 1, 4-butanesultone, which has a six-membered ring (300). In many reactions involving the sultones, no solvent is needed. Although the sultones will react with water (203a) or with alcohols, these materials can often be used as reaction solvents, since the desired reaction often occurs more easily (304).

(1) ALCOHOLS. Alcohols easily form the 3-alkoxypropanesulfonic acids:

$$ROH + \overline{O(CH_2)_3 SO_2} \longrightarrow RO(CH_2)_3SO_3H \qquad (5\text{-}71)$$

The facile reaction of 1-methyl-1, 3-propanesultone with methanol has been used to separate it from 1, 4-butanesultone, which reacts much more slowly (294, 296); the 3-methoxypropanesulfonic acid was then converted to the pure sultone by vacuum distillation. Butanol, dodecanol (296), and ethoxylated p-tert-octylphenol (302) react similarly. Sodium lauroxide forms the corresponding salt (203a, 216, 581). Alkali cellulose forms a water-soluble product (285, 300); in one case a degree of substitution of nearly 2. 0 was attained (203a, 581). Starch, amylopectin, carob bean gum, and guar gum form water-soluble products with degrees of substitution varying from 0. 27 to 0. 55 (609). Amylose reacts over the range 0. 28 - 1. 21 (350).

(2) PHENOLS. Sodium phenoxides similarly form the 3-phenoxy-propanesulfonate salts upon refluxing for two hours in methanol (581). Phenols cited included phenol itself (216, 285, 296, 300), 4-cresol (304), octylphenol (137, 203a, 302, 581), nonylphenol (137, 216), 2, 4-di(tert-amyl)phenol (137), 2, 4, 6-trichlorophenol (70), and 2-naphthol (296, 300). As expected, monosodium salicylate reacts only on the carboxyl group (558) under the conditions used.

(3) ORGANIC ACID SALTS. Salts of organic acids form the 3-acyloxypropanesulfonate salts by refluxing in methanol, or by heating without a solvent at 120 - 150°C:

$$RCOONa + \overline{O(CH_2)_3 SO_2} \longrightarrow RCOO(CH_2)_3SO_3Na \qquad (5\text{-}72)$$

Salts used include those of acetic, caprylic, lauric, palmitic, stearic, oleic, phenylacetic, benzoic (203a, 285, 290, 300, 581), salicylic (558), acrylic, and methacrylic acids (485). The oleic derivative showed good foaming and detergency (300). Most of these derivatives were actually made from the mixture of 1-methyl-1, 3-propanesultone and

1, 4-butanesultone mentioned before (300).

(4) HYDROPEROXIDES. Hydrogen peroxide and organic peroxides in the presence of alkali form the expected peroxysulfonate salts:

$$ROONa + \overline{O(CH_2)_3SO_2} \longrightarrow ROO(CH_2)_3SO_3Na \qquad (5\text{-}73)$$

Organic peroxides used include sec- and tert-butyl, n-octyl, cumene,
and tetralin (699). Hydrogen peroxide reacts at either 1:1 or 1:2 molar
ratios.

(5) AMINES. Ammonia, primary, secondary, and tertiary aliphatic, aromatic, and heterocyclic amines form inner salts or sulfo-
betaines:

$$R_3N + \overline{O(CH_2)_3SO_2} \longrightarrow R_3\overset{+}{N}(CH_2)_3SO_3^- \qquad (5\text{-}74)$$

Amines used include aniline, 4-toluidine, 4, 4'-diaminobiphenyl, 4-
aminophenol, decyl-, dodecyl-, and octadecylamines, dimethylaniline,
pyridine, quinoline, isoquinoline, octylphenoxyethyldimethylamine,
and bisimidazolines (made by reacting long-chain fatty acids with tri-
ethylene tetramine)(27, 174, 203a, 216, 285, 296, 300, 301, 304, 581, 696).
1-Aminoanthraquinone (285, 300) and nitroparaphenylenediamine (352)
formed water-soluble dyes. Sulfanilamide, sulfanilanilide, and sulfathiazole yielded fungicides (223), with reaction occurring preferentially on the amino group. Iminothioesters (138) and sodium carbazole
(285) both sulfopropylate on nitrogen. Phenylhydrazine and 1-phenyl-
3-methyl-5-pyrazolone behave similarly (302b).

(6) TRIVALENT PHOSPHORUS COMPOUNDS. Various products
result, depending on the nature of the starting compound (269, 270):

$$R_3P + \overline{O(CH_2)_3SO_2} \longrightarrow R_3\overset{+}{P}(CH_2)_3SO_3^- \qquad (5\text{-}75)$$

$$R_2PH + \overline{O(CH_2)_3SO_2} \longrightarrow R_2P(CH_2)_3SO_3H \qquad (5\text{-}76)$$

$$(RO)_3P + \overline{O(CH_2)_3SO_2} \longrightarrow (RO)_2P(:O)(CH_2)_3SO_3R \qquad (5\text{-}77)$$

(7) FATTY ACID AMIDES. Alkali metal amides (potassium phthalimide, the sodium derivatives of acetamide, lauramide, and stearamide) sulfopropylate on nitrogen (216, 285, 295, 300, 581):

$$RCONHNa + \overline{O(CH_2)_3SO_2} \longrightarrow RCONH(CH_2)_3SO_3Na \qquad (5\text{-}78)$$

The lauric derivative shows good foaming and detergency. The free amides, on the other hand, alkylate on oxygen (304):

$$RCONH_2 + \overline{O(CH_2)_3SO_2} \longrightarrow RC(:NH^+_2)O(CH_2)_3SO_3^- \qquad (5\text{-}79)$$

(8) SULFONAMIDES. Alkali metal N-alkyl 4-toluenesulfonamides likewise sulfopropylate on nitrogen (293, 304, 581). Substituting alkyl groups include short (methyl) and long (octadecyl) chains.

(9) SULFINATE SALTS. Sulfones are formed (304):

$$RSO_2Na + \overline{O(CH_2)_3SO_2} \longrightarrow RSO_2(CH_2)_3SO_3Na \qquad (5\text{-}80)$$

(10) THIOL DERIVATIVES. Sulfopropylation on sulfur occurs with a wide variety of compounds, including sodium hydrosulfide (300), sodium disulfide (at 2:1 molar ratio) (70), potassium thiocyanate (287, 300), and the salts of thiophenol (70, 296, 300, 304), benzylthiol (260), tert-dodecanethiol (219), mercaptothiazole (70), mercaptobenzthiazole (221), trimercaptocyanuric acid (at 3:1 molar ratio) (261, 367, 698), thioacetic acid (260), and thiobenzoic acid (260). Dithiocarbamate salts used include those made from ammonia, diethylamine, diethanolamine, piperidine, piperazine, and pentamethylene diamine (70, 71, 259). Sodium isopropyl and n-butyl xanthates react similarly (71, 259). Dibenzylsulfide yields a sulfonium sulfonate (222). The dithiocarbamate derivatives are additives for electroplating baths (260, 261, 367).

(11) THIOAMIDES. Thiourea alkylates on sulfur forming a thiouronium inner salt (70, 216, 271):

$$NH_2CSNH_2 + \overline{O(CH_2)_3SO_2} \longrightarrow NH_2C(:NH_2^+)S(CH_2)_3SO_3^- \qquad (5\text{-}81)$$

Alkyl and aryl substituted thioureas, thiosemicarbazones, 4-methylthiouracil, and dithizone behave similarly. In the presence of alkalies, the corresponding sodium salts are formed. Thioamides (thioacetanilide, thiobenzanilide, rhodanine) form similar salts (272).

(12) MALONIC ESTER. Sodio diethyl malonate forms $(C_2H_5 -$ $OCO)_2CH(CH_2)_3SO_3Na$ (216, 254), proposed as a comonomer to improve dyeability of polyesters.

(13) METALLOORGANIC COMPOUNDS. Reaction occurs easily as follows:

$$RMe + \overline{O(CH_2)_3}SO_2 \longrightarrow R(CH_2)_3SO_3Me \qquad (5\text{-}82)$$

Aryl compounds so treated include fluorene sodium (285, 291, 292), phenyl sodium and lithium (291, 292), and 9-phenanthrene potassium (292). Alkyl and arylalkyl materials include benzyl sodium and aluminum, dodecyl sodium, and octadecyl potassium (292). Grignard reagents behaving similarly include ethyl and phenyl magnesium bromides (291, 696). The Friedel - Crafts reaction, using benzene and aluminum chloride, also forms the sulfopropylated hydrocarbon in 56% yield (216).

(14) INORGANIC SALTS. Inorganic salts (KBr, KCl, KI, KCN, KSCN) react as follows (216, 285, 287, 298, 300, 302a, 304, 581):

$$KF + \overline{O(CH_2)_3}SO_2 \longrightarrow F(CH_2)_3SO_3K \qquad (5\text{-}83)$$

2.   2-HYDROXY-3-CHLOROPROPANESULFONIC ACID

This compound is easily prepared as the sodium salt from epichlorohydrin (655);

$$ClCH_2\overline{CHCH_2}O + NaHSO_3 \longrightarrow ClCH_2CHOHCH_2SO_3Na \qquad (5\text{-}84)$$

$$(A)$$

The claim that this reaction yields a sulfite rather than a sulfonate (212) has not been substantiated. The use of aqueous sodium sulfite with methyl formate gives improved results (67). Other less satisfactory synthetic approaches have also been employed (618). As pointed out in Chapter 3, products other than 5-84-A can be formed in this reaction.

Through the reactive chlorine atom, this compound has been condensed with sodium hydrosulfide (121, 422, 430), starch (505), ammonia, and primary, secondary, and tertiary aliphatic, aromatic, and heterocyclic amines (341, 482, 563, 654, 679). Sodium laurate and related soaps form sulfonate esters used as specialty detergents:

$$RCOONa + ClCH_2CHOHCH_2SO_3Na \longrightarrow$$

$$RCOOCH_2CHOHCH_2SO_3Na + NaCl \qquad (5\text{-}85)$$

This reaction is best conducted in the presence of a volatile amide, such as acetamide (655), dimethylformamide (378), formamide (474), or solvents (370) such as ethylene glycol monoethers. The free fatty acid can also be heated with the free sulfonic acid in vacuo at 150°C (123):

$$RCOOH + ClCH_2CHOHCH_2SO_3H \longrightarrow$$

$$RCOOCH_2CHOHCH_2SO_3H + HCl \qquad (5\text{-}86)$$

The monosodium salt of catechol reacts as expected forming the phenolic ether - sulfonate, an antiseptic (700).

3. 3-CHLORO- AND 3-BROMOPROPANESULFONIC ACIDS

Sodium 3-bromopropanesulfonate has been prepared as follows (421):

$$Br(CH_2)_3Br + Na_2SO_3 \longrightarrow Br(CH_2)_3SO_3Na + NaBr \qquad (5\text{-}87)$$

The chloro analogue was made similarly from 1-bromo-3-chloropropane (565, 566). Both compounds have been made by heating 1,3-propanesultone with the appropriate halide (302a).
Like 2-bromoethanesulfonic acid salts (Section II-B-4), these two compounds have been used to prepare thiol sulfonates. With thiourea, both sulfonate salts form the isothiouronium compounds (511, 565), which have been hydrolyzed to the thiol sulfonate; the thiol sulfonate has also been made by reacting the bromosulfonate salt with sodium hydrosulfide (421). The bromosulfonate has been condensed with the free thiol group of the benzal derivative of 1,2,3-propanetrithiol (431), and with the pyridine salt of pentamethylene dithiocarbamic acid (258).
Sodium 3-chloropropane sulfonate reverts to propanesultone upon heating (228):

$$Cl(CH_2)_3SO_3Na \longrightarrow \overline{O(CH_2)_3SO_2} + NaCl \qquad (5\text{-}88)$$

4. 3-PROPANAL- AND 1-METHYL-3-PROPANALSULFONIC ACIDS

Two similar compounds are considered in this section: 3-propan-alsulfonic acid (also designated 3-oxo-1-propanesulfonic acid) (Formula 5-90-A), and its 1-methyl derivative, also called 1-formyl-2-propanesulfonic acid ($OCHCH_2CH(CH_3)SO_3H$). The corresponding 2-methyl compound is known (587) but it has not been used for sulfoalkylation.

a. Preparation

Sodium 3-propanalsulfonate is easily prepared, as its sodium bisulfite adduct, as follows (203, 587, 695):

$$OCHCH{:}CH_2 + 2\ NaHSO_3 \longrightarrow \underset{(A)}{NaO_3SCHOHCH_2CH_2SO_3Na} \quad (5\text{-}89)$$

The hydroxysulfonate group is unstable, and hydrolyzes in the presence of either acids or bases liberating the free aldehydic sulfonate (203, 582):

$$NaO_3SCHOHCH_2CH_2SO_3Na + HCl \longrightarrow$$

$$OCHCH_2CH_2SO_3Na + NaCl + SO_2 \quad (5\text{-}90)$$

$$(A)$$

The adduct, therefore, behaves like the free aldehydic sulfonate in many reactions (582), except when it reacts as a sulfomethylating agent forming disulfonates, as mentioned below. The adduct has better storage stability than the free aldehyde. It is commercially available in experimental quantities (582).

Similar considerations apply to the preparation of the adduct of the 1-methyl analogue from crotonaldehyde and sodium bisulfite. Studies of this reaction (79, 317, 695) have shown that the first mole adds rapidly and reversibly to the aldehyde group, and that the second adds slowly and irreversibly to the olefinic double bond. (This type of reaction is discussed in more general terms in Chapter 3, Section II-B-2.) This aldehydic sulfonate is also easily liberated from its adduct by treatment with sodium bicarbonate.

An analogous reaction occurs with aqueous sulfur dioxide (189):

$$OCHCH{:}CH_2 + 2\ SO_2 + 2H_2O \longrightarrow HO_3SCHOHCH_2CH_2SO_3H \quad (5\text{-}91)$$

Heat liberates sulfur dioxide, forming a solution of the propanal sulfonic acid:

$$HO_3SCHOHCH_2CH_2SO_3H \longrightarrow OCHCH_2CH_2SO_3H + SO_2 + H_2O \quad (5\text{-}92)$$

Crotonaldehyde likewise forms the 1-methyl analogue (280, 316, 568, 665). This preparative approach may be preferable in some cases, since it avoids the presence of salts.

b.   Chemical Reactions

The propanalsulfonate undergoes the normal aldehydic reaction of oxidation to the acid (535, 582), which, as its anhydride, is a useful sulfoacylating agent, as discussed in Section II-C-6. It has also been reduced to the alcoholic sulfonate (203, 286, 587); this constitutes one approach to preparing 1,3-propanesultone. The 1-methyl analogue has been oxidized to the acid, reduced to the alcohol, and converted to the oxime (280). The propanalsulfonate is stated to form an acetylated polyol sultone, as follows, but the structure is not proved:

$$OCHCH_2CH_2SO_3Na + 3\ CH_2O + (CH_3CO)_2O \longrightarrow$$

$$\overline{CH_2C(CH_2OCOCH_3)_2CH_2SO_2O} \tag{5-93}$$

Both sulfonates form polyolsulfonates with excess formaldehyde under alkaline conditions (15).

Long-chain alkylphenols (tert-amyl or tert-octyl) (230) form surface-active agents:

$$OCHCH_2CH_2SO_3Na + 2\ RC_6H_4OH \longrightarrow$$

$$(RC_6H_3OH)_2CHCH_2CH_2SO_3Na + H_2O \tag{5-94}$$

The 1-methyl analogue also forms similar products with these phenols. Reaction with phenol, followed by treatment with formaldehyde, gives an ion-exchange resin (79), and with catechol it forms an intermediate for tanning agents (665). Acetaldehydedisulfonic acid forms similar resins, as mentioned in Section II-B-9.

Poly(vinyl alcohol) can form either water-soluble or -insoluble acetal sulfonates (189), useful as tanning agents, textile finishes (190), and protective colloids (186):

$$(-CH_2CHOHCH_2CHOH-)_x + OCHCH_2CH_2SO_3H \longrightarrow$$

$$CH_2CH_2SO_3H$$
$$|$$
$$O-CH-O$$
$$|\qquad|$$
$$(-CH_2CHCH_2CH-)_x + H_2O \tag{5-95}$$

The 1-methyl analogue forms similar products.

The propanalsulfonate - bisulfite adduct can sulfomethylate amines, e. g. , sulfapyrimidines (54):

$$RNH_2 + NaO_3SCHOHCH_2CH_2SO_3Na \longrightarrow$$

$$RNHCH(SO_3Na)CH_2CH_2SO_3Na + H_2O \qquad (5-96)$$

The 1-methyl compound behaves similarly, and reacts likewise with long-chain amides, forming surface-active agents. Both compounds sulfomethylate malonic acid; decarboxylation also occurs (490):

$$CH_2(COOH)_2 + NaO_3SCHOHCH_2CH_2SO_3Na \longrightarrow$$

$$Na_3SCH(CH_2COOH)CH_2CH_2SO_3Na + CO_2 \qquad (5-97)$$

These two aldehydic sulfonates should find wider application in sulfoalkylation, since they are easily and cheaply prepared and are highly reactive. The propanalsulfonate has been suggested (582) as a raw material for making ion- exchange resins and surface-active agents by unspecified reaction with higher alcohols or amines.

5.   2-CYANOETHANESULFONIC ACID

The sodium salt of this compound is easily prepared in excellent yield from acrylonitrile (95, 465, 559):

$$CH_2:CHCN + NaHSO_3 \longrightarrow NaO_3SCH_2CH_2CN \qquad (5-98)$$

(A)

Since acylonitrile is an inexpensive commercial chemical, this sulfonate is also cheaply accessible. It is available in experimental quantities (19, 99, 355).

Although little work has as yet been done with this compound, it has been shown to undergo typical nitrile reactions (19). Partial hydrolysis yields the amide, which forms detergents with C10 - 16 alcohols (381):

$$H_2NCOCH_2CH_2SO_3Na + ROH \longrightarrow ROCOCH_2CH_2SO_3Na + NH_3 \qquad (5-99)$$

Complete hydrolysis gives disodium 3-sulfopropionate, which, in anhydride form, has been studied as a sulfopropylating agent, as discussed in the following section. Hydrogenation yields sodium 3-aminopropanesulfonate ("homotaurine"), which has been studied somewhat as a sulfopropylating agent, and is stated (19) to be of interest for preparing surface-active agents analogous to "Igepon T. " Dicyandiamide forms sodium 3-sulfopropioguanamine, as follows:

$$2NH_2C(:NH)NHCN + NaO_3SCH_2CH_2CN \longrightarrow$$

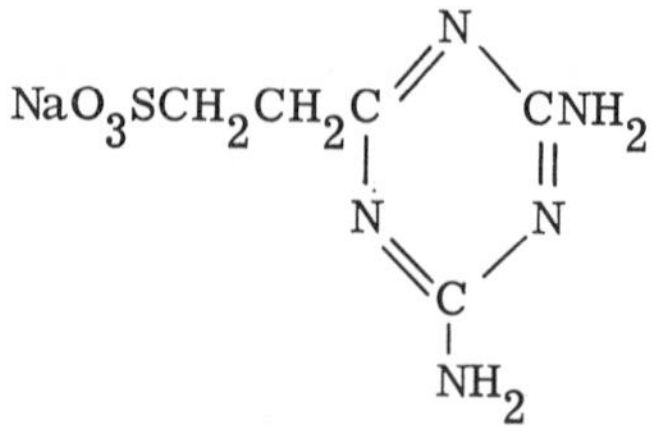

$$NaO_3SCH_2CH_2C \overset{\displaystyle N}{\underset{\displaystyle N}{\diagup\diagdown}} \underset{\displaystyle N}{\overset{\displaystyle CNH_2}{\parallel}}$$

(structure diagram)

(5-100)

This guanamide, being a diamine, may be of interest for the preparation of resins with formaldehyde, and for general use as a sulfoalkylating agent in its own right.

6.   3-SULFOPROPIONIC ANHYDRIDE

This reactive sulfoacylating agent is formed upon heating the acid chloride of the corresponding acid (363, 364):

$$ClO_2SCH_2CH_2COOH \longrightarrow \overline{SO_2CH_2CH_2CO O} + HCl$$

(5-101)

(A)

It forms from sulfochlorinating propionic acid, or by heating 3-sulfopropionic acid with thionyl chloride (364) - the acid chloride apparently being intermediate in both cases. Although the anhydride was first described in 1940 (364), it is thought (19) that a report published in 1886 (534) of the "drying" of the acid to a compound melting at 68 - 69°C may have unknowingly described preparation of the anhydride (m. p. 76 - 77°C) by thermal dehydration. The anhydride is regarded (19) as a commercially promising intermediate, since it can be prepared easily from acrylonitrile or acrylic acid (559) as starting materials. It is commercially available in laboratory quantities (11, 100, 125, 355).

The anhydride reacts with methanol (364) and with ascorbic acid 6-palmitate (635) to form the expected sulfoesters, and with excess ammonia, aniline (364), or substituted anilines (544) to form salts of the sulfonated amides:

$$2RNH_2 + \overline{SO_2CH_2CH_2COO} \longrightarrow RNHCOCH_2CH_2SO_3H \cdot RNH_2$$

(5-102)

Sulfanilamide and sulfathiazole likewise sulfoacylate on the amino group in the presence of pyridine, forming the salts of the latter (204).

7. MISCELLANEOUS SULFOPROPYLATING REAGENTS

The addition of one mole of sodium bisulfite to 1,3,5-triacrylyl-hexahydro-s-triazine (617) forms the following compound:

$$\underset{\substack{\displaystyle CH_2:CHCON \qquad\qquad NCOCH_2CH_2SO_3Na \\ \displaystyle \diagdown C \diagup \\ \displaystyle H_2}}{\overset{\substack{\displaystyle COCH:CH_2 \\ \displaystyle N \\ \diagup \diagdown \\ \displaystyle CH_2 \qquad CH_2 \\ \displaystyle | \qquad\quad |}}{}} \qquad (5\text{-}103)$$

The analogous disulfonate results from the addition of two moles of bisulfite. These compounds can be copolymerized with acrylonitrile yielding fibers with improved dye receptivity. The parent triazine is easily prepared from acrylonitrile and formaldehyde.

Propenesultone has been prepared by a method similar to that used for propanesultone (Reactions 5-67 and 5-68) (300a):

$$HC\!:\!CCH_2OH \xrightarrow[\text{(2)}H^+]{\text{(1)}NaHSO_3} HO_3SCH:CHCH_2OH \xrightarrow{-H_2O}$$

$$O_2\overline{SCH:CHCH_2O} \qquad\qquad (5\text{-}104)$$

This interesting new sultone has been studied relatively little as yet. It should undergo the many reactions of 1,3-propanesultone, plus the numerous nucleophilic addition reactions with compounds containing active hydrogen atoms cited in Section II-B-7 for ethenesulfonic acid and its derivatives. Propenesultone forms copolymers with acrylonitrile (153a).

D. Introduction of Sulfobutyl and Sulfobutyryl Groups

1. 1,4-BUTANESULTONE AND ITS ALKYL DERIVATIVES

a. Preparation

This compound ($\overline{O(CH_2)_4SO_2}$) is prepared in 50% yield by vacuum dehydration-distillation of the corresponding hydroxysulfonic acid (297, 299, 651, 696), or its ether (297, 590). Yield from the former is increased to 89% if the dehydration is effected in the presence of ethylene glycol mono n-butyl ether or xylene (696). The sultone has also been prepared by distilling 4-chlorobutanesulfonic acid (299). It is commercially available in laboratory quantities (11).

Similar procedures have been used to make alkyl 1, 4-butanesultones. The 2-methyl derivative was prepared from the corresponding chlorinated sulfonic acid (299), and the 4-methyl (651), 1-ethyl, 4-ethyl (303), and 4-n-propyl (696) analogues from the hydroxysulfonic acids. Yields of these compounds are generally lower than that of the unsubstituted sultone. In the case of the 4-n-propyl compound, no sultone was obtained unless a diluent was employed in the dehydration step.

b.   Chemical Reactions

1, 4-Butanesultone undergoes reactions similar to those of 1, 3-propanesultone, as discussed in Section II-C-1, but at a considerably slower rate (296). The times required for half hydrolysis (303) show that alkyl substitution also slows the rates: 1, 4-butanesultone, 4. 5 hr.; 1-ethyl-1, 4-butanesultone, 10 hr.; 4-ethyl-1, 4-butanesultone, 97 hr.

Methanol gives 96% conversion of the sultone to 4-methoxybutanesulfonic acid in 48 hr. (294, 296). The sultone also reacts with n-dodecanol, octadecanol, and castor oil (294). Corn starch undergoes sulfobutylation with 0. 04 degree of substitution (609), which is much less than that observed with propanesultone. The expected products were formed from sodium ethoxide (652), sodium phenoxide (297), sodium 2-naphthoxide (696), pyridine (297, 651, 696), dimethylaniline (297), ammonia (297), n-octylamine (696), KCN (297), potassium phthalimide (297), tert-butylhydroperoxide (699), calcium acrylate (485), ethyl magnesium bromide (696), sodium phenylacetylide (652), n-butyl lithium (652), diethyl malonate (652), ethyl acetoacetate (652), and dibenzoylmethane (652). Phenyl magnesium bromide gave a mixture of the magnesium salts of 4-phenylbutane- and 4-bromobutanesulfonic acids (652).

Sulfur compounds reacting as expected with 1, 4-butanesultone include KSCN, sodium thiophenoxide (297), thiourea (271), thioamides (272), sodium isopropyl xanthate (259), and aliphatic and aromatic sulfinate salts (289, 652). 2-Aminobenzenethiol sulfobutylates preferentially on the amino group (86).

1, 4-Butanesultone and its 4-methyl derivative, form 4-arylbutanesulfonic acids by the Friedel-Crafts reaction with benzene, p-xylene and p-dichlorobenzene (651). 2-Methyl-1, 4-butanesultone forms betaines with pyridine and quinoline, and the expected derivatives from KSCN and potassium phthalimide (300).

4-Aminobutanesulfonic acid salts, obtained by reacting 1, 4-butanesultone with ammonia or amines, have been converted to surface-active materials by interaction with epoxides (377), or with long-chain acid chlorides (196). The latter are homologues of "Igepon T. " At higher temperatures, the sultone and amines form sultams (302c).

1,4-Butanesultone has no apparent advantages over 1,3-propane-sultone as a sulfoalkylating agent, and it has the disadvantages of higher molecular weight (with corresponding higher cost), comparative lack of easy accessibility, and slower rate of reaction.

2. 4-SULFOBUTYRIC ACID

γ-Butyrolactone reacts with sodium sulfite at $180°C$, as follows (127):

$$\overline{OCH_2CH_2CH_2C}{:}O + Na_2SO_3 \longrightarrow NaO_3S(CH_2)_3COONa \qquad (5\text{-}105)$$

No reactions of this compound have been reported, but its consideration may be warranted, however, since it appears easy to prepare from inexpensive raw materials. Conversion to a six-membered ring anhydride analogous to compound 5-101-A would be of special interest (cf., Sulfobutyrolactone, Section II-B-14).

E. Miscellaneous Sulfoalkylating Reagents

1. 2-(2-CHLOROETHOXY) ETHANESULFONIC ACID

This compound is prepared as follows (52, 707):

$$ClCH_2CH_2OCH_2CH_2Cl + Na_2SO_3 \longrightarrow$$

$$ClCH_2CH_2OCH_2CH_2SO_3Na + NaCl \qquad (5\text{-}106)$$

Although this sulfonate thus appears cheaply and easily accessible, it has been studied comparatively little, perhaps because it has appeared to offer no advantages over the analogous 2-chloroethanesulfonic acid salts discussed in Section II-B-3. It forms the expected esters and ethers with carboxylic acid salts and sodium phenoxides or alkoxides, respectively (707), and alkylates secondary amines (341); these products have surface activity. As indicated in Chapter 3, Section II-A-5, some compounds of this type, as made by another procedure, have been produced commercially for many years.

2. 2,2-BIS(HYDROXYMETHYL)-1,3-PROPANEDISULFONIC ACID DISULTONE

3,3-Bis(bromomethyl)oxacyclobutane (from pentaerythritol) easily forms the disulfonate by the Strecker reaction. The latter has been converted to the disultone via the dihydroxydisulfonate (240a):

$$(BrCH_2)_2C \underset{\diagdown CH_2}{\overset{\diagup CH_2}{<}} O \xrightarrow{Na_2SO_3} (NaO_3SCH_2)_2C \underset{\diagdown CH_2}{\overset{\diagup CH_2}{<}} O \longrightarrow$$

$$(NaO_3SCH_2)_2C(CH_2OH)_2$$

(5-106-A)

These three interesting bifunctional disulfonates should be capable of extensive derivatization, including the preparation of polymers. The disultone can be regarded as comprising two 1,3-propanesultone moieties. It has in fact been shown (240a) to undergo many of the numerous reactions of 1,3-propanesultone (cf., Section C-1).

III. SULFATOALKYLATION

Sulfatoalkylation is similar in principle to sulfoalkylation, except that the reagents used contain a sulfate, rather than a sulfonate, grouping. It has been employed comparatively seldom.

A. 2-Aminoethyl Hydrogen Sulfate and Its N-Alkyl Derivatives

2-Aminoethyl hydrogen sulfate is easily prepared in good yield as follows (416):

$$NH_2CH_2CH_2OH + H_2SO_4 \longrightarrow \overset{+}{N}H_3CH_2CH_2OSO_3^- + H_2O \quad (5\text{-}107)$$

It is available in laboratory quantities (11,14,148). As indicated in Chapter VI, other aminoalkyl hydrogen sulfates can also be easily prepared from the amino alcohols by sulfation.

Long-chain acid chlorides, such as oleoyl or lauroyl, yield the amide - sulfates (264):

$$RCOCl + NH_2CH_2CH_2OSO_3Na \xrightarrow{NaOH}$$

$$RCONHCH_2CH_2OSO_3Na + NaCl \tag{5-108}$$

The lauric derivative was used briefly in Germany as a commercial detergent (43), but was abandoned because of the hydrolytic instability of the sulfate group. Surfactant amides have also been made from long-chain acid chlorides with the sodium sulfates of N-(n-butyl) aminoethanol and 1-amino-2-propanol (264).

Sodium 2-aminoethyl sulfate has been used to prepare "Solacet" anthraquinone dyes by replacement of a ring bromine atom or hydroxyl group (83, 548, 669):

$$RBr(OH) + NH_2CH_2CH_2OSO_3Na \longrightarrow$$

$$RNHCH_2CH_2OSO_3Na + HBr \ (H_2O) \tag{5-109}$$

This approach, also applied to azo dyes, likewise saw only limited commercial use because of the lability of the sulfate group. This lability has led to some revival of interest in such dyes, however, since the alkyl sulfate group is now known to react with textile fibers (266, 712), as follows in the case of alkali cellulose:

$$RNHCH_2CH_2OSO_3Na + Cell-ONa \longrightarrow$$

$$RNHCH_2CH_2OCell + Na_2SO_4 \tag{5-110}$$

Dibenzanthrone dyes containing sulfonyl chloride groups similarly form sulfonamides of structure $RSO_2NHCH_2CH_2OSO_3Na$ (183), as does also phthalocyaninesulfonyl chloride with sodium 4-amino-butyl sulfate (610); both types are fiber-reactive. Fiber-reactive dyes in general are of increasing interest (712).

Sodium 2-aminoethyl sulfate has been employed to modify urea-formaldehyde wet-strength resins (613), apparently by introduction of the $-CH_2NHCH_2CH_2OSO_3Na$ moiety.

Imino di(ethyl sulfate), $HN(CH_2CH_2OSO_3Na)_2$, couples with diazonium compounds forming dyes (361) of a type which has attracted recent commercial interest (459).

Sodium N-(n-dodecyl)aminoethyl sulfate reacts with cyanuric chloride at 2:1 molar ratio; a surface-active compound results by reaction of the third chlorine atom with ethylene diamine (309).

B. Miscellaneous Organic Sulfating Reagents

The sulfatomethylation of 25 azo dyes was effected with paraformaldehyde, monohydrate sulfuric acid and dry HCl at 5° C (76):

$$RH + CH_2O + H_2SO_4 \xrightarrow{HCl} RCH_2OSO_3H + H_2O \qquad (5\text{-}111)$$

The salts are soluble in water, stable to hydrolysis, and unchanged in shade from the original dye. This technique could find future application with hydrocarbons and other compounds which do not react with the milder formaldehyde - bisulfite system discussed in Section II-A. Sulfatomethylated anthraquinonoid dyes were prepared by treating the chloromethylated compounds with oleum (118).

As indicated elsewhere in this chapter, aliphatic and aromatic sulfonic groups can be introduced into polymers by vinyl polymerization. The sulfate group has been similarly introduced using 1-vinyl-2-ethylhistidol sulfate (5-112), which has been copolymerized with acrylonitrile to improve fiber dyeability (645):

$$\begin{array}{c} CH\!=\!CCH_2CH_2OSO_3K \\ | \quad\quad | \\ CH_2\!=\!CHN \quad\quad N \\ \diagdown \quad \diagup\!\!\diagup \\ C \\ | \\ C_2H_5 \end{array} \qquad (5\text{-}112)$$

As mentioned in Section II-B-5, carbyl sulfate has been employed to introduce the sulfatoethylsulfonyl group into aliphatic and aromatic amines. This moiety is also of interest in fiber-reactive dyes (310a).

IV.   SULFAMALKYLATION

A.   Hydroxymethylsulfamic Acid

Sulfamic acid and its salts react with formaldehyde, but the nature of the initial product has not been established. It has been suggested that in acid solution $CH_2{:}NSO_3H$ is formed (567), and under alkaline conditions $HOCH_2NHSO_3^-$ (680). A 50% yield of a cyclic trimer $(-CH_2N(SO_3K)-)_3$ has actually been isolated (64).

Regardless of its chemical composition, the system formaldehyde-sulfamic acid has been used to a very limited extent to introduce the $-CH_2NHSO_3H$ group into organic compounds in much the same manner as the aldehyde - bisulfite compounds discussed in Section II-A-1 have been employed to introduce the sulfomethyl moiety. Benzamide reacts as follows (626):

$$C_6H_5CONH_2 + HOCH_2NHSO_3H \longrightarrow$$

$$C_6H_5CONHCH_2NHSO_3H + H_2O \qquad (5\text{-}113)$$

A similar type of reaction, plus urea-formaldehyde resin formation, occurs with urea in the preparation of a textile treating resin (368). A polyethylene polyamine behaves likewise, forming a tanning agent (281).

V. SULFOARYLATION

A. Phenolsulfonic Acid

1. PREPARATION

Phenolsulfonic acid, as obtained by the direct sulfonation of phenol (235, 618), comprises a mixture of the 2- and 4-isomers, the ratio depending upon reaction conditions, primarily temperature (cf. , Chapter II).   The free acid (162, 461) and the sodium salt (148, 232) are available as commercial mixtures.

2. RESIN FORMATION

Phenolsulfonic acid and its salts have seen industrial application as monomers and comonomers for preparing water-soluble and -insoluble, sulfonated phenol-formaldehyde-type resins, used as synthetic tanning agents and ion-exchange resins, respectively.   Sulfoarylation is the only practical approach for making these materials, since direct sulfonation of the polymers has not proved satisfactory (440).   Preparation of the tanning agents using numerous variations has been studied at length using empirical methods (103, 180, 600, 601), as have also the preparation and properties of the ion-exchange resins (50, 611).   In both cases, the most effective products are copolymers of sulfonated and unsulfonated phenols, using one of several possible aldehydes or ketones.   Although the water-insoluble phenolsulfonate resins have been largely supplanted in recent years by those based on polystyrene, patents continue to appear on preparative variations for this, as well as for the water-soluble type.

3. ESTERIFICATION

Acrylate and methacrylate esters, made from the acid chlorides with sodium phenolsulfonate, have been polymerized and copolymerized (412, 413).   The lauric and oleic esters, evaluated as detergents, have excellent wetting power, but poor lime stability (246).   The acid chlorides have similarly been used to prepare the benzoic (433) and the ethyl carbonic esters (324, 433).   The ester groups in both compounds withstand treatment with PCl_5 during conversion to the sulfonyl chlorides.   Sulfonate esters were made from 4-toluenesulfonyl chloride (153), and from long-chain sulfonyl chlorides (29).

4.   ETHER FORMATION

Sodium phenolsulfonate has been converted to the methyl, ethyl, n-propyl, n-butyl (96), 9-octadecenyl, butyldodecyl (246), and 2, 4-dinitrophenyl (153) ethers.   The two long-chain ethers were fair surfactants, but had poor lime stability.

5.   MISCELLANEOUS REACTIONS

The phenolic group of the sodium salt ethoxylates normally with styrene oxide to form emulsifiers (510) and with ethylene oxide (102) to give polyester modifiers improving dyeability.   Sodium phenolsulfonate couples with diazotized 4-nitro-4'aminodiphenylsulfone (710).

B.   Sulfanilic and Metanilic Acids

These compounds, 4- and 3-aminobenzenesulfonic acids, respectively, have been available for many years from several commercial sources as dye intermediates.   Sulfanilic acid, being the cheaper of the two, has been favored in sulfoarylation studies.

1.   ACYLATION

Acylation of sodium sulfanilate with long-chain fatty acid chlorides yields foam stabilizers (602), or detergents similar in effectiveness to "Igepon T" (321), which is derived from taurine, as discussed in Section II-B-2.   Chlorinated stearoyl chloride has been similarly reacted with sodium metanilate (335), and oleoyl chloride with sodium N-ethyl metanilate (263).   Sodium N-lauroyl metanilate was manufactured as a commercial detergent, but was discontinued because of deficient foaming and inadequate detergency (34).   Acylation with 2, 4-dimethoxybenzoyl chloride yields an optical bleach (428).   Surface reaction occurs between a methyl methacrylate-maleic anhydride copolymer and sulfanilic acid, presumably by amide or imide formation (573); properties of the sulfoarylated polymer were not studied.

The sulfonyl fluorides of sulfanilic and metanilic acids are of special interest.   They are stable compounds in which the amino group show normal reactivity (137a).   They can be acylated with acrylyl or methacrylyl chlorides (276), and the monomers so formed can be polymerized.   The sulfonyl fluoride groups are stable in neutral or acid medium, but can be hydrolyzed to sulfonate in weakly alkaline medium without destruction of the amide linkages.   Similarly, the sulfonyl fluorides can be reacted with maleic anhydride polymers, followed by hydrolysis.   The sulfonyl fluoride of 4-methoxymetanilic acid has been likewise employed (234).   The 4-cetylmercapto analogue has been used to ammonolyze an ester (233); the amide so formed was then hydrolyzed to the sulfonate.

2. SULFONAMIDE FORMATION

Sodium sulfanilate also forms sulfonamides. Water-soluble dyes were thus prepared from copper phthalocyaninetrisulfonyl chloride (40). Long-chain sulfonyl chlorides yield surface-active compounds (29).

3. ALKYLATION

Sodium sulfanilate can be mono- or dibenzylated with benzyl chloride (7, 74, 75), forming textile assistants. A similar product can be made by alkylation with ar-2-(chloromethyl)tetrahydronaphthalene (109). Experimental detergents have been prepared (321) by reductive alkylation using long-chain oxo aldehydes; this procedure can be operated in one step (344). Polyalkylene polyamino compounds of structure $H(NHCH_2CH_2)_xNHC_6H_4SO_3Na$ can be made from ethylenimine (516). Sodium metanilate was alkylated at 1:1 molar ratio with N, N-(2-hydroxyethyl) oleamide (515), and with sodium N-(n-dodecyl)aminoethyl sulfate (309) to form surface-active agents. A similar use was made of the product from sodium sulfanilate and octadecenyl glycidyl ether (377):

$$ROCH_2\overline{CHCH_2O} + H_2NC_6H_4SO_3Na \longrightarrow ROCH_2CHOHCH_2NHC_6H_4SO_3Na$$

$$(5\text{-}114)$$

Diazomethane converts sulfanilic acid to the betaine (397).

4. ALDEHYDE CONDENSATIONS

Although formaldehyde reacts with sulfanilic acid forming the N, N-dimethyl derivative (200), the sodium salt forms resins (500). Water-soluble sulfanilate-modified urea-formaldehyde or urea-melamine resins have been suggested as textile finishes (598, 701), tanning agents (133), or wet-strength additives for paper (359). Thymol yields a water-soluble antiseptic by reaction with formaldehyde and sodium sulfanilate (240). Long-chain alkyl sulfonamides form detergents with formaldehyde and sodium metanilate (496). Both of these reactions may be Mannich-type condensations, yielding a product of the structure $RSO_2NHCH_2NHC_6H_4SO_3Na$ in the second case. Furfural forms ion-exchange resins (33, 520, 671). 4-Dimethylaminobenzaldehyde (686) and β-furylacrolein (591) form anils with sulfanilic acid.

5. CYANURIC CHLORIDE DERIVATIVES

Sodium sulfanilate reacts easily with cyanuric chloride at 1:1 molar ratio, forming sodium (4-sulfophenylamino)-4, 6-dichloro-s-triazine (388, 636):

$$NaO_3SC_6H_4NHC \underset{N}{\overset{N \diagdown \diagup N}{\diagdown}} \quad (5\text{-}115)$$

This compound is a useful sulfoarylating agent in its own right, since the chlorine atoms are quite reactive. Both chlorine atoms have been replaced by ammonia (351) and by ethanol (165). The former derivative was then converted to a tanning agent by reaction with formaldehyde and a sulfonamide (562). It has also been condensed stepwise with a variety of amino or hydroxy compounds. It is, therefore, of interest for preparing fiber-reactive dyes (388, 712), by first replacing one chlorine atom with an amino-containing dye, and subsequently reacting the other with a hydroxyl group of cellulose. This principle has been applied in dyeing rayon (549), and it can be used with azo (42, 388, 712) and with anthraquinonoid (712) dyes. An optical bleach has been prepared (48) by replacing one chlorine atom with dehydrothiotoluidinesulfonic acid and then hydrolyzing the other. Reaction of one atom with ethylene diamine and the other with starch yields a wrinkle-resistant cotton finish (257). Sodium sulfanilate reacts similarly at 1:1 molar ratio with 2, 4-dichloroquinazoline, forming a dye intermediate (117). A similar type of compound was prepared from sodium metanilate with 2, 4, 5, 6-tetrachloropyrimidine at 1:1 molar (6). Cyanuric chloride was likewise condensed with 1-amino-2, 5-benzenedisulfonate (38). Similar compounds made from sodium taurate and cyanuric chloride were discussed in a previous section (see Eq. 5-41).

Considerably more effective ion-exchange resins can be prepared by treating the cellulose - cyanuric chloride reaction product with sodium sulfanilate, rather than reacting compound 5-115 with cellulose (225).

6. MISCELLANEOUS DERIVATIVES

Long-chain isothiocyanates (545), and isocyanates (658) react as expected, forming detergents. Calcium cyanamide yields the cyanoguanidine (524), and ethyl acetoacetate forms the sulfonated anilide, a photographic chemical (708). This ammonolysis is effected in pyridine solution:

$$CH_3COCH_2COOC_2H_5 + H_2NC_6H_4SO_3Na \longrightarrow$$

$$CH_3COCH_2CONHC_6H_4SO_3Na + C_2H_5OH \quad (5\text{-}116)$$

C. 4-Hydrazinobenzenesulfonic Acid

Although all three isomers of this compound, $H_2NNHC_6H_4SO_3H$, are commercially available (100, 148, 184, 355), the 4-isomer, which is the most cheaply accessible via diazotization of sulfanilic acid (199), is the only one which has been employed to any extent for sulfoarylation.

This compound has proved of special interest because of its reactivity with ketones, which form water-soluble phenylhydrazonesulfonic acids (649, 689). Since the ketones are easily recovered from these materials, this approach has provided a useful method for isolating them from natural sources. α, β-Unsaturated ketones form pyrazolines (5-117-A) (360, 649), compounds also formed from the analogous dimethylaminomethylacetophenones (360); these materials are textile brightening agents.

(5-117)

(A)　　　　　　　　　　(B)

Ethyl acetoacetate easily forms the corresponding phenylmethylpyrazolonesulfonic acid (5-117-B) in 94% yield (199), a useful dye intermediate, also obtainable from ketene (419). Ethyl dihydroxystearoylacetate (450) and diketosuccinic acid (711) similarly form heterocycles. Jacobs (343) has reviewed in some detail the preparation of such dyes from ethyl oxalacetate. The 3-keto group of 1-benzoylisatin also forms a dyestuff (531). An imino group, as in nitroiminophthalimidines (348), behaves similarly, liberating ammonia and forming the phenylhydrazonesulfonic acid salt. Grape sugar (620) and hydrocellulose (466) form derivatives of unstated structure; the second compound did not react with other hydrazines.

Aldehydes, on the other hand, either do not react, or, if they do react, they form addition compounds unstable in the presence of moisture or some solvents (63, 649). The dihydroxybenzaldehydes, exceptionally, do form stable derivatives.

2-(2-Chloromethyl)cymene forms a surface-active agent (110), presumably by alkylation of the hydrazine moiety.

D. 4-Chloromethylbenzenesulfonic Acid

This compound, $ClCH_2C_6H_4SO_3H$, has been prepared as its sodium salt by chlorinating dry, solid, sodium 4-toluenesulfonate suspended in o-dichlorobenzene, at 120°C for 3 hr. (347). Others (195) claim that the reaction does not proceed stepwise and that mixtures are always formed. The sulfonyl chloride is reported to form in fair yield by treating toluene with a mixture of sulfuryl chloride and chlorosulfonic acid (456). An 85% yield is claimed in the chlorination of 4-toluenesulfonyl chloride, catalyzed by light and the addition of PCl_5 (401). Attempts to prepare the sulfonic acid by the direct sulfonation of benzyl chloride with sulfuric acid have proved fruitless. The compound is apparently not available commercially.

The chlorine atom in this compound has the typical high reactivity typical of benzyl halides. It reacts with the primary amino group of 4-methyl-7-aminocoumarin (4, 5) forming optical bleaches, and with the secondary amino group of 2-heptadecyl-2-imidazoline (679), yielding a surface-active compound. It also forms quaternary compounds with dimethylamino-substituted aromatics (495) and heterocyclics (4, 5). Sulfonamides yield tanning agents, apparently by alkylation of the amido group (507). A tanning agent was also prepared by ether formation with ar-tetrahydro-2-naphthol (385), and a surfactant similarly resulted from isooctylphenol (144). Etherification of pine lignin yields a water-soluble sulfonate useful in drilling muds (550). This reactive sulfoarylating agent would undoubtedly attract widespread interest if it were easily available.

E.   4-Styrenesulfonic Acid

This compound, also known as 4-vinylbenzenesulfonic acid, is easily prepared by sulfonating 2-bromoethylbenzene, followed by treatment with alkali to effect simultaneous dehydrobromination and sulfonate salt formation. Sulfonation can be effected with sulfur trioxide (457), or with chlorosulfonic acid (21, 463, 487, 693). The sodium and potassium salts are commercially available (125, 160, 162, 684). They can be purified by recrystallization from water (247, 248), and stabilized by adding sodium nitrite (487).

4-Styrenesulfonic acid has been used to date only for the preparation of water-soluble or -insoluble polymers, either by homopolymerization (693), by copolymerization with a wide variety of other monomers (21, 132, 164, 176, 247, 340, 452, 470, 471, 694), or by grafting to polymers such as cellulose acetate (119) or poly (vinylpyrrolidone) (163). This method of preparing sulfonated polymers can give products of greater purity and uniformity than those made by the direct sulfonation of a polymer (597). The two types consequently have different properties. Use of this reagent will no doubt increase parallel to the increasing attention being given to sulfonated polymers in general. 3- and 4-Styrenesulfonylfluorides copolymerize with styrene and methyl acrylate (275); the sulfonyl fluoride group enhances overall reactivity of the monomer.

The high reactivity of the styrene moiety (170) suggests that this reagent may see future consideration for sulfoarylation reactions other than polymerization.

F. Benzaldehyde-2-Sulfonic and -2, 4-Disulfonic Acids

1. PREPARATION

Of the three benzaldehydemonosulfonic acids, only the 3-isomer can be made by the direct sulfonation of benzaldehyde with oleum (681). The statement that SO_3 can also be employed (409) has not been verified (15). The 2-isomer is prepared by reacting 2-chlorobenzaldehyde with sodium sulfite (235). Benzaldehyde-2, 4-disulfonic acid is made by oxidizing toluene-2, 4-disulfonic acid. The 2-sulfonate (99, 148, 158), the 3-isomer (226), and the 2, 4-disulfonate (99, 100, 184, 355) are commercially available.

2. AROMATIC CONDENSATION REACTIONS

The condensation of aromatic compounds with the 2-isomer at 2:1 molar ratio via the aldehyde group yields triphenylmethane dyes of unusual alkali stability because of the influence of the ortho sulfonic group (140, 199):

$$2RH + HO_3SC_6H_4CHO \longrightarrow HO_3SC_6H_4CH(R)_2 + H_2O \qquad (5\text{-}118)$$

Aromatic compounds so reacted include the cresols (140), dimethylaniline (678), and o-cresotinic acid (256). Benzaldehyde-2, 4-disulfonic acid similarly forms stable dyes with aryl compounds, e. g. , diethylaniline (199). The 2-monosulfonic acid reacts with naphthalene (229, 676), or with alkylated phenols (229), forming syntans and surface-active agents. The 3-isomer also forms tanning agents with phenols or with phenanthrene (676). The disulfonic acid also forms syntans with cresols (676) and wetting agents with naphthalene or with alkylated phenols (229). It has been used to some extent commercially as an intermediate for making ion-exchange resins by condensation with resorcinol, followed by resinification with formaldehyde (400, 646).

3. AZOMETHINE FORMATION

The aldehyde group forms azomethines with primary aromatic amines. The 2-monosulfonic acid salt has thus been employed to render chromed azo dyes (116) and diphenylmethane dyes (415) water-soluble. The azomethines of 1, 2, 4-triaminobenzene derivatives are photographic chemicals (697). The disulfonate salt forms an azomethine useful as an optical bleach with 7-methyl-4-aminocoumarin (5). Reduction of the azomethine from stearic hydrazide yields a textile assistant of the structure $RCONHNHCH_2C_6H_3(SO_3Na)_2$ (114).

4. MISCELLANEOUS REACTIONS

Several reports indicate the utility of benzaldehyde-2-sulfonic acid for rendering poly(vinyl alcohol) derivatives water-soluble by acetal formation. Photographic dyes (128, 438, 439, 447) and electrostatic charge inhibitors for hydrophobic fibers (190, 369) can be thus prepared. The disulfonic acid forms similar acetals (190, 675). The bisulfite adduct of the monosulfonate salt forms a wetting agent, RCONH—CH(SO$_3$Na)C$_6$H$_4$SO$_3$Na, by sulfomethylation of stearamide (115).

G. 2-Sulfobenzoic Anhydride

This compound, prepared from saccharin (618), as follows:

(5-119)

(A)

or from 2-chlorobenzoic acid (235), is commercially available (100, 148, 232, 355).

Applications of this long-used sulfoacylating reagent have been largely along established lines since a previous review (618). A major use of 2-sulfobenzoic anhydride has been acid-catalyzed condensation with a phenolic nucleus via the carbonyl group to form sulfonephthalein dyes (618). More recently, this reaction has been extended to include catechol (672, 673), pyrogallol (674), indole (572), and various diphenylamines (551). One report states that in such condensations, saccharin yields the same product as the anhydride (509). Under alkaline conditions, phenols undergo conventional sulfoacylation; thus, phenol forms sodium 2-(carbophenoxy)benzenesulfonate (423). Alcoholic hydroxyl groups also react. The water solubility of ascorbic acid-6-palmitate is enhanced by conversion to the 5-[2-sulfobenzoate] (635). Sterols are similarly rendered water-soluble (310).

Ammonia (423) and amines are sulfoacylated forming compounds of structure RNHCOC$_6$H$_4$SO$_3$H· H$_2$NR. Sulfa drugs of enhanced water solubility result from similar reaction in pyridine solution with the amino groups of sulfanilamide, sulfathiazole, and sulfadiazine (204). Photographic dyes are thus formed by sulfoacylation of ring-substituted anilines (544). Aliphatic and aromatic diamines can form heterocycles (458):

$$H_2NCH_2CH_2NH_2 + \quad \text{[benzoxathiine structure]} \longrightarrow \text{[product structure]} \qquad (5\text{-}120)$$

Hydrazine similarly forms a three-membered ring.

H. 3-Sulfobenzoic Acid and Acid Chloride

1. PREPARATION

Of the three sulfobenzoic acids, the 3-isomer is the one of most practical interest as a sulfoacylating agent, since it can be made by the direct sulfonation of benzoic acid (237, 618), whereas the other two must be prepared by more expensive indirect methods. All three acids are, however, commercially available in experimental quantities (14, 51, 148, 232, 355).

2. CHEMICAL REACTIONS

3-Sulfobenzoic acid easily undergoes direct esterification, and the lauryl ester was at one time of commercial interest as a specialty surfactant. The methyl ester confers dyeability to polyester (254) and polyamide (323) fibers.

The acid chloride - sulfonic acid (5-121-A), easily prepared from the acid (539), is a more reactive, and therefore a more convenient, sulfoacylating agent:

$$\text{[COOH / SO}_3\text{H benzene]} + SO_2Cl_2 \longrightarrow \text{[COCl / SO}_3\text{H benzene]} + ClSO_3H \qquad (5\text{-}121)$$

$$(A)$$

3-Sulfobenzoyl chloride sulfoacylates via typical acid chloride reactions with 2-naphthol, ammonia, aniline, and benzene (539). Azo dyes containing phenolic groups (22, 197, 250), and dinaphthazine (480) dyes have been made water-soluble by treatment with this reagent. Sterols (404) have been reacted likewise; similar sterol derivatives result from the use of the corresponding diacid chloride (310). 3-Sulfobenzoyl chloride is apparently not commercially available, but the corresponding acid-sulfonyl chloride (5-122-A) can be purchased (11, 148), or, as shown in Chapter 2, it can easily be made by reacting benzoic acid with chlorosulfonic acid. It has been shown (539) that, in the presence of pyridine, compound 5-122-A forms the sulfoacyl derivative of 2-naphthol (5-122-C), rather than the expected ester, 5-122-B, which is in fact formed from the sodium salt of 2-naphthol:

$$
\text{(A)} \quad
\underset{\text{SO}_2\text{Cl}}{\overset{\text{COOH}}{\bigcirc}} + \text{ROH}
\xrightarrow[\text{NaOH}]{\text{Pyridine}}
\begin{cases}
\underset{\text{SO}_3^-}{\overset{\text{COOR}}{\bigcirc}} \quad \text{(C)} \\[2em]
\underset{\text{SO}_2\text{OR}}{\overset{\text{COO}^-}{\bigcirc}} \quad \text{(B)}
\end{cases}
\qquad (5\text{-}122)
$$

The hydroxyl groups in leuco dimethoxybenzanthrone have similarly been sulfoacylated with 3-carboxybenzenesulfonyl chloride in pyridine (104); this is an interesting variation over the usual procedure for solubilizing vat dyes by sulfation, as discussed in Chapter 6. These results suggest that 3-carboxybenzenesulfonyl chloride plus pyridine is a practical sulfoarylating system deserving further study. Other cases in which sulfonyl chlorides also containing carboxyl groups form the acyl, rather than the expected sulfonate, esters are cited in Sections VI, and II-B-11.

3-(Fluorosulfonyl) benzoyl chloride is of special interest because of the extreme difference in the reactivity of the two acid halide groups. The reactive chlorocarbonyl group preferentially undergoes coupling with amino groups [(e. g. , poly(vinyl amine)], while the remaining fluorosulfonyl moiety, being relatively inert, is stable in acid or neutral medium, but is easily hydrolyzed to sulfonate with aqueous alkali (234a). The amide group is stable under the conditions of hydrolysis.

I.   4-Sulfophthalic Anhydride

4-Sulfophthalic anhydride is made by direct sulfonation of the anhydride (618). It (14), the free acid (355), and its sodium salt (11) are commercially available in experimental quantities.

The chemical reactions of this compound in general resemble those of 2-sulfobenzoic acid discussed in Section G. Diester wetting agents have been prepared by esterification with long-chain alcohols, including branched C6 and 7 (152, 593), octadecyl (108), oleyl (108), C9 oxo (709), and hydroxyethylamides of phthalic acid (357). It has been converted to sulfophthaleins with phenol, m-cresol, 3, 5-dimethyl-phenol, and resorcinol (536); subsequent treatment with formaldehyde gave ion - exchange resins. Ion - exchange resins have also been made by simply refluxing the anhydride with excess mixed xylenes, followed by curing of the gel so formed (537). Aminodiphenylamine dyes can be made water-soluble by acylation with this anhydride (215).

Sulfonated phthalocyanine dyes can be made by sulfonating a phthalocyanine, or by heating a salt of sulfophthalic acid, preferably the ammonium salt (664), with urea and a copper salt (669). The dyes thus prepared by sulfoacylation are stated (610) to differ in several important respects from those made by direct sulfonation. The former have the sulfonic group in the 3-position, while the latter have it in the 4-position. The former have better light-fastness and considerably improved fastness to alkali, while the latter are greener in shade and have better affinity for cellulose fibers. Due to their lower cost, the directly sulfonated products are the ones most used commercially. Another procedure for solubilizing phthalocyanine dyes involves reacting the dye with formaldehyde and potassium sulfophthalimide, thereby introducing the sulfophthalimidomethyl moiety (274).

J. 5-Sulfoisophthalic and 2-Sulfoterephthalic Acids

These compounds have been made by direct sulfonation of the corresponding acids (90, 93, 618). Isophthalic acid is the easiest of the three phthalic compounds to sulfonate, and terephthalic the most difficult. 5-Sulfoisophthalic acid is available in experimental quantities (355). Since the two parent acids have become commercially available only comparatively recently, little work has as yet been done with the derived sulfo acids compared to sulfophthalic anhydride, discussed in the preceding section. They are easily diesterified with methanol (254), and the esters have been incorporated into polyester (254) and polyamide (323) fibers by alcoholysis and ammonolysis, respectively, to increase dyeability.

K. Miscellaneous Sulfoarylating Reagents

Sulfoarylation with sultones has been well reviewed through 1959 (472, 473). Tolylsultone (5-123-A) has been made from 2-chlorobenzaldehyde by a three-step procedure. It resembles a typical aliphatic sultone in its reactions with sodium carboxylates, sodium hydrosulfide, sodium acetamide (300), long-chain amines, starch (609) and sodium phenoxides (329).

(5-123)

(A)   (B)   (C)

1,8-Naphthosultone (5-123-B), and the 4-chloromethyl derivative (5-123-C) easily made from it, have also been studied (472, 473). The chloromethyl group is highly reactive, while the sultone group is stable under acid conditions. This has allowed preparation of many derivatives via the Friedel-Crafts and similar reactions. The chloromethyl group was also hydrolyzed to hydroxymethyl, which was then oxidized to carbonyl and to carboxyl groups. The sultone group in many of these compounds can be hydrolyzed to the 1-naphthol-8-sulfonate derivative under alkaline conditions. Further study of these three sulfoarylating agents may be limited by their difficult accessibility compared to other reagents cited in this chapter.

Sodium 4-vinylbenzylsulfonate (CH_2:$CHC_6H_4CH_2SO_3Na$) has been copolymerized with acrylamide (346), and grafted to poly (vinylpyrrolidone) (163), and to cellulose acetate (119). Sodium 4-vinyloxybenzenesulfonate (CH_2:$CHOC_6H_4SO_3Na$) was prepared in 96% yield by dehydrohalogenation of the corresponding bromide (207). It has been copolymerized with acrylonitrile to enhance fiber dyeability. Both of these compounds may find uses similar to those of sodium 4-styrenesulfonate (Section E).

2-Naphthalenesulfonic acid forms commercially important polymeric tanning and dispersing agents by condensation with formaldehyde (180, 479a, 665), but this compound has apparently not been otherwise employed for sulfoarylation.

VI. HETEROCYCLIC SULFONATING REAGENTS

A. Furan-2-Chlorocarbonyl-5-Sulfonic Acid

This compound has been prepared by treating available (148, 232) furan-2-carboxylic acid chloride with SO_3 in methylene chloride solvent at -10°C (249):

$$\begin{array}{ccc}
\text{HC} - \text{CH} & & \text{HC} - \text{CH} \\
\parallel \quad \parallel & + SO_3 \longrightarrow & \parallel \quad \parallel \\
\text{HC} \quad \text{CCOCl} & & \text{HO}_3\text{SC} \quad \text{CCOCl} \\
\diagdown\diagup & & \diagdown\diagup \\
\text{O} & & \text{O}
\end{array} \qquad (5\text{-}124)$$

(A)

It has been used to sulfoacylate azo dyes on phenolic hydroxyl and amino groups (22, 249). It is noteworthy that the same sulfoacylated compounds can result when using either the chlorocarbonyl sulfonic acid (5-124-A), or the carboxylic acid sulfonyl chloride [made from 2-furoic acid and chlorosulfonic acid (249)]. The sulfonyl chlorides of aliphatic and aromatic carboxylic acids behave similarly, as pointed out in Sections V-H, and II-B-11, respectively.

B.   2, 4(2, 6)-Dichloropyrimidine-5-Sulfonic Acid

This compound, prepared as follows from uracil (572a), has been

$$
\begin{array}{ccc}
\underset{\substack{HC \\ }}{\overset{N}{\underset{\parallel}{HOC}}}\overset{N}{\underset{N}{\diagdown COH}} & \xrightarrow{ClSO_3H} & \underset{ClO_2SC}{\overset{N}{\underset{\parallel}{HOC}}}\overset{N}{\underset{N}{\diagdown COH}} \xrightarrow[(2)NaOH]{(1)PCl_5}
\end{array}
$$

$$
\underset{NaO_3SC}{\overset{N}{\underset{\parallel}{ClC}}}\overset{N}{\underset{N}{\diagdown CCl}}
$$

(5-125)

suggested (572a) for rendering dyes water-soluble by reaction of the
halogen atoms with amino groups in the dyes, and for reaction with
cellulose to improve its receptivity to dyes.   This sulfonate has a general structural resemblance to the derivatives of cyanuric chloride
made by reacting the latter with taurine (cf., Section II-B-2), or with
sulfanilic acid (Section V-B), but the chlorine atoms in this compound
are less reactive than those in cyanuric chloride.

REFERENCES

1. Abe, H. , S. Onishi, Y. Kunugi, and K. Matsui, Tanabe Seiyaku Kenkyu Nempo 2, No. 2, 11 (1957); Chem. Abstr. , 52, 9153 (1958).
2. Ackermann, F. ,   U. S. Patent 2, 550, 321; Chem. Abstr. , 45, 7360 (1951).
3. Ackermann, F. ,   U. S. Patent 2, 567, 796; Chem. Abstr. , 46, 754 (1952).
4. Ackermann, F. ,   U. S. Patent 2, 600, 375; Chem. Abstr. , 47, 2501 (1953).
5. Ackermann, F. ,   U. S. Patent 2, 610, 152; Chem. Abstr. , 47, 338 (1953).
6. Ackermann, H. , and P. Dussy, Helv. Chim. Acta, 45, 1683 (1962).
7. Adams, D. A. W. , and W. Baird, U. S. Dept. Commerce, OTS Rept. , PB80, 401, 1946, BIOS Final Rept. 1154.
8. Adams, R. , and J. D. Garber, J. Am. Chem. Soc. , 71, 522 (1949).
9. Aktien-Gesellschaft vorm. B. Siegfried, Swiss Patent 242, 286; Chem. Abstr. , 43, 7958 (1949).
10. Aktieselskabet Benzon, A. , and F. Andersen, British Patent 645, 429; Chem. Abstr. , 45, 2020 (1951).
11. Aldrich Chemical Co. , Milwaukee, Wis.
12. Alles, R. ,   U. S. Patent 2, 837, 489; Chem. Abstr. , 52, 15107 (1958).
13. Alles, R. ,   U. S. Patent 2, 837, 563; Chem. Abstr. , 52, 14224 (1958).
14. Allied Chemical Corp. , Baker and Adamson Dept. , Morristown, N. J.
15. Allied Chemical Corp. , General Chemical Division, unpublished research data.
16. Allied Chemical Corp. , National Aniline Division, National Surfactants, New York, N. Y.
17. van Alphen, J. , and J. Terwan, British Patent 869, 744; Chem. Abstr. , 55, 25297 (1961).
18. Alsbury, A. , K. A. Phillips, and B. Taylor, German Patent 1, 074, 797; Chem. Abstr. , 55, 21628 (1961).
19. American Cyanamid Company, "Sodium β-Sulfopropionitrile, " New York, 1957.
20. Anderson, R. J. , and L. M. Schenck, U. S. Patent 2, 923, 724; Chem. Abstr. , 54, 14733 (1960).
21. Andres, R. J. , and W. Sweeny, U. S. Patent 2, 837, 500; Chem. Abstr. , 52, 15964 (1958).
22. Andrew, H. F. , H. C. Boyd, and R. R. Davies, British Patent 786, 567; Chem. Abstr. , 52, 9608 (1958).
23. Antara Chemicals Division, Butyrolactone Technical Bulletin, New York, 1956.
24. Antara Chemicals Division, Methyltaurine 22 and Methyltaurine 25, New York, 1958.

25. Antara Chemicals Division, Sodium Isethionate Difunctional Intermediate, New York, 1961.

26. Anthes, J. A., and J. R. Dudley, U. S. Patent 2,597,696; Chem. Abstr., 47, 2196 (1953).

27. Armour and Co., Belgian Patent 613,063; Chem. Abstr., 58, 2456 (1963).

28. Armour Chemical Division, α-Sulfoalkyl Acids, Bulletin G-7, 1956.

29. Asinger, F., Chemie und Technologie der Paraffinkohlenwasserstoffe, Akademie-Verlag, Berlin, 1956.

30. Auten, R. W., Paper Trade J., 127, No. 5, 45 (1948).

31. Auten, R. W., Paper Trade J., 127, No. 5, 47 (1948).

32. Auten, R. W., and J. L. Rainey, U. S. Patent 2,407,599; Chem. Abstr., 41, 623 (1947).

33. Auxiliaire des chemins de fer et de l'industrie, French Patent 993,966; Chem. Abstr., 51, 14166 (1957).

34. Ayo, J. J., and M. L. Kastens, Ind. Eng. Chem., 42, 1626 (1950).

35. Backer, H. J., and W. G. Burgers, J. Chem. Soc., 1925, 234.

36. Backer, H. J., and H. Mulder, Rec. Trav. Chim., 52, 454 (1933).

37. Backer, H. J., and H. Mulder, Rec. Trav. Chim., 53, 1120 (1934).

38. Badische Anilin- und Soda Fabrik AG, Belgian Patent 616,686; Chem. Abstr., 59, 6557 (1963).

39. Badische Anilin- und Soda Fabrik AG, British Patent 686,061; Chem. Abstr., 48, 3392 (1954).

40. Badische Anilin- und Soda Fabrik AG, British Patent 827,568; Chem. Abstr., 54, 13674 (1960).

41. Badische Anilin- und Soda Fabrik AG, French Patent 1,292,003.

42. Badische Anilin- und Soda Fabrik AG, German Patent 1,127,016; Chem. Abstr., 57, 3592 (1962).

43. Baird, W., BIOS Final Rept. No. 421, Item No. 22.

44. Baldsiefen, W. D., U. S. Patent 2,600,831; Chem. Abstr., 46, 10026 (1952).

45. Barber, H. J., British Patent 647,214; Chem. Abstr., 45, 7144 (1951).

46. Barber, H. J., H. J. Cottrell, R. F. Fuller, and M. B. Green, J. Appl. Chem. (London), 3, 253 (1953).

47. Barber, H. J., H. J. Cottrell, and M. B. Green, J. Appl. Chem. (London), 3, 259 (1953).

48. Bartkowicz, S., Przemysl Chem., 9, 112 (1953); Chem. Abstr., 48, 8549 (1954).

49. Bauer, H., J. Am. Chem. Soc., 61, 617 (1939).

50. Bauman, W. C., Ind. Eng. Chem., 38, 46 (1946).

51. Beacon Chemical Industries, Inc., Cambridge, Mass.

52. Becker, W., German Patent 692,838; Chem. Abstr., 35, 4607 (1941).

53. Behnisch, R., and J. Klarer, German Patent 820,004; Chem. Abstr., 50, 540 (1956).

54. Behnisch, R. , and J. Klarer, U. S. Patent 2, 696, 454; Chem. Abstr. , 49, 3483 (1955).
55. Behnisch, B. , and P. Poehls, German Patent 870, 266.
56. Behrend, R. , and G. Koolman, Ann. , 394, 228 (1913).
57. Bell, R. P. , and G. A. Wright, Trans. Faraday Soc. , 57, 1386 (1961).
58. Beringer, F. M. , and R. A. Falk, J. Am. Chem. Soc. , 81, 2997 (1959).
59. Berkman, Ya. Pa. , and Yu. Shevchenko, Trudy Ukr. Nauchn. - Issledo. Inst. Kozheven Prom. , 6, 52 (1954); Chem. Abstr. , 51, 13435 (1957).
60. Berkman, Ya. Pa. , L. Shuter, and M. Ya. Rabinovich, Legkaya Prom. , 14, No. 7, 26 (1954); Chem. Abstr. , 48, 13250 (1954).
61. Bersworth, F. , A. E. Martell, and R. G. Lacoste, U. S. Patent 2, 836, 620; Chem. Abstr. , 52, 20060 (1958).
62. Besthorn, E. , and B. Geisselbrecht, Ber. , 53, 1026 (1920).
63. Biltz, H. , Ber. , 68B, 221 (1935).
64. Binnie, W. P. , H. L. Cohen, and G. F. Wright, J. Am. Chem. Soc. , 72, 4457 (1950).
65. Black, D. M. , U. S. Patent 2, 694, 051; Chem. Abstr. , 49, 5016 (1955).
66. Blicke, F. F. , The Mannich Reaction; in Organic Reactions, Vol. 1, Wiley, New York, 1942, pp. 303-341.
67. Blumenfeld, G. , German Patent 1, 075, 596; Chem. Abstr. , 55, 10316 (1961).
68. Bockmuehl, M. , and K. Windisch, German Patent 421, 505.
69. Bodendorf, K. , and N. Senger, Ber. , 72B, 571 (1939).
70. Boehme Fettchemie Gmbh, British Patent 764, 340; Chem. Abstr. , 51, 12956 (1957).
71. Boehme Fettchemie Gmbh, British Patent 764, 613; Chem. Abstr. , 51, 12956 (1957).
72. Boehme Fettchemie Gmbh, German Patent 1, 146, 870; Chem. Abstr. , 59, 11259 (1963).
73. Boehringer, C. F. , und Soehne, Austrian Patent 174, 151; Chem. Zentr. , 125, 1074 (1954).
74. Borodkin, V. F. , Tekstil. Prom. , 14, No. 8, 38 (1954); Chem. Abstr. , 48, 14213 (1954).
75. Borodkin, V. F. , Zh. Prikl. Khim. , 28, 777 (1955); Chem. Abstr. , 50, 3280 (1956).
76. Borodkin, V. F. , and S. S. Kuznetsova, Izv. Vysshikh Uchebn. Zavednii, Khim. i Khim. Tekhnol. , 5, No. 1, 141 (1962); Chem. Abstr. , 57, 15281 (1962).
77. Braitberg, L. D. , M. Robin, H. L. Friedman, and E. T. Tisza, J. Am. Chem. Soc. , 69, 2005 (1947).
78. Bradner, J. D. , W. H. Lockwood, R. H. Nagel, and K. L. Russell, U. S. Dept. Commerce, FIAT Final Rept. No. 1141.
79. Brenner, M. , and C. H. Burckhardt, Helv. Chim. Acta, 34, 1070 (1951).

80. Breslow, D. S. , and R. Hough, J. Am. Chem. Soc. , 79, 5000
     (1957).
81. Breslow, D. S. , R. R. Hough, and J. T. Fairclough, J. Am. Chem.
     Soc. , 76, 5361 (1954).
82. Breslow, D. S. , and G. E. Hulse, J. Am. Chem. Soc. , 76, 6399
     (1954).
83. British Celanese Ltd. , and H. C. Olpin, British Patent 285, 641;
     Chem. Abstr. , 23, 288 (1929).
84. Britt, K. W. , J. E. Donohue, R. P. Goodale, I. J. Gruntfest, L. E.
     Kelley, C. S. Maxwell, and J. P. Weidner, TAPPI Monograph No.
     13, Technical Assn. of the Pulp and Paper Industry, New York,
     1954.
85. Britton, E. C. , and A. R. Sexton, U. S. Patent 2, 821, 535; Chem.
     Abstr. , 52, 5861 (1958).
86. Brooker, L. G. S. , and G. H. Keyes, U. S. Patent 2, 917, 516;
     Chem. Abstr. , 54, 9575 (1960).
87. Brown, H. , D. H. Becking, and T. W. Tomaszewski, U. S. Patent
     2, 841, 602; Chem. Abstr. , 52, 17107 (1958).
88. Bucherer, H. , and A. Schwalbe, Ber. , 39, 2796 (1906).
89. Bunton, C. A. , and E. A. Halevi, J. Chem. Soc. , 1952, 4541.
90. Burckhardt, R. , German Patent 1, 127, 891; Chem. Abstr. , 57,
     9749 (1962).
91. Burnette, L. W. , and M. E. Chiddix, U. S. Patent 2, 880, 219;
     Chem. Abstr. , 53, 14963 (1959).
92. Burnette, L. W. , and M. E. Chiddix, J. Am. Oil Chemists' Soc. , 39,
     477 (1962).
93. Burns, H. W. , U. S. Patent 2, 895, 986; Chem. Abstr. , 54, 1447
     (1960).
94. Cain, C. K. , E. C. Taylor, and L. J. Daniel, J. Am. Chem. Soc. ,
     71, 892 (1949).
95. Carpenter, E. L. , U. S. Patent 2, 312, 878; Chem. Abstr. , 37,
     5199 (1943).
96. Carr, M. H. , and H. P. Brown, J. Am. Chem. Soc. , 69, 1170
     (1947).
97. Cassella Farbwerke Mainkur AG, British Patent 779, 908; Chem.
     Abstr. , 52, 11969 (1958).
98. Catlin, W. E. , and A. M. Jenkins, U. S. Patent 2, 839, 573; Chem.
     Abstr. , 52, 17107 (1958).
99. Chemical Intermediates and Research Laboratories, Cuyahoga
     Falls, Ohio.
100. Chemicals Procurement Laboratories, Inc. , College Point,
     N. Y.
101. Chemische Fabrik von Heyden, German Patent 216, 072-3; Chem.
     Abstr. , 4, 645 (1910).
102. Chemstrand Corp. , British Patent 868, 150; Chem. Abstr. , 55,
     24680 (1961).
103. Chen, P. S. , "500 Syntan Patent Abstracts, 1911-1950", South
     Lancaster, Mass. , Chemical Elements, 1950.

104.   Ciba AG, German Patent 1,146,840; Chem. Abstr. , 59, 5309
        (1963).
105.   Ciba Ltd. , British Patent 655,258; Chem. Abstr. , 46, 4245
        (1952).
106.   Ciba Ltd. , British Patent 662,572; Chem. Abstr. , 46, 11245
        (1952).
107.   Ciba Ltd. , British Patent 662,573; Chem. Abstr. , 46, 6394
        (1952).
108.   Ciba Ltd. , Swiss Patents 234,288-91; Chem. Abstr. , 44, 7873
        (1950).
109.   Ciba Ltd. , Swiss Patent 235,197; Chem. Abstr. , 44, 1543
        (1950).
110.   Ciba Ltd. , Swiss Patent 235,200; Chem. Abstr. , 44, 1543
        (1950).
111.   Ciba Ltd. , Swiss Patent 242,782; Chem. Abstr. , 43, 5217
        (1949).
112.   Ciba Ltd. , Swiss Patent 243,596; Chem. Abstr. , 43, 5216
        (1949).
113.   Ciba Ltd. , Swiss Patent 248,683; Chem. Abstr. , 43, 7729
        (1949).
114.   Ciba Ltd. , Swiss Patent 248,684; Chem. Abstr. , 43, 7730
        (1949).
115.   Ciba Ltd. , Swiss Patent 252,069; Chem. Abstr. , 43, 8712
        (1949).
116.   Ciba Ltd. , Swiss Patent 264,571; Chem. Abstr. , 44, 10326
        (1950).
117.   Ciba Ltd. , Swiss Patent 294,227; Chem. Abstr. , 50, 4212
        (1956).
118.   Ciba SA, Belgian Patent 619,754; Chem. Abstr. , 59, 12960
        (1963).
119.   Cloninger, L. C. , and F. M. Arnesen,   U. S. Patent 3,006,830;
        Chem. Abstr. , 56, 10418 (1962).
120.   Coffman, D. D. , and W. L. Alderson,   U. S. Patent 2,373,870;
        Chem. Abstr. , 39, 3536 (1945).
121.   Cohen, J. B. ,   J. Pharmacol. , 46, 283 (1932).
122.   Coker, J. N. ,   J. Org. Chem. , 27, 1881 (1962).
123.   Colgate Palmolive Co. , Belgian Patent 593,514.
124.   Colgate Palmolive Co. , French Patent 1,270,616.
125.   Columbia Organic Chemicals, Inc. , Columbia, S. C.
126.   Cooper, G. D. ,   J. Org. Chem. , 21, 1214 (1956).
127.   Copenhaver, J. W. , and M. H. Bigelow, Acetylene and Carbon
        Monoxide Chemistry, Reinhold, New York, 1949, p. 158.
128.   Corner, J. O. , and E. L. Martin,   J. Am. Chem. Soc. , 76, 3593
        (1954).
129.   Cross, J. M. , and M. E. Chiddix,   U. S. Patent 2,694,727; Chem.
        Abstr. , 48, 13290 (1954).
130.   Culvenor, C. C. J. , W. Davies, and N. S. Heath,   J. Chem. Soc. ,
        1949, 278.

131. Daimler, K., and K. Platz, U.S. Patent 1,881,172; Chem. Abstr., 27, 575 (1933).

132. Davis, C. W., F. A. Ehlers, and T. G. Taylor, U.S. Patent 2,913,438; Chem. Abstr., 54, 2776 (1960).

133. Dawson, W. O., U.S. Patent 2,550,639; Chem. Abstr., 45, 6864 (1951).

134. Day, H. M., U.S. Patent 2,477,328; Chem. Abstr., 44, 371 (1950).

135. Day, H. M., U.S. Patent 2,497,054; Chem. Abstr., 44, 4607 (1950).

136. Day, H. M., and R. L. De Hoff, U.S. Patent 2,522,569; Chem. Abstr., 45, 1274 (1951).

137. Dazzi, J., U.S. Patent 2,667,506; Chem. Abstr., 48, 6149 (1954).

137a. DeCat, A., and R. VanPoucke, J. Org. Chem., 28, 3426 (1963).

138. Dehydag Deutsche Hydrierwerke Gmbh, British Patent 875,846; Chem. Abstr., 56, 11362 (1962).

139. Demmler, K., H. Distler, F. Miller, and L. Wuertele, German Patent 1,116,405; Chem. Abstr., 57, 1068 (1962).

140. Demont, P., Rev. gen. des mat. col., 24, 65 (1920); Chem. Abstr., 14, 3796 (1920).

141. Dengel, F., German Patent 833,809; Chem. Abstr., 47, 3345 (1953).

142. Despois, R. L., U.S. Patent 2,262,544; Chem. Abstr., 36, 1736 (1942).

143. Desseigne, G., and M. Mathieu, Mem. Serv. Chim. Etat (Paris), 31, 359 (1944); Chem. Abstr., 41, 705 (1947).

144. Deutsche Hydrierwerke, British Patent 516,188; Chem. Abstr., 35, 6023 (1941).

145. Dickert, J. J., and H. D. Hartough, U.S. Patent 2,721,875; Chem. Abstr., 50, 8713 (1956).

146. Dickey, J. B., U.S. Patent 2,422,000; Chem. Abstr., 41, 5306 (1947).

147. Dickey, J. B., and J. G. McNally, U.S. Patent 2,241,769; Chem. Abstr., 35, 5133 (1941).

148. Distillation Products Industries, Eastman Organic Chemicals Dept., Rochester, New York.

149. Distler, H., Paper presented at the 19th International Congress for Pure and Applied Chemistry, London, July 10-17, 1963.

150. Distler, H., and K. Kuespert, U.S. Patent 3,048,625; Chem. Abstr., 57, 16404 (1962).

151. Dmitriev, S. A., N. M. Karavaev, and A. V. Smirnova, Izvest. Akad. Nauk SSSR Otdel. Khim. Nauk, 1961, 1800; Chem. Abstr., 56, 7207 (1962).

152. Doerr, E. L., and R. E. Miller, U.S. Patent 2,828,326; Chem. Abstr., 52, 13796 (1958).

153. Doherty, D. G., W. H. Stein, and M. Bergmann, J. Biol. Chem. 135, 487 (1940).

153a.   Dohr, M. , and G. Tauber, German Patent 1,165,272; Chem.
        Abstr. , 60, 14635 (1964).

154.   Dombrovskii, A. V. , and G. M. Prilutskii, Zh. Obshch. Khim. ,
        25, 1943 (1955); Chem. Abstr. , 50, 8450 (1956).

155.   Donovan, T. S. , U. S. Patent 2,578,292; Chem. Abstr. , 46,
        2435 (1952).

156.   Doser, A. , in Houben-Weyl, Methoden der Organischen Chemie,
        Vol. IX, 4th ed. , Thieme Verlag, Stuttgart, 1955.

157.   Driver, G. W. , British Patent 841,701; Chem. Abstr. , 55,
        5426 (1961).

158.   Du Pont de Nemours and Co. , E. I. , Inc. , Organic Chemicals
        Dept. , Wilmington, Del.

159.   Du Pont de Nemours and Co. , E. I. , Inc. , "Pyrrolidine", New
        Products Bulletin No. 28, 1950.

160.   Du Pont de Nemours and Co. , E. I. , Inc. , "Sodium Styrene Sul-
        fonate Product Data Sheet", A-20797.

161.   Du Pont de Nemours and Co. , E. I. , Inc. , British Patent
        444,639; Chem. Abstr. , 30, 5596 (1936).

162.   Dow Chemical Co. , Midland, Michigan.

163.   Dow Chemical Co. , British Patent 851,491; Chem. Abstr. , 55,
        13923 (1961).

164.   Dow Chemical Co. , British Patent 895,033; Chem. Abstr. , 57,
        4887 (1962).

165.   Dudley, J. R. , J. T. Thurston, F. C. Schaefer, D. Holm-Hansen, C.
        J. Hull, and P. Adams, J. Am. Chem. Soc. , 73, 2986 (1951).

166.   Dyke, W. J. C. , and H. King, J. Chem. Soc. , 1935, 805.

167.   Eibner, A. , Ann. , 316, 89 (1901).

168.   Eilar, K. R. , U. S. Patent 2,668,851; Chem. Abstr. , 48, 9087
        (1954).

169.   Elbel, E. , German Patent 1,121,045; Chem. Abstr. , 58, 9338
        (1963).

170.   Emerson, W. S. , Chem. Rev. , 45, 183 (1949).

171.   Erdtman, H. G. H. , Swedish Patent 130,523; Chem. Abstr. , 45,
        8554 (1951).

172.   Erdtman, H. G. H. , U. S. Patent 2,623,881; Chem. Abstr. , 48,
        719 (1954).

173.   Erickson, J. G. , U. S. Patent 2,758,133; Chem. Abstr. , 51,
        2856 (1957).

174.   Erman, W. F. , and H. C. Kretschmar, J. Org. Chem. , 26, 4841
        (1961).

175.   Ernst, O. , and O. Nicodemus, German Patent 414,426; Chem.
        Zentr. , 96, II, 759 (1925).

176.   Estes, L. L. , U. S. Patent 2,822,385; Chem. Abstr. , 52, 7771
        (1958).

177.   Etat Francais, British Patent 605,973; Chem. Abstr. , 43, 660
        (1949).

178.   Ettel, V. , and J. Hebky, Collection Czech. Chem. Commun. , 15,
        65 (1950); Chem. Abstr. , 44, 8334 (1950).

179. Ettel, V. , and J. Hebky, Czech. Patent 84,847; Chem. Abstr. , 50, 9445 (1956).
180. Faber, K. , and E. Komarek, Ullmanns Encyclopaedie der technischen Chemie, Vol. 11, 3rd ed. , Urban and Schwarzenberg, Munich, 1960.
181. Falk, R. A. , J. F. Gerecht, and I. J. Krems, J. Am. Oil Chemists' Soc. , 35, 171 (1958).
182. Farbenfabriken Bayer AG, British Patent 692,052; Chem. Abstr. , 49, 2686 (1955).
183. Farbenfabriken Bayer AG, British Patent 904,873; Chem. Abstr. , 58, 14160 (1963).
184. Farbwerke Hoechst AG, Frankfurt/M. -Hoechst, German Federal Republic.
185. Farbwerke Hoechst AG, Belgian Patent 611,605; Chem. Abstr. , 57, 14945 (1962).
186. Farbwerke Hoechst AG, Belgian Patent 616,065; Chem. Abstr. , 58, 5870 (1963).
187. Farbwerke Hoechst AG, Belgian Patent 620,445; Chem. Abstr. , 59, 7375 (1963).
188. Farbwerke Hoechst AG, Belgian Patent 624,071; Chem. Abstr. , 59, 9799 (1963).
189. Farbwerke Hoechst AG, British Patent 785,164; Chem. Abstr. , 52, 5887 (1958).
190. Farbwerke Hoechst AG, British Patent 802,150; Chem. Abstr. , 53, 7619 (1959).
191. Farbwerke Hoechst AG, British Patent 886,768; Chem. Abstr. , 54, 24394 (1960) (German analogue).
192. Farbwerke Hoechst AG, French Patent 1,307,710.
193. Farbwerke Hoechst AG, French Patent 1,308,199.
194. Farbwerke Hoechst AG, German Patent 234,711.
195. Feichtinger, H. , and S. Puschhof, German Patent 873,840; Chem. Abstr. , 48, 12173 (1954).
196. Feichtinger, H. , and H. Tummes, U. S. Patent 2,821,536; Chem. Abstr. , 52, 8596 (1958).
197. Felix, F. , A. Heckedorn, E. Reich, and F. Oesterlein, U. S. Patent 2,496,386; Chem. Abstr. , 44, 7560 (1950).
198. Fetscher, C. A. , and S. Lipowski, U. S. Patent 3,063,781.
199. Fierz-David, H. E. , and L. Blangey, Fundamental Processes of Dye Chemistry, Interscience, New York, 1949.
200. Fierz-David, H. E. , and L. Blangey, Helv. Chim. Acta, 23, 213 (1940).
201. Fikentscher, H. , H. Willersinn, E. Penning, and H. Distler, German Patent 1,127,590; Chem. Abstr. , 57, 10039 (1962).
202. Filbert, W. F. , and M. F. Fuller, U. S. Patent 2,820,788; Chem. Abstr. , 52, 6792 (1958).
203. Finch, H. D. , J. Org. Chem. , 27, 649 (1962).
203a. Fischer, R. F. , Ind. Eng. Chem. , Prod. Res. Develop. , to be published.

204. Fish, V. B. , J. R. Stevens, and R. G. D. Moore, J. Am. Chem. Soc. , 69, 1391 (1947).

205. Fodor, G. , D. Beke, and O. Kovacs, Acta Chim. Acad. Sci. Hung. , 1, 194 (1951); Chem. Abstr. , 46, 3514 (1952).

206. Fonzes, L. , and F. Winternitz, Compt. Rend. , 256, 4459 (1963); Chem. Abstr. , 59, 5033 (1963).

207. Fournet, A. , and H. Lemoine, French Patent 1, 228, 861; Chem. Abstr. , 55, 24682 (1961).

208. Frank, K. , German Patent 1, 013, 289; Chem. Abstr. , 53, 20850 (1959).

209. Frankel, M. , and P. Moses, Tetrahedron, 9, 288 (1960).

210. Friedman, H. L. , and L. D. Braitberg, U. S. Patent 2, 477, 731; Chem. Abstr. , 44, 172 (1950).

211. Friedman, H. L. , L. D. Braitberg, A. V. Tolstoouhov, and E. T. Tisza, J. Am. Chem. Soc. , 69, 1795 (1947).

212. Fromm, E. , R. Kapeller, and I. Taubman, Ber. , 61B, 1353 (1928).

213. Fujikawa, F. , Japanese Patent 14080 ('62); Chem. Abstr. , 59, 9880 (1963).

214. Fuller, M. F. , U. S. Patent 2, 883, 375; Chem. Abstr. , 53, 20868 (1959).

215. Fuortes, C. , and E. Gaetani, Italian Patent 588, 315; Chem. Abstr. , 54, 9307 (1960).

216. Furukawa, K. , T. Okada, I. Tamai, and R. Oda, Kogyo Kagaku Zasshi, 59, 221 (1956); Chem. Abstr. , 51, 10362 (1957).

217. Fuson, R. C. , and C. H. McKeever, Organic Reactions, Vol. 1, Wiley, New York, 1942, p. 63.

218. Gaertner, V. R. , J. Am. Oil Chemists' Soc. , 38, 212 (1961).

219. Gaertner, V. R. , U. S. Patent 2, 799, 702; Chem. Abstr. , 51, 15156 (1957).

220. Gaertner, V. R. , U. S. Patent 2, 802, 027; Chem. Abstr. , 51, 18454 (1957).

221. Gaertner, V. R. , U. S. Patent 2, 809, 973; Chem. Abstr. , 52, 6412 (1958).

222. Gaertner, V. R. , U. S. Patent 2, 813, 898; Chem. Abstr. , 52, 10177 (1958).

223. Gaertner, V. R. , U. S. Patent 2, 875, 125; Chem. Abstr. , 53, 15011 (1959).

224. Gaertner, V. R. , U. S. Patent 3, 086, 043; Chem. Abstr. , 59, 11271 (1963).

225. Galbraikh, L. S. , V. A. Derevitskaya, Z. A. Rogovin, and M. A. Chekalin, Vysomolekul. Soedin. , 4, 409 (1962); Chem. Abstr. , 57, 16926 (1962).

226. Gallard-Schlesinger Chemical Mfg. Corp. , Garden City, N. Y.

227. Gandini, A. , Farmaco (Pavio) Ed. Sci. , 1, 83 (1946); Chem. Abstr. , 40, 6417 (1946).

228. Gardenier, K. J. , and H. Kothe, German Patent 1, 107, 220; Chem. Abstr. , 56, 2333 (1962).

229. Geigy, J. R. , AG, British Patent 502, 848; Chem. Abstr. , 33, 6996 (1939).

230. Geigy, J. R. , AG, Swiss Patents 202, 423-7; Chem. Abstr. , 33, 8858 (1939).

231. General Aniline and Film Corp. , British Patent 835, 519; Chem. Abstr. , 55, 4998 (1961).

232. General Laboratory Supply Co. , Paterson, N. J.

233. Gevaert Photo-Producten NV, Belgian Patent 603, 995.

234. Gevaert Photo-Producten NV, Belgian Patent 604, 416.

234a. Gevaert Photo-Producten NV, Belgian Patent 939, 250.

235. Gilbert, E. E. , and P. H. Groggins, in P. H. Groggins, ed. , Unit Processes in Organic Synthesis, 5th ed. , McGraw-Hill, New York, 1958, pp. 303-87.

236. Gilbert, E. E. , C. J. McGough, and J. A. Otto, Ind. Eng. Chem. , 51, 925 (1959).

237. Gilbert, E. E. , B. Veldhuis, E. J. Carlson, and S. L. Giolito, Ind. Eng. Chem. , 45, 2065 (1953).

238. Gladshtein, B. M. , E. I. Polyanskaya, and L. Z. Soborovskii, Zh. Obshch. Khimii, 31, No. 3, 855 (1961); Chem. Abstr. , 55, 23333 (1961).

239. Gluesenkamp, E. W. , and M. Kosmin, U. S. Patent 2, 498, 619; Chem. Abstr. , 44, 4928 (1950).

240. Goebel, H. , U. S. Patent 2, 349, 654; Chem. Abstr. , 39, 1021 (1945).

240a. Goethals, E. , Bull. Soc. Chim. Belges, 72, 11 (1963).

241. Gold, M. H. , and L. J. Druker, U. S. Patent 2, 477, 870; Chem. Abstr. , 43, 9079 (1949).

242. Gold, M. H. , L. J. Druker, R. Yotter, C. J. B. Thor, and G. Lang, J. Org. Chem. , 16, 1495 (1951).

243. Goldberg, A. A. , J. Chem. Soc. , 1942, 716.

244. Goldberg, A. A. , J. Chem. Soc. , 1943, 4.

245. Goldberg, A. A. , and D. M. Besly, British Patent 563, 559; Chem. Abstr. , 40, 2940 (1946).

246. Goto, T. , and J. Mikumo, J. Chem. Soc. Japan Ind. Chem. Sect. , 55, 387 (1952); Chem. Abstr. , 48, 1711 (1954).

247. Grabiel, C. E. , and D. L. Decker, J. Polymer Sci. , 59, 425 (1962).

248. Grabiel, C. E. , L. R. Morris, P. J. Sienknecht, and R. N. Farris, Ind. Eng. Chem. , 52, 845 (1960).

249. Graenacher, C. , A. E. Siegrist, and H. Bruengger, U. S. Patent 2, 623, 050; Chem. Abstr. , 48, 2778 (1954).

250. Graenacher, C. , and H. Bruengger, U. S. Patent 2, 753, 239; Chem. Abstr. , 52, 3355 (1958).

251. Grassie, V. R. , U. S. Patent 2, 580, 351-2; Chem. Abstr. , 46, 2802 (1952).

252. Grassie, V. R. , C. L. P. Vaughan, and L. F. McBurney, Abstracts of Papers presented at the 124th Meeting of the American Chemical Society, Chicago, Ill. , Sept. 6-11, 1953, p. 6E.

253. Green, A. G. , and M. Coplans, U. S. Patent 2, 214, 527; Chem. Abstr. , 35, 857 (1941).

254. Griffing, J. M. , and W. R. Remington, U. S. Patent 3, 018, 272; Chem. Abstr. , 57, 8762 (1962).

255. Grinev, A. N. , A. S. Mezentsev, and D. V. Sibiryakova, Antibiotki, 6, 894 (1961); Chem. Abstr. , 56, 7439 (1962).

256. Grotowsky, H. , German Patent 447, 754; Chem. Zentr. , 1927, II, 2236.

257. Grunau AG, Belgian Patent 596, 735.

258. Guendel, W. , U. S. Patent 3, 023, 215; Chem. Abstr. , 57, 4553 (1962).

259. Guendel, W. , and H. Haas, U. S. Patent 2, 844, 584; Chem. Abstr. , 52, 16198 (1958).

260. Guendel, W. , W. Strauss, and H. Haas, U. S. Patent 2, 830, 014; Chem. Abstr. , 52, 12626 (1958).

261. Guendel, W. , W. Strauss, and H. Haas, U. S. Patent 2, 849, 351; Chem. Abstr. , 53, 1963 (1959).

262. Guenther, F. , and H. Haussmann, U. S. Patent 1, 932, 177; Chem. Abstr. , 28, 671 (1934).

263. Guenther, F. , F. Muenz, and H. Haussmann, U. S. Patent 1, 932, 176; Chem. Abstr. , 28, 671 (1934).

264. Guenther, F. , F. Muenz, and H. Haussmann, U. S. Patent 1, 932, 180; Chem. Abstr. , 28, 672 (1934).

265. Gushin, H. , and F. J. Zelman, U. S. Patent 2, 844, 607; Chem. Abstr. , 53, 743 (1959).

266. Guthrie, J. D. , Am. Dyestuff Reptr. , 41, P13 (1952).

267. Guthrie, J. D. , Ind. Eng. Chem. , 44, 2187 (1952).

268. Guthrie, J. D. , L. H. Chance, and C. L. Hoffpauir, U. S. Patent 2, 681, 846; Chem. Abstr. , 48, 12417 (1954).

269. Haas, H. , German Patent 937, 949; Chem. Abstr. , 50, 12108 (1956).

270. Haas, H. , German Patent 938, 186; Chem. Abstr. , 50, 12096 (1956).

271. Haas, H. , U. S. Patent 2, 833, 781; Chem. Abstr. , 52, 11912 (1958).

272. Haas, H. , and W. Guendel, U. S. Patent 2, 822, 366; Chem. Abstr. , 52, 10155 (1958).

273. Habicht, L. , Originalfassung Intern. Kongr. Grenzflaechenaktive Stoffe, 3, Cologne, Ger. , 1, 116 (1960); Chem. Abstr. , 57, 3284 (1962).

274. Haddock, N. H. , British Patent 914, 249; Chem. Abstr. , 58, 11505 (1963).

275. Hart, R. , Makromol. Chem. , 49, 33 (1961).

276. Hart, R. , and D. Timmerman, J. Polymer Sci. , 48, 151 (1960).

277. Hartough, H. D. , J. W. Schick, and J. J. Dickert, J. Am. Chem. Soc. , 72, 1572 (1950).

278. Harvel Corp. , British Patent 637, 741; Chem. Abstr. , 44, 8371 (1950).

279. Harvey, C. E. , British Patent 789, 032; Chem. Abstr. , 52, 11448 (1958).
280. Haubner, G. , Monatshefte fuer Chemie, 12, 546 (1891).
281. Hees, W. , German Patent 819, 404; Chem. Abstr. , 46, 11777 (1952).
282. Heisel, P. , German Patent 853, 442; Chem. Abstr. , 49, 12531 (1955).
283. Helberger, J. H. , Angew. Chem. , 73, 69 (1961).
284. Helberger, J. H. , Ann. , 588, 71 (1954).
285. Helberger, J. H. , Reichsamt Wirtschaftaufbau, Chem. Ber. Pruf. Nr. 15 (U. S. Dept. Commerce, OPB Rept. 52, 013) 269 (1942); Chem. Abstr. , 41, 4101 (1947).
286. Helberger, J. H. , U. S. Dept. Commerce, OTS Rept. PB70, 309; Frame 8004-5.
287. Helberger, J. H. , German Patent 823, 447; Chem. Abstr. , 49, 3239 (1955).
288. Helberger, J. H. , German Patent 915, 693; Chem. Abstr. , 49, 10357 (1955).
289. Helberger, J. H. , and W. Grublewsky, German Patent 901, 288; Chem. Abstr. , 49, 3249 (1955).
290. Helberger, H. , and R. Heyden, German Patent 894, 116; Chem. Abstr. , 48, 4234 (1954).
291. Helberger, J. , and R. Heyden, German Patent 895, 598; Chem. Abstr. , 48, 4234 (1954).
292. Helberger, J. H. , and R. Heyden, German Patent 904, 894; Chem. Abstr. , 49, 3264 (1955).
293. Helberger, J. , and R. Heyden, German Patent 907, 892; Chem. Abstr. , 49, 3249 (1955).
294. Helberger, J. H. , and R. Heyden, German Patent 930, 687; Chem. Abstr. , 50, 10129 (1956).
295. Helberger, J. H. , R. Heyden, and G. Manecke, German Patent 901, 054; Chem. Abstr. , 49, 3248 (1955).
296. Helberger, J. H. , J. R. Heyden, and H. Winter, Ann. , 586, 147 (1954).
297. Helberger, J. H. , and H. Lanterman, Ann. , 586, 158 (1954).
298. Helberger, J. H. , and G. Manecke, German Patent 895, 559; Chem. Abstr. , 48, 12792 (1954).
299. Helberger, J. H. , G. Manecke, and H. Fischer, Ann. , 562, 23 (1949).
300. Helberger, J. H. , G. Manecke, and R. Heyden, Ann. , 565, 22 (1949).
300a. Helberger, J. H. , and G. Mueller, German Patent 1, 146, 870; Chem. Abstr. , 59, 11259 (1963).
301. Helberger, J. H. , and J. B. Niederl, German Patent 1, 018, 421; Chem. Abstr. , 54, 22397 (1960).
302. Helberger, J. H. , and J. B. Niederl, German Patent 1, 040, 042; Chem. Abstr. , 55, 5424 (1961).

302a.   Helberger, J. H. , and J. F. Sproviero, Ann. , $\underline{666}$, 67 (1963).

302b.   Helberger, J. H. , and J. F. Sproviero, Ann. , $\overline{666}$, 78 (1963).

302c.   Helferich, B. , and V. Boellert, Ann. , $\underline{647}$, 37 (1961).

303.   Helferich, B. , and V. Boellert, Chem. Ber. , $\underline{94}$, 505 (1961).

304.   Henkel International Gmbh, Technical Bulletin 1, 3-Propansulton, Duesseldorf, Germany, 1961.

305.   Henkel et Cie Gmbh, British Patent 887,466; Chem. Abstr. , $\underline{56}$, 12049 (1962).

306.   Hennes, J. H. , U. S. Patent 3,009,950; Chem. Abstr. , $\underline{56}$, 7138 (1962).

307.   Hennsler, H. , E. Zahn, and I. Gross, British Patent 880,822; Chem. Abstr. , $\underline{56}$, 4911 (1962).

308.   Henry, T. A. , and W. H. Gray, British Patent 562,216; Chem. Abstr. , $\underline{39}$, 605 (1945).

309.   Hentrich, W. , and E. Schirm, U. S. Patent 2,394,306; Chem. Abstr. , $\underline{40}$, 2328 (1946).

310.   Hershberg, E. B. , and D. H. Gould, U. S. Patent 3,089,881; Chem. Abstr. , $\underline{59}$, 11619 (1963).

310a.   Heyna, J. , Angew. Chem. Intern. Ed. Engl. , $\underline{2}$, No. 1, 20 (1963).

311.   Hinman, R. L. , and L. Locatell, J. Am. Chem. Soc. , $\underline{81}$, 5655 (1959).

312.   Hioki, M. , and H. Okeda, Japanese Patent 3027 ('51); Chem. Abstr. , $\underline{47}$, 832 (1953).

313.   Hoffmann, H. , and E. Mundlos, Chem. Ber. , to be published.

314.   Hollander, C. S. , U. S. Patent 2,480,859; Chem. Abstr. , $\underline{44}$, 5378 (1950).

315.   Hollander, C. S. , and L. H. Bock, U. S. Patent 2,535,677-8; Chem. Abstr. , $\underline{45}$, 3408 (1951).

316.   Hoover, G. I. , and K. W. Hunten, J. Phys. Chem. , $\underline{34}$, 1367 (1930).

317.   Hori, M. , J. Agr. Chem. Soc. Japan, $\underline{18}$, 155 (1942); Chem. Abstr. , $\underline{45}$, 4202 (1951).

318.   Horsley, L. H. , and A. R. Sexton, U. S. Patent 2,945,056; Chem. Abstr. , $\underline{55}$, 4432 (1961).

319.   Horst, K. , and H. Schild, German Patent 884,644; Chem. Abstr. , $\underline{48}$, 7921 (1954).

320.   Hoyt, L. F. , BIOS Misc. Rept. No. 11 (1945).

321.   Hoyt, L. F. , U. S. Dept. Commerce, OTS Rept. PB3,868.

322.   Huber, F. R. , and L. M. Schenck, U. S. Patent 3,013,035-6; Chem. Abstr. , $\underline{57}$, 2076 (1962).

323.   Huffman, W. A. H. , U. S. Patent 3,039,990; Chem. Abstr. , $\underline{57}$, 11416 (1962).

324.   Hultquist, M. E. , R. P. Germann, J. S. Webb, W. B. Wright, B. Roth, J. M. Smith, Jr. , and Y. SubbaRow, J. Am. Chem. Soc. , $\underline{73}$, 2558 (1951).

325.   IG Farbenindustrie AG, FIAT Final Rept. 1313, I, 56 (1948).

326.   IG Farbenindustrie AG, U. S. Dept. Commerce, OTS Rept. PB3,868.

327. IG Farbenindustrie AG, U.S. Dept. Commerce, OTS Rept. PB30,071.
328. IG Farbenindustrie AG, U.S. Dept. Commerce, OTS Rept. PB30,109.
329. IG Farbenindustrie AG, U.S. Dept. Commerce, OTS Rept. PBL44,775.
330. IG Farbenindustrie AG, U.S. Dept. Commerce, OTS Rept. PB70,183, Frames 710-718.
331. IG Farbenindustrie AG, U.S. Dept. Commerce, OTS Rept. PB70,183, Frames 784-7.
332. IG Farbenindustrie AG, U.S. Dept. Commerce, OTS Rept. PB70,183, Frames 1084-95.
333. IG Farbenindustrie AG, U.S. Dept. Commerce, OTS Rept. PB70,183, Frames 1161-5,1304-6.
334. IG Farbenindustrie AG, U.S. Dept. Commerce, OTS Rept. PB70,183, Frames 1215-22.
334a. IG Farbenindustrie AG, U.S. Dept. Commerce, OTS Rept. PB84,030, Frames 3831-2.
335. IG Farbenindustrie AG, British Patent 459,791; Chem. Abstr., 31, 4419 (1937).
336. IG Farbenindustrie AG, British Patent 529,382; Chem. Abstr., 35, 7981 (1941).
337. Imperial Chemical Industries, Ltd., British Patent 815,167; Chem. Abstr., 54, 328 (1960).
338. Ivanov, D., and N. Marekov, Croat. Chem. Acta, 29, 347 (1957); Chem. Abstr., 53, 16054 (1959).
339. Izumi, M., Japanese Patent 3564 ('57); Chem. Abstr., 52, 4678 (1958).
340. Izumi, Z., H. Kiuchi, and M. Watanabe, J. Polymer Sci., A1, 705 (1963).
341. Jaccard, G., U.S. Patent 2,543,852; Chem. Abstr., 45, 4472 (1951).
342. Jacobi, B., and H. Fikentscher, German Patent 572,204; Chem. Abstr., 27, 2965 (1933).
343. Jacobs, T.L., Pyrazoles and Related Compounds, in Heterocyclic Compounds, Vol. 5, R. C. Elderfield, ed., Wiley, New York, 1957.
344. Jahrstorfer, M., and J. Brandeis, German Patent 854,653; Chem. Abstr., 52, 8597 (1958).
345. Johnson, T.B., and I. B. Douglass, J. Am. Chem. Soc., 63, 1571 (1941).
346. Jones, G.D., U.S. Patent 2,909,508; Chem. Abstr., 54, 4057 (1960).
347. Jones, R.V., U.S. Patent 2,678,947; Chem. Abstr., 49, 4713 (1955).
348. Jones, W.O., U.S. Patent 2,537,352; Chem. Abstr., 45, 4052 (1951).

349. Jullander, I. , Swedish Patent 171, 657; Chem. Abstr. , 55, 9874 (1961).

350. Kafka, M. , in Houben-Weyl, Methoden der Organischen Chemie, Vol. XIV/2, Thieme Verlag, Stuttgart, 1963.

351. Kaiser, D. W. , J. T. Thurston, J. R. Dudley, F. C. Schaefer, I. Hechenbleikner, and D. Holm-Hansen, J. Am. Chem. Soc. , 73, 2984 (1951).

352. Kaiser, W. J. , and A. Sturm, German Patent 1, 114, 775; Chem. Abstr. , 56, 7452 (1962).

353. Kalle and Co. , U. S. Dept. Commerce, OTS Rept. PB83, 606, Frames 6977-82.

354. Kamlet, J. , U. S. Patent 2, 305, 260; Chem. Abstr. , 37, 2888 (1943).

355. K and K Laboratories, Jamaica, New York.

356. Kanegafuche Spinning Co. , Ltd. , Japanese Patent 4650 (1962).

357. Katzman, M. , and B. R. Harris, U. S. Patent 2, 238, 902; Chem. Abstr. , 35, 4878 (1941).

358. Kay-Fries Chemicals, Inc. , Organic Intermediates, 1961.

359. Keim, G. I. , U. S. Patent 2, 512, 720; Chem. Abstr. , 44, 8695 (1950).

360. Kendall, J. D. , and G. F. Duffin, U. S. Patent 2, 640, 056; Chem. Abstr. , 47, 9623 (1953).

361. Kern, J. G. , U. S. Patent 2, 122, 424; Chem. Abstr. , 32, 6671 (1938).

362. Kern, W. , and R. C. Schulz, in Houben-Weyl, Methoden der Organischen Chemie, Vol. 14/1, IV ed. , Thieme Verlag, Stuttgart, 1961.

363. Kharasch, M. S. , U. S. Patent 2, 383, 320; Chem. Abstr. , 40, 595 (1946).

364. Kharasch, M. S. , T. H. Chao, and H. C. Brown, J. Am. Chem. Soc. , 62, 2393 (1940).

365. Kienle, R. H. , and C. A. Amick, U. S. Patent 2, 409, 127; Chem. Abstr. , 41, 601 (1947).

366. Kin, Z. , Przeglad Papier. , 16, No. 5, 131 (1960); Chem. Abstr. , 55, 15920 (1961).

367. Kirstahler, A. , W. Strauss, and W. Willmund, U. S. Patent 2, 849, 352; Chem. Abstr. , 53, 1963 (1959).

368. Kitasato, M. , and I. Koike, Japanese Patent 846 (1953); Chem. Abstr. , 48, 1732 (1954).

369. Klockgether, H. , and A. Ossenbrunner, German Patent 960, 334; Chem. Abstr. , 53, 16775 (1959).

370. Kluge, A. , and E. Koczorowski, Fette, Seifen, Anstrichmittel, 63, 835 (1961); Chem. Abstr. , 56, 2525 (1962).

371. Knoevenagel, E. , Ber. , 37, 4073 (1904).

372. Knoevenagel, E. , and H. Lebach, Ber. , 37, 4094 (1904).

373. Knoevenagel, E. , and E. Mercklin, Ber. , 37, 4087 (1904).

374. Koepke, G. , W. Pelz, and H. Schellenberger, German Patent 1, 130, 287; Chem. Abstr. , 57, 15294 (1962).

375.   Komori, S. , T. Agawa, and T. Kataoka, Yukagaku, 10, 153 (1961); Chem. Abstr. , 55, 26483 (1961).

375a.   Komori, S. , M. Okahara, and S. Ito, Kogyo Kagaku Zasshi, 66, No. 5, 693 (1963); Chem. Abstr. , 60, 9487 (1964).

376.   Komori, S. , S. Sakakibara, and A. Fujiwara, Kogyo Kagaku Zasshi, 61, 319 (1958); Chem. Abstr. , 55, 6361 (1961).

377.   Konishi, E. , M. Kawada, and A. Taniuchi, Japanese Patent 755 ('61); Chem. Abstr. , 55, 21628 (1961).

378.   Kooijman, P. L. , and H. Buesink, U. S. Patent 3, 097, 218.

379.   Kosmin, M. , U. S. Patent 2, 658, 072; Chem. Abstr. , 48, 3049 (1954).

380.   Kosmin, M. , U. S. Patent 2, 785, 968; Chem. Abstr. , 51, 9997 (1957).

381.   Kosmin, M. , U. S. Patent 2, 818, 426; Chem. Abstr. , 52, 6822 (1958).

382.   Kosmin, M. , U. S. Patent 2, 857, 261; Chem. Abstr. , 53, 11313 (1959).

383.   Kosmin, M. , U. S. Patent 2, 875, 122; Chem. Abstr. , 53, 12576 (1959).

384.   Kosmin, M. , U. S. Patent 2, 913, 324; Chem. Abstr. , 54, 2650 (1960).

384a.   Kottenhahn, A. P. , J. Org. Chem. , 28, 3433 (1963).

385.   Kraenzlein, G. , and A. Voss, German Patent 408, 871; Chem. Zentr. , 1925, I, 1671.

386.   Kraenzlein, G. , A. Voss, and H. Gaertner, German Patent 426, 424; Chem. Zentr. , 1926, II, 1228.

387.   Kraessig, H. , Makromol. Chem. , 8, 208 (1952); Chem. Abstr. , 47, 1976 (1953).

388.   Krazer, B. , and H. Zollinger, Helv. Chim. Acta, 43, 1513 (1961).

389.   Kressman, T. R. E. , and J. A. Kitchener, J. Chem. Soc. , 1949, 1190.

390.   Krzikalla, H. , and A. Tartter, German Patent 800, 410; Chem. Abstr. , 45, 1619 (1951).

391.   Krzikalla, H. , and A. Tartter, German Patent 801, 992; Chem. Abstr. , 45, 5179 (1951).

392.   Krzikalla, H. , and A. Tartter, German Patent 807, 686; Chem. Abstr. , 48, 7064 (1954).

393.   Kuentzel, A. , and J. Plapper, Leder, 6, 176 (1955); Chem. Abstr. , 49, 16487 (1955).

394.   Kuentzel, A. , and J. Plapper, Leder, 7, 60 (1956); Chem. Abstr. , 50, 15110 (1956).

395.   Kuespert, K. , and H. Distler, German Patent 1, 110, 628; Chem. Abstr. , 56, 3358 (1962).

396.   Kugita, H. , Japanese Patent 5062 ('60); Chem. Abstr. , 55, 464 (1961).

397.   Kuhn, R. , and W. Brydowna, Ber. , 70, 1333 (1937).

398. Kumetat, K. , and S. Gassner, U. S. Patent 2,163,146; Chem. Abstr. , 33, 7685 (1939).

399. Kunichika, S. , and T. Katagiri, Kogyo Kagaku Zasshi, 64, 929 (1961); Chem. Abstr. , 57, 7480 (1962).

400. Kunin, R. , and R. J. Myers, Ion Exchange Resins, Wiley, New York, 1950.

401. Kurata, S. , Yamaguchi Daigaku Kogakubu Gakuho, 12, 128 (1961); Chem. Abstr. , 57, 14988 (1962).

402. Kutner, A. , and D. S. Breslow, J. Polymer Sci. , 38, 274 (1959).

403. Kvalnes, D. E. , and C. W. Croco, U. S. Patent 2,541,822; Chem. Abstr. , 45, 7143 (1951).

404. Laboratoires francais de chimiotherapie, British Patent 853,402; Chem. Abstr. , 55, 17694 (1961).

405. Lacoste, R. G. , and A. E. Martell, J. Am. Chem. Soc. , 77, 5512 (1955).

406. Lambert, A. , and J. D. Rose, J. Chem. Soc. , 1949, 46.

407. Landau, E. F. , W. F. Whitmore, and P. Doty, J. Am. Chem. Soc. , 68, 816 (1946).

408. Lange, G. , F. Ebel, R. Schroedel, and W. Hensel, German Patent 1,107,356; Chem. Abstr. , 56, 11755 (1962).

409. Lauer, K. , J. prakt. Chem. , 143, 127 (1935).

410. Lauer, W. M. , and C. M. Langkammerer, J. Am. Chem. Soc. , 57, 2360 (1935).

411. Ledrut, J. H. T. , U. S. Patent 2,650,219; Chem. Abstr. , 48, 12181 (1954).

412. LeFevre, W. J. , and D. P. Sheetz, U. S. Patent 3,024,221; Chem. Abstr. , 57, 2078 (1962).

413. LeFevre, W. J. , and D. P. Sheetz, U. S. Patent 3,033,833; Chem. Abstr. , 57, 7466 (1962).

414. LeHenaff, P. , Compt. Rend. , 256, 3090 (1963).

415. Lehmann, E. , H. Kleiner, and H. J. Manderla, U. S. Patent 2,926,060; Chem. Abstr. , 54, 11494 (1960).

416. Leighton, P. A. , W. A. Perkins, and M. L. Renquist, J. Am. Chem. Soc. , 69, 1540 (1947).

417. Lepetit, R. , Atti Accad. Lincei, 26, I, 126 (1917); Chem. Abstr. , 12, 366 (1918).

418. Lepetit, R. , German Patent 209,695; Chem. Abstr. , 3, 2241 (1909).

419. Levin, P. A. , Zh. Obshch. Khim. , 27, 2864 (1957); Chem. Abstr., 52, 8125 (1958).

420. Lindgren, B. O. , Acta Chem. Scand. , 4, 1365 (1950).

421. Lipovich, I. M. , J. Appl. Chem. USSR (English Transl.), 18, 718 (1945); Chem. Abstr. , 40, 6407 (1946).

422. Lipovich, I. M. , and E. M. Mones, J. Appl. Chem. USSR (English Transl.), 18, 20 (1945); Chem. Abstr. , 39, 5399 (1945).

423. Loev, B. , and M. Kormendy, J. Org. Chem. , 27, 2448 (1962).

424. Logemann, W. , Farmaco (Pavia) Ed. Sci. , 7, 4304 (1952); Chem. Abstr. , 47, 5938 (1953).

425. Logemann, W. , U. S. Patent 2, 759, 944; Chem. Abstr. , 51,
      11398 (1957).

426. Logemann, W. , F. Lauria, and D. Artini, Nature, 185, 532
      (1960).

427. Logemann, W. , and G. P. Miori, Arzneimittel-Forsch. , 5, 213
      (1955); Chem. Abstr. , 49, 11244 (1955).

428. Long, R. S. , and D. W. Hein, U. S. Patent 2, 671, 790; Chem.
      Abstr. , 49, 4024 (1955).

429. Lorentzen, C. P. , U. S. Patent 2, 967, 872; Chem. Abstr. , 55,
      9298 (1961).

430. Lumiere, A. , French Patent 548, 343; Chem. Zentr. , 1925, I,
      1011.

431. Lysenko, N. M. , and V. E. Petrun'kin, Zh. Obshch. Khim. , 31,
      2252 (1961); Chem. Abstr. , 56, 2321 (1962).

432. Mack, L. , U. S. Patent 2, 366, 452; Chem. Abstr. , 39, 1882
      (1945).

433. Magnusson, S. , J. E. Christian, and G. L. Jenkins, J. Am. Pharm.
      Assoc. Sci. Ed. , 36, 257 (1947).

434. Malm, C. J. , L. J. Tanghe, and R. E. Glegg, Ind. Eng. Chem. , 51,
      1483 (1959).

435. Marekov, N. , Compt. Rend. Acad. Bulgare Sci. , 12, 231 (1959);
      Chem. Abstr. , 54, 20961 (1960).

436. Marekov, N. , Compt. Rend. Acad. Bulgare Sci. , 12, 325 (1959);
      Chem. Abstr. , 54, 22439 (1960).

437. Marekov, N. , and N. Petsev, Izvest, Khim. Inst. Bulgar, Akad.
      Nauk, 6, 345 (1958); Chem. Abstr. , 54, 20944 (1960).

438. Martin, E. L. , U. S. Patent 2, 513, 189; Chem. Abstr. , 44, 9841
      (1950).

439. Martin, E. L. , U. S. Patent 2, 902, 365; Chem. Abstr. , 53, 23078
      (1959).

440. Martin, R. W. , The Chemistry of Phenolic Resins, Wiley, New
      York, 1956.

441. Marvel, C. S. , and C. F. Bailey, Org. Syn. , Vol. 2, 563 (1943).

442. Marvel, C. S. , and M. S. Sparberg, Org. Syn. , Vol. 2, 558 (1943).

443. Maxwell, C. S. , Paper presented at the 142nd American Chem-
      ical Society Meeting, Sept. 11, 1962.

444. Maxwell, C. S. , U. S. Patent 2, 582, 840; Chem. Abstr. , 46, 3768
      (1952).

445. Mazak, P. , and J. Suszko, Roczniki Chem. , 9, 431 (1929);
      Chem. Abstr. , 23, 4187 (1929).

446. McIlwain, H. , J. Chem. Soc. , 1941, 75.

447. McQueen, D. M. , and D. W. Woodward, J. Am. Chem. Soc. , 73,
      4930 (1951).

448. Mehta, C. M. , and J. M. Trevedi, Current Sci. (India), 32, 17
      (1963); Chem. Abstr. , 58, 8939 (1963).

449. Meito Sangyo Co. , Ltd. , Japanese Patent 15618 ('62); Chem.
      Abstr. , 59, 10151 (1963).

450.   Menzel, K. H. , and H. Ulrich, German Patent 1,127,220; Chem. Abstr. , 57, 16811 (1962)

451.   Mietzsch, F. , J. Klarer, and R. Behnisch, French Patent 816,988; Chem. Abstr. , 32, 2293 (1938).

452.   Milhiser, F. R. , U. S. Patent 2,837,501; Chem. Abstr. , 52, 15964 (1958).

453.   Millmaster Chemical Company, George F. Smith Division, New York.

454.   Miralles, J. A. , and J. A. Miralles, Spanish Patent 197,072; Chem. Abstr. , 49, 2504 (1955).

455.   Miyatake, K. , and T. Yoshikawa, Japanese Patent 6734 ('56); Chem. Abstr. , 52, 8207 (1958).

456.   Mochizuki, G. , Japanese Patent 6915 ('51); Chem. Abstr. , 48, 719 (1954).

457.   Mock, R. A. , U. S. Patent 2,821,549; Chem. Abstr. , 52, 9206 (1958).

458.   Moehrke, H. , H. Koch, and H. von Freyberg, German Patent 865,305; Chem. Zentr. , 125, 6346 (1954).

459.   Mohr, R. , and H. Hertel, Chem. Ber. , 96, 114 (1963).

460.   Molteni, H. A. , N. H. Masarky, and G. Barsky, U. S. Reissue Patent 23,823; Chem. Abstr. , 48, 8566 (1954).

461.   Monsanto Chemical Co. , St. Louis, Mo.

462.   Monsanto Chemical Co. , British Patent 611,244.

463.   Moralli, G. J. , Bull. Soc. Chim. France, 1953, 1044.

464.   Morgner, M. , and R. Wilharm, German Patent 1,113,814; Chem. Abstr. , 56, 4953 (1962).

465.   Morton, M. , and H. Landfield, J. Am. Chem. Soc. , 74, 3523 (1952).

466.   Mueller, I. F. , Helv. Chim. Acta, 22, 208 (1939).

467.   Mueller, W. , H. Distler, and A. Palm, Belgian Patent 607,888.

468.   Muenz, F. , in Houben-Weyl, Methoden der Organischen Chemie, Vol. IX, IV ed. , Thieme Verlag, Stuttgart, 1955.

469.   Mulligan, B. , and J. M. Swan, Textile Res. J. , 31, 18 (1961).

470.   Murdock, S. A. , T. G. Traylor, and T. B. Lefferdinck, U. S. Patent 2,829,066; Chem. Abstr. , 52, 13322 (1958).

471.   Murdock, S. A. , T. G. Traylor, and T. B. Lefferdinck, U. S. Patent 3,026,288; Chem. Abstr. , 57, 3659 (1962).

472.   Mustafa, A. , Chem. Rev. , 54, 195 (1954).

473.   Mustafa, A. , in Organic Sulfur Compounds, N. Kharasch, ed. , Pergamon Press, New York, 1961, p. 183.

474.   Nagayama, S. , Japanese Patent 1715 ('62); Chem. Abstr. , 58, 7833 (1963).

475.   Nagy, D. E. , U. S. Patent 2,592,587; Chem. Abstr. , 46, 6421 (1952).

476.   Nagy, D. E. , U. S. Patent 2,621,164; Chem. Abstr. , 47, 3613 (1953).

477.   Nakajima, S. , I. Tanaka, and M. Sasho, Japanese Patent 7634 ('58); Chem. Abstr. , 54, 2378 (1960).

478. Nauman, R. V. , P. W. West, F. Tron, and G. C. Gaeke, Jr. , Anal. Chem. , 32, 1307 (1960).
479. Neelakantan, I. , and W. H. Hartung, J. Org. Chem. , 24, 1943 (1959).
479a. Negoro, K. , H. Hiyama, and K. Oshima, Kogyo Kagaku Zasshi, 62, 844 (1959); Chem. Abstr. , 57, 8512 (1962).
480. Neresheimer, H. , and W. Bruck, German Patent 758, 555; Chem. Abstr. , 52, 4196 (1958).
481. Neugebauer, W. , U. Ostwald, and K. Sponsel, U. S. Patent 2, 132, 181; Chem. Abstr. , 33, 381 (1939).
482. Nicodemus, O. , and W. Schmidt, German Patent 651, 733; Chem. Abstr. , 32, 686 (1938).
483. Nicodemus, O. , and W. Schmidt, U. S. Patent 1, 932, 907; Chem. Abstr. , 28, 491 (1934).
484. Nicodemus, O. , W. Schmidt, A. Ossenbeck, and E. Tietze, U. S. Patent 1, 999, 614; Chem. Abstr. , 29, 4028 (1935).
485. Niederhauser, W. D. , E. Broderick, and F. F. Owings, U. S. Patent 2, 964, 557; Chem. Abstr. , 55, 6377 (1961).
486. Nishimura, M. , S. Kobayashi, and M. Sugihara, Kogyo Kagaku Zasshi, 62, 1930 (1959).
487. Nix, S. J. , U. S. Patent 2, 822, 386; Chem. Abstr. , 52, 7771 (1958).
488. Northey, E. H. , The Sulfonamides and Allied Compounds, Reinhold, New York, 1948.
489. Norton, F. H. , U. S. Patent 2, 840, 601; Chem. Abstr. , 52, 20060 (1958).
490. Nottbohm, O. , Ann. , 412, 49 (1917).
491. Nyquist, A. S. , U. S. Patent 2, 610, 171; Chem. Abstr. , 47, 235 (1953).
492. Oda, R. , and K. Teramura, Bull. Inst. Chem. Res. , Kyoto Univ. , 32, 159 (1954); Chem. Abstr. , 51, 4357 (1957).
493. Oda, R. , Z. Yoshida, and Y. Shimada, J. Chem. Soc. Japan, Ind. Chem. Sect. , 55, 782, 786 (1952); Chem. Abstr. , 49, 3915 (1955).
494. Okazaki, J. , et al. , Japanese Patent 6464 (1951); Chem. Abstr. , 47, 11233 (1953).
495. Ono, K. , J. Soc. Org. Syn. Chem. Japan, 7, 12 (1949).
496. Orthner, L. , G. Balle, K. Horst, and H. Schild, U. S. Patent 2, 243, 437; Chem. Abstr. , 35, 5600 (1941).
497. Orthner, L. , K. Platz, and U. Lampert, German Patent 859, 447; Chem. Abstr. , 52, 14665 (1958).
498. Orthner, L. , M. Reuter, and F. Landauer, German Patent 1, 097, 431; Chem. Abstr. , 55, 25296 (1961).
499. Overberger, C. G. , D. E. Baldwin, and H. P. Gregor, J. Am. Chem. Soc. , 72, 4864 (1950).
500. Pagani et Cie. , German Patent 654, 714; Chem. Abstr. , 32, 3513 (1938).

501. Paris, L. F. , French Patent 983, 479; Chem. Abstr. , 49, 7257 (1955).

502. Park, H. F. , U. S. Patent 2, 727, 057; Chem. Abstr. , 50, 10758 (1956).

503. Parke, Davis and Co. , British Patent 896, 774; Chem. Abstr. , 57, 12612 (1962).

504. Parkes, G. D. , and S. J. M. Fisher, J. Chem. Soc. , 1936, 83.

505. Paschall, E. F. , U. S. Patent 2, 806, 857; Chem. Abstr. , 52, 768 (1958).

506. Patnaik, S. , and S. S. G. Sircar, J. Indian Chem. Soc. , 30, 577 (1953); Chem. Abstr. , 48, 4180 (1954).

507. Pense, W. , W. Asch, and G. Balle, German Patent 844, 784; Chem. Abstr. , 49, 5875 (1955).

508. Perkin, W. H. , and A. W. Fyfe, British Patent 238, 717; Chem. Abstr. , 20, 2078 (1926).

509. Perrier, L. H. , French Patent 1, 108, 210; Chem. Abstr. , 53, 11317 (1959).

510. Petrie, P. S. , and E. C. Britton, U. S. Patent 2, 694, 087; Chem. Abstr. , 49, 9298 (1955).

511. Petrun'kin, V. E. , Tiolovye Soedin. v Med., Ukr. Nauch. -Issled. Sanit. -Khim. Inst. , Tr. Nauch. Konf. , 1957, 7 (Pub. 1959); Chem. Abstr. , 54, 24378 (1960).

512. Phillips, M. A. , Ind. Chemist, 26, 29 (1950).

513. Pieper, G. , in Houben-Weyl, Methoden der Organischen Chemie, Vol. II/III, IV ed. , Thieme Verlag, Stuttgart, 1958.

514. Platz, K. , and L. Mack, German Patent 854, 796; Chem. Abstr., 52, 8580 (1958).

515. Ploetz, E. , German Patent 832, 890; Chem. Abstr. , 47, 2199 (1953).

516. Ploetz, E. , German Patent 857, 495; Chem. Abstr. , 52, 10188 (1958).

517. Poehls, P. , and R. Behnisch, German Patent 708, 465; Chem. Abstr. , 37, 3106 (1943).

518. Porath, J. , Arkiv Kemi, 11, 97 (1956); Chem. Abstr. , 51, 15684 (1957).

519. Porath, J. , U. S. Patent 2, 891, 057; Chem. Abstr. , 53, 17508 (1959).

520. Produits chimiques de Ribecourt, French Patent 958, 216; Chem. Abstr. , 45, 10440 (1951).

521. Pruetz, A. , and P. Rathfelder, Ber. , 94, 58 (1961).

522. Putnam, R. C. , and S. I. Hayes, Jr. , U. S. Patent 2, 872, 278; Chem. Abstr. , 53, 9708 (1959).

523. Raschig, F. , and W. Prahl, Ann. , 448, 265 (1926).

524. Redmon, B. C. , and D. E. Nagy, U. S. Patent 2, 455, 807; Chem. Abstr. , 43, 2635 (1949).

525. Regestad, S. O. , and O. Samuelson, Svensk Kem. Tidskr. , 61, 8 (1949); Chem. Abstr. , 43, 4083 (1949).

526.   Reich, G. , and W. Roedel, German Patent 1, 081, 470; Chem.
        Abstr. , 55, 13888 (1961).
527.   Reichert, B. , Die Mannich-Reaktion, Springer Verlag, Berlin,
        1959.
528.   Reppe, W. , et al. , Ann. , 596, 163 (1955).
529.   Reppe, W. , et al. , Ann. , 601, 81 (1956).
530.   Reuter, M. , German Patent 845, 509; Chem. Abstr. , 50, 2669
        (1956).
531.   Riesz, E. , Rev. fac. humanidad. cienc. , (Montevideo), 1952,
        117; Chem. Abstr. , 47, 2490 (1953).
532.   Rondestvedt, C. S. , Jr. , and P. K. Chang, J. Am. Chem. Soc. , 77,
        6532 (1955).
533.   Rose, F. L. , U. S. Patent 2, 425, 396; Chem. Abstr. , 41, 6898
        (1947).
534.   Rosenthal, T. , Ann, 233, 15 (1886).
535.   Rosenthal, T. , Ann. 233, 36 (1886).
536.   Rowland, S. P. , U. S. Patent 2, 453, 687; Chem. Abstr. , 43,
        1216 (1949).
537.   Rowland, S. P. , U. S. Patent 2, 456, 085; Chem. Abstr. , 43, 3233
        (1949).
538.   Ruggieri, R. , Giorn. med. militaire, 107, 239 (1957); Chem.
        Abstr. , 52, 2021 (1958).
539.   Ruggli, P. , and F. Gruen, Helv. Chim. Acta, 24, 197 (1941).
540.   Rumpf, P. , Compt. Rend. , 212, 83 (1941).
541.   Rust, J. B. , and W. B. Canfield, U. S. Patent 2, 861, 054; Chem.
        Abstr. , 53, 5698 (1959).
542.   Sakamuki, T. , and M. Tanino, Japanese Patent 6279 (1955);
        Chem. Abstr. , 51, 16570 (1957).
543.   Sallmann, R. , and C. Graenacher, U. S. Patent 2, 479, 782;
        Chem. Abstr. , 44, 2549 (1950).
544.   Salminen, I. , and A. Weissberger, U. S. Patent 2, 694, 718;
        Chem. Abstr. , 49, 3704 (1955).
545.   Salzberg, P. L. , U. S. Patent 2, 139, 697; Chem. Abstr. , 33,
        2252 (1939).
546.   Salzer, W. , and E. Auhagen, German Patent 902, 736; Chem.
        Abstr. , 49, 11698 (1955).
547.   Sandoz, Ltd. , British Patent 529, 355; Chem. Abstr. , 35, 7981
        (1941).
548.   Sandoz, Ltd. , Swiss Patent 234, 787; Chem. Abstr. , 43, 9467
        (1949).
549.   Sause, R. , and W. E. Stephen, British Patent 794, 180; Chem.
        Abstr. , 52, 19155 (1958).
550.   Scarth, V. , U. S. Patent 2, 775, 580; Chem. Abstr. , 51, 4708
        (1957).
551.   Schaefer, G. , and F. Quint, German Patent 928, 006; Chem.
        Zentr. , 1955, 10632.
552.   Scheibler, H. , and P. Baumgartner, Ber. , 55, 1358 (1922).
553.   Scheibler, H. , and H. Neef, Ber. , 59, 1500 (1926).

554.   Schenck, L. M., U. S. Patent 2, 898, 352; Chem. Abstr. , 54, 6162 (1960).

555.   Schenck, L. M. , U. S. Patent 2, 987, 526; Chem. Abstr. , 56, 3585 (1962).

556.   Schenck, L. M. , U. S. Patent 3, 004, 049; Chem. Abstr. , 56, 2526 (1962).

557.   Schenck, L. M. , and L. G. Nunn, Jr. , Belgian Patent 610, 499.

558.   Schenck, R. T. , U. S. Patent 2, 900, 410; Chem. Abstr. , 54, 1811 (1960).

559.   Schenck, R. T. , and I. Danishevsky, J. Org. Chem. , 16, 1683 (1951).

559a.   Scherer, O. , G. Staehler, and K. Reichner, German Patent 1, 104, 968; Chem. Abstr. , 56, 4620 (1962).

560.   Schick, J. W. , and E. F. Degering, Ind. Eng. Chem. , 39, 906 (1947).

561.   Schiller, A. M. , and T. J. Suen, Ind. Eng. Chem. , 48, 2132 (1956).

562.   Schirm, E. , German Patent 877, 759; Chem. Abstr. , 50, 4540 (1956).

563.   Schmidt, W. , U. S. Patent 2, 265, 200; Chem. Abstr. , 36, 1955 (1942).

564.   Schramm, C. H. , U. S. Patent 2, 694, 723; Chem. Abstr. , 49, 13289 (1955).

565.   Schramm, C. H. , H. Lemaire, and R. H. Karlson, J. Am. Chem. Soc. , 77, 6231 (1955).

566.   Schramm, C. H. , and C. T. Walling, U. S. Patent 2, 797, 239; Chem. Abstr. , 51, 12956 (1957).

567.   Schroeter, G. , German Patent 601, 105; Chem. Abstr. , 28, 7261 (1934).

568.   Schroeter, R. , in Houben-Weyl, Methoden der Organischen Chemie, Vol. VII/1, Thieme Verlag, Stuttgart, 1954.

569.   Schulze, H. , Canadian Patent 618, 120.

570.   Schwalenberg, A. , German (East) Patent 13, 968; Chem. Abstr. , 53, 11231 (1959).

571.   Schwalenberg, A. , German (East) Patent 15, 289; Chem. Abstr. , 54, 3203 (1960).

572.   Seibert, W. , German Patent 1, 033, 350; Chem. Abstr. , 54, 17898 (1960).

573.   Seymour, R. B. , I. Branum, Jr. , and F. W. Hayward, Ind. Eng. Chem. , 41, 1482 (1949).

574.   Sexton, A. R. , U. S. Patent 2, 693, 488; Chem. Abstr. , 49, 14795 (1955).

575.   Sexton, A. R. , and E. C. Britton, U. S. Patent 2, 810, 747; Chem. Abstr. , 52, 9197 (1958).

576.   Sexton, A. R. , and E. C. Britton, U. S. Patent 2, 820, 818; Chem. Abstr. , 52, 9195 (1958).

577.   Sexton, A. R. , and E. C. Britton, U. S. Patent 2, 830, 082; Chem. Abstr. , 52, 13783 (1958).

578. Sexton, A. R. , and E. C. Britton, U. S. Patent 2, 968, 664; Chem. Abstr. , 55, 11887 (1961).
579. Sheetz, D. P. , U. S. Patent 2, 914, 499; Chem. Abstr. , 54, 20274 (1960).
580. Sheetz, D. P. , U. S. Patent 2, 923, 734; Chem. Abstr. , 54, 12000 (1960).
581. Shell Chemical Company, "Propanesultone, " Technical Information Bulletin PD145, New York, March 1963.
582. Shell Development Co. , "Sodium 1-Hydroxy-1, 3-Propanedisulfonate, " Preliminary Information Sheet, 1960.
583. Shimomura, T. , et al. , Japanese Patent 2182 (1954); Chem. Abstr. , 49, 14801 (1955).
584. Shoji, J. , M. Hamada, S. Watanabe, and K. Chiba, J. Antibiotics (Japan), B12, 365 (1959); Chem. Abstr. , 54, 9205 (1960).
585. Shriner, R. L. , and A. H. Land, J. Org. Chem. , 6, 888 (1941).
586. Smith, C. W. , U. S. Patent 2, 566, 810; Chem. Abstr. , 46, 2576 (1952).
587. Smith, C. W. , D. G. Norton, and S. A. Ballard, J. Am. Chem. Soc. , 75, 748 (1953).
588. Smith, J. M. , Jr. , U. S. Patent 2, 502, 897; Chem. Abstr. , 44, 5905 (1950).
589. Smith, T. L. , and J. H. Elliott, J. Am. Chem. Soc. , 75, 3566 (1953).
590. Snoddy, A. O. , Org. Syn. , 37, 55 (1957).
591. Societa per Azioni Ferrania, French Patent 1, 296, 104; Chem. Abstr. , 58, 2438 (1963).
592. Societa des usines chimiques Rhone-Poulenc, French Patent 1, 167, 618; Chem. Abstr. , 55, 3621 (1961).
593. Soc. pour l'ind. chim. a Bale, Swiss Patent 215, 398; Chem. Abstr. , 42, 4200 (1948).
594. Soc. pour l'ind. chim. a Bale, Swiss Patent 227, 509; Chem. Abstr. , 43, 4019 (1949).
595. Soc. pour l'ind. chim. a Bale, Swiss Patent 231, 254; Chem. Abstr. , 43, 2632 (1949).
596. Societe Industrielle pour la Fabrication des Antibiotiques, British Patent 874, 028; Chem. Abstr. , 56, 6079 (1962).
597. Spinner, I. H. , J. Ciric, and W. J. Graydon, Can. J. Chem. , 32, 143 (1954).
598. Spirk, L. , Chem. Listy, 36, 69 (1942); Chem. Abstr. , 37, 4254 (1943).
599. Stalinovy Zavody, Narodni Podnik, French Patent 974, 879; Chem. Zentr. , 123, 3435 (1952).
600. Stather, F. , H. Herfeld, R. Schubert, and R. Bellmann, Ges. Abhandl. Deut. Lederinst. Freiberg/Sa. , 5, 3 (1950); Chem. Abstr. , 46, 5874 (1952).
601. Stather, F. , and H. Nebe, Ges. Abhandl. Deut. Lederinst. Freiberg/Sa. , 7, 34, (1951); Chem. Abstr. , 46, 5875 (1952).

602. Stayner, R. D. , U. S. Patent 2, 874, 127; Chem. Abstr. , 53, 8670 (1959).
603. Stayner, R. D. , and R. A. Stayner, U. S. Patent 2, 665, 978; Chem. Abstr. , 48, 4213 (1954).
604. Steindorff, A. , K. Daimler, and K. Platz, German Patent 657, 357; Chem. Abstr. , 32, 4252 (1938).
605. Stewart, J. M. , and H. P. Cordts, J. Am. Chem. Soc. , 74, 5880 (1952).
606. Stewart, T. D. , and L. H. Donnally, J. Am. Chem. Soc. , 54, 3559 (1932).
607. Stillich, O. , J. prakt. Chem. (2), 74, 51 (1906).
608. Stirton, A. J. , J. Am. Oil Chemists' Soc. , 39, 490 (1962).
609. Strating, J. , G. Moes, and W. F. Vogel, British Patent 879, 133; Chem. Abstr. , 57, 2314 (1962).
610. Struve, W. S. , in The Chemistry of Synthetic Dyes and Pigments, H. A. Lubs, ed. , Reinhold, New York, 1955.
611. Stults, F. C. , R. W. Moulton, and J. L. McCarthy, Chem. Eng. Progr. Symp. Ser. , 48, No. 4, 38 (1952).
612. Suen, T. J. , U. S. Patent 2, 559, 578; Chem. Abstr. , 45, 9912 (1951).
613. Suen, T. J. , and A. M. Schiller, U. S. Patent 2, 646, 419; Chem. Abstr. , 47, 10279 (1953).
614. Suen, T. J. , and A. M. Schiller, U. S. Patent 2, 761, 834; Chem. Abstr. , 50, 15130 (1956).
615. Sundberg, R. L. , U. S. Patent 2, 857, 370; Chem. Abstr. , 53, 6658 (1959).
616. Sundberg, R. L. , M. E. Chiddix, and E. P. Williams, U. S. Patent 2, 860, 160; Chem. Abstr. , 53, 7994 (1959).
617. Sunden, O. , and S. B. Stinemur, U. S. Patent 3, 012, 015; Chem. Abstr. , 57, 1090 (1962).
618. Suter, C. M. , The Organic Chemistry of Sulfur, New York, Wiley, New York, 1944.
619. Suter, C. M. , R. K. Bair, and F. G. Bordwell, J. Org. Chem. , 10, 470 (1945).
620. Suzuki, T. , and S. Sakurai, British Patent 242, 721; Chem. Abstr. , 20, 3696 (1926).
621. Takahashi, M. , Japanese Patent 636 ('59); Chem. Abstr. , 53, 10762 (1959).
622. Takata, Y. , Yakugaku Zasshi, 80, 1640 (1960); Chem. Abstr. , 55, 8303 (1961).
623. Takata, Y. , K. Yamamoto, and Y. Takata, Japan. J. Pharm. Chem. , 26, 702 (1954); Chem. Abstr. , 49, 13083 (1955).
624. Takeda, A. , Contrib. Boyce Thompson Inst. , 20, 191 (1959).
625. Tanabe Seiyaku Co. , Ltd. , Belgian Patent 594, 743.
626. Tanimoto, S. , and R. Oda, J. Chem. Soc. Japan Ind. Chem. Sect. , 56, 942 (1953); Chem. Abstr. , 49, 6878 (1955).
627. Tanizawa, K. , Japanese Patent 4016 ('51); Chem. Abstr. , 47, 9356 (1953).

628. Teramura, K. , Mem. Fac. Ind. Arts Kyoto Tech. Univ. Sci. Technol. , 8, 53 (1959); Chem. Abstr. , 55, 562 (1961).

629. Terent'ev, A. P. , Vestn. Moskov. Univ. , 6, 9 (1947); Chem. Abstr. , 44, 1480 (1950).

630. Terent'ev, A. P. , A. N. Kost, A. M. Yurkevich, E. E. Khaskina, and L. I. Obreimova, Vestn. Mosk. Univ. , 8, No. 6, Ser. Fiz. -Mat. i Estestven. Nauk No. 4, 121 (1953); Chem. Abstr. , 49, 8104 (1955).

631. Terent'ev, A. P. , and M. N. Preobrazhenskaya, Zhr. Obshch. Khim. , 26, 3468 (1956); Chem. Abstr. , 51, 9632 (1957).

632. Terent'ev, A. P. , and L. A. Yanovskaya, Dokl. Akad. Nauk SSSR, 75, 235 (1950); Chem. Abstr. , 45, 8445 (1951).

633. Terent'ev, A. P. , and L. A. Yanovskaya, Zhr. Obshch. Khim. , 23, 618 (1953); Chem. Abstr. , 48, 6958 (1954).

634. Testa, E. , L. Fontanella, and V. Aresi, Ann. , 656, 114 (1962).

635. Thirtle, J. R. , I. F. Salminen, and A. Weissberger, French Patent 1, 112, 594; Chem. Zentr. , 130, 1667 (1959).

636. Thurston, J. T. , J. R. Dudley, D. W. Kaiser, I. Hechenbleikner, F. C. Schaefer, and D. Holm-Hansen, J. Am. Chem. Soc. , 73, 2981 (1951).

637. Tiedmann, H. H. , U. S. Patent 2, 861, 090; Chem. Abstr. , 53, 5711 (1959).

638. Tillotson, E. W. , U. S. Patent 2, 287, 071; Chem. Abstr. , 37, 231 (1943).

639. Timell, T. , Ing. Vetenskaps Akad. Handl. , 205, 9 (1950); Chem. Abstr. , 45, 2199 (1951).

640. Timell, T. , Svensk Papperstid. , 51, 254 (1948); Chem. Abstr. , 43, 396 (1949).

641. Timell, T. , Swedish Patent 124, 025; Chem. Abstr. , 43, 9446 (1949).

642. Timmler, H. , and R. Wegler, German Patent 1, 134, 070; Chem. Abstr. , 57, 14945 (1962).

643. Tishchenko, D. , and A. Kislitsyn, Zhr. Prikl. Khim. , 34, 1612 (1961); Chem. Abstr. , 55, 27045 (1961).

644. Tishchenko, D. , and I. P. Uvarov, Gidrolizn. i Lesokhim. Prom., 2, 9 (1956); Chem. Abstr. , 50, 16149 (1956).

645. Toho Rayon K. K. , Belgian Patent 606, 175.

646. Topp, N. E. , U. S. Dept. Commerce, OTS Rept. PB41, 238; BIOS Final Rept. No. 621, Item No. 22.

647. Touey, G. P. , U. S. Patent 2, 811, 519; Chem. Abstr. , 52, 4180 (1958).

648. Touey, G. P. , and J. E. Kiefer, U. S. Patent 3, 008, 952; Chem. Abstr. , 56, 11865 (1962).

649. Treibs, W. , and H. Roehnert, Chem. Ber. , 84, 433 (1951).

650. Truce, W. E. , and C. C. Alfieri, J. Am. Chem. Soc. , 72, 2740 (1950).

651. Truce, W. E. , and F. D. Hoerger, J. Am. Chem. Soc. , 76, 5357 (1954).

652. Truce, W. E. , and F. D. Hoerger, J. Am. Chem. Soc. , 77, 2496 (1955).

653. Truce, W. E. , and F. D. Hoerger, J. Am. Chem. Soc. , 77, 2497 (1955).

654. Tsunoo, S. , Ber. , 68B, 1334 (1935).

655. Tucker, N. B. , U. S. Patent 2,289,391; Chem. Abstr. , 37, 483 (1943).

656. Ueda, T. , and N. Ito, Japanese Patent 20 (1951); Chem. Abstr., 47, 3876 (1953).

657. Ulinski, A. , and D. Staszewska, Roczniki Chem. , 35, 1495 (1961); Chem. Abstr. , 57, 5786 (1962).

658. Ulsperger, E. , J. Prakt. Chem. , 15, 67 (1961).

659. Unilever, Ltd. , Belgian Patent 578, 179.

660. Unilever, Ltd. , Belgian Patent 593, 737.

661. Unilever, Ltd. , British Patent 848, 463; Chem. Abstr. , 55, 7872 (1961).

662. Unilever, Ltd. , French Patent 1, 332, 754.

663. Urban, R. , U. S. Patent 2, 537, 868; Chem. Abstr. , 45, 6661 (1951).

664. U. S. Dept. Commerce, FIAT Final Rept. No. 1313, PB 85, 172, Vol. III.

665. U. S. Dept. Commerce, OTS Leather Series, Rept. No. 2, PB95, 789.

666. VEB Farbenfabriken Wolfen, Belgian Patent 557, 931.

667. Vejdelek, Z. J. , Chem. Listy, 50, 674 (1956); Chem. Abstr. , 50, 8639 (1956).

668. Veldstra, H. , W. Kruyt, E. J. van der Steen, B. Aberg, M. Kooistra, J. F. Michels, and C. van de Westeringh, Rec. Trav. Chim. , 73, 23 (1954); Chem. Abstr. , 48, 6515 (1954).

669. Venkataraman, K. , The Chemistry of Synthetic Dyes, Academic Press, New York, 1952.

670. Vieillefosse, R. , Bull. Soc. Chim. France, 1947, 351.

671. Vignoli, L. , and J. Sice, Bull. Soc. Chim. France, 12, 877 (1945).

672. Vodak, Z. , Chem. Listy, 48, 552 (1954); Chem. Abstr. , 49, 4576 (1955).

673. Vodak, Z. , British Patent 754, 367; Chem. Abstr. , 51, 8803 (1957).

674. Vodak, Z. , and O. Leminger, Chem. Listy, 50, 943 (1956); Chem. Abstr. , 50, 16717 (1956).

675. Vol'f, L. A. , A. I. Meos, and S. A. Inkina, Zhr. Prikl. Khim. , 35, 2047 (1962); Chem. Abstr. , 58, 4692 (1963).

676. Voss, A. , German Patent 423, 033; Chem. Zentr. , 1926, I, 3376.

677. Wacker-Chemie Gmbh, French Patent 1, 302, 218.

678. Waintraub, S. M. , Zavodsk. Lab. , 10, 542 (1941); Chem. Abstr. , 38, 3220 (1944).

679. Waldmann, E. , and A. Chwala, Austrian Patent 160, 231; Chem. Abstr. , 47, 11256 (1953).

680. Walker, J. F. , U. S. Patent 2, 321, 958; Chem. Abstr. , 37, 6770 (1943).
681. Wallach, O. , and M. Wuesten, Ber. , 16, 150 (1883).
681a. Walling, C. T. , L. F. McKenney, and R. Geitz, U. S. Patent 2, 903, 466; Chem. Abstr. , 54, 2177 (1960).
682. Wallingford, V. H. , U. S. Patent 3, 023, 232; Chem. Abstr. , 57, 2080 (1962).
683. Ward, G. A. , Ph. D. Dissertation, Northwestern University, 1961; Dissertation Abstr. , 22, No. 7, 2167 (1962).
684. Wateree Chemical Co. , Lugoff, S. C.
685. Weil, J. K. , R. G. Bistline, Jr. , and A. J. Stirton, J. Am. Oil Chemists' Soc. , 32, 370 (1955).
686. Werner, A. E. A. , Sci. Proc. Roy. Dublin Soc. , 23, 214 (1944); Chem. Abstr. , 38, 4257 (1944).
687. Werner, H. , and H. Distler, German Patent 1, 098, 202; Chem. Abstr. , 55, 24106 (1961).
688. Wesche, H. , and L. Weiz, German (East) Patent 21, 772; Chem. Abstr. , 56, 8722 (1962).
689. Wheeler, O. H. , Chem. Rev. , 62, 205 (1962).
690. White, T. , and J. R. B. Hastings, U. S. Patent 2, 674, 591; Chem. Abstr. , 48, 7923 (1954).
691. Wicklatz, J. E. , U. S. Patent 2, 600, 287; Chem. Abstr. , 47, 1726 (1953).
692. Wieland, T. , E. Fischer, and F. Moewus, Ann. , 561, 47 (1949).
693. Wiley, R. H. , and S. F. Reed, J. Am. Chem. Soc. , 78, 2171 (1956).
694. Wiley, R. H. , and W. A. Trinler, J. Polymer Sci. , 28, 163 (1958).
695. Willems, J. , Bull. Soc. Chim. Belges, 64, 409 (1955).
696. Willems, J. , Bull. Soc. Chim. Belges, 64, 747 (1955).
697. Willems, J. F. , W. Koerber, and F. Huegebaert, German Patent 1, 113, 138; Chem. Abstr. , 57, 15295 (1962).
698. Willmund, W. , and A. Kirstahler, British Patent 877, 957; Chem. Abstr. , 56, 14307 (1962).
699. Wirth, H. , U. S. Patent 2, 860, 144; Chem. Abstr. , 53, 14002 (1959).
700. Wolff, A. , German Patent 258, 473; Chem. Abstr. , 7, 2666 (1913).
701. Wooding, W. M. , U. S. Patent 2, 688, 570; Chem. Abstr. , 49, 616 (1955).
702. Yamasiti, S. , and T. Yoshizaki, U. S. Patent 2, 313, 695; Chem. Abstr. , 37, 5168 (1943).
703. Yoshikawa, T. , Yakugaku Zasshi, 78, 479 (1958); Chem. Abstr. , 52, 17265 (1958).
704. Yoshizaki, T. , J. Chem. Soc. Japan Ind. Chem. Sect. , 54, 415 (1951); Chem. Abstr. , 48, 1953 (1954).
705. Yoshizaki, T. , J. Chem. Soc. Japan Ind. Chem. Sect. , 55, 352 (1952); Chem. Abstr. , 48, 1706 (1954).

706.   Yoshizaki, T. , J. Chem. Soc. Japan Ind. Chem. Sect. , 56, 85
        (1953); Chem. Abstr. , 48, 8560 (1954).
707.   Young, H. A. , and H. Spitzmueller, U. S. Patent 2, 394, 834;
        Chem. Abstr. , 40, 2658 (1946).
708.   Zeiss Ikon AG, U. S. Dept. Commerce, OTS Rept. PB83, 606.
709.   Zerweck, W. , and O. Troesken, German Patent 849, 106; Chem.
        Abstr. , 49, 9299 (1955).
710.   Zhedek, M. S. , S. S. Shtal, and M. A. Gorinshtein, Zh. Prikl.
        Khim. , 25, 441 (1952); Chem. Abstr. , 47, 1394 (1953).
711.   Ziegler, J. H. , and M. Locher, Ber. , 20, 834 (1887).
712.   Zollinger, H. , Angew. Chem. , 73, No. 4, 125 (1961).

CHAPTER 6

SULFATION

I. INTRODUCTION

Sulfation involves the formation of a compound containing an oxygen-sulfur bond, $ROSO_3H$, usually by reaction of an alkene with H_2SO_4, or of a hydroxy compound with SO_3, or an appropriate derivative thereof. Sulfonation, in contrast, involves the formation of a carbon-sulfur bond.

A brief general comparison of the two quite similar and important processes of sulfation and sulfonation appears of interest, with respect to their uses, and the techniques and reagents used. Sulfation is industrially important for the production of alcohols and detergents from alkenes, of detergents from long-chain alcohols, and of leuco vat dyes. The preparation of such types of products, including detergents, dye intermediates and ion-exchange resins, may likewise be considered as the primary practical use for sulfonation. Sulfation, on the other hand, differs in also having substantial biological and biochemical importance, since alkyl, steroid, aryl, and carbohydrate sulfates are synthesized in living systems (315), and their preparation in the laboratory is, therefore, of corresponding interest. The four basic techniques of sulfonation, as discussed in Chapters 2-5, have all been applied to sulfation, but that involving the direct use of SO_3 and its compounds is by a very large margin the only one of broad practical interest, although the others are preferred in isolated cases. The reagents employed for both processes are similar, but the more inert materials are generally favored for the sulfation of hydroxy compounds because of their much greater sensitivity to acid conditions or susceptibility to ring sulfonation. The SO_3-amine adducts have thus been widely employed for sulfation, often in aqueous medium, but they are almost never used for sulfonation, except for acid-sensitive heterocyclic compounds, and even then only under anhydrous conditions. Sulfamic acid, which has rarely been employed for sulfonation, is used for sulfating compounds when it is desired to avoid ring sulfonation. Chlorosulfonic acid, a favored reagent for the sulfation of many alcohols, is employed for sulfonation almost exclusively for preparing aromatic sulfonyl chlorides.

II. THE SULFATION OF ALKENES AND CYCLOALKENES WITH SULFURIC ACID

A. Short-Chain Alkenes

Alkenes are easily sulfated with sulfuric acid by the following over-all reaction:

$$RCH:CH_2 + H_2SO_4 \longrightarrow RCH(CH_3)OSO_3H \qquad (6\text{-}1)$$

The sulfation of the lower alkenes derived from petroleum (ethylene, propylene, the butylenes) with concentrated acid is operated on a large commercial scale intermediate to producing the corresponding alcohols. The higher alkenes, made from shale oil or by petroleum cracking, are sulfated to detergents. Other reactions occur during sulfation, including oxidation, polymerization and tar formation. Disulfation is also noted (cf., Section VI):

$$2RCH:CH_2 + H_2SO_4 \longrightarrow \left[RCH(CH_3)\right]_2SO_4 \qquad (6\text{-}2)$$

Both the mono- and dialkyl sulfates can be hydrolyzed to the alcohol, as follows:

$$RCH(CH_3)OSO_3H + \left[RCH(CH_3)\right]_2SO_4 + 3H_2O \longrightarrow$$

$$3RCHOHCH_3 + 2H_2SO_4 \qquad (6\text{-}3)$$

Ether formation is a side reaction during hydrolysis:

$$\left[RCH(CH_3)\right]_2SO_4 + RCHOHCH_3 \longrightarrow RCH(CH_3)SO_4H +$$

$$\left[RCH(CH_3)\right]_2O \qquad (6\text{-}4)$$

The sulfation of alkenes proceeds according to Markownikoff's rule, forming the secondary sulfates from monosubstituted or 1, 2-disubstituted ethylenes. 1, 1-Disubstituted ethylenes may form the tertiary sulfates, but they have not been isolated as such, even though the corresponding tertiary alcohols are formed. (The controversy over the existence of tertiary sulfates is discussed in Section III-A-1.) As pointed out in Section II-C, the hydration of some alkenes can occur without the necessary formation of a sulfate intermediates. Some highly halogenated alkenes form primary sulfates, e.g., 1, 1, 1-tri-chloropropene (Section II-D), and alkenes of structure $RCF:CF_2$, where R is fluorinated alkyl (Section VIII-B). This difference in behavior would be expected in view of the electron-withdrawing power of the halogen atoms compared to the electron-donating character of alkyl groups.

Commercial process factors involved in the sulfation of the lower alkenes have been thoroughly reviewed up to about 1956 by Asinger (13), and to a lesser extent by others (10, 127, 144, 240). Work prior to 1941 has been discussed by Suter (369). Ethylene sulfation is of major commercial interest, since hundreds of millions of gallons of ethanol are produced annually by this procedure. The success of this process has been made possible by good yields, continuous operation on a large scale, and an efficient procedure for reconcentrating the spent acid from the hydrolysis step to permit its reuse in the sulfation reaction. This sulfation is usually effected with 96 - 98% acid at 70 - 80°C under 5 - 15 atm. pressure. The rate of reaction (6-1) is largely contact-controlled (173); efficient agitation is, therefore, essential. The initial rate of sulfation can be doubled by adding silver nitrate, but it later falls to normal. The addition of 20 mole-% diethyl sulfate increases the rate of reaction to the point that it is no longer contact-controlled. Of major importance was the discovery that the costly reconcentration step could be obviated by sulfating at 150°C with 70% acid under higher pressure, followed by adding just enough water for hydrolysis (129). This substantial advantage is somewhat offset by the requirement of costly tantalum equipment because of the extremely corrosive operating conditions.

Propylene is sulfated under milder condition as shown in Table 6-1 (13, 129). Reconcentration is unnecessary if 70% acid is used (129). Thermal (122) and kinetic (264) factors for propylene sulfation have been determined. The rate of sulfation has been noted to increase sharply with pressure increase (264), and with the addition of kerosene to the reaction mixture (331).

The sulfation of isobutylene with 30 - 60% acid at 30 - 50°C and from 3 to 6 atm. pressure gave very little polymer formation (262). Steaming out the tert-butanol gave 42% acid, which could be reused for sulfation without reconcentration. Thermal and reactor design factors have been studied for the three butylene isomers (399).

TABLE 6-1

Sulfation of Propylene

Process	Acid strength (%)	Temp. (°C)	Pressure (Atm.)
"Strong acid"	92	20	8-10
"Weak acid"	70	65-90	25
Batch	75	40	20

Cyclohexene has likewise been sulfated under varied conditions, as shown in Table 6-2.

TABLE 6-2

Sulfation of Cyclohexene

Reagent	Temp. (°C)	Conversion(%)	Yield (%)	Reference
20% oleum	0	–	34-54	362
80% acid	40	62	89	302
65 - 75% acid	40-60	77	95	157

B.   Long-Chain Alkenes

The sulfation of long-chain alkenes (C8 - 18) has been of commercial interest for many years for the production of detergents. Although many types of long-chain alkenes have been sulfated experimentally (13, 334, 335), commercial operation has been limited to those obtained from shale oil or by the cracking of petroleum wax. The manufacture of such detergents has been described in some detail (187, 366). Process studies (33, 74, 216, 366) have shown the suitable sulfation conditions which might comprise operation at 10-15°C with 90-98% acid, a 5-min. contact time, and an acid-alkene molar ratio of approximately 2:1. Efficient mixing is essential, since the acid and hydrocarbon are immiscible. If 96% acid is added to 1-dodecene at 0°C, dialkyl sulfate is formed almost exclusively at first, but this is converted to an 80% yield of monoalkyl sulfate as more acid is added (85a). The yield can be increased to 90% by using 98% acid at -15°C with pentane as solvent. The product obtained by these procedures is almost exclusively the 2-isomer. On the other hand, if the olefin is added to the acid, the position of the entering sulfate group is entirely random on the secondary carbon atoms.

An interesting comparative study (217) of five types of reactors used for long-chain alkene sulfation showed that the circulating type used commercially for isobutane alkylation was best, since it has a large cooling area for a small amount of liquid and can be scaled up to any desired commercial size. Workup of the sulfation mixture includes tar removal (by centrifuging), breakdown of undesired dialkyl sulfates (by holding at 90°C for 8 hr. with aqueous sodium carbonate), and removal of unreacted hydrocarbon (by solvent extraction). This type of detergent is not manufactured in the United States in part because of these processing difficulties.

C. The Mechanism of Alkene Sulfation

The mechanism of alkene sulfation has been studied surprisingly little considering its very extensive industrial use for preparing alcohols. Although the high reactivity of sulfuric acid toward olefins is to be generally expected because of its high acidity and ion-solvating power and its low basicity (175), the detailed nature of the reactions involved is still not clear (238). Following introduction of the carbonium ion concept by Whitmore in 1934, sulfation was thought simply to involve protonation of the alkene, followed by attack of the ion by bisulfate anion to yield the alkyl sulfate, which was then hydrolyzed to the alcohol. It was subsequently pointed out (312) that, in the sulfation of the n-butenes, only 30-40% of the butene content of the acid reaction mixture was alkylsulfuric acid. The remainder was considered to be in the form of alkoxonium ion, since no free alcohol could be extracted using immiscible organic solvents. The reactions were assumed to be:

$$ROSO_3^- + H_3O^+ \overset{\text{Rapid}}{\underset{}{\rightleftharpoons}} ROH_2^+ + HOSO_3^- \tag{6-5}$$

$$ROH_2^+ + H_2O \rightleftharpoons ROH + H_3O^+ \tag{6-6}$$

Taft and co-workers (296) suggested that a facile protonation step appeared to precede the rate-determining formation of carbonium ion; this was considered to be a π complex. In their work, alkene hydration was catalyzed by acids other than sulfuric (e.g., nitric), showing that alkyl sulfate formation is not an essential. They further showed that (231) the olefin to carbonium ion reaction is not necessarily reversible. This conclusion was also reached independently by others (338) in a study of the sulfation of ethylene and of isobutylene with D_2SO_4. These concepts can be summarized (44) as follows for hydration in which the sulfate is not an intermediate:

$$C=C + H_3O^+ \rightleftharpoons \left[\begin{array}{c} C = C \\ | \\ H \end{array} \right]^+ + H_2O \tag{6-7}$$

$$(A)$$

$$(A) + H_2O \longrightarrow R^+. \quad . \; . \; . OH_2 \text{ (rate-determining)} \qquad (6-8)$$
$$\underset{(B)}{}$$

$$(B) \rightleftharpoons ROH_2^+ \qquad (6-9)$$
$$\underset{(C)}{}$$

$$(C) + H_2O \rightleftharpoons ROH + H_3O^+ \qquad (6-10)$$

Reaction 6-5 is also involved when the sulfate is formed intermediate to alcohol formation. Because Taft's earlier conclusions, as outlined above, were based in part on the Hammett-Zucker hypothesis, which has more recently been shown to be invalid in many instances, the π-complex mechanism must be reevaluated in competition with the simpler concept of a rate-determining proton transfer (which has not been ruled out by Taft's studies).

Kinetic studies of the sulfation of long-chain alkenes have led to the conclusion that a carbonium ion intermediate is involved (73). The reaction rate decreases with increase in chain length, possibly because of steric hindrance. At equilibrium, comparable amounts of alkyl sulfate and alkoxonium ion are present (74). These studies were complicated by the heterogeneity of the systems being investigated.

D. Chlorination-Sulfation of Alkenes

Simultaneous chlorination and sulfation of 1,1,1-trichloropropene yields bis-(2,3,3,3-tetrachloropropyl)sulfate (137).

$$2Cl_3CCH:CH_2 + 2Cl_2 + H_2SO_4 \longrightarrow (Cl_3CCHClCH_2O)_2SO_2$$
$$+ 2HCl \qquad (6-11)$$

It was later shown (162) that ethylene, chlorine and 98% acid at room temperature form equal amounts of 2-chloroethyl acid sulfate and bis-(2-chloroethyl)sulfate:

$$3CH_2:CH_2 + 3Cl_2 + 2H_2SO_4 \longrightarrow ClCH_2CH_2OSO_3H +$$
$$+ (ClCH_2CH_2O)_2SO_2 + 3HCl \qquad (6-12)$$

This approach was extended by others to propylene and to cyclohexene using tert-butyl hypochlorite (413) instead of chlorine. The analogous substituted bis-(2-chloroethyl)sulfates were also formed in these cases, but the one obtained from propylene was the isopropyl derivative, rather the anti-Markownikoff n-propyl sulfate noted from 1,1,1-trichloropropene. This difference in the direction of addition would be expected, since the trichloromethyl group is electron-withdrawing, and the methyl group is electron-donating.

The mechanisms of these reactions were not discussed, and it is not apparent whether or not chlorination follows sulfation. However, electrophilic attack in the 2-position of an alkyl sulfate can occur fairly easily, as has been shown for ethyl- and n-propyl sulfates, which undergo sulfonation in that position (cf. Section III-A-3).

III. THE SULFATION OF ALIPHATIC AND CYCLOALIPHATIC HYDROXY COMPOUNDS

A. Saturated Monohydric Alcohols

1. GENERAL CONSIDERATIONS

In this section is considered the sulfation of straight- and branched-chain alcohols of varying chain length, of ether-alcohols (i. e., epoxide condensates of long-chain alcohols and of alkylated phenols), and of alcohols also containing amide, ester, or similar groups. Many of these sulfates are technically important as detergents, while others have been prepared only in the laboratory. This subject has been discussed broadly by Suter through 1941 (369), and others have reviewed the preparation of such detergent sulfates through 1956 (334, 335). The long-chain, alkyl acid sulfates have been isolated as pure compounds with definite melting points (249).

Most of the known compounds of sulfur trioxide are apparently capable of sulfating alcoholic groups. The question, therefore, becomes one of the comparative merits of the various reagents and procedures, with many possibilities from which to choose. This point is brought out by two reports. A study of the sulfation of a tridecyl alcohol-ethylene oxide adduct (1:4 mole ratio) (121) showed that four reagents (sulfur trioxide vapor, chlorosulfonic acid, 20% oleum and sulfamic acid) all gave 93-99% yields of good quality sulfate. The results of the second study, involving comparison of nine reagent systems (401), are summarized in Table 6-3. Only two of those tried (sulfamic acid and oleum in ether) were concluded to be unsatisfactory.

Primary alcohols undergo sulfation without difficulty. The same can be said of secondary alcohols in general, although they react less easily than the primary compounds with sulfamic or sulfuric acids. Long-chain secondary alcohols also tend to dehydrate with sulfuric acid or with SO_3 vapor. The existence of tertiary alcohol sulfates is controversial. Fieser reported (132) the preparation of such compounds by brief heating of the alcohols with SO_3-pyridine at 100°C. He showed that they decompose very rapidly in aqueous medium in the range pH 4-10 and in strong acid. The validity of these results, and in fact the existence of such sulfates, was later questioned by Deno and Newman (100), who were unable to prepare tert-butyl sulfate from the alcohol with SO_3-pyridine or sulfuric acid at room temperature. (It seems doubtful, however, that these conditions would favor formation of the

TABLE 6-3

Sulfation of a C12-14 Alcohol Mixture with Various Reagents

Reagent	Acid-alcohol mole ratio	Reaction temp. (°C)	Product quality			
			% Active	% Oil[a]	% Yield[b]	Color[c]
96% H$_2$SO$_4$ alone	2. 3	55	14. 2	3. 4	80. 6	3
96% H$_2$SO$_4$ with CCl$_4$	2	15	32. 8	4. 8	87. 2	2
20% Oleum alone	3	35	9. 4	2. 0	82. 4	-
20% Oleum in ether	1. 2	15	14. 7	10. 8	57. 7	-
Sulfamic acid	1. 05	130	19. 6	12. 0	61. 9	-
ClSO$_3$H alone	1. 03	35	40. 5	1. 6	96. 2	4
ClSO$_3$H in ether	1. 1	10	38. 7	0. 3	99. 3	1
SO$_3$ vapor	1. 02	35	44. 0	3. 0	93. 6	6
SO$_3$ in SO$_2$	1. 15	-10	31. 2	1. 2	96. 2	5

[a]On "as is" basis.

[b]Based on alcohol.

[c]The lower the number, the lighter the color.

desired sulfate). Three tertiary alcohols were later apparently successfully sulfated with SO$_3$-dioxane at room temperature in 3 min., as indicated in Section III-A-4. The existence of these sulfates was assumed by titration, rather than from actual isolation, however. Others noted only dehydration with these reagents at 0°C (373). It was later stated (420) that tert-butyl alcohol can be sulfated in 35% yield with sulfamic acid-pyridine in 3 hr. at 105°C; milder conditions suitable for other alcohols were unsatisfactory. In view of these conflicting reports, it appears that the preparation of tertiary alkyl sulfates should be systematically reconsidered. Di-(tert-butyl)sulfate, described as a dry, white solid softening at 0°C, and slowly decomposing at room temperature, has been prepared from the alcohol and SO$_2$Cl$_2$

in isopentane at -30°C (50). It is described as a powerful tertiary butylating agent.

2. SULFURIC ACID AND OLEUM

Alcohols sulfate reversibly with sulfuric acid as follows:

$$ROH + H_2SO_4 \rightleftharpoons ROSO_3H + H_2O \tag{6-13}$$

Even under the most favorable conditions at equimolar ratios of acid and alcohol, the reaction is only 65% complete (100). A kinetic and mechanistic study (100) has shown that it proceeds by a bimolecular displacement mechanism like that of the acid-catalyzed esterification of alcohols with carboxylic acids; no oxygen-alkyl fission occurs. The experimentally determined rate law is

$$\frac{d(ROSO_3H)}{dt} = k\ (ROH)(H_2SO_4)(H^+ \text{ activity}) \tag{6-14}$$

However, more recent work, reviewed by Long and Paul (238), has led to the conclusion that under somewhat different conditions it could be unimolecular, although it is admitted that for the concentrated H_2SO_4 solutions used it is not easy to distinguish a unimolecular rate step from a bimolecular one. Primary alcohols sulfate at a rate ten times that of secondary alcohols. Steric effects are minor, since neopentyl alcohol sulfates at a rate comparable to that of secondary alcohols. Tian has studied the sulfation rates of C1-4 alcohols at 0°C over a wide range of reactant ratios (381, 382), and noted that with excess acid the initial rate is unexpectedly 500 times that observed with excess alcohol.

Several side reactions occur in monosulfating alcohols with sulfuric acid. The extent of dialkyl sulfate formation has been studied with higher fatty alcohols (305). Sperm alcohol forms dialkyl sulfates, alkylene disulfates, and ethers (395), while decanol gives decene, decenal, and short-chain hydrocarbons (322), in addition to the desired monosulfate.

In spite of these side effects, sulfuric acid and oleum have occasionally been employed for preparative sulfation of alcohols, even though the yields are poor. Examples include C1-3 (77), even-carbon, straight-chain, primary C8-18 alcohols (139) in 40% yield using concentrated acid, neododecanol, in 83% yield with 20% oleum (112), lauric ethanolamide using 93% acid (84), and long-chain monoesters of ethylene glycol with oleum at 40°C (242). In the last case, extensive solvolytic cleavage of the ester group would be expected (23).

A number of expedients have been tried toward improving the yields in sulfating long-chain alcohols with sulfuric acid, all involving methods for driving the equilibrium of Reaction (6-13) to the right. An obvious measure is the addition of excess acid. As shown in Table 6-3, 80-87% sulfation can thus be achieved with the long-chain alcohols using 2-2.3 moles of 96% acid per mole of alcohol. With stoichiometric concentrated acid, 1-tetradecanol sulfates in 55% yield, and the various secondary isomers give conversions as low as 25% (202). Doubling the quantity of acid raised the yields to 83 and 65%; dehydration was noted increasingly as a side reaction as the hydroxyl group was moved in from the end of the chain. Another approach involves the removal of water, by distillation in the presence of carbon tetrachloride (402), by adding a chemical which reacts with water, such as boron sulfate (422), or by sulfating in vacuo (342), for example at 6 mm. for 1 hr. at 40°C. The yields fell at higher pressures, even with increased acid. Long-chain alcohols can be sulfated 55-75% by heating to 130°C with the sulfate of an organic amine (166).

The sulfation of lauryl alcohol with sulfuric acid has been operated industrially for many years by a continuous "flash" procedure using 170% of theory of 99% acid with a reaction time of 60 sec. or less, followed by immediate "quenching" by neutralization (412). The alcohol and acid are mixed and passed through a reaction coil where no attempt is made to control the temperature by cooling; it rises to 60-70°C. Immediate quenching is not only desirable for fast throughput, but is necessary to avoid side reactions. About 10-15% of the alcohol remains unreacted. The heat effects encountered in this process have been calculated (144). A somewhat similar process, operated on a pilot scale in Germany (19), involves simultaneous feeding of the alcohol and acid to a disc rotating at 800 r.p.m. The reaction mixture is thus thrown centrifugally on the cooled walls of the surrounding container, which quenches the reaction. This process employs about the same quantity of the same strength acid and operates under conditions similar to those of the flash process. Lauryl alcohol can also be sulfated with oleum, employing similar concepts (83, 130). Apparently, this type of sulfation procedure has been applied mostly to the reaction mixture of detergent alkylate with oleum (comprising a mixture of sulfonic acid with sulfuric acid), where it is desired to obtain a mixture of sulfonate and alkyl sulfate, and where the residual alcohol and sodium sulfate are acceptable (130). As discussed later, chlorosulfonic acid or SO$_3$ vapor give a better yield of a product much lower in inorganic salts.

3. SULFUR TRIOXIDE

Sulfur trioxide converts alcohols to the acid sulfates:

$$ROH + SO_3 \longrightarrow ROSO_3H \tag{6-15}$$

Methanol has been reacted with SO$_3$ vapor at -5°C (253), or with liquid SO$_3$ in carbon tetrachloride solvent (350). Vacuum distillation of the acid sulfate yields dimethyl sulfate, a process once used commercially, but now supplanted by the direct reaction of SO_3 with dimethyl ether, as discussed in Section VI:

$$2CH_3OH \xrightarrow{\text{SO}_3} 2CH_3OSO_3H \longrightarrow (CH_3O)_2SO_2 + H_2SO_4 \qquad (6\text{-}16)$$

The sulfation of absolute ethanol with SO_3 in liquid SO_2 solvent gives 74-86% of the acid sulfate, depending upon the length of time before analysis (52); the equilibrium

$$2C_2H_5OSO_2H \rightleftharpoons (C_2H_5O)_2SO_2 + H_2SO_4 \qquad (6\text{-}17)$$

has been established experimentally from both directions at 45% monosulfate, 25% disulfate, and 30% sulfuric acid. Treatment of absolute ethanol at 0°C with SO_3 vapor (1 mole), then addition of a second mole at 50°C, gives ethionic acid in good yield (52):

$$C_2H_5OH \xrightarrow{\text{SO}_3} C_2H_5OSO_3H \xrightarrow{\text{SO}_3} HO_3SCH_2CH_2OSO_3H \qquad (6\text{-}18)$$

This unusual reaction, which has also been run in liquid SO_2 (133), suggests that the sulfatomethylene moiety activates the adjacent methyl group in somewhat the same manner as carbonyl. A quasi-six-membered ring has been suggested as intermediate (52). Chlorination also occurs in this position (cf., Section II-D).

Sulfur trioxide is suitable for sulfating the higher primary alcohols. As shown in Table 6-3, in the sulfation of a mixture of 1-dodecanol and 1-tetradecanol, SO_3 vapor and SO_3 in liquid SO_2 in comparison with other reagents gave comparatively high yields, low unreacted alcohol, low inorganic salts, but somewhat darker colors (401). Passage of sulfur trioxide vapor diluted with air into the undiluted alcohol at 30-40°C gives good results on a laboratory scale for the primary straight-chain alcohols derived from coconut oil (octyl, decyl, and dodecyl) (148) and for the primary branched-chain C10 and C13 alcohols prepared by the Oxo process (121, 148). Lauryl alcohol has been sulfated in this way on a pilot plant (80) and on a commercial scale (236). It has also been sulfated commercially in a continuous process with SO_3 vapor (209). The aqueous sodium sulfate product contains no sodium chloride, and is therefore desirably much less viscous than that made with $ClSO_3H$. Hexadecyl and octadecyl alcohols have been sulfated similarly in the laboratory at 70-80°C, since they are solids at room temperature (148). Long-chain secondary alcohols have not been successfully sulfated with SO_3, since excessive dehydration occurs.

The use of solvents has been suggested to facilitate the sulfation of higher alcohols with SO_3 - especially of those compounds which are solid or excessively viscous at the reaction temperature. The organic sulfate reaction product itself has been suggested (351) as the reaction solvent in a "dominant bath" procedure, but such an approach gives a product of poor quality since the sulfate is rapidly degraded under acidic conditions. Liquid sulfur dioxide has been proposed as solvent with decyl, dodecyl, and tetradecyl alcohols (133), and for C12 and 13 Oxo alcohols (169, 186). As shown in Table 6-3, this procedure gives a good yield and fairly low oil, but dark product color. Tetrachloroethylene has been used with hydroabietyl alcohol (174).

Polyether alcohols, made by the ethoxylation of long-chain alcohols or of alkylated phenols, are likewise converted by SO_3 to sulfates of value as commercial surface-active agents. Examples are given in Table 6-4. The reagent, introduced as air-diluted vapor into the organic compound at 30-40°C, has been compared with $ClSO_3H$ (147), and with $ClSO_3H$, sulfamic acid, and 20% oleum (121) for sulfating the alcohol-derived condensates; all reagents gave good yields of acceptable products. The alkylphenol-based materials have been similarly sulfated with SO_3 vapor on a laboratory (147) and on a pilot plant (80)

TABLE 6-4

Sulfation of Polyether Alcohols (Ethylene Oxide Condensates)
with SO_3

Substrate	Moles Ethylene oxide	Reagent	Reference
2-Butyloctanol-1	3-5	SO_3 in liquid SO_2	221
Lauryl	3	SO_3 vapor	146
Tridecyl (Oxo)	3, 4	SO_3 vapor	14, 121, 146, 218
7-Ethyl-2-methyl-4-undecanol	5	SO_3 in liquid SO_2	220
Tallow (1-octadecanol)	4	SO_3 vapor	146
Octylphenol	3, 5, 12	SO_3 vapor	147
Nonylphenol	4, 9	SO_3 vapor	80, 147
Dodecylphenol	6	SO_3 vapor	147

scale, in the former case in comparison with sulfamic acid. The two reagents differ in that SO_3 gives some ring sulfonate, while sulfamic acid forms none. Products made by the two reagents give different test results in some performance tests (120), but not in others (147).

4. SULFUR TRIOXIDE ADDUCTS

Sulfur trioxide adducts convert alcohols to the sulfate salts:

$$ROH + SO_3 \cdot Base \longrightarrow ROSO_3H \cdot Base \qquad\qquad (6\text{-}19)$$

Ethanol (24) and 2-butanol (100) react with SO_3-pyridine at 25°C in 1 hr. or less to give good yields of the sulfates. Optically active 2-butanol also has been sulfated with the same reagent in 1 hr. at 100°C in 90% yield (72), with retention of optical purity and configuration; SO_3-dioxane gave similar results. Sulfur trioxide-pyridine sulfates benzyl alcohol in carbon disulfide (397). Primary and tertiary alcoholic derivatives of 1,4-naphthoquinone were sulfated on a semi-micro scale by heating for two minutes with SO_3-pyridine in excess pyridine at 100°C (132). Monoethanolamides of long-chain fatty acids have been reacted in a melt at 190°C with SO_3-picoline (110). The trimethylamine adduct sulfates both 1- and 2-propanols (165); the former reacts first in a mixture of the two alcohols, thereby effecting separation. As noted previously, primary alcohols sulfate ten times as rapidly as secondary with sulfuric acid. Ethanol has been sulfated with SO_3-trimethylphosphine oxide (62). Isoamyl alcohol is sulfated by acetyl sulfate without acetylation (287), but some acylation does occur when using n-butyryl sulfate (288). Long-chain ethanolamides (303) and C5-19 long-chain secondary alcohols (338a) have also been sulfated with acetyl sulfate.

Sulfur trioxide-dioxane quantitatively sulfates many alcohols, and this reaction has been used for their analytical determination (377, 378). With monohydric alcohols, sulfation is complete at room temperature in three minutes, but polyhydric alcohols may require two hours. The procedure was found applicable to primary (ethanol, 1-butanol, isobutanol, 1-nonanol, benzyl alcohol, and a phenylpropanol), secondary (1,1,1-trichloro-2-propanol, 2-octanol, cyclohexanol, and menthol), and tertiary (2-methyl-2-hexanol, 2-methyl-2-butanol, and 3-hydroxy-3-amyltetrahydrofuran) saturated alcohols. Polyhydric alcohols included 1,3- and 1,4-butanediols, pinacol, pentaerythritol, mannitol, glucose, galactose, and fructose. Unsaturated alcohols (allyl, 2-methyl-4-penten-2-ol, and 1,4-butynediol) reacted only on the hydroxyl groups. However, others (373) report that at 0°C SO_3-dioxane does not sulfate tert-butyl alcohol; only dehydration was noted, forming sulfuric acid. This discrepancy may be explained by differing reaction times, or by the instability of tertiary alkyl sulfates, which decompose rapidly in aqueous solution in the presence of either acids or bases (132). This subject is discussed further in Section III-A-1.

Sulfur trioxide-dioxane sulfates borneol and menthol (379).

Numerous complexes of SO_3 have been suggested in the patent literature for the sulfation of long-chain alcohols (334), but these have not been used commercially for the saturated compounds. Sulfur trioxide-dioxane has been proposed for lauryl (370) and for a C17 Oxo alcohol (56), and SO_3-thioxane for C15-19 secondary alcohols (261). Alcohols from oxidized petroleum fractions have been sulfated semi-commercially with SO_3-pyridine at 50 - 95°C using a 30 min. reaction time (201). Stearyl alcohol has been sulfated with SO_3-dimethylaniline using chlorobenzene as solvent (352), and 7-ethyl-2-methyl-4-undecanol with SO_3-bis(2-chloroethyl)ether (224). Sulfur trioxide-N-methyl ethylene carbamate sulfates lauryl alcohol at 45°C (346).

5. CHLOROSULFONIC ACID

The sulfation of alcohols with chlorosulfonic acid proceeds as follows:

$$ROH + ClSO_3H \longrightarrow ROSO_3H + HCl\uparrow \qquad (6\text{-}20)$$

This sulfation procedure has been recommended as the best all-round method for laboratory use (90, 401), since it is simple and rapid, reaction is nearly complete, and product quality is good, as shown in Table 6-3. No reaction solvent is necessary for alcohols liquid at about 30°C, at which temperature the sulfation is usually run, but chloroform, carbon tetrachloride or tetrachloroethylene can be used with solids. This procedure is not only suitable for long-chain alcohols (121, 249, 407), but for their ethoxylated derivatives (35, 146), glycerol diethers (336), long-chain fatty acid hydroxy amides (102, 277, 361), and ester-alcohols (23, 37). Long-chain secondary alcohols can be sulfated with $ClSO_3H$; SO_3 vapor, on the other hand, leads to excessive dehydration of this type of alcohol.

The ethyl ether-$ClSO_3H$ complex, used at 10°C, is milder than the acid alone, and, as shown in Table 6-3, is outstanding for yield and quality of sulfate. It is therefore a standard laboratory procedure not only for primary and secondary C8 - 28 long-chain alcohols (81, 141a, 169, 299), but for alcohols containing ether (223, 275), amide (98), nitro (99), and thioether (106) groups. In the last case, the ether solvent was recovered by distillation from the product sulfate. A mixture of $ClSO_3H$ and acetic acid has given excellent results in the sulfation of C5 - 19 long-chain secondary alcohols (338a); this mixture is presumably largely acetyl sulfate (CH_3COOSO_3H).

Long-chain alcohols are similarly sulfated batchwise on an industrial scale. Standard procedure involves adding the acid to the undiluted alcohol at about 30°C (144, 160). Chloroform (25-35% by weight on the alcohol) is sometimes added as solvent. Glass-lined kettles are used to avoid corrosion.

Although $ClSO_3H$ is an excellent reagent for laboratory and even industrial sulfation of long-chain alcohols on a batch scale, two factors have hindered its use on a continuous large scale basis. One of these is the exceptionally corrosive nature of hydrogen chloride, which necessitates the use of stainless steel or glass apparatus. The unbalanced patterns of heat and gas evolution also present problems. During addition of the first half of the acid, much of the hydrogen chloride formed is retained in the reaction mixture by exothermic formation of the alkoxonium chloride. As the second half is added, most of the hydrogen chloride is endothermically evolved as gas with considerable foaming. Overall, 60% of the total heat is evolved by the time only 20% of the acid has been added (412). A simple expedient for overcoming these problems is saturation of the alcohol with hydrogen chloride before adding the acid (149); this also lowers the melting point of the alcohol, permitting a lower sulfation temperature. This approach has apparently not been used commercially, however. Continuous sulfation with $ClSO_3H$ has been achieved in Germany (383), using special equipment, and in France (353) by employing liquid SO_2 as a reaction solvent which adiabatically removes the heat of reaction by vaporization. An Italian continuous process operates in vacuo (316), which removes the hydrogen chloride, reduces corrosion and gives a purer sulfate. Continuous processing apparently has not been generally adopted in the United States, although commercial units are available (83).

6. SULFAMIC ACID

Sulfamic acid forms the ammonium sulfate upon heating with an alcohol:

$$ROH + NH_2SO_3H \longrightarrow ROSO_3H \cdot NH_3 \qquad (6-21)$$

Since it is less reactive and more expensive than other sulfating agents, it has been used only where the others fail. With long-chain primary alcohols, as shown in Table 6-3, it gives poor yields and dark-colored products (121, 401). However, with long-chain alcohol-ethylene oxide condensates it yields sulfates of good color in excellent yield (121). Since other, cheaper reagents give similar results (121), there is no practical reason for preferring sulfamic acid with these compounds. Phenolic ethylene oxide condensates, on the other hand, are preferably sulfated with sulfamic acid, since other reagents differ in forming some undesired ring sulfonate (54, 147, 191); the reaction requires about two hours at 125°C. Sulfamic acid has also been used to sulfate an ethoxylated phenol-formaldehyde resin (205).

Although it was initially reported that secondary alcohols could not be sulfated with sulfamic acid, it was later noted (72) that they did react with difficulty and in poor yield, for example 22% with sec-butanol. It was also found that the yield could be raised to 60-70% by adding pyridine (72). Pyridine was also added when sulfating primary alcohols. A series of seven C3 - 6 alcohols (77), menthol, and allyl alcohol (420) were thus sulfated in 30 - 60 min. at 100°C. Pyridine was compared with urea, thiourea, acetamide, and γ-picoline as catalysts for sulfating dodecyl and hexadecyl alcohols (213); urea was found best. These catalysts were also used for catalyzing the sulfation of long-chain secondary alcohols, glycol monoesters, and glycerol mono- and diesters (243). As noted subsequently in this chapter, sulfamic acid-urea is more effective than the acid alone for sulfating starch and cellulose.

Long-chain alcohols have been sulfated with diammonium imidodisulfonate $(NH(SO_3NH_4)_2)$ at 140°C in a dialkylamide solvent (256a).

B. Polyhydric Alcohols

A variety of reagents have been used to sulfate polyhydric alcohols, as noted in Table 6-5. Glycerol could be di- but not trisulfated with SO_3 vapor (155); trisulfation was, however, effected with oleum. The polyethylene glycols used varied in molecular weight from 200 - 6000. Sulfation of poly(vinyl alcohol) with H_2SO_4-ethanol yields a product soluble in water and ethanol (134), whereas acid or oleum without ethanol are stated to either give no reaction or unusable gels. As noted in the next section, similar acid-alcohol mixtures have been used to sulfate cellulose. The glycol formates, from cyclohexene, 1-hexadecene and a C15 olefin, react as follows (104):

$$RCH(OCOH)CH(OCOH)R + 2\ ClSO_3H \longrightarrow$$

$$RCH(OSO_3H)CH(OSO_3H)R + 2\ CO + 2\ HCl \qquad (6\text{-}22)$$

C. Carbohydrates and Nitrogenous Polysaccharides

1. SULFURIC ACID

Water-soluble sulfated derivatives of cellulose have been of industrial interest for many years as possible substitutes for similar natural products. Biological interest has centered on preparing sulfated sugars and compounds related to the naturally-occurring anticoagulant heparin (311). In many cases with these materials, the problem comprises finding suitable conditions for sulfating a solid of low solubility and high melting point, but of unusual sensitivity to degradation by acidic reagents.

Although unmodified sulfuric acid has been suggested for sulfating cellulose under mild conditions [e. g., 5°C using methylene chloride as liquid reaction medium (208) or at -10°C in liquid SO_2 (141)], it has usually been found necessary to convert it into a less reactive form. One method has involved using the H_2SO_4-bis(2-chloroethyl)ether ad-

TABLE 6-5

Sulfation of Polyhydric Alcohols

Compound	Reagent	Solvent	Temp. ($^\circ$C)	Degree of sulfation	Reference
Ethylene and propylene glycols	H_2SO_4	None	40	Mono	138
Ethylene glycol	SO_3	SO_2	50	Di	133
Glycerol	H_2SO_4	None	-	Di	211
Glycerol	SO_3 vapor	None	40	Di	155
Lauric mono- glyceride	SO_3	SO_2	-	Mono	133
C12-18 mono- glycerides	$ClSO_3Na$	None	-	Mono	36
Oleic and linoleic mono- glycerides	SO_3-pyridine	None	10	Mono	36
Polyethylene glycol	SO_3	SO_2	-	Partial	150
Polyethylene and polypro- pylene glycols	SO_3-amine	None	100	Mono	225
Polypropylene glycol	$ClSO_3H$	$CHCl_2$	10	Di	364
Polyethylene glycol ethers and esters	H_2SO_4	CCl_4	35	-	219
Glycol-adipic acid poly- esters	$ClSO_3H$	Ether	-	-	176
Hydroxylated polybuta- diene	SO_3-pyridine	Benzene- pyridine	90	Partial	198

(continued)

TABLE 6-5 (CONTINUED)

Compound	Reagent	Solvent	Temp. (°C)	Degree of sulfation	Reference
Poly(vinyl alcohol)	SO_3-pyridine	None	110	Complete	128
Poly(vinyl alcohol)	$ClSO_3Na$	Benzene-pyridine	35	60%	195
Poly(vinyl alcohol)	H_2SO_4	None	200	-	82
Poly(vinyl alcohol)	H_2SO_4	Ethanol	-	70%	134
Shellac	H_2SO_4	None	145	-	103
Glycol for-mates	$ClSO_3H$	Ether	10	80% mono, 20% di	104
Bis(2-Hydro-xyethyl) sulfone	60% oleum	$CHCl_3$	10	Di	393

duct below 0°C with 1,2-dichloroethane as solvent (38). The approach which has come closest to commercial realization is treatment with sulfuric acid in the presence of an aliphatic alcohol containing three or more carbons (e.g., isopropyl, n-butyl, or amyl) at 0 - 20°C (136, 207, 244, 276, 410), possibly in the presence of an auxiliary solvent such as liquid SO_2 (245) at its boiling point (-10°C). The acid is partially converted to the alkyl acid sulfate, and the sulfation reaction may then involve sulfate interchange between the acid sulfate and cellulose:

$$ROH + H_2SO_4 \rightleftharpoons ROSO_3H + H_2O \qquad (6-23)$$

$$Cell \cdot OH + ROSO_3H \rightleftharpoons Cell \cdot OSO_3H + ROH \qquad (6-24)$$

Water-soluble products containing one sulfate group for every two or three anhydroglucose units can be prepared by this method without excessive degradation (410). As noted in Section III-B, this approach has been used to sulfate poly(vinyl alcohol). Apparently, the structure of the aliphatic alcohol used is critical, since poly(vinyl alcohol) could be sulfated with ethanol, but not with methanol, and cellulose requires a C3 alcohol or higher.

2. SULFUR TRIOXIDE ADDUCTS

Sulfur trioxide used as vapor, or (preferably) in carbon disulfide solution, was first reported in 1928 to sulfate three hydroxyl groups in each six-carbon unit of cellulose (387). Use of less than three moles of SO_3 gave the same trisulfate and unreacted cellulose. This sulfate was water-soluble, but did not form a viscous solution, an observation which, in the light of subsequent work, probably indicates substantial degradation during sulfation. Subsequently, chitosan was sulfated with SO_3 dissolved in liquid SO_2 for 10 - 24 hr. at $-10°C$ (392); the same system was used for chondroitin sulfuric acid (254), and for glucosamine (255). Other attempts to sulfate such materials with free SO_3 have not been reported, probably because of excessive degradation.

It was soon noted that cellulose formed a different product at $100°C$ with SO_3-pyridine. It contained 2.9 sulfate groups per glucose unit, and, unlike the material made with free SO_3, formed water solutions of higher viscosity and, therefore, probably of considerably higher molecular weight (140, 388). Starch similarly gave a material with two sulfate groups per unit (374).

This general technique has been used extensively since that time, with only minor variations, for sulfating many carbohydrates and related materials. The usual procedure involves heating the organic compound with SO_3-pyridine from 1 - 8 hr. in excess pyridine at from 60 - 100°C. Occasionally, auxiliary or alternative solvents such as chloroform (105, 116, 411), benzene (196), formamide (2, 324), or dimethylformamide (411) are employed. One to three sulfate groups are thus introduced per glucose unit in carbohydrates. The nitrogen-containing compounds are not only sulfated on hydroxyl and thiol groups, but are also sulfamated on the amino groups. Other groups react as shown in Table 7-3. The formation of sulfamate, as well as sulfate, groups in the same molecule may not be undesirable from the standpoint of preparing heparin analogues, since that compound has been shown (415) to contain both types of groups. In the case of one compound (5-fluorodeoxyuridine), which contains both a primary and a secondary alcohol group, the former was found to sulfate 2.4 times as fast as the latter with SO_3-pyridine in excess pyridine (412a). As indicated in Section III-A-2, primary alcohols sulfate ten times as fast as secondary with sulfuric acid.

Compounds so sulfated include: adenosine (116), alginic acid (6, 31, 348), degraded alginic acid (234), amylose (324), anhydroglucose (109), various aminoglucose derivatives (414), cyclo-(heptamylose) and cyclo-(hexamylose) (32), cellulose (32, 140, 197, 375, 388), chitin (32, 196), chitosan (415), N-deacetylated chondroitin sulfate (416), dextramic acid (89), dextran (2, 283, 307, 308, 309), degraded dextran (310), dextrin (311), 5-fluorodeoxyuridine (412a), galactose (286), a D-galactose derivative (153), glucofuranosides (285), glucose (105, 107, 286, 357, 411), polymerized glucose (151, 237, 417), glycogen (32),

gum arabic (32), various hexoses (390), various methylhexosides
(108), ovomucoid (313), pectic acid (31), degraded pectic acid (3),
pectin (79), degraded pectin (210), polyuronic acids (3), riboflavin
(117), saponins (314), starch (32, 197, 374), sucrose (374), tannin
heterosides (254), degraded xylan (294, 403, 415), and yeast (32).
Monosaccharide sulfates are usually made via a sugar derivative,
rather than by direct sulfation of the sugar itself.

The use of excess pyridine has been thought to minimize degradation of the acid-sensitive polysaccharides during sulfation. Cellulose
with 2.82 sulfate groups per glucose unit showed a degree of polymerization of 750 - 1000 units per mole (375). Since the latter figure
is accepted as a possible minimum for unsulfated cellulose, degradation in this case may be minor. On the other hand, polygalacturonic
acid methyl ester methyl glycoside was seriously degraded to about
half its original molecular weight during sulfation (3).

Recent work has emphasized lower sulfation temperatures in an
effort to avoid such degradation, and the elimination of pyridinium
chloride from the sulfation mixture, since it has been shown (254)
that preparations of enhanced physiological activity result. Sulfur trioxide-dimethylformamide has been used for sulfating chitosan at
room temperature (415). The use of excess dimethylformamide as
reaction solvent conveniently dissolves both the SO_3 complex and the
organic compound, yielding a homogeneous system, while SO_3-pyri-
dine is only slightly soluble in excess pyridine. However, SO_3-di-
methylformamide caused some degradation, since chitosan (415)
yielded a product with a degree of polymerization of 530 units per
mole, while SO_3-pyridine gave 1280 units at 100°C. Both products had
one sulfate and one sulfamate group per monomer unit, but that prepared with dimethylformamide had superior use properties, since it
was much less toxic with about equal physiological activity. Sulfur
trioxide-formamide has been employed for sulfating alginic acid, xylan,
pectin and methyl cellulose (294, 403). This system gave some degradation of amylose (289).

A further, and possibly ultimate, move toward even milder sulfating conditions has involved the combined use of low temperature,
a long reaction time, a powerful solvent, and an SO_3-amine complex
considerably less reactive than SO_3-dimethylformamide. Sulfur tri-
oxide-triethylamine, used with dimethylformamide solvent at 0°C for
24 hr. (409, 410), was shown to introduce 0.5 - 1.0 sulfate group per
monomer unit before degradation began. In a similar approach,
laminarin reacted with SO_3-pyridine in formamide at -5°C for 20 hr.
(273).

The low reactivity of the SO_3-amine complexes has permitted their
use in a cold aqueous alkaline medium. Starch (204, 419) is thus sulfated with complexes of triethylamine, tributylamine, or N-methyl-
morpholine at room temperature in 16 - 24 hr. Reports vary regarding the activity of SO_3-pyridine in aqueous alkaline medium. One

study (cf., Table 7-3) indicates that sulfation does not occur; with chitosan sulfamation was quantitative in 20 hr. (404), but no sulfation was noted. However, starch is reported (419) to undergo sulfation under these conditions, although no data are presented. A fairly detailed study of the sulfation of wheat flour with SO_3-trimethylamine in aqueous alkali showed a maximum 51% efficiency in utilization of the reagent, which declined to 34% as the amount of reagent was increased (343).

Other SO_3 complexes have been employed to a lesser extent for this type of sulfation. Sulfur trioxide-bis(2-chloroethyl) ether at -5°C for 1.5 hr. was used for cellulose (38); 1,2-dichloroethane was employed as reaction solvent. Sulfur trioxide-dioxane, used in excess, quantitatively sulfates all the hydroxyl groups in glucose and galactose and four of the hydroxyl groups in fructose at room temperature in 1 - 2 hr. (376).

3. ACETYL SULFATE

It has long been known that a minor degree of sulfation occurs during the usual commercial sulfuric acid-catalyzed acetylation of cellulose. It was later found that water-soluble, acetate-sulfates could be made by simply increasing the quantity of sulfuric acid (9). The reaction can be conducted homogeneously (93) or heterogeneously (85, 94), and similar cellulose sulfates containing C3 - 6 acyl groups have been made (246, 385). The properties of the commercially available sodium cellulose acetate sulfate have been described (113). Commercial interest in this type of product has supplanted that in cellulose sulfate made by the alcohol-sulfuric process as described in Section III-C-1.

4. CHLOROSULFONIC ACID

Carbohydrates and related compounds have been sulfated with chlorosulfonic acid. Usually the reaction has been conducted at about 0°C in the presence of a solvent to achieve monosulfation, although fatty amine glucosides (123) and N-alkyl-D-gluconamides (252) could also be tri- and tetrasulfated by raising the temperature to 25°C, and acylated glucamines (333) were sulfated at 50°C with ethylene glycol diethyl ether as reaction solvent. Cellulose was degraded to sulfo-dextrens (241) at 0°C. D-Glucose (317), 2-amino-2-deoxy-D-glucose (318), and glucosamine (268) were predissolved in sulfuric acid before treatment with chlorosulfonic acid. The last compound formed the disulfate in 77% yield. Degraded chitosan was sulfated in formamide (400), and laminarin-2-aminoethyl ether in liquid SO_2 (273).

5. SULFAMIC ACID

Sulfamic acid, being a comparatively inert solid reagent, would not appear well suited to the sulfation of carbohydrates. Cellulose is reported (380) to undergo degradation when heated with it alone, but in the presence of urea as catalyst satisfactory solid phase sulfation occurs at 140°C in 30 min. Starch has been sulfated similarly (248), and also with the related compound trisodium nitrilotrisulfonate (282):

$$ROH + N(SO_3Na)_3 \longrightarrow ROSO_3Na + HN(SO_3Na)_2 \qquad (6-25)$$

D. Alkenols and Alkynols

In sulfating unsaturated alcohols, it is usually desired to effect sulfation without attack of the double bond. In general, the more in- ert the reagent used, the more nearly is this goal achieved. Conver- sely, strong reagents attack both reactive sites. The point was brought out in a study of the sulfation of oleyl and elaidyl alcohols with nine reagents (406), giving results as follows, with product purity - a rough indication of the degree of double bond attack - indicated for each compound: SO_3-pyridine (96%); sulfamic acid (93); SO_3-dioxane (90); $ClSO_3H$-urea (87), $ClSO_3H \cdot NaCl$ (66), and H_2SO_4-urea (54). Sul- furic acid at 5 - 10°C, $ClSO_3H$ and SO_3 in liquid SO_2 at -10°C showed excessive attack and product purity was not determined. Sulfur tri- oxide-pyridine had previously been shown to give excellent results in sulfating oleyl alcohol with no attack of the double bond (368). This procedure has been employed industrially for making oleyl sulfate, which is an outstanding detergent (19). Assuming efficient recovery and recycle of the pyridine, this method is attractive economically, but complete removal of residual base, which has an unpleasant and persistent odor, has proved difficult on a commercial scale. The cur- rent industrial approach involves the use of sulfamic acid, which, as with the alcohols cited in Section III-A-6, reacts more rapidly, com- pletely, and at a lower temperature in the presence of catalysts like morpholine (263), triethylamine (40), or urea (213). Sulfur trioxide- N-methylethylene carbamate is also stated not to attack the double bond (346). The claim has been made (267) that the degree of dilution of SO_3 vapor determines the degree of double bond attack; little reac- tion with it occurs if 4% vapor is used for the first half of the sulfa- tion, and 2% for the second half. Another approach, employed with sperm alcohol (266), involves sulfation to the 50% point with SO_3 gas, followed by treatment with $ClSO_3H$-urea; 99% sulfation with 90% double bond retention is claimed.

For certain industrial purposes, it is not always desirable to avoid at least some attack of the double bond in the sulfation of oleyl alcohol, since empirically-prepared materials of this kind have been found best for special uses. Oleyl alcohol has thus been sulfated with 98% acid at

45°C (19), 100% acid below 30°C (181), ClSO₃H in chloroform as solvent (18), ClSO₃H-urea without a solvent (39), and ClSO₃H-urea with formamide in chloroform as solvent (18).

Sulfur trioxide-dioxane is stated to react with alcoholic groups more rapidly than with unsaturated linkages, but to sulfonate the latter also when present in excess (369). However, allyl alcohol, 2-methyl-4-penten-2-ol and 2-butyn-1, 4-diol showed nearly quantitative sulfation of the hydroxyl groups in 3 min. even using a large excess of reagent (378), indicating a longer time requirement for the other reaction. This reagent gave only slightly more attack of the double bond in oleyl alcohol than SO₃-pyridine (406).

Sulfur trioxide-pyridine, as mentioned before in connection with oleyl alcohol, reacts almost exclusively with the hydroxyl group. It has also been used to disulfate 2-butyne-1, 4-diol (300), and to monosulfate propargyl alcohol (278), geraniol (largely 2, 6-dimethyl-2, 6-octadiene-8-ol) (397), lomatiol [2-hydroxy-3-(3-methyl-4-hydroxy-2-buten-1-yl)-1, 4-naphthoquinone] (132), the latter on a semi-micro scale at 100°C in 2 min. An ethylene-allyl alcohol telomer, of molecular weight 246 with terminal unsaturation, was likewise sulfated with SO₃-pyridine using ethyl ether as solvent (235).

Sulfamic acid has also been employed to sulfate materials other than oleyl alcohol with minimum attack of the double bond. 11- and 13-Docosen-1-ols were thus converted to detergents (212). Methyl ricinoleate was sulfated at 145°C in 50 min. (214). Allyl alcohol, on the other hand, reacted at 95°C in 40 min. (420). Acetylenic polyether alcohols are also satisfactorily sulfated with sulfamic acid; the reaction occurs at 115°C, apparently without attack of the triple bond (250).

E. Amino Alcohols

Interest in the sulfation of amino alcohols has increased parallel to greater use of the sulfates for aminoalkylating cellulosic materials, and for preparing ethylenimine derivatives, to which the sulfates are easily converted by treatment with aqueous alkalies.

Wenker showed that 2-aminoethanol is converted to the sulfate inner salt by heating at atmospheric pressure with equivalent sulfuric acid (408):

$$H_2SO_4 \cdot H_2NCH_2CH_2OH \longrightarrow H_3\overset{+}{N}CH_2CH_2O\overset{-}{S}O_3 + H_2O \qquad (6\text{-}26)$$

Application of this compound for sulfatoalkylation is discussed in Chapter 5. The use of reduced pressure with the Wenker approach was later found (229) to give higher yields of a better quality product. This convenient method has been extended to the sulfation of 3-amino-1-propanol, in 90% yield at 190°C (172), to 2-aminocycloheptanol and the corresponding cyclooctanol (203), and to N-phenylaminoethanol and four 1-phenyl-2-amino-1-alkanols (53). A series of eight amino alcohols was sulfated by azeotropic removal of water with refluxing toluene

(289a). The heating step of the Wenker method has been obviated by simply adding oleum to the amino alcohol at $0°C$, presumably employing sufficient free SO_3 to effect sulfation. 2-Aminoethanol, five of its N, N-dialkyl derivatives (189), and 2-hydroxy-1, 3-diaminopropane (363) have been so treated, the last in 89% yield using 15% oleum. 2-(Dimethylamino) ethanol gives the sulfate with SO_3 dissolved in 1, 2-dichloroethane at $0°C$ (193). A mixture of products was obtained when using this approach with 2-aminoethanol (5).

A convenient and widely applicable procedure for sulfating amino alcohols comprises treatment of them with $ClSO_3H$ at $0°C$, using a solvent such as chloroform or 1, 2-dichloroethane. This approach, applied to seven compounds of varied types, showed that the monohydroxymonoamines form the inner salts with HCl evolution, the monohydroxydiamines give the hydrochlorides of the salts, and the dihydroxymonoamines yield the salt-acid sulfates (301). This method has also been used with N-(2-ethylhexyl)-2-aminoethanol (184), bis-(2-hydroxyethyl)methylamine (188), and compounds of the structure $(RCH_2)_2NCH_2CH_2OH$, where R = long-chain alkylphenyl (365). Ethoxylated long-chain amines have been sulfated with SO_3-dioxane (111).

The techniques described in this section result in the sulfation, rather than sulfamation, of amino alcohols. As shown in Chapter 7, these alcohols are selectively sulfamated by SO_3-pyridine in aqueous medium. By a proper choice of reagent it is, therefore, possible to effect either O-sulfation or N-sulfonation (i. e., sulfamation) of these materials.

F. Sterols

The sulfation of steroids is of biological interest, since many of them are excreted from the body as the water-soluble sulfates. Except for several with phenolic character, these compounds can be considered as high molecular weight polycyclic secondary alcohols, also containing other reactive groups which must not be attacked during sulfation. It is, therefore, logical that the choice of reagents has been confined to two fairly inert compounds -SO_3-pyridine and sulfamic acid, especially the former, which has always been employed under anhydrous conditions with a solvent, usually chloroform. The reaction is commonly run at room temperature, but reaction times have varied widely. Cholesterol and cholestan-3-β-ol took 2 hr. (251), equilin (154) 24, and estradiol-3-monobenzoate (178) 68. The same system at reflux $(61°C)$ was employed for estrone (319), and for 7α- and 7β-hydroxycholesterols (8). Benzene with SO_3-pyridine at $55°C$ was used with cholesterol, lanosterol, and γ-lanostadienol (34). A ternary solvent mixture (benzene, pyridine, and acetic anhydride) is reported to give quantitative sulfation using SO_3-pyridine at $50 - 60°C$ in 20 min. with cholesterol, ergosterol, and lanosterol (349); dibromocholesterol was sulfated similarly at $37°C$. Hydrocortisone was semisulfated in the 21-position (158). Sulfation on a semimicro scale is effected by heating with SO_3-pyridine in excess pyridine for 2 min. This technique was applied to androsterone, isoandrosterone, and dehydroisoandrosterone (67), to three 3-hydroxy-20-oxopregnane isomers (423), and to one pregnene analogue (423).

Estrone is sulfated with sulfamic acid at 100°C, using pyridine or dimethylaniline as solvents which also function as reaction catalysts (167, 168, 291).

In the steroids cited in this section, the hydroxyl group is alcoholic, except in equilin, equilenin, and estrone, where it is phenolic.

G. Oximes and Hydroxylamines

Ketoximes resemble alcohols in ease of sulfation. Acetoxime and acetophenone oxime sulfate quantitatively in a few minutes with SO_3-dioxane at room temperature (378). Benzoin oxime is similarly sulfated both on the alcoholic and on the oximino group. Quinone monoxime was sulfated with SO_3-pyridine using carbon tetrachloride solvent (66), and cyclohexanone oxime with $ClSO_3H$ in ether at 0°C (271). The sodium salt of the last compound was converted to the chlorosulfonate (96):

$$R_2C{:}NONa \xrightarrow{SO_2Cl_2} R_2C{:}NOSO_2Cl + NaCl \qquad (6\text{-}27)$$

1, 2-Cyclohexanone dioxime, with SO_3 in liquid SO_2, gave a 23% yield of 5-cyanovaleric acid (384), apparently by a Beckmann rearrangement followed by ring cleavage and dehydration.

In contrast to the ketoximes, a series of four aldoximes gave inconclusive results upon attempted sulfation with SO_3-dioxane (378). Dehydration to the corresponding nitrile may have occurred preferentially.

As shown in Chapter 7, Section II-L, hydroxylamines (RNHOH) undergo sulfamation rather than sulfation, although the N-acylated analogues do form sulfates.

IV. UNSATURATED AND HYDROXYLATED ACIDS, ESTERS, GLYCERIDES, AND AMIDES

Sulfation is the predominant reaction in the commercial preparation of the so-called "sulfonated" fatty oils, as from sperm, tallow, peanut, soybean, castor, olive, and various fish oils, as well as the derived esters, amides, and free acids. Such compounds have been manufactured on an entirely empirical basis since 1875, when sulfonated castor oil (Turkey red oil) was first introduced as a textile assistant. The chemistry of these empirical sulfations has been well reviewed (230, 334, 335).

With all of these oils except castor, sulfation of double bonds is the predominate reaction. In the case of castor oil (the triglyceride of 12-hydroxy-9,10-oleic acid, however, sulfation under the usual industrial conditions occurs almost exclusively at the hydroxyl group (230). Commercial process conditions, which have varied little over the years, involve gradual addition of cold 96% acid (often 20 - 40% of the weight of the oil) to the oil, with efficient agitation and cooling in a batch operation at room temperature or below. The acid is present in excess, since sulfation is an equilibrium reaction and, with the olefinic oils, stops when the acid strength reaches 85%. Reaction conditions used with some commonly sulfonated oils are summarized in Table 6-6. Reaction solvents are not commonly employed, but

TABLE 6-6

Reaction Conditions for the Preparation of
"Sulfonated" Fatty Oils

Oil	Lb. Sulfonating Agent per lb. Oil[a]	Time (hr.)	Temp. (°C)	Reference
Castor	0.25-0.30	3	30	20, 145, 230
Castor	0.21	9	25-30	145
Olive	0.38	3	20	70
Shark	0.20	3	25	145
Sperm	0.09	3	25	145
Neat's foot	0.10	>2	15-25	145
Cod	0.12	-	7-18	145
Cod	0.28	10	35	144
Oleic acid	0.23	1	52	144
Oleic acid	0.40 (98% acid)	1.5	20	118
Oleic esters	0.30-0.50 (98% acid)	3	25	119
Oleic N-ethylanilide	1.0 (100% acid)	10-15	0	145
Butyl ricinoleate	1.0	6.5	0	145

[a]96% H_2SO_4 used, except as indicated.

chlorinated hydrocarbons (230) and highly refined petroleum oils (118) have been used in isolated instances. The acid removal and neutralization step is a very critical one, since hydrolysis of the sulfate and glyceride linkages occurs easily. The conditions used in this operation determine most of the important characteristics of the sulfonated oils.

Treatment of unsaturated compounds of these types with SO_3 and its adducts is discussed in Chapter 2. Sulfonates, rather than sulfates, are thus formed. Sulfation of the hydroxyl group of castor oil with SO_3-pyridine (340) and with SO_3-N-methyl ethylene carbamate (345) occurs without attack of the double bond. Such reagents have not been used commercially.

Burton and Byrne have made the most significant recent studies of fatty oil sulfation, giving detailed consideration to castor oil (69), ricinoleic acid (68), neat's foot oil (71a), olive oil (70), and various fish oils (71), as reacted with sulfuric acid, acetyl sulfate, and $ClSO_3H$ at various temperatures and times of reaction.

V. ALKYL HYDROGEN SULFATES BY ETHER CLEAVAGE

The reaction of SO_3 with ethers to form dialkyl sulfates is discussed in Section VI, and with cyclic ethers to yield cyclic sulfates in Section VII. Ethers also undergo fission to alkyl hydrogen sulfates with sulfuric acid in the following overall sense:

$$ROR' + H_2SO_4 \longrightarrow ROSO_3H + R'^{\oplus} \qquad (6\text{-}28)$$

Jaques and Leisten (190), in a study of the reaction of 99. 6% acid with 13 alkyl and 4 alkyl aryl ethers, have assessed the relationship between structural factors and bond cleavage and deduced a reaction mechanism previously unsuspected. The alkyl ethers ionize in H_2SO_4 as strong or moderately strong bases, as shown by the van't Hoff i factor. The conjugate acid of the ether reacts with SO_3 in a mobile equilibrium to form a complex, which, in a rate-determining stage, collapses into a carbonium ion and an alkyl hydrogen sulfate:

$$\overset{..}{R}\overset{..}{O}R \underset{}{\overset{H^+}{\rightleftarrows}} R\overset{H^{\oplus}}{\overset{..}{O}}R \underset{}{\overset{SO_3}{\rightleftarrows}} R\overset{\overset{\displaystyle H^{\oplus}}{\underset{\underset{SO_3^{\ominus}}{\oplus}}{O}}}{} R \xrightarrow{\text{Slow}} ROSO_3^{\ominus} + H^{\oplus} + R^{\oplus} \quad (6\text{-}29)$$

(The fission of the alkyl aryl ethers, on the other hand, appears to follow a different but more conventional course, with cleavage of the conjugate acid occurring without the participation of SO_3.) The alkyl ethers undergo cleavage in such a manner as to produce the more stable carbonium ion. For ethers with the same R group, the rate of cleavage decreased in the following order of R' groups: 2-sulfatoethyl >2-chloroethyl>methyl>ethyl.

The ether cleavage reaction has been considered for the preparation of detergents. A mixture of a long-chain fatty acid, pentamethylene oxide and $ClSO_3H$ reacts as follows (293):

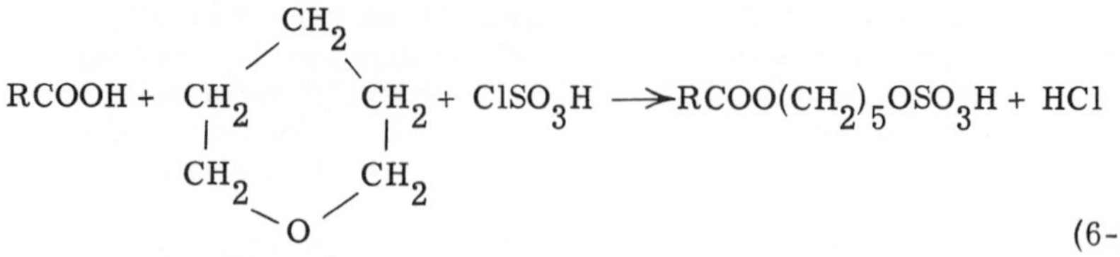

$$RCOOH + \begin{array}{c} CH_2 \\ CH_2 \quad CH_2 \\ | \quad\quad | \\ CH_2 \quad CH_2 \\ O \end{array} + ClSO_3H \longrightarrow RCOO(CH_2)_5OSO_3H + HCl$$

(6-30)

Long-chain derivatives of this ether also cleave to form surface-active sulfates (41, 63). A long-chain tetrahydrofurfuryl ether apparently cleaves as follows with sulfuric acid at 60 °C (65):

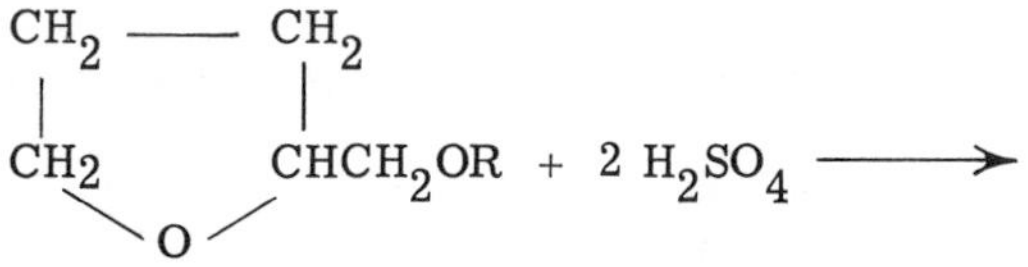

$$\begin{array}{c} CH_2 \text{——} CH_2 \\ | \quad\quad\quad | \\ CH2 \quad\quad CHCH_2OR \\ O \end{array} + 2\ H_2SO_4 \longrightarrow$$

$$HO_3SO(CH_2)_3CH(OSO_3H)CH_2OR + H_2O$$

(6-31)

Amides and esters containing the tetrahydrofuran moiety behave similarly (64, 247).

VI. DIALKYL SULFATES

Developments in the preparation of dialkyl sulfates have occurred along established lines since the subject was thoroughly reviewed by Suter through 1941 (369).

Dimethyl sulfate was once prepared industrially by vacuum distillation of the acid sulfate by reaction 6-16. Other dialkyl sulfates cannot be prepared in this way, since they are both less stable and higher-boiling.

The absorption of ethylene in 98% acid at 60 °C forms a mixture containing 45% monosulfate, 43% disulfate, and 12% sulfuric acid (355). The following reactions are involved:

$$CH_2{:}CH_2 + H_2SO_4 \rightleftharpoons C_2H_5OSO_3H \tag{6-32}$$

$$CH_2{:}CH_2 + C_2H_5OSO_3H \rightleftharpoons (C_2H_5O)_2SO_2 \tag{6-33}$$

$$2C_2H_5OSO_3H \rightleftharpoons (C_2H_5O)_2SO_2 + H_2SO_4 \tag{6-34}$$

Attempts to vacuum distill the dialkyl sulfate from such a mixture results in excessive decomposition. One expedient involves the application of more ethylene under pressure to convert all the acid to the desired sulfate (369). Other approaches involve chemical removal of the acid as bisulfate by adding sodium sulfate (355) or sodium chloride (156), or removal of the dialkyl sulfate in a stream of inert gas (124). If 96% acid is added to 1-dodecene at 0°C, the initial product is almost entirely di(2-dodecyl)sulfate, but this is converted to the monosulfate as more acid is added (85a). Isopropanol forms the dialkyl sulfate with 100% acid at 90°C (265), and n-butanol reacts likewise in 3 hr. under reflux for azeotropic removal of water (367).

Ethers, being Lewis bases, form complexes with SO_3 of varying degrees of stability; some of these rearrange to dialkyl sulfates (cf., reaction 6-29):

$$R_2O \xrightarrow{SO_3} R_2O^{\oplus} \cdot SO_3^{\ominus} \longrightarrow (RO)_2SO_2 \qquad (6\text{-}35)$$

Dimethyl sulfate is manufactured in excellent yield and purity on a continuous basis from the ether and liquid SO_3 (144), a procedure said to be inapplicable to diethyl and other ethers. Monochloro- (180, 194) and sym.-dichloromethyl (159, 180) ethers form the sulfates with SO_3; in the latter case, a maximum 31% yield was obtained under pressure at 180°C. Unsym.-difluoromethyl ether similarly (359) gives a 50% yield of sulfate, but the hexafluoro analogue did not react at 180°C (360), while the tri- and tetrafluoro ethers gave only decomposition products. Ethyl ether forms the sulfate if carefully treated in the cold with one mole of SO_3 (182); excess reagent causes sulfonation in the β position, as with ethanol. Bis-(2-chloroethyl) ether, as discussed in Chapter 1, forms an SO_3 complex, which rearranges smoothly to bis-(2-chloroethyl) sulfate in 91% yield (371). A low yield of the analogous bromo sulfate was obtained similarly, but attempts to extend the reaction to di-(n-propyl) and to bis-(3-chloropropyl) ethers were unsuccessful. Dioxane, a diether, forms two complexes, but these have not been converted to sulfates.

Of special interest, because of the controversy associated with tertiary alkyl sulfates (see Section III-A-1), is the preparation of di-(tert-butyl) sulfate from the alcohol with sulfuryl chloride at -30°C in isopentane (50). The sulfate, described as a dry, white solid softening at 0°C and decomposing slowly at room temperature, is a powerful tert-butylating agent.

VII. CYCLIC SULFATES

When previously reviewed through 1941 (369), there was only one procedure for preparing cyclic sulfates, namely by reacting a dibromide with silver sulfate. Other methods are now available.

One approach involves direct reaction of a cyclic ether with SO_3, the same general procedure as described above for the conversion of open-chain ethers to dialkyl sulfates. Ethylene oxide thus yields the cyclic sulfate with SO_3-dioxane (161) or with free SO_3 in the gas phase (206):

$$\begin{array}{c} CH_2 \\ | \quad\quad O \\ CH_2 \end{array} \xrightarrow{\quad SO_3 \quad} \begin{array}{c} CH_2-O \\ | \quad\quad\quad SO_2 \\ CH_2-O \end{array} \qquad (6\text{-}36)$$

Although the yield is poor, the simplicity of this method, taken with the easy accessibility of many epoxides, suggests broader future application.

Tetrahydrofuran reacts as follows using a mixture of $ClSO_3H$ and 60% oleum (232):

$$\begin{array}{c} CH_2-CH_2 \\ | \quad\quad | \\ CH_2 \quad CH_2 \\ \quad\; O \end{array} \xrightarrow{\quad SO_3 \quad} \begin{array}{c} \quad\; CH_2 \\ CH_2 \quad\quad CHCH_3 \\ | \quad\quad\quad\quad | \\ O \quad\quad\quad\; O \\ \quad\; SO_2 \end{array} \qquad (6\text{-}37)$$

It is not surprising that the yield in this reaction is low (9%), and that the unstable seven-membered ring, which would result from direct sulfation, is not formed.

A second approach to the cyclic sulfates involves permanganate oxidation of the corresponding sulfites, which are easily accessible. The sulfates of about a dozen glycols have been prepared by this approach (22, 135, 233).

$$\begin{array}{c} R_2C-O \\ | \quad\quad\quad SO \\ R_2C-O \end{array} \xrightarrow{\quad O \quad} \begin{array}{c} R_2C-O \\ | \quad\quad\quad SO_2 \\ R_2C-O \end{array} \qquad (6\text{-}38)$$

The use of nitrogen tetroxide or ozone for this type of oxidation would be of interest, since (as discussed in Chapter 4) they can react rapidly and cleanly, and are advantageously applied under anhydrous conditions.

Another technique has involved acidolysis of the cyclic sulfites:

$$\begin{array}{c} CH_2-O \\ | \quad\quad\quad SO \\ CH_2-O \end{array} + H_2SO_4 \longrightarrow \begin{array}{c} CH_2-O \\ | \quad\quad\quad SO_2 \\ CH_2-O \end{array} + H_2O + SO_2 \qquad (6\text{-}39)$$

This procedure has been employed to prepare ethylene and propylene sulfates (58); use of SO_3, or an SO_3 adduct, might be preferable as

avoiding the presence of water. Another approach involves ester interchange, which occurs at 130°C in 2 hr. (57):

$$
\begin{array}{c}
CH_2OCOCH_3 \\
| \\
CH_2OCOCH_3
\end{array}
+ (CH_3O)_2SO_2 \longrightarrow
\begin{array}{c}
CH_2-O \\
| \qquad\ \ SO_2\ + \\
CH_2-O
\end{array}
$$

$$2\ CH_3COOCH_3 \tag{6-40}$$

The success of both of these approaches apparently depends upon the
formation of a volatile product.

Carbohydrates with vicinal chlorosulfate groups form the cyclic
sulfates upon treatment with pyridine (192):

$$
\begin{array}{c}
| \\
HC-OSO_2Cl \\
| \\
HC-OSO_2Cl \\
|
\end{array}
\xrightarrow{\text{Pyridine}}
\begin{array}{c}
| \\
HC-O \\
| \qquad SO_2\ +\ SO_2Cl_2 \\
HC-O \\
|
\end{array}
\tag{6-41}
$$

This reaction is inoperative with diaxial configurations.

A somewhat similar type of reaction may also be involved in the
following sulfation (257, 258):

$$
\begin{array}{c}
Cl \\
| \\
F_3CC \quad HCrO_4^- \\
\| \\
F_3CC \\
| \\
Cl
\end{array}
\longrightarrow
\begin{array}{c}
Cl \quad O\ OH \\
| \quad |/ \\
F_3CC-O-Cr-O \\
| \ominus| \\
F_3CC \\
| \\
Cl
\end{array}
\xrightarrow{SO_3}
\begin{array}{c}
Cl \quad O\ OH \\
| \quad |/ \\
F_3CC-O-Cr-O \\
| \\
F_3CC-O-S\overset{\ominus}{\ }O \\
| \qquad | \\
Cl \qquad O
\end{array}
\longrightarrow
$$

$$\tag{6-42}$$

$$
\begin{array}{c}
Cl \\
| \\
F_3CC-O \\
| \qquad\ \ SO_2\ +\ HCrO_3^- \\
F_3CC-O \\
| \\
Cl
\end{array}
$$

This reaction, which proceeds in fair yield, may alternatively involve
the epoxide as intermediate, since their formation is considered probable in the oxidation of alkenes with CrO_3 (405). Conversion of the
epoxide to the cyclic sulfate would then proceed by reaction 6-36. Since
this alkene is known to form a sultone with SO_3 (Chapter 2, Section II-
B-3), another alternative would involve oxidation of the sultone to the
cyclic sulfate. The success of this sulfation suggests that the combined
oxidation-sulfation approach may be generally applicable for the direct
preparation of cyclic sulfates from alkenes. Use of SO_3 or an adduct

might be preferable to that of oleum, as might also the use of OsO_4 rather than CrO_3, since the former easily oxidizes alkenes to five-membered ring osmates under anhydrous conditions.

Ethylene and trimethylene sulfates have also been made as follows (1):

$$\underset{\substack{|\\CH_2-OH}}{\overset{\substack{CH_2-O\\|}}{}}\!\!\!\!\!SO_2OH \quad \xrightarrow{SOCl_2} \quad \left[\underset{\substack{|\\CH_2-OH}}{\overset{\substack{CH_2-O\\|}}{}}\!\!\!\!\!SO_2Cl\right] \longrightarrow$$

$$\underset{\substack{|\\CH_2-O}}{\overset{\substack{CH_2-O\\|}}{}}\!\!\!\!\!SO_2 + HCl \qquad (6\text{-}43)$$

The intermediate shown is hypothetical.

Aldehydes without hydrogen atoms on the carbon adjacent to the carbonyl group can form cyclic sulfates through that group. Formaldehyde gives "methylene sulfate" with oleum (369), a reaction conducted more efficiently with SO_3 in 1, 2-dichloroethane solvent at 10-35°C (344):

$$2CH_2O + 2SO_3 \longrightarrow CH_2\underset{\substack{O-SO_2-O}}{\overset{\substack{O-SO_2-O}}{}}CH_2 \qquad (6\text{-}44)$$

Chloral also combines with SO_3 forming a complex unidentified product containing ten carbon and three sulfur atoms (152), presumably also formed by reaction with the carbonyl group.

o-Benzoquinone, and seven of its analogues, form cyclic sulfates as follows (323):

$$+ SO_2 \xrightarrow{\text{Light}} \qquad (6\text{-}45)$$

Paraquinones did not react similarly, which is not unexpected since they have a lower energy content than the ortho analogues, and a diffi-cultly-formed, seven-membered ring would result. α-Diketones, which lack the driving force of aromatic resonance energy, were like-wise unreactive. An intermediate oxygen diradical is proposed. In one case, a similar cyclic sulfate was formed from the dihydroxy compound with oleum, but none resulted from the action of SO_2Cl_2 on its dipotassium salt.

VIII. FLUORO- AND CHLOROSULFONATE ESTERS

A. The Action of Sulfonating Agents on Halogenated Alkanes and Cycloalkanes

Many halogenated alkanes are miscible in all proportions with SO_3, $ClSO_3H$, or FSO_3H, but not with H_2SO_4. Although they can react, as noted in Table 6-7, some of them can be employed quite satisfactorily as reaction solvents if care is taken to maintain a sufficiently low reaction temperature, and if the solvent reacts less easily with the reagent than the compound being sulfonated. The presence of fluorine increases stability; fluorotrichloromethane is, therefore, a useful solvent for SO_3, especially since it boils at 24°C. 1, 2-Dichloroethane is used extensively as a solvent for SO_3 sulfonations. At room temperature, it reacts only to the extent of 3% in 4 days to form the products shown in Table 6-7. High-boiling impurities in technical 1, 2-dichloroethane react with SO_3, whereas the distilled material does not (297). Methylene chloride also is used as solvent in SO_3 sulfonations.

From all the examples listed in Table 6-7, it is noted that halogenated alkanes react by replacement by one or more halogen atoms by oxygen. Monohalogenated alkanes thus form sulfates or halosulfonates. This reaction seems logical when it is considered that the SO_3 and the alkyl halide are polarized as follows:

$$RCl \rightleftharpoons \overset{\delta+}{R}\ldots\overset{\delta-}{Cl} \xrightarrow{\overset{\delta+\ \ \delta-}{SO_3}} ROSO_2Cl \qquad (6\text{-}45\text{-}a)$$

Gem. di- and trihalogenated alkanes likewise yield acid chlorides or similar products, except for the difluoroiodo compounds, which behave like the dihydro analogues, and 1, 1-dichloroethane, which is stated to form the chlorosulfonate. In several compounds containing CCl_2 groups (hexachlorocyclopentadiene, hexachlorodifluorocyclopentene (78), octachloroindene (114), and decachloroindane (114)), these are converted by SO_3 to keto groups; dimerization also occurs in the first case. The CCl_2 group in the first compound yields a $C(Cl)OSO_2Cl$ moiety with $ClSO_3H$, and $C(Cl)OSO_2F$ with FSO_3H. The reaction of carbon tetrachloride with SO_3 has been used for the practical preparation of both of the products indicated in Table 6-7. Phosgene evolution occurs upon gently warming a mixture of the two; distillation of the residue gives pyrosulfuryl chloride. Ethyl chloride resembles ethanol in undergoing secondary sulfonation in the β position.

TABLE 6-7. The Action of Sulfonating Agents on Halogenated Alkanes and Cycloalkanes

Compound	Reagent	Products	Reference
CH_3Cl	SO_3	$CH_3OSO_2OSO_2Cl$	391
$CHCl_3$	SO_3	CO, $ClSO_3H$, $S_2O_5Cl_2$	11
$CHBr_3$	SO_3	CO, other products	11
CCl_4	SO_3	$COCl_2$, $S_2O_5Cl_2$	11, 215, 269, 290, 332
C_2H_5Cl	SO_3	$C_2H_5OSO_2Cl$,	259, 270, 295
		$HO_3SCH_2CH_2OSO_2Cl$	
$R_fCH_2CH_2I$	Oleum	$R_fCH_2CH_2OSO_3H$	110a
C_2H_5I	SO_3	$C_2H_5OSO_3H$, HI, I_2	418
$ClCH_2CH_2Cl$	SO_3	$ClCH_2CH_2OSO_2Cl$,	
		$ClCH_2CH_2OSO_2OH$	43
$BrCH_2CH_2Br$	SO_3	$BrCH_2CH_2OSO_3H$	30, 418
CH_3CHCl_2	SO_3	$CH_3CHClOSO_2Cl$	199
Cl_3CCCl_3	SO_3	Cl_3CCOCl, $S_2O_5Cl_2$	12, 292
$HOCH_2CH_2Cl$	H_2SO_4	$HOCH_2CH_2OSO_3H$	274
$F_3C(CF_2CF_2)_XI$	$ClSO_3H$	$F_3C(CF_2CF_2)OSO_2Cl$	170
$F_3C(CF_2CF_2)_XI$	FSO_3H	$F_3C(CF_2CF_2)OSO_2F$	171
C_5Cl_6	SO_3	$C_{10}Cl_{10}O$	143
C_5Cl_6	$ClSO_3H$	$C_{10}Cl_{11}OSO_2Cl$	179
C_5Cl_6	FSO_3H	$C_{10}Cl_{11}OSO_2F$	5
$C_6H_6Cl_6$	SO_3	$C_6H_2Cl_3SO_3H$, $ClSO_3H$ (low temperature)	5, 16
$C_6H_6Cl_6$	SO_3	C_6Cl_6, SO_2, H_2SO_4 (high temperature)	26
$C_6H_6Br_6$	SO_3	C_6Br_6	26

Hexachlorocyclohexane ("benzene hexachloride") reacts with SO_3 at room temperature (5, 16):

$$C_6H_6Cl_6 + 4SO_3 \longrightarrow C_6H_2Cl_3SO_3H + 3ClSO_3H \qquad (6\text{-}46)$$

Apparently, dehydrochlorination occurs to a mixture of trichlorobenzenes, which then undergoes sulfonation; the hydrogen chloride forms $ClSO_3H$. At 220°C, however, an 81% yield of hexachlorobenzene is formed in 5 hr. (26). The authors propose the initial formation of a complex between 1 mole of halide and 3 moles of SO_3, which then decomposes directly to hexachlorobenzene by the abstraction of six protons. A more likely sequence may involve the preceding reaction of 6-46, then reaction 6-47, a known type:

$$C_6H_2Cl_3SO_3H + 3\ ClSO_3H + 2\ SO_3 \longrightarrow C_6Cl_6 + 3\ SO_2 +$$

$$3\ H_2SO_4 \qquad (6\text{-}47)$$

Hexabromobenzene reacts similarly, but in only 33% yield.

B. Halosulfonate Esters from Alkenes

The sulfation of alkenes with chloro- or fluorosulfonic acids to form the corresponding halosulfonates is discussed in this section. These compounds are sometimes called chloro- and fluorosulfuric acids, and halosulfates, respectively.

Chlorosulfonic acid, either without a solvent or with carbon tetrachloride or chloroform, forms the chlorosulfonate esters from ethylene (389), propylene, the three butylene isomers and "isononylene" (185), apparently as follows:

$$CH_3CH{:}CH_2 + ClSO_3H \longrightarrow CH_3CH(OSO_2Cl)CH_3 \qquad (6\text{-}48)$$

(As noted in Chapter 2, a substituted 2-chloroethanesulfonic acid results when this reaction is run with diethyl ether as solvent.)

Fluorosulfonic acid behaves similarly, forming fluorosulfonates from ethylene (386), 1,1-difluoro-, 1,1-difluoro-2-chloro- (76), and 1,1,2-trifluoroethylenes (97), and from compounds of structure RCF: CF_2, where R is fluorinated alkyl (115, 142). In all of these cases the oxygen atom is always attached to the F_2C group, as has also been noted when SO_3 reacts with such alkenes forming sultones (See Chapter 2).

$$RCF{:}CF_2 + FSO_3H \longrightarrow RCFHCF_2OSO_2F \qquad (6\text{-}49)$$

Perfluorocyclopentene and tetrafluoroethylene add peroxydisulfuryl difluoride (339):

$$F_2C{:}CF_2 + (FSO_2O\text{-})_2 \longrightarrow FSO_2OCF_2CF_2OSO_2F \qquad (6\text{-}50)$$

C. Halosulfonate Esters from Hydroxy Compounds

The preparation of chlorosulfonates from alcohols and SO_2Cl_2 is well known (369):

$$ROH + ClSO_2Cl \longrightarrow ROSO_2Cl + HCl \qquad (6\text{-}51)$$

This standard procedure was used with alcohols of structure $Cl(CH_2)_nOH$ (354). A prolonged reaction time with n-propanol gave anomalous secondary reaction in the 2-position, forming a cyclic sulfate-sulfonate, as shown in Chapter 3, Section II-A-1. With comparatively unreactive alcohols, such as $HCF_2CF_2CH_2OH$, the sodium salt is used rather than the alcohol itself (87, 88); the corresponding dialkyl sulfates can also be made with appropriate molar ratios.

Two phenolic fluorosulfonates (4-chlorophenyl- and 4-methoxyphenyl-) were prepared in good yield from $ClSO_2F$ and pyridine (92). This approach renders this type of compound easily accessible, since $ClSO_2F$ and FSO_2F are commercially available (4). Previously known methods are laborious.

D. Halosulfonate Esters from Chlorosilanes

Chlorosilanes form chlorosulfonate esters in a manner somewhat analogous to the chlorinated aliphatic hydrocarbons (328), except that the silanes yield diesters, whereas the chlorinated hydrocarbons form ketones:

$$(CH_3)_2SiCl_2 \xrightarrow[\;ClSO_3H\;]{SO_3 \text{ or}} (CH_3)_2Si(Cl)OSO_2Cl \xrightarrow[\;ClSO_3H\;]{SO_3 \text{ or}}$$

$$(CH_3)_2Si(OSO_2Cl)_2 \qquad (6\text{-}52)$$

Trimethylchlorosilane behaves likewise. Methyltrichlorosilane, however, yields only the monoester, apparently for steric reasons. In 2-phenylethyltrichlorosilane, the aromatic ring is also sulfonated (17).

An analogous methoxysilane (326) and silicone (327) behave similarly:

$$(CH_3)_3SiOCH_3 \xrightarrow[-78\,°C]{SO_3} (CH_3)_3SiOSO_2OCH_3 \qquad (6\text{-}53)$$

$$\left[-(CH_3)_2SiO-\right]_X \xrightarrow[\substack{-SO_3}]{\substack{+SO_3 \\ Low\ temp. \\ 150°C}} \left[-(CH_3)_2SiOSO_2O-\right]_X \qquad (6\text{-}54)$$

In all these cases, cleavage of the Si—Cl$_2$ or Si—O bond occurs with insertion of SO$_3$ and with no attack on the Si—aliphatic carbon bonds. A similar effect was noted with $(CH_3)_3SiN(C_2H_5)_2$ (cleavage of Si—N, see Chapter 7), and with $(CH_3)_3SiC_6H_5$ (cleavage of Si—aromatic carbon bond, see Chapter 2).

E. Miscellaneous Approaches to Halosulfonate Esters

Chlorination of sulfite esters is a known, but seldom-used (369) approach to chlorosulfonate esters. Ethylene sulfite, easily prepared from ethylene oxide and SO$_2$, has been thus chlorinated (398):

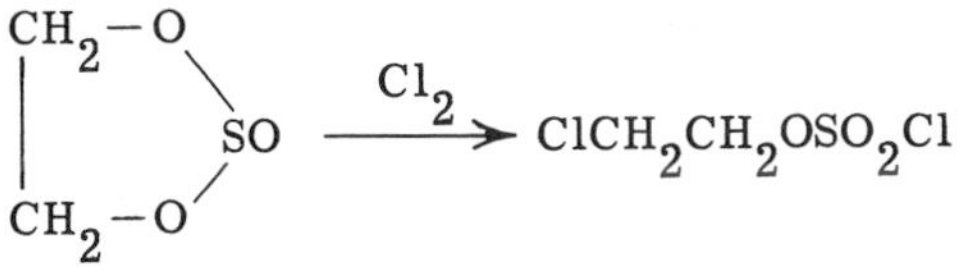

$$\begin{array}{c} CH_2-O \\ | \qquad \quad \diagdown \\ | \qquad \quad \quad SO \xrightarrow{\ Cl_2\ } ClCH_2CH_2OSO_2Cl \qquad (6\text{-}55) \\ | \qquad \quad \diagup \\ CH_2-O \end{array}$$

Bis-(2-octyl) sulfite has been similarly converted to the chlorosulfonate (95).

Chlorosulfonate esters have been made in the past from SO$_2$ and alkyl hypochlorites (369), but extension of this approach to a hypofluorite is relatively recent (394):

$$F_3COF + SO_2 \longrightarrow F_3COSO_2F \qquad (6\text{-}56)$$

The reaction was conducted in the gas phase at 170-85°C, and other products were also formed, including the dialkyl sulfate.

A similar fluorosulfonate was noted from the following reaction (360):

$$(F_2CH)_2O + SO_3 \longrightarrow F_2CHOSO_2F \qquad (6\text{-}57)$$

None of the expected dialkyl sulfate was formed.

Electrolysis of dimethylsulfate in anhydrous HF yields fluorinated methyl fluorosulfonates and fluorinated derivatives of dimethylsulfate (358).

IX. THE SULFATION OF PHENOLS

Since phenolic compounds in general undergo ring sulfonation with extreme ease, their sulfation must usually be effected with inert reagents such as the SO_3-amines or sulfamic acid.

Properly constituted phenols can, in isolated cases, be sulfated with strong reagents. Chlorosulfonic acid usually forms the sulfonic acids, although at low temperature a small yield of aryl hydrogen sulfate is formed (59). 4-Hydroxyazobenzene, on the other hand, gives a good yield of chlorosulfonate, $ROSO_2Cl$ (284). Iodinated phenols can be sulfated with concentrated acid below $0°C$, even though a ring position ortho to the hydroxyl group is still open for ring sulfonation (256). Pentachlorophenol forms the sulfate with SO_3 (200); in this case no ring positions are available for sulfonation.

A. Sulfur Trioxide-Amine Complexes

The favored reagents for phenol sulfation are SO_3-amine complexes used at moderate temperatures, often below room temperature and never above $100°C$; at higher temperatures sulfonation occurs, as in the case of phenol with SO_3-pyridine at $170°C$ (24). Amine complexes have almost invariably been used, except for one reference to the sulfation of phenol with SO_3-dioxane (372). The reaction can be conducted either in anhydrous (Table 6-8), or in aqueous alkaline (Table 6-9) medium. Potassium pyrosulfate was employed in early studies of phenol sulfation (369); it gave 25-30% yields. However, in the presence of dimethylaniline, the yield rose to 85%, possibly because of intermediate formation of the SO_3-amine complex. A reagent recently found useful for low temperature anhydrous sulfation of complex, sensitive phenols is $ClSO_3H$-dimethylformamide (75). As noted in Section III-F, phenolic steroids are sulfated with SO_3-pyridine, but always under anhydrous conditions.

A study of the sulfation of phenol, the three cresols, the three nitrophenols, the three hydroxybenzoic acids, and 2- and 4-chlorophenols with SO_3-trimethylamine in aqueous sodium carbonate at 50 and $100°C$ (281) showed yields to decrease as alkalinity, dilution, or temperature increased. Yields varied from less than 1 to 84%. When sulfating under anhydrous conditions, the older standard technique involved adding $ClSO_3H$ to pyridine in chloroform, then adding the phenol in pyridine, and finally refluxing briefly; carbon disulfide or carbon tetrachloride were also used as solvents. A more satisfactory method (131) comprises dissolving the phenol in pyridine, cooling to $0°C$, adding the $ClSO_3H$, and at once adding aqueous potassium hydroxide to form the potassium salt. This method is more rapid, and gives better yields of lighter-colored products. The same procedure can be employed with dimethylaniline, but pyridine works better with phenol, the cresols, and polyalkylated phenols.

Ortho isomers sulfate with difficulty compared to the other two. With the cresols and chlorophenols, 40 - 70% yields of ortho sulfates can be obtained, however (281). With the nitrophenols, on the other hand, the maximum reported yield of ortho sulfate is 34% (281), compared to 94% for the para isomer (61). Salicylic acid gave less than 1%

TABLE 6-8

Sulfation of Phenols in Anhydrous Medium with
SO$_3$-Amine Adducts

Complex amine	Phenol	Solvent	Temp. (°C)	Reference
Pyridine	Phenol	None	50	24
Pyridine	Phenol, thymol, eugenol	CS$_2$	45	397
Pyridine	2- and 4-Nitro-phenols	Benzene	80	61
Pyridine	Phenolphthalein	CCl$_4$	77	320
Pyridine	Alkoxyhydroxy-phenylethylamines	CHCl$_3$	25	171a
Pyridine	Phenol, cresols	Pyridine	0	131
Pyridine	4-Hydroxybenzoic acid	Pyridine	0	101
Pyridine	Dodecylphenol	Pyridine	25	306
Pyridine	Dibromosalicyl	Pyridine	45	222
Pyridine	Hydroquinone	Pyridine	65	51
Pyridine	N-Acetyl- and N-lauroyl 1-tyrosines	Pyridine	100	304
Quinoline	Phenol	Quinoline	0	131
Dimethylaniline	Phenol, three cre-sols, eugenol, iso-eugenol	CS$_2$	45-100	61
Dimethylaniline	Five xylenols	CS$_2$	45-100	86
Dimethylaniline	Seventeen phenols, substituted with carbonyl, alkyl, and aryl groups	CS$_2$	45-100	60
Dimethylaniline	2-, 3-, and 4-Aminophenols	CS$_2$	25	45
Dimethylaniline	Methyl salicylate	Dimethyl-aniline	25	279
Dimethylaniline	Phenol	SO$_2$	-10-25	61

TABLE 6-9

Sulfation of Phenols in Aqueous Medium with
SO_3-Amine Adducts

Complexing amine	Phenol	Reference
Trimethylamine	Phenol	281
Trimethylamine	2-, 3-, and 4-Cresols	281
Trimethylamine	2-, 3-, and 4-Hydroxybenzoic Acids	281
Trimethylamine	2-, and 4-Chlorophenols	281
Trimethylamine	2-, 3-, and 4-Nitrophenols	281
Trimethylamine	2-Methyl-5-nitrophenol	280
Trimethylamine	Guaiacol	227
Triethylamine	2-, and 4-Phenylphenols	165
N-Ethylmorpholine	Phenol	227
N-Ethylmorpholine	Hydroquinone	321
Pyridine	Phenol	24

sulfate, while the other two isomers formed 43 - 69% (281). 4-Phenyl-
phenol sulfates much faster than the 2-isomer, a difference which can
be exploited for isomer separation (165). This difference in isomer
reactivity may be explained by steric effects, or by the difference in
the degree of dissociation of the phenolic hydrogen (7, 165). In the case
of salicylic acid, interaction of the hydroxyl and carboxyl groups may
be responsible (281), since methyl salicylate is sulfated in good yield
with SO_3-dimethylaniline (279).

The naphthols can be sulfated, similarly to the phenols, in either
anhydrous or aqueous medium. 2-Naphthol reacted with SO_3-pyridine
in carbon disulfide (397), and both naphthols have been sulfated at
100°C for 4 - 8 hr. with SO_3-dimethyl- or diethylanilines (61). 2-
Nitro-1-naphthol reacted with SO_3-dimethylaniline in carbon disulfide
(46), and 6-nitro-2-naphthol with SO_3-pyridine at 25°C in excess pyridine (42). A study (131) has shown that the two naphthols are preferably sulfated with SO_3-dimethylaniline rather than with SO_3-pyridine;

the reverse is true of phenol and the cresols. The preferred procedure involves cooling the naphthol, dissolved in dimethylaniline, to
0°C, adding $ClSO_3H$, and then immediately converting to the potassium
salt with aqueous KOH.

2-Naphthol is quantitatively sulfated by SO_3-trimethylamine in
aqueous alkaline solution at room temperature (227). 1-Bromo-2-
naphthol reacted similarly with SO_3-N-ethylmorpholine.

5-Benzamido- and 8-benzamido-1-naphthols have been sulfated with
SO_3-triethylamine in both anhydrous and aqueous medium (165). In the
former case, using excess pyridine as solvent at room temperature for
24 hr., only the 5-isomer sulfated, since it is less sterically hindered.
However, in aqueous medium only the 8- isomer reacted, since the 5-
isomer is much less soluble and is therefore less available for reaction.

Aminophenols and aminonaphthols can be either sulfated or sulfamated by the same reagents under the same general conditions. These
reactions are discussed in Chapter 7.

The preparation of aryl fluorosulfonate esters, $ROSO_2F$, is cited
in Section VIII-C, and of aryl cyclic sulfates in Section VII.

B. Sulfamic Acid

Phenol forms the ammonium sulfate with sulfamic acid at 100°C
(177); higher temperatures lead to ring sulfonation:

$$ROH + NH_2SO_3H \longrightarrow ROSO_3NH_4 \qquad (6\text{-}58)$$

Sulfamic acid has been employed relatively little for sulfating phenols
since the method was first developed in 1912.

The use of pyridine as catalyst and reaction solvent allowed reduction of the time of reaction from 24 hr., as first used, to about 1 hr.
at 80-100°C. This procedure was applied to phenol, thymol, 2- and 4-
hydroxybenzoic acids and to the monosulfation of resorcinol, hydroquinone and resacetophenone (420); catechol formed a mixture of the mono-
and disulfates. Several hydroxyflavonoids (quercetin, fisetin, isor-
hamnetic acid, etc.) (421) and the phenolic steroid estrone (167, 168,
291) were sulfated similarly. Sulfamic acid-pyridine appears to offer
no special advantages over SO_3-pyridine.

C. Persulfates (The Elbs Reaction)

Aromatic and heterocyclic phenols and amines in aqueous alkaline
solution are directly converted to sulfates by the action of ammonium
or potassium persulfate by nucleophilic displacement on peroxide oxygen:

$$C_6H_5OH + K_2S_2O_8 \longrightarrow HOC_6H_4OSO_3K + KHSO_4 \qquad (6\text{-}59)$$

This procedure, known as the Elbs reaction, has found extensive application, not only for synthesis, but as an aid to the structure determination of complex phenolic compounds. Yields are usually poor, i. e., in the range 15 - 50%, but separation and purification of the desired sulfate are ordinarily not difficult. Two good reviews cover the Elbs sulfation (239, 337) through 1960.

Phenols are sulfated in a free para position, but if this position is blocked, substitution occurs ortho to the hydroxyl group, as with 4-nitro- or 4-chlorophenols (105, 330, 347). No case of meta substitution has ever been noted. An effort to improve the poor yields ordinarily associated with the Elbs reaction, involving the use of three moles of persulfate instead of the usual one, showed (15) that no change resulted for para sulfation, but that considerable enhancement was noted where sulfation occurred ortho to the hydroxyl group, as with 4-methyl-, 4-chloro-, and 4-nitrophenols. Disulfation can occur, and in the case of salicylic acid, the disulfate is the major product if excess persulfate is used (330); hydrolysis yields 2, 3, 5-trihydroxybenzoic acid. In other cases, inability to stop the oxidation at the mono stage is no doubt a major reason for low yields. The phenolic sulfates are usually hydrolyzed to the corresponding dihydric phenols, which has constituted a major synthetic use for this reaction. The monoethers of the dihydric phenols result when alkylation precedes hydrolysis. The scope of this reaction has been extended to include 2- and 3-hydroxy-pyridines (28), and 4-hydroxy-pyrimidine (183).

Primary (46, 47, 341), secondary (48), and tertiary (46, 341) aromatic amines react under similar conditions and with comparable yields to form the orthoaminophenylsulfates, therein differing from the phenols. Para sulfation occurs if the ortho positions are blocked. The reaction has been successfully applied to a variety of amines, including aniline, dimethylaniline, 1- and 2-naphthylamines (46), aminostilbenes, aminoazobenzenes, xylidines, sulfanilamide (341), diphenylamine, an aminobiphenyl (48), and anthranilic acid (49). The last compound forms a mixture of the ortho and para sulfates. 2-, and 4-Aminopyridines, and indoles (48, 49) similarly undergo sulfation.

Baker and Brown, who studied the Elbs sulfation at some length (21), proposed a reaction mechanism based on attack of a resonance hybrid of the phenoxide ion by the sulfate-ion radical, $\cdot OSO_3^{\ominus}$. A subsequent kinetic and mechanistic study by Behrman and Walker (29) indicated, however, that phenolate ion attacks the peroxy bond of the persulfate ion $(-OSO_3)_2^{2-}$ with displacement of a sulfate ion. Cleavage of the persulfate molecule by either heterolysis or homolysis, prior to attack of the phenolate ion, was ruled out as inconsistent with their results. The reaction was found to be first order with respect to both persulfate and phenolate ions. Kinetic data with forty monosubstituted phenols suggested rate-limiting electrophilic attack at carbon, but Hammett $\sigma - \rho$ plots gave a more satisfactory correlation with attack at oxygen (27), although applicability of the Hammett correlation to this reaction is questioned.

Efforts to extend the Elbs sulfation technique to acetanilide, 2-acetamidonaphthalene, various aromatic hydrocarbons, nitrobenzene, and benzoic acid (47) were unsuccessful.

D. The Preparation of Leuco Vat Dyes and Related Sulfates

Sulfation of the leuco (or hydroxy) forms of vat dyes, especially those derived from anthraquinone, has been used increasingly in industry since 1924 to achieve water solubility with consequent easy application to textile fibers. Oxidation of the organic sodium sulfate in acid solution reconverts it on the fiber to the original insoluble keto form of the dye, thereby fixing it firmly. Combined reduction and sulfation of the dye is effected by heating with a metal (copper, iron, or zinc) and SO_3-pyridine (or other amine complexes) by the reactions

$$2 \begin{pmatrix} O \\ \| \\ C \\ / \ \backslash \end{pmatrix} + Cu + 2\,(SO_3 \cdot Py) \longrightarrow \begin{pmatrix} OSO_3 \\ | \\ C \\ / \ \diagdown \end{pmatrix}_2 Cu(Py)_2 \xrightarrow{2NaOH}$$

$$2 \begin{pmatrix} OSO_3Na \\ | \\ C \\ / \ \diagdown \end{pmatrix} + CuO + 2Py + H_2O \qquad (6\text{-}60)$$

This direct and widely applicable procedure is used to produce over 50 individual dyes (396). The general method involves adding $ClSO_3H$ to excess pyridine at 20 °C, and then simultaneously adding the dye and the metal with agitation in the range 40 - 80 °C over several hours. Aqueous sodium hydroxide is added next and the mixture is steamed to recover pyridine; the yields of leuco sulfate are 80-90% (396). Pyridine has been the most commonly used base, but picolines are more suitable for certain dyes. Also, the metal and its degree of subdivision, as well as the temperature and time of heating, vary from case to case. A similar procedure, employing iron powder at 70 °C for 3 hr., was used in the laboratory for preparing the disulfates of anthraquinol, 6, 12-dihydroxyanthracene, and 3, 8-dihydroxy-1, 2, 6, 7-dibenzpyrene (51). With 2-aminoanthraquinone and 2, 6-diaminoanthraquinone, use of equivalent SO_3-pyridine at 40 °C yields the disulfate sulfamate (298).

9-Hydroxyanthracene (anthranol) derivatives (1- and 2-acetamino-, and 3-chloro-) are sulfated in 1 hr. with SO_3-pyridine at 85 °C in excess pyridine (126); the same reagent was used with 3-acetoxyanthranol (125). Anthranol sulfates are also made under the same conditions from anthrone, 4-chloroanthrone, and sodium 2-anthronesulfonate (126); 10-acetoxyanthrone reacted likewise in an anhydrous melt with SO_3-triethylamine for 3 min. at 115 °C (321):

$$\text{Anthrone} \xrightarrow{\text{SO}_3\text{-Amine}} \tag{6-61}$$

In the anhydrous vat dye reduction-sulfation procedure cited before, SO_3-pyridine has usually given better results than the complexes of cheaper bases (396). However, the discovery that the dyes could be reduced and sulfated in aqueous medium permitted use of the adducts from trimethyl- and triethylamines, and from N-ethylmorpholine (226, 228, 321). Reduction can be effected with sodium hydrosulfite, and sulfation can be done at 30 - 50°C in 1 - 4 hr., with pH control varying critically from one dye to another. When a free amino group is present, as in 2-aminoanthraquinone, the reduced compound is sulfamated as well as sulfated (226). Reduction and sulfation can be done simultaneously (163, 164). Aqueous sulfation at room temperature with SO_3-triethylamine has also been employed with 2-hydroxyanthraquinone (227), and with anthranol (321).

X. ALIPHATIC AND AROMATIC THIOSULFATES

The preparation, properties, and uses of these compounds, also known as Bunte salts, or the salts of S-alkyl and S-aryl esters of thiosulfuric acid, have been well reviewed (260). The usual approach to the aliphatic compounds has involved reaction of alkyl halides, usually chlorides, with sodium thiosulfate:

$$\text{RCl} + \text{NaSSO}_3\text{Na} \longrightarrow \text{RSSO}_3\text{Na} + \text{NaCl} \tag{6-62}$$

As mentioned in Chapter 4, aliphatic Bunte salts made by this general procedure are useful intermediates for preparing the corresponding sulfonyl chlorides.

The procedures ordinarily employed for making O-sulfates have been almost entirely neglected in preparing the S analogues, partly because, in the aliphatic series at least, the approach cited above via the halides is so simple and direct. n-Butanethiol and thiophenol form the thiosulfates at -78°C with SO_3-diethyl ether in difluorodichloromethane as solvent (329):

$$\text{RSH} + \text{SO}_3 \longrightarrow \text{RSSO}_3\text{H} \tag{6-63}$$

Di-(2-ethylhexyl) dithiophosphoric acid reacts similarly with chlorosulfonic acid in liquid SO_2 at -17°C (55):

$$(\text{RO})_2\text{PSSH} + \text{ClSO}_3\text{H} \longrightarrow (\text{RO})_2\text{PSSSO}_3\text{H} + \text{HCl} \tag{6-64}$$

At a higher temperature thiophenol is oxidized (325):

$$2C_6H_5SH + SO_3 \longrightarrow (C_6H_5S-)_2 + SO_2 + H_2O \qquad (6-65)$$

Sulfur trioxide-pyridine gives a quantitative yield of thiosulfate at 100°C (25):

$$C_6H_5SH + SO_3 \cdot py \longrightarrow C_6H_5SSO_3H \cdot py \qquad (6-66)$$

XI. SULFATION WITH SULFUR DIOXIDE

Although sulfur dioxide and its compounds are often employed for sulfonation, as indicated in Chapter 3, they are only rarely used for sulfation.

Long-chain hydroperoxides form sulfates with SO_2 (272):

$$ROOH + SO_2 \longrightarrow ROSO_2OH \qquad (6-67)$$

As noted in Chapter 3 (Section II-A-3), hydroperoxides can form either sulfonates or sulfates with sodium sulfite, depending upon the proportions of reagents used.

Sulfoxidation, studied extensively for preparing sulfonates as noted in Chapter 3, (Section II-A-2), has also been employed for sulfating alcohols (91):

$$ROH + SO_2 + O_2 \xrightarrow{\text{Light}} ROSO_2OH \qquad (6-68)$$

Methyl, n-butyl, and n-octyl alcohols were sulfated in this manner.

The formation of cyclic aryl sulfates by photochemical reaction of SO_2 with orthoquinones is discussed in Section VII.

XII. MISCELLANEOUS SULFATION PROCEDURES

Sulfation with organic sulfating agents ("sulfatoalkylation") is discussed in Chapter V.

A series of patents (356) describes the sulfation of long-chain ethanolamides by SO_3 interchange with naphthalenesulfonic acids:

$$ROH + C_{10}H_7SO_3H \longrightarrow ROSO_3H + C_{10}H_8 \qquad (6-69)$$

This reaction seems theoretically possible at elevated temperatures (e.g., at 160°C), but hardly at that claimed (40°C).

Sulfation by the oxidation of organic sulfur compounds, often used for sulfonation as discussed in Chapter 4, has seldom been employed for sulfation. This approach has proved useful for preparing cyclic sulfates, as indicated in Section VII.

REFERENCES

1. Agfa Wolfen Filmfabrik, Belgian Patent 558,201.
2. Aktiebolaget Pharmacia, Swedish Patent 165,090; Chem. Abstr.,
    54, 5494 (1960).
3. Alburn, H. E., and J. Seifter, U.S. Patent 2,729,633; Chem. Abstr.,
    50, 8144 (1956).
4. Allied Chemical Corporation, Baker & Adamson Dept., Morris-
    town, New Jersey.
5. Allied Chemical Corporation, General Chemical Division, unpub-
    lished research data.
6. Alpine Chemische A.G., Austrian Patent 198,429; Chem. Abstr.,
    52, 16238 (1958).
7. American Cyanamid Company, "Trialkylamine-Sulfur Trioxide
    Compounds", New York, 1955.
8. Apotheker, D., J. L. Owades, and A. E. Sobel, J. Am. Chem. Soc.,
    76, 3684 (1954).
9. Araki, T., Japanese Patent 176,243; Chem. Abstr., 45, 5406
    (1951).
10. Aries, R. S., in Kirk-Othmer, Encyclopedia of Chemical Technology,
    Vol. I, 1st ed., Interscience, New York, 1947, p. 280.
11. Armstrong, H. E., Ber., 2, 712 (1869).
12. Armstrong, H. E., Proc. Roy. Soc. (London), 18, 502 (1870).
13. Asinger, F., Chemie und Technologie der Monoolefine, Akademie
    Verlag, Berlin, 1957.
14. Atlas Powder Co., British Patent 766,706; Chem. Abstr., 51,
    10933 (1957).
15. Babu Rao, K., and N. V. Subba Rao, J. Sci. Ind. Res. (India), 14B,
    130 (1955); Chem. Abstr., 49, 10877 (1955).
16. Badische Anilin- & Soda-Fabrik A.G., German Patent Application
    B33945 (June 21, 1956).
17. Bailey, D. L., U.S. Patent 2,968,643; Chem. Abstr., 55, 10387
    (1961).
18. Baird, W., U.S. Dept. Commerce, OTS Rept., PB28,754, 1946.
19. Baird, W., U.S. Dept. Commerce, OTS Rept., PB79,578, BIOS
    Final Rept. 1151 (1946).
20. Baker Castor Oil Co., Sulfonated Castor Oil, Bayonne, New
    Jersey, 1959.
21. Baker, W., and N. C. Brown, J. Chem. Soc., 1948, 2303.
22. Baker, W., and B. F. Burrows, J. Chem. Soc., 1961, 2257.
23. Bauman, R. B., and I. J. Krems, J. Am. Chem. Soc., 81, 1620 (1959).
24. Baumgarten, P., Ber., 59B, 1976 (1926).
25. Baumgarten, P., Ber., 63B, 1330 (1930).
26. Becke, F., and L. Wuertele, Chem. Ber., 91, 1011 (1958).
27. Behrman, E. J., J. Am. Chem. Soc., 85, 3478 (1963).
28. Behrman, E. J., and B. M. Pitt, J. Am. Chem. Soc., 80, 3717
    (1958).

29. Behrman, E. J., and P. P. Walker, J. Am. Chem. Soc., 84, 3454 (1962).

30. Beilstein, F., and E. Wiegand, Ber., 15, 1368 (1882).

31. Berger, L., and J. Lee, XII Intern. Congr. Pure Appl. Chem., Abstracts of Papers, 1951, p. 343.

32. Bergstrom, S., Naturwissenschaften, 23, 706 (1935); Chem. Abstr., 30, 1073 (1936).

33. Birch, S. F., J. Inst. Petrol. 38, 69 (1952).

34. Birchenough, M. J., and H. Burton, J. Chem. Soc., 1952, 2443.

35. Bistline, R. G., Jr., A. J. Stirton, J. K. Weil, and E. W. Maurer, J. Am. Oil Chemists' Soc., 34, 516 (1957).

36. Biswas, A. K., and B. K. Mukherji, J. Am. Oil Chemists' Soc., 37, 171 (1960).

37. Blake, E. S., U. S. Patent 2,630,449; Chem. Abstr., 48, 3997 (1954).

38. Blaser, B., and M. Rugenstein, German Patent 925,045; Chem. Abstr., 52, 1608 (1958).

39. Boehme Fettschemie Gmbh, British Patent 734,191; Chem. Abstr., 50, 1334 (1956).

40. Boehme Fettchemie Gmbh, British Patent 884,618.

41. Boehme Fettchemie Gmbh, German Patent 852,695; Chem. Zentr., 124, 1581 (1953).

42. Booth, J., E. Boyland, and D. Manson, Biochem. J., 60, 62 (1955).

43. Bordwell, F. G., and G. W. Crosby, J. Am. Chem. Soc., 78, 5367 (1956).

44. Boyd, R. H., R. W. Taft, Jr., A. P. Wolf, and D. Christman, J. Am. Chem. Soc., 82, 4729 (1960).

45. Boyland, E., and D. Manson, J. Chem. Soc., 1958, 532.

46. Boyland, E., D. Manson, and P. Sims, J. Chem. Soc., 1953, 3623.

47. Boyland, E., and P. Sims, J. Chem. Soc., 1954, 980.

48. Boyland, E., and P. Sims, J. Chem. Soc., 1958, 4198.

49. Boyland, E., P. Sims, and D. C. Williams, Biochem. J., 62, 546 (1956).

50. Brader, W. H., Jr., U. S. Patent 3,083,221; Chem. Abstr., 59, 8595 (1963).

51. Bradley, W., and J. G. Lee, J. Chem. Soc., 1957, 3549.

52. Breslow, D. S., R. R. Hough, and J. T. Fairclough, J. Am. Chem. Soc., 76, 5361 (1954).

53. Brois, S. J., J. Org. Chem., 27, 3532 (1962).

54. Brown, C. B., U. S. Dept. Commerce, OTS Rept., PB63, 822 (1946).

55. Brugmann, W. H., Jr., U. S. Patent 2,694,084; Chem. Abstr., 49, 10617 (1955).

56. Bruner, W. M., U. S. Patent 2,633,473; Chem. Abstr., 47, 6162 (1953).

57. Brunken, J., and G. Glackner, German (East) Patent 15,024; Chem. Abstr., 54, 3201 (1960).

58. Brunken, J., and E. J. Poppe, German (East) Patent 18,485; Chem. Abstr., 55, 8296 (1961).
59. Burckhardt, G. N., J. Chem. Soc., 1933, 337.
60. Burckhardt, G. N., C. Horrex, and D. I. Jenkins, J. Chem. Soc., 1936, 1654.
61. Burckhardt, G. N., and A. Lapworth, J. Chem. Soc., 1926, 684.
62. Burg, A. B., and W. E. McKee, J. Am. Chem. Soc., 73, 4590 (1951).
63. Burgdorf, K., German Patent 874,308; Chem. Abstr., 48, 2396 (1954).
64. Burgdorf, K., German Patent 877,612; Chem. Zentr., 125, 3834 (1954).
65. Burgdorf, K., German Patent 887,340; Chem. Abstr., 48, 4233 (1954).
66. Burmistrov, S. I., and A. G. Taranenko, Uk. Khim. Zh., 22, 620 (1956); Chem. Abstr., 51, 5726 (1957).
67. Burstein, S., and S. Lieberman, J. Am. Chem. Soc., 80, 5235 (1958).
68. Burton, D., and E. E. Byrne, J. Soc. Leather Trades' Chemists, 36, 309 (1952).
69. Burton, D., and E. E. Byrne, J. Soc. Leather Trades' Chemists, 37, 243 (1953).
70. Burton, D., and E. E. Byrne, J. Soc. Leather Trades' Chemists, 37, 321 (1953).
71. Burton, D., and E. E. Byrne, J. Soc. Leather Trades' Chemists, 38, 10 (1954).
71a. Burton, D., and L. F. Byrne, J. Soc. Leather Trades' Chemists, 47, 208 (1963); Chem. Abstr., 59, 10352 (1963).
72. Burwell, R. L., Jr., J. Am. Chem. Soc., 71, 1769 (1949).
73. Butcher, K. L., and G. M. Nickson, J. Appl. Chem. (London), 10, 65 (1960).
74. Butcher, K. L., and G. M. Nickson, Trans. Faraday Soc., 54, 1195 (1958).
75. Butenandt, A., E. Biekert, N. Koga, and P. Traub, Z. Physiol. Chem., 321, 258 (1960).
76. Calfee, J. D., and P. A. Florio, U. S. Patent 2,628,972; Chem. Abstr., 48, 1413 (1954).
77. Calhoun, G. M., and R. L. Burwell, Jr., J. Am. Chem. Soc., 77, 6441 (1955).
78. Campbell, D. H., Ph. D. Dissertation, Purdue University, 1955; Dissertation Abstr., 15, 697 (1955).
79. Cannava, A., and B. Chiarlo, Med. sper., 26, 114 (1955); Chem. Abstr., 50, 8911 (1956).
80. Carlson, E. J., G. Flint, E. E. Gilbert, and H. R. Nychka, Ind. Eng. Chem., 50, 276 (1958).
81. Carrington, R. A. G., and H. C. Evans, J. Chem. Soc., 1957, 1701.
82. Chemische Fabrik Budenheim A. G., British Patent 727,476; Chem. Abstr., 49, 12756 (1955).

83. Chemithon Corporation, "Chemithon Detergent Process Equipment," Seattle, Wash., 1961.

84. Chimiotechnie union chimique du nord et du Rhone (Soc. anon.), French Patent 979,000; Chem. Abstr., 48, 2764 (1954).

85. Claes, F. A., R. C. Gerbaux, and J. T. Lemmerling, Belgian Patent 581,794; Chem. Abstr., 55, 25250 (1961).

85a. Clippinger, E., Ind. Eng. Chem. Prod. Res. Develop., 3, No. 1, 3 (1964).

86. Cocker, W., and D. O'Meara, Chem. Ind. (London), 1953, 63.

87. Cohen, W. V., J. Org. Chem., 26, 4021 (1961).

88. Cohen, W. V., U. S. Patent 3,017,421; Chem. Abstr., 56, 15366 (1962).

89. Commonwealth Engineering Co. of Ohio, Belgian Patent 577,947.

90. Continental Oil Co., "Procedure for Sulfation of Alfol Alcohols," Prod. Bull. AD-5-60, 1960.

91. Cramer, G., and K. Schimmelschmidt, German Patent 907,054; Chem. Abstr., 49, 3243 (1955).

92. Cramer, R., and D. D. Coffman, J. Org. Chem., 26, 4164 (1961).

93. Crane, C. L., U. S. Patent 2,582,009; Chem. Abstr., 46, 3275 (1952).

94. Crane, C. L., U. S. Patent 2,622,079; Chem. Abstr., 47, 3565 (1953).

95. Cross, A. H. J., and W. Gerrard, J. Chem. Soc., 1949, 2686.

96. Csuros, Z., K. Zech, and S. Zech, Acta Chim. Hung. 1, 83 (1951); Chem. Abstr., 46, 5003 (1952).

97. Davis, R. A., U. S. Patent 2,878,156; Chem. Abstr., 53, 10652 (1959).

98. DeBenneville, P. L., U. S. Patent 2,632,766; Chem. Abstr., 47, 6686 (1953).

99. Dehydag Deutsche Hydrierwerke Gmbh, German Patent 881,509; Chem. Abstr., 48, 12435 (1954).

100. Deno, N. C., and M. S. Newman, J. Am. Chem. Soc., 72, 3852 (1950).

101. Desai, N. B., V. Ramanathan, and K. Venkataraman, J. Sci. Ind. Res. (India), 14B, 330 (1955); Chem. Abstr., 50, 12008 (1956).

102. Desnuelle, P., and O. Micaelli, Bull. Soc. Chim. France, 17, 671 (1950).

103. Dhar, A. N., J. Sci. Ind. Res. (India), 13B, 384 (1954); Chem. Abstr., 49, 640 (1955).

104. Dinerstein, R. A., and R. E. Van Strien, U. S. Patent 2,595,341; Chem. Abstr., 47, 1186 (1953).

105. Dodgson, K. S., and B. Spencer, in Methods of Biochemical Analysis, Vol. 4, D. Glick, ed., Interscience, New York, 1957, p. 211.

106. Doerr, E. L., U. S. Patent 2,909,554; Chem. Abstr., 54, 2167 (1960).

107. Duff, R. B., J. Chem. Soc., 1949, 1597.

108. Duff, R. B. , and E. G. V. Percival, J. Chem. Soc. , 1941, 830.
109. Duff, R. B. , and E. G. V. Percival, J. Chem. Soc. , 1947, 1675.
110. Duperray, J. N. , French Patent 1, 004, 350; Chem. Abstr. , 51, 7044 (1957).
110a. Du Pont de Nemours and Co. , E. I. , Belgian Patent 640, 971.
111. Dupre, J. , U. S. Patent 3, 079, 416; Chem. Abstr. , 56, 3586 (1962) (German analogue).
112. Eastman Chemical Products, Inc. , "Eastman Neoalcohols, " 1961.
113. Eastman Chemical Products, Inc. , "Sulfacel Sodium Cellulose Acetate Sulfate, " 1959.
114. Eaton, P. , E. J. Carlson, P. Lombardo, and P. Yates, J. Org. Chem. 25, 1225 (1960).
115. Edens, W. L. , U. S. Patent 3, 083, 220; Chem. Abstr. , 59, 6258 (1963).
116. Egami, F. , and N. Takahashi, Bull. Chem. Soc. Japan, 28, 666 (1955); Chem. Abstr. , 50, 7193 (1956).
117. Egami, F. , and R. Takahashi, Japanese Patent 2624 ('59); Chem. Abstr. , 54, 13151 (1960).
118. Emery Industries Inc. , Technical Bulletin No. 203B, Cincinnati, Ohio, 1958.
119. Emery Industries Inc. , Technical Bulletin No. 402, Cincinnati, Ohio, 1956.
120. Enjay Chemical Company, "Sulfated Ethoxylates of Tridecyl Alcohol in Light-Duty Liquid Detergents, " Technical Bulletin No. 17, New York, N. Y. , undated.
121. Enjay Chemical, "Sulfation Procedures for Tridecyl Alcohol and Ethoxylated Tridecyl Alcohol, " Technical Bulletin C-21, 1960.
122. Entelis, S. G. , and G. V. Korovina, Dokl. Akad. Nauk SSSR, 134, 856 (1961); Chem. Abstr. , 55, 15100 (1961).
123. Erickson, J. G. , U. S. Patent 2, 838, 487; Chem. Abstr. , 53, 1170 (1959).
124. Evans, R. , and L. Totherick, U. S. Patent 2, 816, 126; Chem. Abstr. , 52, 6392 (1958).
125. Fairweather, D. A. W. , and J. Thomas, U. S. Patent 1, 929, 866; Chem. Abstr. , 28, 174 (1934).
126. Fairweather, D. A. W. , and J. Thomas, U. S. Patent 1, 970, 083; Chem. Abstr. , 28, 6322 (1934).
127. Faith, W. L. , D. B. Keyes, and R. L. Clark, Industrial Chemicals, Wiley, New York, 1950.
128. Farbenfabriken Bayer A. G. , German Patent 1, 086, 434; Chem. Abstr. , 55, 19331 (1961).
129. Farbwerke Hoechst A. G. , German Patent 1, 035, 632; Chem. Abstr. , 54, 19482 (1960).
130. Fedor, W. S. , B. Strain, L. Theoharous, and D. D. Whyte, Ind. Eng. Chem. , 51, 14 (1959).

131.   Feigenbaum, J., and C. A. Neuberg, J. Am. Chem. Soc., 63, 3529 (1941).

132.   Fieser, L. F., J. Am. Chem. Soc., 70, 3232 (1948).

133.   Fincke, J. K., U. S. Patent 2,634,287; Chem. Abstr., 47, 6161 (1953).

134.   Fingauz, I. M., A. F. Vorob'eva, G. A. Shirikova, and M. P. Doku-chaeva, J. Polymer Sci., 56, 245 (1962).

135.   Foster, A. B., E. B. Hancock, and W. G. Overend, Chem. Ind. (London), 1956, 1144.

136.   Frank, G., U. S. Patent 2,559,914; Chem. Abstr., 45, 8770 (1951).

137.   Freidlina, R. K., V. N. Kost, and A. N. Nesmeyanov, Izv. Akad. Nauk SSSR, Otdel. Khim. Nauk, 1956, 1202; Chem. Abstr., 51, 5685 (1957).

138.   Fuchs, W. M., and E. Gavatin, U. S. Patent 2,511,911; Chem. Abstr., 44, 8568 (1950).

139.   Gale, L. E., and P. M. Scott, J. Am. Pharm. Assoc., 42, 283 (1953).

140.   Gebauer-Fuelnegg, E., W. Stevens, and O. Dingler, Ber., 61B, 2000 (1928).

141.   Gershenovich, A. I., and M. A. Rabinovich, Primeneniya Sinte-tich. Zhirozamenitelei v Proizv. Myla i Moyushchikh Sredstv, Moscow, Sb. 1962, 133; Chem. Abstr., 59, 1847 (1963).

141a.   Getmanskii, I. K., Russian Patent 154,360; Chem. Abstr., 60, 6747 (1964).

142.   Gibbs, H. H., W. L. Edens, and R. N. Griffin, Division of Indus-trial and Engineering Chemistry, 138th Meeting, American Chemical Society, New York, Sept., 1960.

143.   Gilbert, E. E., and S. Giolito, U. S. Reissue Patent 24,435; Chem. Abstr., 52, 7358 (1958).

144.   Gilbert, E. E., and P. H. Groggins, in Unit Processes in Organic Synthesis, 5th ed., McGraw-Hill, New York, 1958.

145.   Gilbert, E. E., and E. P. Jones, Ind. Eng. Chem., 43, 2043 (1951).

146.   Gilbert, E. E., and B. Veldhuis, J. Am. Oil Chemists' Soc., 36, 208 (1959).

147.   Gilbert, E. E., and B. Veldhuis, J. Am. Oil Chemists' Soc., 37, 298 (1960).

148.   Gilbert, E. E., B. Veldhuis, E. J. Carlson, and S. L. Giolito, Ind. Eng. Chem., 45, 2065 (1953).

149.   Girard, A., French Patent 1,063,068; Chem. Zentr., 126, 2328 (1955).

150.   Gluesenkamp, E. W., U. S. Patent 2,498,618; Chem. Abstr., 44, 4928 (1950).

151.   Goldsmith, P. D. J., K. L. Kelley, and C. W. Mishett, J. Am. Pharm. Assoc., 45, 223 (1956).

152.   Grabowski, J., Ber., 6, 1070 (1873).

153.   Grant, D., and A. Holt, J. Chem. Soc., 1960, 5026.

154.   Grant, G. A. , and W. L. Glen, U. S. Patent 2, 597, 723; Chem.
        Abstr. , 47, 5460 (1953).
155.   Gray, F. W. , U. S. Patent 2, 868, 812; Chem. Abstr. , 53, 8671
        (1959).
156.   Great Britain Ministry of Supply, British Patent 774, 384;
        Chem. Abstr. , 51, 15549 (1957).
157.   Greene, R. B. , U. S. Patent 2, 504, 517; Chem. Abstr. , 44, 5574
        (1950).
158.   Griebsch, E. , and W. Garn, German Patent 1, 047, 780; Chem.
        Abstr. , 55, 3661 (1961).
159.   Grignard, V. , C. Toussaint, and J. Cazin, Bull. Soc. Chim.
        France, 43, 537 (1928).
160.   Gushee, D. E. , and O. L. Scherr, Ind. Eng. Chem. , 51, 798
        (1959).
161.   Ham, G. E. , J. Org. Chem. , 25, 864 (1960).
162.   Ham, G. E. , J. Org. Chem. , 26, 4148 (1961).
163.   Hardy, E. M. , and W. B. Hardy, U. S. Patent 2, 649, 453; Chem.
        Abstr. , 48, 1014 (1954).
164.   Hardy, W. B. , and E. M. Hardy, U. S. Patent 2, 647, 124; Chem.
        Abstr. , 48, 4851 (1954).
165.   Hardy, W. B. , and M. Scalera, J. Am. Chem. Soc. , 74, 5212
        (1952).
166.   Harrington, R. C. , Jr. , U. S. Patent 2, 849, 450; Chem. Abstr. ,
        53, 3057 (1959).
167.   Hasbrouck, R. B. , U. S. Patent 2, 642, 427; Chem. Abstr. , 48,
        6474 (1954).
168.   Hasbrouck, R. B. , U. S. Patent 2, 666, 066; Chem. Abstr. , 48,
        12816 (1954).
169.   Hatch, L. F. , "Higher Oxo Alcohols, " Enjay Co. , Inc. New
        York, 1957.
170.   Hauptschein, M. , and M. Braid, J. Am. Chem. Soc. , 83, 2500
        (1961).
171.   Hauptschein, M. , and M. Braid, J. Am. Chem. Soc. , 83, 2505
        (1961).
171a.   Hegedues, B. , Helv. Chim. Acta, 46, 2604 (1963).
172.   Heine, H. W. , R. W. Greiner, M. A. Boote, and B. A. Brown, J.
        Am. Chem. Soc. , 75, 2505 (1953).
173.   Hellin, M. , and J. C. Jungers, Bull. Soc. Chim. France, 1957,
        386; Chem. Abstr. , 51, 11827 (1953).
174.   Henke, C. O. , and M. A. Prahl, U. S. Patent 2, 076, 563; Chem.
        Abstr. , 31, 4017 (1937).
175.   Hine, J. , Physical Organic Chemistry, 2nd ed. McGraw-Hill,
        1962.
176.   Hoelscher, F. , German Patent 803, 835; Chem. Abstr. , 45,
        5953 (1951).
177.   Hofmann, K. A. , and E. Biesalski, Ber. , 45, 1394 (1912).
178.   Holden, G. W. , and R. Bromley, J. Am. Chem. Soc. , 72, 3807
        (1950).

179. Hooker Chemical Co., Bulletin No. 65, Niagara Falls, New York, 1961.
180. Houben, J., and H. R. Arnold, Ber., 40, 4306 (1908).
181. Hoyt, L. F., U. S. Dept. Commerce, OTS Rept. PB3868, 1945.
182. Huebner, R., Ann., 223, 198 (1884).
183. Hull, R., British Patent 756, 189; Chem. Abstr., 51, 8812 (1957).
184. I. G. Farbenindustrie A. G., U. S. Dept. Commerce, OTS Rept. PB70, 183.
185. I. G. Farbenindustrie A. G., U. S. Dept. Commerce, OTS Rept., PB73, 911, Frames 4816-18, 1935.
186. I. G. Farbenindustrie A. G., U. S. Dept. Commerce, OTS Rept., PB96, 623.
187. Inskeep, G. D., and A. Mussard, Ind. Eng. Chem., 47, 2 (1955).
188. Ishidate, M., Y. Sakwai, and S. Owari, Pharm. Bull. (Tokyo), 5, 203 (1957); Chem. Abstr., 52, 6241 (1958).
189. Jakubovic, A. O., and B. N. Brook, Polymer, 2, No. 1, 18 (1961).
190. Jaques, D., and J. A. Leisten, J. Chem. Soc., 1961, 4963.
191. Jefferson Chemical Co., "Surfonic Surface Active Agents," Houston, Texas, 1958.
192. Jennings, H. J., and J. K. N. Jones, Can. J. Chem., 41, 1151 (1963).
193. Johnson, D. A., U. S. Patent 2, 966, 518; Chem. Abstr., 55, 16491 (1961).
194. Jones, L. W., and H. F. Whalen, J. Am. Chem. Soc., 47, 1351 (1925).
195. Jones, R. V., U. S. Patent 2, 623, 037; Chem. Abstr., 47, 4131 (1953).
196. Jones, R. V., U. S. Patent 2, 689, 244; Chem. Abstr., 49, 9840 (1955).
197. Jones, R. V., U. S. Patent 2, 697, 093; Chem. Abstr., 49, 2766 (1955).
198. Jones, R. V., U. S. Patent 2, 714, 605; Chem. Abstr., 50, 7126 (1956).
199. Jones, R. V., U. S. Patent 2, 860, 123; Chem. Abstr., 53, 4797 (1959).
200. Kaji, A., K. Hashimoto, and S. Kano, J. Chem. Soc. Japan, 82, 782 (1961); Chem. Abstr., 57, 13665 (1962).
201. Karnaukh, A. M., Maslob. -Zhir. Prom., 24, No. 3, 28 (1958); Chem. Abstr., 52, 17760 (1958).
202. Karnaukh, A. M., and Z. P. Deinekhovskaya, Maslob. -Zhir. Prom., 27, No. 5, 28 (1961); Chem. Abstr., 55, 25729 (1961).
203. Kashelikar, D. V., and P. E. Fanta, J. Am. Chem. Soc., 82, 4927 (1960).
204. Kerr, R. W., E. F. Paschall, and W. H. Minkema, U. S. Patent 2, 967, 178; Chem. Abstr., 55, 7705 (1961).

205. Kirkpatrick, W. H. , and V. L. Seale, U. S. Patent 3, 049, 511; Chem. Abstr. , 58, 7774 (1963).
206. Klass, D. L. , U. S. Patent 3, 100, 780; Chem. Abstr. , 60, 2766 (1964).
207. Klug, E. D. , U. S. Patent 2, 753, 337; Chem. Abstr. , 50, 15083 (1956).
208. Klug, E. D. , and H. M. Spurlin, U. S. Patent 2, 714, 591; Chem. Abstr. , 49, 16432 (1955).
209. Knaggs, E. A. , Soap Chem. Spec. , 38, No. 5, 237 (1962).
210. Knoll, A. G. , German Patent 1, 033, 196.
211. Koen, N. , German Patent DDR 2261; Chem. Zentr. , 126, 5449 (1955).
212. Komori, S. , T. Agawa, and T. Kataoka, Yukagaku, 10, 153 (1961); Chem. Abstr. , 55, 26483 (1961).
213. Komori, S. , S. Sakakibara, and K. Nambu, J. Oil Chemists' Soc. , Japan, 1, 73 (1952); Chem. Abstr. , 47, 3224 (1953).
214. Komori, S. , S. Sakakibara, and T. Takahashi, J. Chem. Soc. , Japan Ind. Chem. Sect. , 57, 83 (1954); Chem. Abstr. , 49, 2099 (1955).
215. Konovaloff, D. , Compt. Rend. , 95, 1285 (1882).
216. Kooijman, P. L. , Intern. Congr. Pure Appl. Chem. (London), 11, 499 (1947); Chem. Abstr. , 45, 1502 (1954).
217. Kooijman, P. L. , H. J. Tadema, and H. Hoog, Congr. Mondial Detergence Prod. Tensio-Actifs 1 er Paris, 1954, 379 (Publ. 1956); Chem. Abstr. , 51, 17203 (1957).
218. Kosmin, M. , British Patent 757, 937; Chem. Abstr. , 51, 8460 (1957).
219. Kosmin, M. , U. S. Patent 2, 606, 178; Chem. Abstr. , 46, 11776 (1953).
220. Kosmin, M. , U. S. Patent 2, 644, 831; Chem. Abstr. , 47, 9641 (1953).
221. Kosmin, M. , U. S. Patent 2, 644, 833; Chem. Abstr. , 48, 4234 (1954).
222. Kuhn, R. , and L. Birkofer, Ber. , 84, 659 (1951).
223. Lambrech, J. A. , U. S. Patent 2, 573, 769; Chem. Abstr. , 46, 5087 (1952).
224. Law, G. H. , and R. W. McNamee, U. S. Patent 2, 088, 027; Chem. Abstr. , 31, 6673 (1937).
225. Lecher, H. Z. , and T. H. Chao, U. S. Patent 2, 606, 202; Chem. Abstr. , 47, 4901 (1953).
226. Lecher, H. Z. , M. Scalera, and E. M. Hardy, U. S. Patent 2, 396, 582; Chem. Abstr. , 40, 3270 (1946).
227. Lecher, H. Z. , M. Scalera, and E. M. Hardy, U. S. Patent 2, 402, 647; Chem. Abstr. , 40, 5774 (1946).
228. Lecher, H. Z. , M. Scalera, and C. T. Lester, U. S. Patent 2, 403, 226; Chem. Abstr. , 40, 6264 (1946).
229. Leighton, P. A. , W. A. Perkins, and M. L. Renquist, J. Am. Chem. Soc. , 69, 1540 (1947).

230. Levy, J. , J. Am. Oil Chemists' Soc. , 38, 36 (1961).
231. Levy, J. B. , R. W. Taft, Jr. , and L. P. Hammett, J. Am. Chem. Soc. , 75, 1253 (1953).
232. Lichtenberger, J. , and L. Durr, Bull. Soc. Chim. France, 1956, 664.
233. Lichtenberger, J. , and J. Hincky, Bull. Soc. Chim. France, 1961, 1495.
234. Lindner, F. , U. S. Patent 2, 758, 110; Chem. Abstr. , 50, 16048 (1956).
235. Lindsey, R. V. , Jr. , U. S. Patent 2, 733, 255; Chem. Abstr. , 50, 6821 (1956).
236. Lohr, J. W. , J. Am. Oil Chemists' Soc. , 35, 532 (1958).
237. London, E. , R. S. Theobald, and G. D. Twigg, Chem. Ind. (London), 1955, 1060.
238. Long, F. A. , and M. A. Paul, Chem. Rev. , 57, 935 (1957).
239. Loudon, J. D. , Progress in Organic Chemistry, Vol. 5, Butterworth, London, 1961.
240. Lumbroso, F. , Compt. Rend. Congr. Intern. Chim. 31^e, Liege, 1958, 1, 624 (1959).
241. Lyandzberg, G. Ya. , Zh. Prikl. Khim. , 31, 1900 (1958); Chem. Abstr. , 53, 10055 (1959).
242. Maerkische Seifen-Industrie, German Patent 762, 967; Chem. Abstr. , 48, 12432 (1954).
243. Malkemus, J. D. , J. R. Ramsay, and D. J. Potter, U. S. Patent 2, 452, 943; Chem. Abstr. , 43, 3024 (1949).
244. Malm, C. J. , and C. L. Crane, U. S. Patent 2, 539, 451; Chem. Abstr. , 45, 4453 (1951).
245. Malm, C. H. , and C. L. Crane, U. S. Patent 2, 675, 377; Chem. Abstr. , 48, 9691 (1954).
246. Malm, C. J. , M. E. Rowley, and G. D. Hiatt, U. S. Patent 2, 969, 355; Chem. Bastr. , 55, 10887 (1961).
247. Mannes, L. , and R. Hirth, German Patent 848, 949; Chem. Zentr. , 124, 3015 (1953).
248. Martin, I. , and O. B. Wurzburg, U. S. Patent 2, 857, 377; Chem. Abstr. , 53, 7041 (1959).
249. Maurer, E. W. , A. J. Stirton, and J. K. Weil, J. Am. Oil Chemists' Soc. , 37, 34 (1960).
250. Mayhew, R. L. , and E. P. Williams, U. S. Patent 3, 089, 888; Chem. Abstr. , 59, 11254 (1963).
251. McKenna, J. , and J. K. Norymberski, J. Chem. Soc. , 1957, 3889.
252. Mehltretter, C. L. , M. S. Furry, R. L. Mellies, and J. C. Rankin, J. Am. Oil Chemists' Soc. , 29, 202 (1952).
253. Merck, E. , German Patent 133, 542.
254. Meyer, K. H. , R. P. Piroue, and M. E. Odier, Helv. Chim. Acta, 35, 574 (1952).
255. Meyer, K. H. , and D. E. Schwartz, Helv. Chim. Acta, 33, 1651 (1950).

256. Michel, R., and J. Roche, U. S. Patent 2, 970, 165; Chem. Abstr., 55, 12312 (1961).
256a. Miyamoto, K., Y. Aritomi, H. Ichida, and S. Irie, German Patent 1, 159, 429; Chem. Abstr., 60, 13142 (1964).
257. Moore, L. O., and J. W. Clark, Paper presented at the Second International Symposium on Fluorine Chemistry, Estes Park, Colo., July 17-20, 1962.
258. Moore, L. O., and J. W. Clark, U. S. Patent 3, 055, 913; Chem. Abstr., 58, 1347 (1963).
259. Mueller, M., Ber., 6, 227 (1873).
260. Milligan, B., and J. M. Swan, Rev. Pure Appl. Chem., 12, 72 (1962).
261. Nawiasky, P., and G. E. Sprenger, U. S. Patent 2, 219, 748; Chem. Abstr., 35, 1067 (1941).
262. Nazarova, S. S., Zh. Prikl. Khim., 33, 448 (1960); Chem. Abstr., 54, 11453 (1960).
263. Neighbors, R. F., U. S. Patent 2, 649, 469; Chem. Abstr., 48, 8250 (1954).
264. Nemtsov, M. S., Khim. Prom., 1960, 633; Chem. Abstr., 55, 15070 (1961).
265. Nerad, Z., E. Wittenberg, and J. Kluege, Czech. Patent 83, 739; Chem. Abstr., 51, 2848 (1957).
266. Nippon Soda Co., Ltd., Japanese Patent 222 ('62).
267. Nippon Soda Co., Ltd., Japanese Patent 2611 ('62).
268. Noguchi, J., Japanese Patent 23, 324 ('61); Chem. Abstr., 58, 1526 (1963).
269. Oddo, G., and A. Sconzo, Gazz. Chim. Ital., 57, 83 (1927).
270. Oehler, K., German Patent 19, 847.
271. Ogata, Y., M. Okano, and K. Matsumoto, J. Am. Chem. Soc., 77, 4643 (1955).
272. Oldham, W. J., and M. M. Wirth, U. S. Patent 2, 645, 656; Chem. Abstr., 48, 1018 (1954).
273. O'Neill, A. N., Can. J. Chem., 33, 1097 (1955).
274. Oppenheim, A., Ber., 3, 735 (1870).
275. Orthner, L., C. Platz, K. Horst, J. Nelles, and H. Keppler, German Patent 917, 602; Chem. Abstr., 49, 9299 (1955).
276. Ott, E., H. M. Spurlin, and M. W. Grafflin, eds. Cellulose and Cellulose Derivatives, 2nd. ed., Part 2, (High Polymers Series, Vol. 5) Interscience, New York, 1954, pp. 755-760.
277. Paquot, C., J. Rech. Centre Natl. Rech. Sci., Lab. Bellevue (Paris), 1950, 169.
278. Parker, E. D., and J. D. Guthrie, U. S. Patent 2, 727, 805; Chem. Abstr., 50, 8221 (1956).
279. Parrod, J., and V. Armand, U. S. Patent 2, 478, 834; Chem. Abstr., 45, 2022 (1951).
280. Parrod, J., N. Rist, L. Robert, and M. Rahier, Bull. Soc. Chim. France, 1951, 418.
281. Parrod, J., and L. Robert, Compt. Rend., 230, 450 (1950).

282. Paschall, E. F. , U. S. Patent 2, 775, 586; Chem. Abstr. , 51, 4746 (1957).

283. Payne, H. G. , and P. J. Baker, Am. J. Med. Technol. , 19, 219 (1953).

284. Pearl, I. A. , and A. R. Ronzio, J. Org. Chem. , 12, 785 (1947).

285. Percival, E. G. V. , J. Chem. Soc. , 1945, 119.

286. Percival, E. G. V. , and T. H. Soutar, J. Chem. Soc. , 1940, 1475.

287. vanPeski, A. J. , Rec. Trav. Chim. , 40, 103 (1921).

288. vanPeski, A. J. , Rec. Trav. Chim. , 40, 736 (1921).

289. Pfannemueller, B. , in Houben-Weyl, Methoden der Organischen Chemie, Vol. XIV/2, Thieme Verlag, Stuttgart, 1963.

289a. Pizzarello, R. A. , A. F. Schneid, and P. Resnick, U. S. Patent 3, 133, 950.

290. Prandtl, W. , and P. Borinski, Z. Anorg. Allgem. Chem. , 62, 24 (1909).

291. Price, W. H. , U. S. Patent 2, 917, 522; Chem. Abstr. , 54, 6823 (1960).

292. Prud'homme, M. , Compt. Rend. , 70, 1137 (1870).

293. Pueschel, F. , H. Frotscher, and K. Burgdorf, German (East) Patent DDR 2833; Chem. Zentr. , 125, 10618 (1954).

294. Pulver, R. , German Patent 924, 211; Chem. Abstr. , 52, 1247 (1958).

295. Purgold, T. , Ber. , 6, 502 (1873).

296. Purlee, E. L. , and R. W. Taft, Jr. , J. Am. Chem. Soc. , 78, 5807 (1956).

297. Ratcliff, G. A. , Ph. D Dissertation, Cornell University; Dissertation Abstr. , 14, 2018 (1954).

298. Ratti, R. , U. S. Patent 1, 934, 143; Chem. Abstr. , 28, 491 (1934).

299. Ravenscroft, P. H. , and M. E. Turney, J. Am. Oil Chemists' Soc. , 32, 418 (1955).

300. Reeves, W. A. , G. L. Drake, O. J. McMillan, and J. D. Guthrie, Textile Res. J. , 25, 41 (1955).

301. Reeves, W. A. , and J. D. Guthrie, J. Am. Chem. Soc. , 75, 4101 (1953).

302. Reichspatentamt, Berlin, U. S. Dept. Commerce, OTS Rept. , PB83, 606, FIAT Microfilm Reel F148, Frames 6157-7166, 1937-45.

303. Reinisch, W. B. , and K. R. Dutton, British Patent 717, 903.

304. Reitz, H. C. , R. E. Ferrel, H. S. Olcott, and H. Fraenkel-Conrat, J. Am. Chem. Soc. , 68, 1031 (1946).

305. Reznikov, I. G. , and N. A. Kurasova, Maslob. -Zhir. Prom. , 28, No. 11, 23 (1962); Chem. Abstr. , 59, 3761 (1963).

306. Richmond, J. L. , U. S. Patent 2, 190, 733; Chem. Abstr. , 34, 4187 (1940).

307. Ricketts, C. R. , Biochem. J. , 51, 120 (1952); Chem. Abstr. , 46, 5723 (1952).

308. Ricketts, C. R. , J. Chem. Soc. , 1956, 3752.

309. Ricketts, C. R., Progress in Organic Chemistry, Vol. 5, Butterworths, London, 1961.
310. Ricketts, C. R., British Patent 695,787; Chem. Abstr., 48, 1636 (1954).
311. Ricketts, C. R., and K. W. Walton, Chem. Ind. (London), 1951, 1062.
312. Robey, R. F., Ind. Eng. Chem., 33, 1076 (1941).
313. Roubal, Z., British Patent 796,477; Chem. Abstr., 52, 20922 (1958).
314. Roubal, Z., Z. Placer, and Z. Slabochova, Czech. Patent 93,204; Chem. Abstr., 54, 23207 (1960).
315. Roy, A. B., in, Advances in Enzymology, Vol. 22, F. F. Nord, ed., Interscience, New York, 1960.
316. Rudelli, G., Tinctoria, 56, No. 9, 60 (1959).
317. Saito, T., and J. Noguchi, Nippon Kagaku Zasshi, 82, 471 (1961); Chem. Abstr., 56, 11678 (1962).
318. Saito, T., J. Noguchi, and K. Komatsu, Nippon Kagaku Zasshi, 82, 472 (1961); Chem. Abstr., 56, 11679 (1962).
319. Salkin, R., U. S. Patent 2,636,042; Chem. Abstr., 48, 7648 (1954).
320. Salkin, R., U. S. Patent 2,767,196; Chem. Abstr., 51, 8788 (1957).
321. Scalera, M., W. B. Hardy, E. M. Hardy, and A. W. Joyce, J. Am. Chem. Soc., 73, 3094 (1951).
322. Schaurich, K., J. Prakt. Chem., 15, 322 (1962).
323. Schenck, G. O., and G. A. Schmidt-Thomee, Ann., 584, 199 (1955).
324. Schill, H., in Houben-Weyl, Methoden der Organischen Chemie, Vol. XIV/2, Thieme Verlag, Stuttgart, 1963.
325. Schiller, R., and R. Otto, Ber., 9, 1638 (1876).
326. Schmidt, M., and H. Schmidbaur, Angew. Chem., 70, 469 (1958).
327. Schmidt, M., and H. Schmidbaur, Angew. Chem., 70, 470 (1958).
328. Schmidt, M., and H. Schmidbaur, Ber., 95, 47 (1962).
329. Schmidt, M., and G. Talsky, Chem. Ber., 94, 1352 (1961).
330. Schock, R. U., Jr., and D. L. Tabern, J. Org. Chem., 16, 1772 (1951).
331. Schultze, G. R., J. Moos, and K. D. Ledwoch, Erdoel Kohle, 11, 12 (1958); Chem. Abstr., 52, 7677 (1958).
332. Schutzenberger, P., Compt. Rend., 69, 352 (1869).
333. Schwartz, A. M., U. S. Patent 2,717,894; Chem. Abstr., 50, 8720 (1956).
334. Schwartz, A. M., and J. W. Perry, Surface Active Agents and Detergents, Vol. 1, Interscience, New York, 1949.
335. Schwartz, A. M., J. W. Perry, and J. Berch, Surface Active Agents and Detergents, Vol. 2, Interscience, New York, 1958.
336. Scott, N. D., German Patent 757,749; Chem. Abstr., 48, 12418 (1954).
337. Sethna, S. M., Chem. Rev., 49, 91 (1951).

338.   Shilov, A. E. , R. D. Sabirova, and V. I. Gorshkov, Dokl. Akad.
        Nauk SSSR, 119, 533 (1958); Chem. Abstr. , 53, 6988 (1959).
338a.   Shimokai, K. , and M. Fukushima, Yukagaku, 12, 516 (1963);
        Chem. Abstr. , 60, 7032 (1964).
339.   Shreeve, J. M. , and G. H. Cady, J. Am. Chem. Soc. , 83, 4521
        (1961).
340.   Siebenbuerger, H. , U. S. Patent 1, 942, 577; Chem. Abstr. , 28,
        1716 (1934).
341.   Sims, P. , J. Chem. Soc. , 1958, 44.
342.   Slominskii, L. I. , and M. K. Yakubov, Maslob. Zhir. Prom. , 26,
        No. 11, 22 (1961); Chem. Abstr. , 55, 9910 (1961).
343.   Smith, H. E. , C. R. Russell, and C. E. Rist, Cereal Chem. , 39,
        273 (1962).
344.   Smith, J. L. , U. S. Patent 2, 805, 228; Chem. Abstr. , 52, 5455
        (1958).
345.   Smith, J. L. , and R. C. Harrington, Jr. , U. S. Patent 2, 891, 962;
        Chem. Abstr. , 54, 1546 (1960).
346.   Smith, J. L. , and R. C. Harrington, Jr. , U. S. Patent 2, 957, 014;
        Chem. Abstr. , 55, 19786 (1961).
347.   Smith, J. N. , J. Chem. Soc. , 1951, 2861.
348.   Snyder, E. G. , U. S. Patent 2, 508, 433; Chem. Abstr. , 44, 7870
        (1950).
349.   Sobel, A. E. , and P. E. Spoerri, J. Am. Chem. Soc. , 63, 1259
        (1941).
350.   Soc. Anon. des Produits Chim. de Fontaines, German Patent
        193, 830; Chem. Abstr. , 2, 1861 (1908).
351.   Soc. Anon. d'Innovations Chimiques dite: Sinnova ou Sadic,
        British Patent 799, 199; Chem. Abstr. , 53, 5114 (1959).
352.   Soc. pour l'Ind. Chim. a Bale, French Patent 41, 843; Chem.
        Abstr. , 27, 4540 (1933).
353.   Societe Anon. d'Innovations Chimiques dite: Sinnova ou Sadic,
        British Patent 680, 629; Chem. Abstr. , 47, 11221 (1953).
354.   Societe Anon. d'Innovations Chimiques dite: Sinnova ou Sadic,
        French Patent 965, 161; Chem. Abstr. , 46, 6137 (1952).
355.   Societe Anonyme des Manufactures des Glace et des Produits
        Chimiques de Saint-Gobain, Chauny et Cirey, French Patent
        1, 006, 211; Chem. Abstr. , 51, 12128 (1957).
356.   Societe des laboratoires de recherches pour applications indus-
        trielles, French Patents 981, 934-9; Chem. Abstr. , 48, 4867-8
        (1954).
357.   Soda, T. , and H. Egami, J. Chem. Soc. Japan, 61, 683 (1940).
358.   Sokol'skii, G. A. , and M. A. Dmitriev, Zh. Obshch. Khim. , 31,
        1107, 1110 (1961); Chem. Abstr. , 55, 27012 (1961).
359.   Sokol'skii, G. A. , and M. A. Dmitriev, Zh. Obshch. Khim. , 31,
        1653 (1961); Chem. Abstr. , 55, 27013 (1961).
360.   Sokol'skii, G. A. , and M. A. Dmitriev, Zh. Obshch. Khim. , 31,
        2743 (1961); Chem. Abstr. , 56, 9938 (1962).

361. Spada, A. , and E. Gavioli, Farmaco (Pavia) Ed. Sci. , 7, 441
      (1952); Chem. Abstr. , 47, 894 (1953).
362. Sperling, R. , J. Chem. Soc. , 1949, 1932.
363. Spivack, J. D. , U. S. Patent 2, 931, 804; Chem. Abstr. , 55, 1651
      (1961).
364. Stayner, R. D. , U. S. Patent 2, 802, 789; Chem. Abstr. , 51,
      17207 (1957).
365. Stayner, R. D. , and R. A. Stayner, U. S. Patent 2, 697, 657;
      Chem. Abstr. , 49, 6632 (1955).
366. Stewart, D. , and E. McNeill, Chem. Age (London), 63, 48
      (1950).
367. Strel'tsova, S. G. , and S. B. Serebryanii, Uk. Khim. Zh. , 19,
      664 (1953); Chem. Abstr. , 49, 11544 (1955).
368. Stirton, A. J. , J. K. Weil, A. A. Stawitzke, and S. James, J. Am.
      Oil Chemists' Soc. , 29, 198 (1952).
369. Suter, C. M. , The Organic Chemistry of Sulfur, Wiley, New
      York, 1944.
370. Suter, C. M. , U. S. Patent 2, 098, 114; Chem. Abstr. , 32, 191
      (1938).
371. Suter, C. M. , and P. B. Evans, J. Am. Chem. Soc. , 60, 536
      (1938).
372. Suter, C. M. , P. B. Evans, and J. M. Kiefer, J. Am. Chem. Soc. ,
      60, 538 (1938).
373. Suter, C. M. , and J. D. Malkemus, J. Am. Chem. Soc. , 63, 978
      (1941).
374. Tamba, R. , Biochem. Z. , 141, 274 (1923).
375. Terayama, H. , J. Polymer Sci. , 15, 575 (1955).
376. Terent'ev, A. P. , A. N. Kost, A. M. Yurkevich, E. E. Khaskira, and
      L. I. Obreimova, Vestn. Mosk. Univ. , 8, No. 6, Ser. Fiz. -Mat.
      i Estestven. Nauk, No. 4, 121 (1953); Chem. Abstr. , 49, 8104
      (1955).
377. Terent'ev, A. P. , and N. B. Kupletskaya, Dokl. Akad. Nauk SSSR,
      90, 807 (1953); Chem. Abstr. , 50, 2368 (1956).
378. Terent'ev, A. P. , and N. B. Kupletskaya, Zh. Obshch. Khim. , 26,
      451 (1956); Chem. Abstr. , 50, 9235 (1956).
379. Terent'ev, A. P. , and V. M. Potapov, Zh. Obshch. Khim. , 26,
      1225 (1956); Chem. Abstr. , 50, 16709 (1956).
380. Thomas, J. C. , U. S. Patent 2, 511, 229; Chem. Abstr. , 44, 8657
      (1950).
381. Tian, A. , Bull. Soc. Chim. France, 1950, 1223.
382. Tian, A. , Compt. Rend. , 228, 836 (1949).
383. Tischbirek, G. , U. S. Patent 2, 931, 822; Chem. Abstr. , 54,
      18354 (1960).
384. Tokura, N. , R. Tada, and K. Yokoyama, Bull. Chem. Soc. Japan,
      34, No. 12, 1812 (1961); Chem. Abstr. , 57, 3312 (1962).
385. Touey, G. P. , and J. E. Kiefer, U. S. Patent 2, 969, 356; Chem.
      Abstr. , 55, 12851 (1961).

386. Traube, W., U.S. Patent 1, 510, 425; Chem. Abstr., 19, 76 (1925).
387. Traube, W., B. Blaser, and C. Grunert, Ber., 61B, 754 (1928).
388. Traube, W., B. Blaser, and E. Lindemann, Ber., 65B, 603 (1932).
389. Traube, W., and R. Justh, Brennstoff-Chem., 4, 150 (1923); Chem. Abstr., 17, 3858 (1923).
390. Turvey, J. R., and M. J. Clancy, Nature, 183, 537 (1959).
391. UCLAF, British Patent 895, 464; Chem. Abstr., 57, 13684 (1962).
392. Upjohn Co., British Patent 746, 870; Chem. Abstr., 51, 1258 (1957).
393. Valentine, L. M., British Patent 915, 573; Chem. Abstr., 58, 13795 (1963).
394. Van Meter, W. P., and G. H. Cady, J. Am. Chem. Soc., 82, 6006 (1960).
395. Varlamov, V. S., and T. M. Ivanova, Maslob. -Zhir. Prom., 28, No. 12, 19 (1962); Chem. Abstr., 58, 11581 (1963).
396. Venkataraman, K., The Chemistry of Synthetic Dyes, Vol. 2, Academic Press, New York, 1952, pp. 1046-55.
397. Verley, A., Bull. Soc. Chim. (3), 25, 46 (1901).
398. Viard, M. J., U.S. Patent 2, 684, 977; Chem. Abstr., 49, 11005 (1955).
399. Vishnevskii, N. A., J. App. Chem. USSR (English Transl.), 34, No. 4, 920 (1961).
400. Vogler, K., U.S. Patent 2, 831, 851; Chem. Abstr., 52, 14098 (1958).
401. Waddelow, R. W., and E. L. Hatlelid, Southwest Regional Meeting, American Chemical Society, Oklahoma City, Okla., Dec., 1960.
402. Waldmann, E., and A. Chwala, Austrian Patent 160, 231; Chem. Abstr., 47, 11256 (1953).
403. Wander, A., A. G., Swiss Patent 305, 572; Chem. Abstr., 50, 15110 (1956).
404. Warner, D. T., and L. L. Coleman, J. Org. Chem., 23, 1133 (1958).
405. Waters, W. A., Quart. Rev. (London), 12, 277 (1958).
406. Weil, J. K., A. J. Stirton, and R. G. Bistline, Jr., J. Am. Oil Chemists' Soc., 31, 444 (1954).
407. Weil, J. K., A. J. Stirton, and E. W. Maurer, J. Am. Oil Chemists' Soc., 32, 148 (1955).
408. Wenker, H., J. Am. Chem. Soc., 57, 2328 (1935).
409. Whistler, R. L., and W. Spencer, Arch. Biochem. Biophys., 95, 36 (1961).
410. Whistler, R. L., and W. W. Spencer, in, Methods in Carbohydrate Chemistry, Vol. 3, Academic Press, New York 1963, pp. 265-267.

411.   Whistler, R. L., W. W. Spencer, and J. N. BeMiller, in R. L.
        Whistler and M. L. Wolfram, Eds. Methods in Carbohydrate
        Chemistry, Vol. 2, Academic Press, New York, 1963, pp.
        299-303.
412.   Whyte, D. D., J. Am. Oil Chemists' Soc., 32, 313 (1955).
412a.   Wigler, P. W., and H. U. Choi, J. Am. Chem. Soc., 86, No. 8,
        1636 (1964).
413.   Winkler, D. E., and G. W. Hearne, J. Org. Chem., 25, 1835
        (1960).
414.   Wolfram, M. L., R. A. Gibbons, and A. J. Huggard, J. Am. Chem.
        Soc., 79, 5043 (1957).
415.   Wolfram, M. L., and T. M. S. Han, J. Am. Chem. Soc., 81, 1764
        (1959).
416.   Wolfram, M. L., and B. O. Juliano, J. Am. Chem. Soc., 82, 2588
        (1960).
417.   Wood, J. W., and P. T. Mora, J. Am. Chem. Soc., 80, 3700
        (1958).
418.   Wroblevsky, E., Z. Chemie, 1868, 563.
419.   Wurzburg, O. B., M. W. Rutenberg, and L. J. Ross, U. S. Patent
        2, 786, 833; Chem. Abstr., 51, 10936 (1957).
420.   Yamaguchi, S., Nippon Kagaku Zasshi, 80, 171 (1959); Chem.
        Abstr., 55, 5396 (1961).
421.   Yamaguchi, S., Nippon Kagaku Zasshi, 81, 1332 (1960); Chem.
        Abstr., 56, 445 (1962).
422.   Yoshida, S., Japanese Patent 178, 560; Chem. Abstr., 45,
        9902 (1951).
423.   Zenik, R., B. Desfosses, and R. Emiliozzi, Compt. Rend., 250,
        1671 (1960).

CHAPTER 7

SULFAMATION

I. INTRODUCTION

Sulfamation, sometimes termed N-sulfonation, involves the formation of compounds of the general structure R_2NSO_3H, as well as the corresponding salts, acid halides, and esters.

Previous reviews (13, 104), as well as the present one, indicate that, as with sulfonation and sulfation, the approach mostly used for sulfamation involves the direct reaction of an amino compound with one of the compounds of SO_3 described in Chapter 1. Sulfamation with sulfites is of definite secondary interest, but procedures involving the oxidation of organic sulfur compounds - often used for sulfonation (cf., Chapter 4), and occasionally for sulfation (cf., Chapter 6) - have apparently not been developed at all for this purpose. Sulfamation by alkylation methods ("sulfamalkylation") has been employed in a few cases, as noted in Chapter 5. Developments over nearly the past fifteen years have comprised almost entirely the extension of methods previously known.

As would be expected from the highly nucleophilic character of the amino group, sulfamation occurs easily, even with reagents of low reactivity (such as the SO_3-amine complexes) at room temperature and in aqueous medium. Conversely, free SO_3 has not been employed for sulfamation because of the violence of the reaction. In an interesting comparative study of various methods for sulfamating aliphatic and aromatic amines made in 1944 (12), it was concluded that $ClSO_3H$ is the most satisfactory reagent, since SO_3-amine complexes are difficult to prepare and store. However, the amine complexes, especially SO_3-pyridine, have since then proved by a large margin to be the preferred laboratory reagents for sulfamation. The commercial availability of liquid SO_3, since 1948, has simplified their preparation, and three of these reagents (SO_3-trimethylamine, SO_3-triethylamine, and SO_3-pyridine) have more recently become available in laboratory quantities.

When reviewed in 1950, sulfamates were described as primarily laboratory curiosities without specific uses (104). The widely developing use of sodium cyclohexylsulfamate as a sweetening agent has since then prompted investigation of various alternate methods of synthesis, as well as the preparation of other sulfamates which might have the same property. The discovery that heparin, the naturally-occurring blood anticoagulant, contains sulfamate as well as sulfate groups, has resulted in a notable increase in interest in sulfamates of this type on the part of biochemists and pharmaceutical manufacturers.

II. SULFAMATION WITH COMPOUNDS OF SULFUR TRIOXIDE

A. Inorganic Nitrogen Compounds

The sulfamation of inorganic nitrogen compounds, although properly outside the scope of this discussion, will be mentioned briefly, since similar chemistry is involved and some of the compounds so formed could prove of future use for the preparation of sulfamates.

Sulfur trioxide reacts violently with ammonia, even explosively when both materials are liquids (98), to yield a mixture of several products, including the ammonium salts of sulfuric, sulfamic and imidodisulfonic acids, sulfamide, polymeric sulfimides $[(-HNSO_2-)_x$, where x = 3 and 4], and long-chain polymeric sulfimidic acids (8-10, 13, 98). Numerous patents have appeared on improved procedures for conducting this difficult reaction (which involves the exothermic, instantaneous formation of high-melting solids from two gases), for obtaining certain of the products in preference to others, and for separating the complex product mixture. Upon digestion of the mixture with excess sulfuric acid, all of the compounds are hydrolyzed either to sulfamic acid (which can be separated by filtration), or to ammonium acid sulfate, which remains dissolved. This procedure is used commercially to some extent for making sulfamic acid, as indicated in Chapter 1.

Hydrazine can be mono- and disulfamated in good yield with SO_3-pyridine (14, 43), but the tri- and tetrasulfamates cannot be so prepared:

$$H_2NNH_2 \xrightarrow{SO_3-Py} H_2NNHSO_3H \xrightarrow{SO_3-Py} HO_3SHNNHSO_3H \qquad (7-1)$$

Hydroxylamine forms the O-sulfonic acid with SO_3-nitromethane (43), oleum (59c), or $ClSO_3H$ (89), which suggests that it may react as $^+NH_3O^-$, rather than as NH_2OH (43):

$$^+NH_3O^- + {}^+SO_3{}^- \longrightarrow {}^+NH_3OSO_3{}^- \qquad (7-2)$$

N-substituted hydroxylamines, on the other hand, form N-substituted hydroxysulfamic acids, as shown in Section II-L.

Sodium azide reacts as follows at 50°C (39):

$$NaN{=}\overset{+}{N}{=}\overset{-}{N} + ClSO_3H \longrightarrow NaO_3SN{=}\overset{+}{N}{=}\overset{-}{N} + HCl \qquad (7-3)$$

This interesting compound could be of value for preparing sulfamates; with water or methanol it simply reverts to hydrazoic acid and sulfate ion.

A reaction of special interest for organic synthesis is the following (11):

$$ClCN + SO_3 \longrightarrow ClO_2SNCO \qquad (7\text{-}4)$$

This compound forms novel sulfamic acid derivatives by reaction of the isocyanate group with alkenes, alcohols, phenols (45), and amides (41).

B. Aliphatic Amines

Although the vapors of methyl-, ethyl-, and diethylamines have been reacted directly with SO_3 vapor to form the sulfamates, isolated as the barium salts (22), this approach has not been generally used because the violence of the reaction leads to the formation of mixtures, as with the SO_3-ammonia reaction mentioned in the preceding section. This method has been employed to prepare surface-active compounds from imidazoline-substituted poly(ethyleneamines) (88). On the other hand, SO_3 reacts smoothly and quantitatively as follows, although the method appears hardly practical for preparative purposes (86):

$$(CH_3)_3SiN(C_2H_5)_2 \xrightarrow{SO_3} (CH_3)_3SiO_3SN(C_2H_5)_2 \xrightarrow{H_2O}$$

$$(CH_3)_3SiOH + (C_2H_5)_2NSO_3H \qquad (7\text{-}5)$$

Compounds of SO_3, which are milder than free SO_3, are the usual reagents for converting amines to sulfamates:

$$RNH_2 + SO_3 \cdot Base \xrightarrow{NaOH} RNHSO_3Na + Base \qquad (7\text{-}6)$$

The reaction can be conducted in cold aqueous alkaline solution, or under anhydrous conditions between room temperature and $100\,^{\circ}C$. Methyl- and diethylamines were thus reacted with SO_3-pyridine at room temperature in aqueous alkaline solution (17). n-Butylamine was sulfamated with SO_3-dioxane at room temperature, forming the butylamine salt of the sulfamic acid (60). Benzylamine was converted to the unstable disulfamate with SO_3-pyridine at $100\,^{\circ}C$ in excess pyridine as solvent (82). In aqueous acid this disulfamate was rapidly hydrolyzed to the more stable monosulfamate. Long-chain amines (decyl, pentadecyl, N-alkylaryl) were similarly monosulfamated with SO_3-pyridine under anhydrous conditions (45a).

Audrieth and Sveda (12) concluded, in a comparative study of the preparation of a series of aliphatic, alicyclic and aromatic sulfamates, that the use of $ClSO_3H$, with a solvent like chloroform, was best for laboratory use:

$$3RNH_2 + ClSO_3H \longrightarrow RNHSO_3H \cdot H_2NR + RNH_2 \cdot HCl \qquad (7\text{-}7)$$

This method has been used commercially with dibutylamine (15); the solvent in this case was 2-chlorotoluene.

n-Butylamine gave the amine salt of the sulfamate by heating it at 190°C with sulfamic acid (60), a standard type of procedure:

$$2RNH_2 + NH_2SO_3H \longrightarrow RNHSO_3H \cdot H_2NR + NH_3 \qquad (7\text{-}8)$$

A more recent modification of this method (107) involves heating excess amine with diammonium imidodisulfonate at 170-185°C:

$$4RNH_2 + NH(SO_3H \cdot NH_3)_2 \longrightarrow 2RNHSO_3H \cdot H_2NR + 3NH_3 \qquad (7\text{-}9)$$

The reaction was run in an autoclave, or at atmospheric pressure with high-boiling amines. Twelve primary and secondary amines gave yields varying from 30 to 93%; ammonia formed 84% of sulfamic acid.

C. Cyclohexyl- and Other Alicyclic Amines

The preparation of sodium cyclohexylsulfamate has been studied at length because of its widespread use as a sweetening agent. It was first (12) made from the amine and $ClSO_3H$:

$$3\,C_6H_{11}NH_2 + ClSO_3H \longrightarrow C_6H_{11}NHSO_3H \cdot NH_2C_6H_{11} +$$
$$C_6H_{11}NH_2 \cdot HCl \qquad (7\text{-}10)$$

Neutralization with caustic soda forms the sodium salt and liberates two moles of amine for recovery and recycle. This approach was also employed for sulfamating cycloheptyl- and cyclooctylamines (25), 2-methylcyclohexylamine (12), ac-tetrahydronaphthylamine, and three related secondary amines (dicyclohexyl, cyclohexyl methyl, and cyclohexyl ethyl). None of these compounds has the sweetening power of the cyclohexyl compound.

A second approach has involved reaction of the amine with sulfamic acid by reaction 7-8 at 140 - 180°C (1), a method used commercially. Reaction is facilitated by adding a quantity of high-boiling tertiary amine equimolar to the cyclohexylamine used. (As stated in Chapter 6, the addition of a tertiary amine has a similar effect when sulfating various hydroxy compounds with sulfamic acid.) Recycle of a mole of cyclohexylamine is eliminated, and the desired product is obtained directly, if sodium sulfamate is used instead of sulfamic acid (5, 59a):

$$C_6H_{11}NH_2 + NH_2SO_3Na \longrightarrow C_6H_{11}NHSO_3Na + NH_3 \qquad (7\text{-}11)$$

This reaction is conducted at 200°C in refined paraffin oil as a dispersing medium. Triammonium nitrilotrisulfonate reacts similarly at 170°C (69, 72):

$$6C_6H_{11}NH_2 + N(SO_3H \cdot NH_3)_3 \longrightarrow$$

$$3C_6H_{11}NHSO_3H \cdot H_2NC_6H_{11} + 4 NH_3 \qquad (7\text{-}12)$$

Diammonium imidodisulfonate $[HN(SO_3H \cdot NH_3)_2]$ reacts similarly at 1:4 molar ratio with the amine (70, 107) by reaction 7-9. Ammonium sulfamate has been used at 1:2 (60a). Trisodium nitrilotrisulfonate reacts only at 1:1 molar ratio, therein differing from the ammonium salt.

Recent industrial interest has focussed on methods of using SO_3, which is cheaper than sulfamic acid. Direct reaction of free SO_3 - either as liquid or as vapor - with cyclohexylamine under various conditions forms a mixture (6), of which the desired amine salt is a constituent. This approach has therefore not been commercialized, although procedures of this kind, involving reaction of the two vapors, have been patented (2a, 106). Sulfur trioxide-tertiary amine complexes, on the other hand, react smoothly and in good yield. Under anhydrous conditions, SO_3-triethylamine requires only 30 min. at 15°C (2); this reaction has also been run in boiling water (67). The SO_3-dimethylaniline complex reacts below 10°C using carbon tetrachloride as dispersing medium (47a). Sulfur trioxide-pyridine, employed among other reagents in the original preparative studies of N-cyclohexylsulfamate (12), is of current commercial interest. In this type of reaction, an SO_3 complex of an amine stronger than cyclohexylamine (e. g., triethylamine) yields the tertiary amine salt of N-cyclohexylsulfamic acid; treatment with aqueous sodium hydroxide then gives the sodium sulfamate and liberates the tertiary amine for recycle. On the other hand, SO_3 complexes of tertiary bases weaker than cyclohexylamine (e. g., pyridine or dimethylaniline) form the cyclohexylamine salt of the desired sulfamic acid, plus equivalent free tertiary base. In such cases, conducting the reaction in the presence of aqueous sodium hydroxide by Equation 7-6 obviates recycle of a mole of cyclohexylamine, since the sodium salt is formed in situ as the reaction proceeds.

As indicated in Section III-C, cyclohexylsulfamic acid is also formed from SO_2 with the hydroxylamine.

D. Amino Alcohols

As indicated in Table 7-3, amino alcohols are selectively sulfamated, without sulfation, using SO_3-pyridine in cold aqueous-alkaline solution between pH 7 and 11:5. This approach has been employed with simple (e. g., 3-aminopropanol, bis-(2-hydroxyethyl) amine, DL-serine), as well as more complex (chitosan, neo-hyaluronic acid, neochondroitin sulfate) compounds (101, 102). The sulfamates of the last three compounds (101) were then sulfated on oxygen with SO_3 in liquid SO_2. 2-Aminoethanol is both sulfamated and sulfated with the same reagent in excess anhydrous pyridine at 60 - 100°C (82, 105). As indicated in

Chapter 6, nitrogenous polysaccharides form sulfamate-sulfates under similar conditions. As was also pointed out in Chapter 6, amino alcohols can be selectively sulfated without sulfamation. Any desired combination is, therefore, possible by a correct choice of conditions.

E. Aromatic Amines

In contrast to sulfamic acid itself and the N-mono-, dialkyl-, and cycloalkyl-sulfamic acids, which are stable in acid form, the aromatic sulfamic acids are stable only as salts (49). Methods applicable to the preparation of aliphatic sulfamic acids involving the use of sulfuric acid or oleum, as from isocyanates or carbamates, are not applicable in the aromatic series because of this instability of the sulfamic acid, and the ease of ring sulfonation (23, 24).

1. ANILINE DERIVATIVES

Aromatic amines are usually sulfamated with SO_3-pyridine under anhydrous conditions between room temperature and 100°C. This approach often using excess pyridine as the reaction medium, has been employed with aniline (34), methylaniline (56), 4-aminobiphenyl (34), 4-amino-4'-nitrodiphenylsulfone (16), 4, 4'-bis-(4-aminobenzoylamino)-stilbene-2, 2'-disulfonic acid and its methylamino analogue - both disulfamated (4), 2-(4-aminophenyl)-6-methylbenzthiazole, and its methylamino analogue (3). para-Phenylenediamines, N-monosubstituted with methyl, 4-tolyl, or 4-methoxyphenyl, were disulfamated similarly (57), as was also 3, 5-diaminobenzoic acid (99).

As shown in Table 7-1, sulfamate yields from nitroanilines increase with increasing α methylation of the complexing pyridine (92); since steric hindrance also increases correspondingly, this may be a factor. Apparently, the second methyl group has much less effect than the first. This approach, using SO_3-2-methylpyridine, was extended to the sulfamation of 1-amino-4-benzamidoanthraquinone (62) and to the disulfamation of 1, 3-diamino-4, 6-dinitrobenzene, and 4, 4'-diamino-3, 3'-dinitrobiphenyl (93).

Sulfur trioxide-quinoline in excess quinoline sulfamates N-(4-aminophenyl)-acetoacetamide and 1-(3'-aminophenyl)-3-methyl-5-pyrazolone (51). Diphenylamine has been sulfamated with SO_3-dimethylaniline (56).

In a mixture of 2- and 4-ethylanilines, the 4-isomer sulfamates exclusively first for steric reasons, using SO_3-triethylamine in chloroform for 5 hr. at room temperature (57); isomer separations can be effected in this way.

The amine complexes effect sulfamation in cold aqueous medium, since loss of the adduct by hydrolysis occurs more slowly. Aniline has been so treated with SO_3-pyridine (17). The trimethylamine complex reacts in aqueous suspension with 2, 5-diethoxyaniline (7).

TABLE 7-1

Sulfamation of Nitroanilines with SO_3-Methylpyridines

Compound Sulfamated	Percentage yield of sulfamate			
	Pyridine	2-Methyl- pyridine	4-Methyl- pyridine	2,6-Dimethyl- pyridine
2,4-Dinitroaniline	60-80	100	-	-
2,6-Dinitroaniline	0	21	-	26
4-Nitrodiphenylamine	6	70	3	83

Equimolar SO_3-dioxane is said to convert aniline at 0°C to N-phenylsulfamic acid (49), but this acid is so unstable that the only product actually isolated is its aniline salt, together with a small quantity of by-product sulfanilic acid. The sulfamation of aromatic amines with excess SO_3-dioxane at room temperature is quantitative in 5 min. (95, 97), allowing use of this approach for their analytical determination. Apparently, the arylsulfamic acids are sufficiently stable in solution for this short time to permit their estimation by back-titration. This approach has been used with aniline, the three toluidines, 4-anisidine, benzidine, a xylidine, methylaniline, and ethylaniline. Diphenylamine is sulfonated on the ring even with cooling. Nitroanilines and 2,4-dichloroaniline react only partially; sulfanilamide reacts on the amino, but not on the sulfonamide group.

Although it has long been known that sulfamic acid will sulfamate aniline (77), this procedure has been largely neglected. 4-Aminodiphenylamine, and its ring-substituted alkyl and alkoxy derivatives (55) react thus by refluxing for 2 hr. in chlorobenzene. This type of sulfamation comprises the first step of a modified aniline black dyeing process (46).

Chlorosulfonic acid is a practical reagent for sulfamating aromatic amines, as demonstrated for aniline, 4-ethoxyaniline, and 4-toluidine (12), but it has been employed comparatively seldom. The formation of a mole of amine hydrochloride could be a disadvantage compared to sulfamation with SO_3-amine complexes, where the amine sulfamate salt is the sole major product [cf., Eq. (7-10)].

The following sulfamation, which proceeds quantitatively at room temperature, indicates that aromatic amines incapable of ring sulfonation can be reacted with oleum (66):

$$ (7-13) $$

2. NAPHTHYLAMINES AND AMINOANTHRAQUINONES

Sulfur trioxide-pyridine in excess pyridine sulfamates 1- and 2-naphthylamines (34), and disulfamates 1-amino-4-(phenylamino)-naphthalene (57). At 0°C, 1-naphthylamine is sulfamated quantitatively with excess SO_3-dioxane in 5 min. (97); slight ring sulfonation also occurs under similar conditions with 2-naphthylamine.

2-Aminoanthraquinone and 2,6-diaminoanthraquinone, with SO_3-pyridine and powdered copper in excess pyridine at 40°C, form the sulfamate-disulfate leuco vat dyes (80).

3. AMINOPHENOLS AND AMINONAPHTHOLS

Although phenolic hydroxyl groups are sulfated, and aromatic amino groups are sulfamated, by the same reagents under the same general conditions, limited evidence (33, 35) indicates that either type of product can be obtained from the aminophenols and the aminonaphthols without substantial contamination by the other. Available data, summarized in Table 7-2, indicate that equivalent complexing base yields sulfate, excess base sulfamate. The preparation of 2-aminophenylsulfates by the Elbs persulfate oxidation is discussed in Chapter 6.

On the other hand, even with excess dimethylaniline, 2-amino-6-naphthol hydrochloride forms the sulfate (33), rather than the expected sulfamate. 2-Amino-7-naphthol is reported to form the sulfamate with SO_3-quinoline even with a deficiency of base (52). 2-Amino-1-naphthol, as hydrochloride and as phthalamate, yields only sulfate, regardless of the reagent used, and whether or not excess base is present (33).

F. Isocyanates, Ureas, Urethanes

It has long been known that isocyanic acid reacts with sulfuric acid in the following overall sense (59):

$$ 2HNCO + 2H_2SO_4 \longrightarrow H_2NSO_3H + H_2NCONHSO_3H + CO_2 \qquad (7-14) $$

TABLE 7-2

Sulfamation of Aminophenols and Aminonaphthols with
SO_3-Amine Complexes

Compound	Complexing base	Amount base used	Product	Reference
2-, 3-, and 4-Aminophenols	Dimethylaniline	Equivalent	Sulfate	33
2-Amino-6-naphthol hydro-chloride	Dimethylaniline	Equivalent	Sulfate	33
2-Aminophenol	Dimethylaniline	Excess	Sulfamate	33
2-, 3-, and 4-Aminophenols	Pyridine	Excess	Sulfamate	33, 35
3-(4'-Amino benzoylamino-)-phenol	Pyridine	Excess	Sulfamate	52
2-Hydroxynaph-thalene-3-car-boxylic acid-4'-amino-anilide	None	SO_3 in tetra-chloro-ethylene used	Sulfamate	52
2-Amino-7-naphthol; 5-amino-2-naphthol	Quinoline	Excess	Sulfamate	51
2-Amino-6-naphthol hydro-chloride	Pyridine	Excess	Sulfamate	33

Bieber later noted (23) that aliphatic isocyanates (ethyl-, hexamethyl-enedi-) behave similarly, forming the corresponding sulfamic acids. He proposed a quasi-four-membered ring transition state, with elimination of CO_2 and sulfamation occurring simultaneously:

$$RNCO \xrightleftharpoons{H_2SO_4} \overbrace{RNH=C=O}^{+} \overbrace{-OSO_3H}^{-} \rightleftharpoons RNH-\overset{\overset{O}{\|}}{C} \longrightarrow$$
$$HO_3S-O$$

$$\underset{HO_3S}{\overset{RNH}{|}} + CO_2 \qquad (7\text{-}15)$$

Cyclohexyl isocyanate similarly forms the sulfamic acid (97a).

Bieber also noted (23) that 1,3-dimethylurea forms the sulfamic acid with oleum and suggested the following sequence:

$$CH_3NH\overset{\overset{O}{\|}}{C}NHCH_3 \xrightarrow{SO_3} CH_3NH\overset{\overset{O}{\|}}{C}N(SO_3H)CH_3 \xrightarrow{H_2SO_4}$$

$$CH_3NHSO_3H + \overbrace{CH_3NH=C=O}^{+} \overbrace{-OSO_3H}^{-} \qquad (7\text{-}16)$$

$$\overbrace{CH_3NH=C=O}^{+} \overbrace{-OSO_3H}^{-} \longrightarrow CH_3NHSO_3H + CO_2 \qquad (7\text{-}16\text{-}A)$$

A somewhat similar path was proposed earlier for the conversion of urea to sulfamic acid with oleum (13), a process used commercially as noted in Chapter 1. Urea can be monosulfamated with SO_3 vapor (18), acetyl sulfate (31), or by fusion with SO_3-pyridine at 120 °C (19). The last procedure also gives the disulfamate at 150 °C with two moles of reagent:

$$H_2NCONH_2 \xrightarrow{SO_3} NH_2CONHSO_3H \xrightarrow{SO_3} HO_3SNHCONHSO_3H \qquad (7\text{-}17)$$

Methylguanidine sulfate likewise undergoes monosulfamation with SO_3-pyridine at 100 °C (82).

Carbamates and N-alkyl carbamates were found by Bieber (24) to form sulfamates with oleum:

$$CH_3NHCOOC_2H_5 \xrightarrow[H_2SO_4]{SO_3} CH_3NHSO_3H + CO_2 + C_2H_5^+ \qquad (7\text{-}18)$$

Since the carbamates do not yield sulfamates with sulfuric acid, it was concluded that, like the ureas, they must first undergo sulfamation with SO_3, followed by alkyl-oxygen cleavage. Sulfamation does not occur with sulfuric acid because the cleavage occurs first. Possible mechanisms have been discussed at some length (24).

Dialkyl carbamyl chlorides are quantitatively converted to the sulfamyl chlorides as follows (91):

$$R_2NCOCl \xrightarrow{SO_3} R_2NSO_2Cl + CO_2 \qquad (7-19)$$

As indicated in Section III-C, sulfamyl chlorides also result from the interaction of SO_2 with a chloramine.

G. Amides

Amides, like urea as mentioned in the preceding section, have been sulfamated by fusion with solid SO_3-pyridine for a few minutes at 100 - 150°C. Acetamide and benzamide thus gave 80% yields in 2 min., benzenesulfonamide 60% at 200°C in 5 min. (20). Diketopiperazine was disulfamated by this melt technique (21):

$$(7-20)$$

This type of amido group is apparently quite difficult to sulfamate, since it does not respond to SO_3-pyridine at 100°C under anhydrous conditions, as shown in Table 7-3. An N-alkylamide is, however, reported to react normally (45b), as are also heptamide, adipamide (82), and palmitamide (45b). Benzamide is sulfamated with sulfamic acid in pyridine at 80°C (59b). Myristamide and stearamide form the amide α sulfonic acids, among other products, with SO_3 in liquid SO_2 (64); the sulfamic acids may be the intermediates. Acetamide did not react with excess SO_3-dioxane at room temperature in 3 min. (96); more drastic conditions are apparently required.

Boivin (30a) found that amides give 90% yields of the nitriles upon heating at 210°C with ammonium sulfamate, and proposed the following sequence:

$$RCONH_2 + NH_2SO_3NH_4 \longrightarrow RCONHSO_3NH_4 + NH_3 \qquad (7\text{-}21)$$

$$RCONHSO_3NH_4 \longrightarrow RCN + NH_4SO_4H \qquad (7\text{-}22)$$

Reaction 7-22 was demonstrated by preparation and pyrolysis of the N-acylsulfamates. Baumgarten and Marggraf had earlier shown that nitriles resulted from heating the acylsulfamate salts, or directly from heating an amide with SO_3-pyridine (20). Benzamide is converted to the nitrile with free SO_3, presumably via the sulfamic acid (40).

H. Amino Acids, Polypetides, and Proteins

A series of 20 common amino acids and simple peptides was treated with SO_3-pyridine in cold, aqueous alkaline medium, with the various groups reacting as shown in Table 7-3 (21). Proteins (zein, casein, corn gluten) react with SO_3-trimethyl- or -triethylamines in aqueous alkali at 45 - 60°C in 2 hr. or less (54). Sulfamation, and sulfation of phenolic hydroxyl groups, appear the sole reactions under these conditions.

Many other functional groups react under anhydrous conditions in excess pyridine at 100°C, as is indicated in Table 7-3. Glycine ethyl ester hydrochloride forms a disulfamate (82), which is rapidly hydrolyzed to the monosulfamate with aqueous acid. A series of 17 proteins and related compounds was sulfamated under these conditions (81, 82). Insulin was progressively sulfamated in a similar manner, but the products formed were all less active physiologically (87).

I. Amino-Substituted Heterocyclic Compounds

Primary amino groups on heterocyclic compounds are sulfamated by conventional procedures. 2-Aminothiazole and several of its derivatives react with $ClSO_3H$ (48) or with 25% oleum at 0°C:

$$(7\text{-}23)$$

2-Amino-5-nitro- derivatives of thiazole, pyridine, and pyrimidine were sulfamated with SO_3-triethylamine in 1, 2-dichloroethane (78). 2-Aminopyridine formed no sulfamate with $ClSO_3H$ or oleum, but did give a poor yield with SO_3 in 1, 2-dichloroethane (48).

TABLE 7-3

Reaction of Various Functional Groups with SO_3-Pyridine

Group	Medium[a]	
	Cold aqueous alkali	Hot anhydrous pyridine
Amino NH_2	+	+
Amido NH_2	-	+
Imidazole NH	+	-
Indole NH	-	+
Imino NH	+	+
Amido NH (peptide)	-	-[b]
Guanidyl (NH and NH_2)	-	+
Alcoholic OH	-	+
Phenolic OH	+	+
Thiol	Not determined	+

[a] + indicates that reaction occurs; - indicates no reaction.

[b] + in the case of reaction 7-20.

An unusual aspect of the 2-thiazolylsulfamic acids and of 2-pyridyl-sulfamic acid is their extreme stability (49, 90). This phenomenon, which is reflected in their low solubility in water, low conductance, and the high pH of their aqueous solutions, is apparently explained by the formation of an inner salt with a stable five-membered ring, as shown in Equation 7-23. A further indication is the rearrangement of 2-amino-4-methylthiazole-5-sulfonic acid to the sulfamic acid by heating at 165°C for 5 hr. (48, 79).

J. Imino Groups in Heterocyclic Rings

An imino group forming part of a heterocyclic ring undergoes sulfamation by the usual procedures. Chlorosulfonic acid has been employed with pyrrolidine, and with hexa-, hepta-, and octamethylen-
imines (25). Sulfur trioxide-pyridine, with excess pyridine as solvent,
was used at 60 - 100°C with 3-indoleacetic acid (82) and carbazole
(56). Carbazole was also sulfamated with SO$_3$-dimethylaniline in
chlorobenzene or 1,2-dichloroethane as solvent at 15°C (32). Sulfur
trioxide-pyridine in ice water or SO$_3$-trimethylamine in water at 100°C
were used with piperidine (83); the product formed is claimed to be the
2-sulfonate, rather than the much more probable sulfamate. Anabasine
(2-(3-pyridyl)piperidine) was similarly reacted with SO$_3$-pyridine in
aqueous medium (74). Anabasine (76), piperidine, and dipiperidyl
(75) react so rapidly and quantitatively with SO$_3$-dioxane that the procedure can be used for their analytical determination. Indole gave the
sulfamate with SO$_3$-pyridine in cold aqueous medium, as well as at
80°C (94). The free indole sulfamic acids are relatively unstable and
rearrange to the sulfonic acids upon prolonged heating, as indicated
in Chapter 2. The unusual cyclic compound S$_7$NH yields the sulfamic
acid with SO$_3$ at 0°C (42). Pyrrolidine and piperidine gave 62 and 79%
yields of the sulfamate salts at 170-85°C with diammonium imidodisulfonate (107). Sulfamic acid was used with morpholine (103).

K. Cyanides and Nitriles

Hydrogen cyanide combines with SO$_3$ at 7:3 molar ratio (50), but
the composition of the product(s) was not established. A study of the
reaction of KCN, and (CN)$_2$, with SO$_3$ (58a) showed that mixtures were
formed, from which small amounts of S$_2$O$_5$(NCO)$_2$ could be isolated.
This is reminiscent of the formation of ClO$_2$SNCO from ClCN and SO$_3$,
which, however, proceeds cleanly and in good yield (cf., Section II-A).
Another material isolated from the reaction of (CN)$_2$ with SO$_3$ may be
formed as follows:

$$(CN)_2 + 2 SO_3 \longrightarrow \quad \text{(7-23-A)}$$

Acetonitrile reacts as follows (38):

$$2 CH_3CN + SO_3 \longrightarrow \quad \text{(7-24)}$$

(A)

Benzonitrile, and 4-tolunitrile behave similarly (37). The two equations above, and Equation 7-13, suggest that five- and six-membered rings containing the $-C=NSO_2O-$ moiety can form quite easily from appropriate substrates. With oleum, acetonitrile reacts as follows, possibly via reaction 7-24 (38):

$$7 - 24 - A \xrightarrow{\text{H}_2\text{O}} CH_3C(:NSO_3H)NHCOCH_3 \qquad (7\text{-}25)$$

On the other hand, several reports state that acetonitrile and other aliphatic nitriles are monosulfonated in the α position by SO_3 and various of its complexes. These reactions are discussed in Chapter 2.

L. Hydroxylamines

Ethyl-, n-propyl-, and isopropylhydroxylamines form the N-alkyl-hydroxysulfamic acids with solid SO_3 in chloroform suspension (84):

$$RNHOH \xrightarrow{\text{SO}_3} RN(OH)SO_3H \qquad (7\text{-}26)$$

This type of compound was also made in one case from a nitroso compound with bisulfite, as noted in Section III-B. Hydroxylamine itself, on the other hand, forms only the O-sulfonic acid with SO_3 and other reagents, as indicated in Section III-B.

N-Phenylhydroxylamine likewise undergoes sulfamation with SO_3 in carbon tetrachloride, or with SO_3-nitromethane, SO_3-pyridine, or sulfamic acid-pyridine (36), and under more drastic conditions (longer time, excess reagent, polar solvent), the N, O-disulfonic acid results. N-Acyl-N-phenylhydroxylamines form the sulfates.

As shown in Section III-C, hydroxylamines form the sulfamates with sulfur dioxide.

III. SULFAMATION WITH COMPOUNDS OF SULFUR DIOXIDE

A. Nitro Compounds

The interaction of various aromatic nitro compounds under basic conditions with bisulfites yields sulfamates by the Piria reaction (13, 104):

$$C_6H_5NO_2 + 3NaHSO_3 \longrightarrow C_6H_5NHSO_3Na + 2NaHSO_4 \qquad (7\text{-}27)$$

If the solution is not kept basic, the free sulfamic acids, being unstable, form aminosulfonic acids, as discussed in Chapter 3. The nitro compound is thought (13, 44) to undergo reduction to the hydroxylamine, which then yields the sulfamate as follows:

$$RNHOH + NaHSO_3 \longrightarrow RNHSO_3Na + H_2O \qquad (7\text{-}28)$$

Nitro compounds so sulfamated include 3-nitrotoluene (28), 4-nitrodiphenylamine (58), 4-nitro-4'-aminodiphenylsulfone (53), and the 3,5-dinitrobenzenesulfonate of testosterone (68), which was disulfamated.

Bogdanov, who has studied the Piria and related reactions at some length (cf., Chapter 3), found that the sulfamation of 3-nitrobenzoic, 3-nitrobenzenesulfonic acids (29), and of 4-nitrotoluene (27) was inhibited by adding certain phenolic compounds capable of sulfonation, including hydroquinone, 2-naphthol-4-sulfonic acid, and 2-hydroxy-3-naphthoic acid, while phenols not easily sulfonated (e. g., hydroquinonedisulfonic acid) did not inhibit the reaction.

The conversion of aliphatic nitro compounds to the corresponding sulfamates with inorganic sulfites is apparently known only in the case of nitrocyclohexane (12), where sodium hydrosulfite ($Na_2S_2O_4$) was used. A reaction which is apparently of the same general type occurs at room temperature with SO_2 in the presence of primary and secondary amines (103), forming the amine salts of imidodisulfonic acid by the following overall sequence:

$$R_2CHNO_2 + R'NH_2 \longrightarrow R_2C \overset{O^-}{\underset{+}{=}}\!NO^- \cdot R'NH_3^+ \qquad (7\text{-}29)$$

$$R_2C \overset{O^-}{\underset{+}{=}}\!NO^- \cdot R'NH_3^+ + R'NH_2 + 2\,SO_2 \longrightarrow R_2C = NR' +$$
$$HN(SO_3^- \cdot R'NH_3^+)_2 \qquad (7\text{-}30)$$

Primary and secondary nitro compounds (1- and 2-nitropropanes, nitrocyclohexane) undergo this reaction. The fact that tertiary nitro compounds do not react in this way is evidence that reaction 7-29 may be the first step with those nitro compounds which are operative. Cyclohexanone oxime similarly forms a salt of sulfamic acid with SO_2 and an aliphatic amine, which is further evidence for the sequence 7-29, 7-30):

$$R_2C=NOH + R'NH_2 + SO_2 \longrightarrow R_2C = NR' + H_2NSO_3^- \cdot R'NH_3^+ \qquad (7\text{-}31)$$

B. Nitroso and Isonitroso Compounds

A 5-isonitrosopyrimidine forms the 5-sulfamate with sodium bisulfite (85), a known, but little used, type of reaction for oximes in general (104). 5-Nitroso-8-hydroxyquinoline sulfate gives the 5-(N-sulfohydroxylamine) derivative (100) with sodium bisulfite, instead of the expected sulfamate. This apparently novel reaction can be regarded as simple addition of bisulfite to the nitroso group:

$$RNO + HSO_3Na \longrightarrow RN(OH)SO_3Na \qquad (7\text{-}32)$$

The Piria reaction is thought (44) to proceed via (7-28); apparently reaction 7-32 has not been considered as a possible alternative. The following reaction can also occur:

$$RNO + NaHSO_3 + H_2O \longrightarrow RNHOH + NaHSO_4 \qquad (7\text{-}33)$$

As indicated in Section II-L, N-sulfohydroxylamines can be made by direct sulfonation of certain hydroxylamines.

C. Hydroxylamines

Ethyl-, n-propyl-, and isopropylhydroxylamines form the sulfamates with SO_2 (84):

$$RNHOH + SO_2 \longrightarrow RNHSO_3H \qquad (7\text{-}34)$$

This known type of reaction (104) was also applied to cyclohexylhydroxylamine (63). An interesting variant of this method comprises preparation of sulfamyl chlorides from chloramines (26):

$$R_2NCl + SO_2 \longrightarrow R_2NSO_2Cl \qquad (7\text{-}35)$$

D. Miscellaneous

Bogdanov, in the course of extended studies of sulfamates and related compounds, noted that aniline could be sulfamated with $K_2SO_3 \cdot 2$ NO, HgNaSO3, or HON(SO3K)2 (30).

Sulfamation can occur by ring cleavage of an arylene 2, 1, 3-oxidiazole-1-oxide (41a):

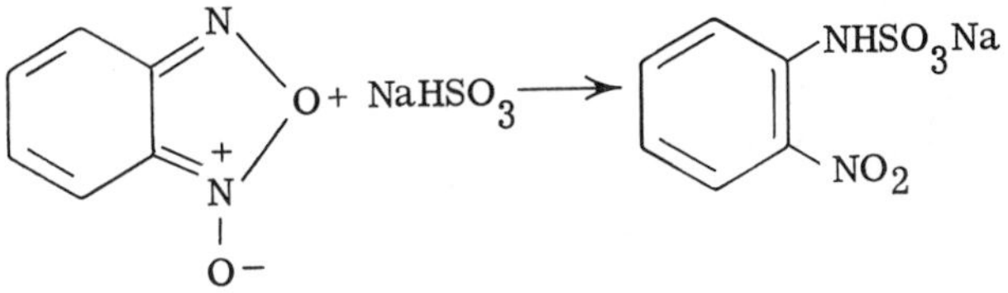

REFERENCES

1. Abbott Laboratories, British Patent 662,800; Chem. Abstr., 46, 11236 (1952).
2. Abbott Laboratories, British Patent 669,200; Chem. Abstr., 47, 5437 (1953).
2a. Abbott Laboratories, South African Patent 329 ('63).
3. Ackermann, F., U.S. Patent 2,550,321; Chem. Abstr., 45, 7360 (1951).
4. Ackermann, F., U.S. Patent 2,567,796; Chem. Abstr., 46, 754 (1952).
5. Aiko, I., K. Saruwatari, and M. Matsushima, Japanese Patent 3781 ('60); Chem. Abstr., 55, 1481 (1961).
6. Allied Chemical Corporation, General Chemical Division, Unpublished research data.
7. American Cyanamid Company, "Trialkylamine-Sulfur Trioxide Compounds," New York, 1955.
8. Appel, R., and M. Goehring, Angew. Chem., 64, 616 (1952).
9. Appel, R., and W. Huber, Z. Anorg. Allgem. Chem., 275, 338 (1954).
10. Appel, R., and W. Huber, Chem. Ber., 89, 386 (1956).
11. Appel, R., and W. Senkpiel, Chem. Ber., 91, 1195 (1958).
12. Audrieth, L. F., and M. Sveda, J. Org. Chem., 9, 89 (1944).
13. Audrieth, L. F., M. Sveda, H. H. Sisler, and M. J. Butler, Chem. Rev., 26, 49 (1940).
14. Audrieth, L. F., and S. F. West, J. Am. Chem. Soc., 77, 5000 (1955).
15. Baird, W., U.S. Dept. Commerce, OTS Rept. PB34,004 BIOS Final Rept. 239, 1946.
16. Bauer, H., J. Am. Chem. Soc., 73, 2113 (1951).
17. Baumgarten, P., Ber., 59B, 1976 (1926).
18. Baumgarten, P., Ber., 69B, 1929 (1936).
19. Baumgarten, P., and I. Marggraf, Ber., 64B, 301 (1931).
20. Baumgarten, P., and I. Marggraf, Ber., 64B, 1582 (1931).
21. Baumgarten, P., I. Marggraf, and E. Dammann, Z. Physiol. Chem., 209, 145 (1932); Chem. Abstr., 26, 5069 (1932).
22. Beilstein, F., and E. Wiegand, Ber., 16, 1264 (1883).
23. Bieber, T. I., J. Am. Chem. Soc., 75, 1405 (1953).
24. Bieber, T. I., J. Am. Chem. Soc., 75, 1409 (1953).
25. Blicke, F. F., H. E. Millson, Jr., and N. J. Doorenbos, J. Am. Chem. Soc., 76, 2498 (1954).
26. Bodenbrenner, K., and R. Wegler, German Patent 1,028,129; Chem. Abstr., 54, 14276 (1960).
27. Bogdanov, S. V., J. Gen. Chem. USSR (English Transl.), 13, 584 (1943); Chem. Abstr., 39, 698 (1945).
28. Bogdanov, S. V., J. Gen. Chem. USSR (English Transl.), 13, 797 (1943); Chem. Abstr., 39, 918 (1945).

29. Bogdanov, S. V. , J. Gen. Chem. USSR (English Transl.), 15, 967 (1945); Chem. Abstr. , 40, 6456 (1946).
30. Bogdanov, S. V. , and N. N. Karandasheva, J. Gen. Chem. USSR (English Transl.), 17, 87 (1947); Chem. Abstr. , 42, 138 (1948).
30a. Boivin, J. L. , Can. J. Res. , 28B, 671 (1950).
31. Boivin, J. L. , and A. L. Lovecy, Can. J. Chem. , 33, 1222 (1955).
32. Borodkin, V. F. , J. Appl. Chem. USSR (English Transl.), 23, 803 (1950); Chem. Abstr. , 46, 8089 (1952).
33. Boyland, E. , and D. Manson, J. Chem. Soc. , 1958, 532.
34. Boyland, E. , D. Manson, and S. F. D. Orr, Biochem. J. , 65, 417 (1957).
35. Boyland, E. , D. Manson, and P. Simms, J. Chem. Soc. , 1953, 3623.
36. Boyland, E. , and R. Nery, J. Chem. Soc. , 1962, 5217.
37. Eitner, P. , Ber. , 25, 461 (1892).
38. Eitner, P. , Ber. , 26, 2833 (1893).
39. Elsner, H. , and H. Ratz, German Patent 886, 298; Chem. Abstr. , 52, 13774 (1958).
40. Engelhardt, A. , Z. Chemie, 1864, 85.
41. Farbwerke Hoechst A. G. , German Patent 1, 144, 718; Chem. Abstr. , 59, 6368 (1963).
41a. Farbwerke Hoechst A. G. , German Patent 1, 155, 119.
42. Goehring, M. , and H. Hohenschutz, Naturwissenschaften, 40, 291 (1953).
43. Goehring, M. , and H. K. A. Zahn, Chem. Ber. , 89, 179 (1956).
44. Goldblum, K. B. , and R. E. Montonna, J. Org. Chem. , 13, 179 (1948).
45. Graf, R. , Chem. Ber. , 96, 56 (1963).
45a. Guenther, F. , and H. Holsten, U. S. Patent 2, 108, 886; Chem. Abstr. , 32, 3056 (1938).
45b. Guenther, F. , and H. Holsten, U. S. Patent 2, 108, 887; Chem. Abstr. , 32, 3056 (1938).
46. Hall, A. J. , Textile Inds. Fibers, 13, 322 (1952).
47. Hardy, W. B. , and M. Scalera, J. Am. Chem. Soc. , 74, 5212 (1952).
47a. Hayashi, M. , and M. Morita, Japanese Patent 3570 ('62); Chem. Abstr. , 58, 8932 (1963).
48. Hurd, C. D. , and N. Kharasch, J. Am. Chem. Soc. , 68, 653 (1946).
49. Hurd, C. D. , and N. Kharasch, J. Am. Chem. Soc. , 69, 2113 (1947).
50. Hutchings, L. E. , U. S. Patent 2, 908, 550; Chem. Abstr. , 54, 3889 (1960).
51. I. G. Farbenindustrie A. G. , British Patent 328, 032; Chem. Abstr. , 24, 5166 (1930).
52. I. G. Farbenindustrie A. G. , German Patent 530, 826; Chem. Abstr. , 26, 154 (1932).
53. Inoue, I. , and M. Kojima, Japanese Patent 7663 ('51); Chem. Abstr. , 48, 719 (1954).
54. Kerr, R. W. , U. S. Patent 2, 858, 300; Chem. Abstr. , 53, 2658 (1959).

55. Koike, E., I. Sugiyama, and M. Sugawara, Japanese Patent 9791 ('60); Chem. Abstr., 55, 9344 (1961).
56. Kraenzlein, G., H. Greune, M. Thiele, and F. Helwert, U.S. Patent 1,933,985; Chem. Abstr., 28, 491 (1934).
57. Lantz, R., Bull. Soc. Chim. France, 1948, 489; Chem. Abstr., 42, 5865 (1948).
58. Lantz, R. L., and G. H. V. Kremer, U.S. Patent 2,637,743; Chem. Abstr., 47, 9038 (1953).
58a. Lehmann, H. A., L. Riesel, K. Hoehne, and E. Maier, Z. Anorg. Allgem. Chem., 310, 298 (1961).
59. Linhard, M., Ann., 535, 267 (1938).
59a. Loder, D. J., U.S. Patent 2,804,472; Chem. Abstr., 52, 8191 (1958).
59b. Marx, K., K. Brodersen, and M. Quaedvlieg, German Patent 570,956; Chem. Abstr., 27, 4246 (1933).
59c. Matsuguma, H. J., and L. F. Audrieth, Inorg. Syn. 5, 122 (1957).
60. McCasland, G. E., and R. B. Hadgraft, J. Am. Chem. Soc., 73, 5507 (1951).
60a. McQuaid, H. S., U.S. Patent 2,804,477; Chem. Abstr., 52, 8191 (1958).
61. Meuwsen, A., and H. Tischer, Z. Anorg. Allgem. Chem., 294, 282 (1958).
62. Mingasson, G. R. H., G. Kremer, and R. F. M. Sureau, French Patent 1,270,593; Chem. Abstr., 57, 15284 (1962).
63. Mori, S., E. Mishima, and K. Hirao, Japanese Patent 9029 ('60); Chem. Abstr., 55, 9309 (1961).
64. Moyer, W. W., U.S. Patent 2,195,187; Chem. Abstr., 34, 5208 (1940).
65. Mueller, P., and R. Trefzer, U.S. Patent 3,060,231.
66. Neeff, R., and O. Bayer, German Patent 1,032,253; Chem. Abstr., 54, 19717 (1960).
67. Nogura, J. S., Spanish Patent 255,221; Chem. Abstr., 56, 2351 (1962).
68. Nomine, G., and M. Vignau, U.S. Patent 2,933,513; Chem. Abstr., 54, 16481 (1960).
69. Okuda, N., Yakugaku Zasshi, 81, 1531 (1961); Chem. Abstr., 56, 9985 (1962).
70. Okuda, N., Yakugaku Zasshi, 81, 1535 (1961); Chem. Abstr., 56, 9985 (1962).
71. Okuda, N., Yakugaku Zasshi, 81, 1544 (1961); Chem. Abstr., 56, 9985 (1962).
72. Okuda, N., and K. Suzuki, U.S. Patent 3,043,864; Chem. Abstr., 58, 7846 (1963).
73. Okuda, N., and K. Suzuki, Yakugaku Zasshi, 81, 1540 (1961); Chem. Abstr., 56, 9985 (1962).
74. Otroshchenko, O. S., and A. S. Sadykov, Zh. Obshch. Khim., 24, 917 (1954); Chem. Abstr., 49, 8316 (1955).

75. Otroshchenko, O. S., A. S. Sadykov, and N. I. Salit, Zh. Prikl. Khim.,
     34, 2768 (1961); Chem. Abstr., 56, 10915 (1962).
76. Otroshchenko, O. S., A. S. Sadykov, and L. S. Smirova, Zh. Prikl.
     Khim., 34, 2797 (1961); Chem. Abstr., 56, 15608 (1962)
77. Paal, C., Ber., 27, 1241 (1894).
78. Parker, R. P., and J. S. Webb, U. S. Patent 2, 574, 155; Chem.
     Abstr., 46, 9614 (1952).
79. Postovskii, I. Y., and T. S. Mamykina, Zh. Obshch. Khim., 23,
     1765 (1953); Chem. Abstr., 49, 300 (1955).
80. Ratti, R., U. S. Patent 1, 934, 143; Chem. Abstr., 28, 491 (1934).
81. Reitz, H. C., U. S. Patent 2, 344, 267; Chem. Abstr., 38, 3396
     (1944).
82. Reitz, H. C., R. E. Ferrel, H. S. Olcott, and H. Fraenkel-Conrat, J.
     Am. Chem. Soc., 68, 1031 (1946).
83. Rubtsov, M. V., Dokl. Akad. Nauk SSSR, 79, 267 (1951); Chem.
     Abstr., 46, 3051 (1952).
84. Ryer, A. I., and G. B. L. Smith, J. Am. Chem. Soc., 73, 5675
     (1951).
85. Scheuing, G., and W. Konz, German Patent 834, 993; Chem.
     Abstr., 48, 1446 (1954).
86. Schmidt, M., and H. Schmidbaur, Angew. Chem., 70, 657 (1958).
87. Sluyterman, L. A. E., and J. M. K. Van Den Bosch, Biochem.
     Biophys. Acta, 38, 102 (1960).
88. Smith, A. H., U. S. Patent 2, 967, 868; Chem. Abstr., 55, 15513
     (1961).
89. Sommer, F., O. F. Schulz, and M. Nassau, Z. Anorg. Allgem. Chem.,
     147, 142 (1925).
90. Sprague, J. M., and A. H. Land, "Thiazoles and Benzothiazoles, "
     in Heterocyclic Compounds, Vol. V, R. C. Elderfield, Wiley,
     New York, 1957.
91. Stein, E., German Patent 946, 710; Chem. Abstr., 53, 2260
     (1959).
92. Sureau, R. F. M., and P. M. J. Obellianne, U. S. Patent 2, 789, 132;
     Chem. Abstr., 51, 15571 (1957).
93. Sureau, R. F. M., and P. M. J. Obellianne, U. S. Patent 2, 853, 359;
     Chem. Abstr., 53, 3721 (1959).
94. Terent'ev, A. P., S. K. Golubeva, and L. V. Tsymbal, J. Gen. Chem.
     USSR (English Transl.), 19, 781 (1949); Chem. Abstr., 47, 3262
     (1953).
95. Terent'ev, A. P., and N. B. Kupletskaya, Dokl. Akad. Nauk SSSR,
     90, 807 (1953); Chem. Abstr., 50, 2368 (1956).
96. Terent'ev, A. P., and N. B. Kupletskaya, Zh. Obshch. Khim., 26,
     451 (1956); Chem. Abstr., 50, 9235 (1956).
97. Terent'ev, A. P., N. B. Kupletskaya, and E. V. Andreeva, Zh.
     Obshch. Khim., 26, 881 (1956); Chem. Abstr., 50, 11885 (1956).
97a. Thompson, W. W., U. S. Patent 2, 800, 501; Chem. Abstr.,
     51, 17987 (1957).
98. Uchida, S., and Y. Ito, Chem. Soc. Japan Ind. Chem. Sect., 57,
     105 (1954); Chem. Abstr., 49 2685 (1955).

99.   UCLAF, British Patent 879,050; Chem. Abstr., 56, 14173
       (1962).
100.   Urbanski, T., Roczniki Chem., 25, 297 (1951); Chem. Abstr.,
       48, 4546, 9370 (1954).
101.   Warner, D. T., British Patent 838,709; Chem. Abstr., 55, 389
       (1961).
102.   Warner, E. T., and L. L. Coleman, J. Org. Chem., 23, 1133
       (1958).
103.   Wehrmeister, H. L., J. Org. Chem., 25, 2132 (1960).
104.   Wheeler, K. W., in An Outline of Organic Nitrogen Compounds,
       University Lithoprinters, Ypsilanti, Michigan, 1950.
105.   Wolfram, M. L., and B. O. Juliano, J. Am. Chem. Soc., 82,
       2588 (1960).
106.   Yamaguchi, H., Japanese Patent 17,559 (1960); Chem. Abstr.,
       55, 22187 (1961).
107.   Yamaguchi, H., Nippon Kagaku Zasshi, 82, 483 (1961); Chem.
       Abstr., 56, 9926 (1962)

CHAPTER 8

DESULFONATION

I. INTRODUCTION

Desulfonation, as defined herein, comprises effecting the reverse of the various types of reactions employed for preparing sulfonates as discussed in preceding chapters. In the aromatic series, where desulfonation has been most used, this involves hydrolytic cleavage to sulfuric acid and the aromatic compound by reaction 8-7. Other cleavage reactions of the aromatic sulfur - carbon bond, such as caustic fusion to a phenol, are not included here under this concept. The very few known examples of the desulfonation of heterocyclic compounds suggest that they behave in a manner analogous to the aromatic sulfonates. On the other hand, the aliphatic sulfonates - in the meager number of cases known to date - involve cleavage to sulfites by reversal of some of the procedures listed in Chapter 3. It is thus becoming increasingly evident that many types of sulfonation reactions are reversible; until very recently this was considered limited to aromatic compounds. The subject as a whole is of increasing theoretical and preparative importance.

Aromatic desulfonation was first observed by Armstrong and Field in 1874, and the characteristic features of the reaction, including the dependence of the desulfonation temperature upon chemical structure, and of reaction rate upon acid strength, were noted shortly afterwards. But systematic physicochemical study of the process was not attempted until the recent investigations made by Spryskov, Leitman, Kilpatrick, Cerfontain, and their various associates. Meanwhile, the desulfonation reaction has seen increasing practical application both in the laboratory and commercially, a trend furthered by the need for simple and efficient means for separating the aromatic hydrocarbon isomers made available in recent years by the cracking of petroleum.

Unquestionably, an important recent development is the realization that the sulfonation of benzenoid compounds under reversible conditions can be made to yield "abnormal" isomers as major products, depending upon the extent to which true equilibrium is established. The classical view of substituent groups as being chiefly ortho - para directing on the one hand, or meta directing on the other, is now known to be true only of kinetically-controlled sulfonation, with the thermodynamically-controlled result being opposite. Thus, the sulfonation of benzenoid compounds is now thought to proceed according to the same general principles as those long accepted for naphthalene and its derivatives.

II. ALIPHATIC AND ALICYCLIC COMPOUNDS

Although reversibility is a characteristic usually associated with aromatic sulfonation, it is becoming evident that at least some aliphatic reactions behave similarly.

The direct sulfonation of long-chain aliphatic acids in the α position with SO_3 is discussed in Chapter 2; this reaction proceeds easily in the range 25 - 100°C. It has now been found (82) that α-sulfostearic acid quantitatively regenerates stearic acid upon refluxing with ortho-dichlorobenzene at 180°C, presumably with the formation of dichlorobenzenesulfonic acid. This interesting reaction deserves further study as the first known example of aliphatic-aromatic transsulfonation. This type of reaction is known in the aromatic series, as mentioned in Chapter 1, Section VIII.

Several of the sulfite reactions for preparing aliphatic sulfonates, as discussed in Chapter 3, are also reversible.

A variety of aliphatic sulfonyl chlorides, prepared by free radical chain sulfochlorination of paraffins via reactions 3-1 through 3-4, are smoothly converted to alkyl halides and SO_2 by heating at 150°C (2, 76) by the same general type of mechanism (17, 21):

Initiation:

$$RSO_2Cl \longrightarrow R\cdot + \cdot SO_2Cl \tag{8-1}$$

$$\text{and/or } RSO_2Cl \longrightarrow RSO_2\cdot + Cl\cdot \tag{8-2}$$

$$RSO_2Cl + R'\cdot \longrightarrow RSO_2\cdot + R'Cl \tag{8-3}$$

Propagation:

$$RSO_2Cl + R\cdot \longrightarrow RSO_2\cdot + RCl \tag{8-4}$$

$$RSO_2\cdot \rightleftharpoons R\cdot + SO_2 \tag{8-5}$$

Equation 8-1 is favored for thermal desulfonation, and Equation 8-3 for initiation by peroxides. This reaction has been extended to sulfonyl bromides (16) and exploited for the preparation of long-chain perfluorinated carboxylic acids (77) in the following way:

$$R_fSO_2Cl + CH_2{:}CHCH_2CH_2COOH \longrightarrow$$

$$R_fCH_2CHClCH_2CH_2COOH + SO_2 \tag{8-6}$$

$(R_f$ = perfluoralkyl)

Alkenes add bisulfite, forming alkanesulfonates, as shown in Chapter 3. The reverse type of reaction will occur, as evidenced by the formation of unsaturated oils by heating water-soluble petroleum sulfonates (6). A mechanistic study of this reaction with sulfonates of known structure would be of interest.

The addition of bisulfite to heteroconjugated alkenes is known to be reversed under suitably alkaline conditions. This has been noted with the adduct made from a cinnamic acid derivative (46), and from 2-methylnaphthoquinone (Eq. 3-78). The Bucherer reaction (Eq. 3-82) likewise involves desulfonation under basic conditions. The addition of sulfurous acid to tetracyanoethylene is reversed by gentle heating, per Equation 3-54.

III. AROMATIC COMPOUNDS

A. General Discussion

Many types of aromatic sulfonates are hydrolytically desulfonated by heating in aqueous medium by the following overall reaction:

$$RSO_3H + H_2O \longrightarrow RH + H_2SO_4 \qquad (8-7)$$

Suter (75) and Muth (49) have generally reviewed aromatic desulfonation through 1941 and 1954, respectively.

This type of reaction generally proceeds rapidly and in good yield, especially in the presence of an added mineral acid (sulfuric, phosphoric, hydrochloric, or hydrobromic), which accelerates the reaction catalytically. From desulfonation studies of hydroxy-, alkyl-, and nitroaminobenzenesulfonic acids conducted in 90% acetic acid in the presence of HBr or H_2SO_4 as catalysts, it was concluded (3) that the reaction velocity is independent of sulfonic acid concentration, conforms to a first order equation, and is proportional to the hydrogen ion activity of the solution, but is independent of the nature of the inorganic anion. The reversible relation between sulfonation and desulfonation is summarized as:

$$ArSO_3^- + H_3O^+ \rightleftharpoons Ar\overset{SO_3}{\underset{H}{\diagup}} \cdots OH_2 \rightleftharpoons ArH + H_2O \cdot SO_3 \qquad (8-8)$$

and it is concluded that "sulfonation and desulfonation are thus essentially determined by the distribution of the acids, proton and SO_3 ---, between the bases phenyl anion and water." It had been earlier observed (11) that for each 10°C rise in temperature the reaction velocity increases 2.5 - 3.5 times, and that a similar increase in rate was observed at any given temperature for one molar increase in the concentration of the mixed acid in the solution. Long and Paul (41), in a discussion of the current status of thought regarding the mechanism of desulfonation, note that the reason for observed variations in the dependence of reaction rate on acidity may result from the conversion of sizeable amounts of the reactant to the conjugate acid:

$$ArSO_3H + H^+ \rightleftharpoons ArSO_3H_2^+ \tag{8-9}$$

$$ArSO_3H_2^+ \rightleftharpoons ArH + SO_3 + H^+ \text{ (slow)} \tag{8-10}$$

Another possible mechanism would involve transfer of a proton to the un-ionized sulfonic acid as the rate determining step. They conclude, however, that further study is required before a plausible mechanism for desulfonation can be formulated.

Other studies (68) indicated, on the contrary, that the nature of the catalyst anion is important, with activity decreasing rapidly in the order HCl, H_2SO_4, H_3PO_4, as shown in Table 8-1, and that the increase in reaction rate is not directly proportional to the increase in acid concentration. The rate-determining step is concluded to involve reaction of the catalyst anion with a complex of structure $RSO_3H \cdot H_3O^+$ (39, 69).

TABLE 8-1

Comparison of Acid Catalysts for Desulfonating
1-Naphthalenesulfonic Acid

Per cent hydrolysis	(25 hr., 100°C, 4.5 moles H_2O) Per cent strength of acid catalyst		
	HCl	H_2SO_4	H_3PO_4
4	6	14	25
25	24.5	47	76
35	27	52	80

If aqueous solutions of the sulfonic acids are heated in sealed tubes, with or without added acid catalysts, only partial hydrolysis will occur gradually over a long period of time at a suitably low temperature, as indicated in Tables 8-1 and 8-3. If, however, the aqueous sulfonic acid is heated in an open vessel using efficient agitation, with the passage of a current of steam, it is found that substantially complete hydrolysis occurs rapidly (e.g., in an hour or less), and at a temperature roughly characteristic of each compound. A number of these "desulfonation temperatures" are quoted in Table 8-2. Volatile organic compounds are thus steam distilled from the reaction mixture as rapidly as formed by hydrolysis.

Hydrolysis will not occur if the sulfuric acid strength is kept too high by the maintenance of too elevated a temperature with the consequent net loss of water, since then the equilibrium of Equation 8-8 cannot be driven to the right, and the rate of resulfonation becomes equal to that of desulfonation. This effect was noted with 1, 2, 3-trimethylbenzene above acid strengths of 70% (37); with 2-chlorobenzenesulfonic acid disulfonation became pronounced with 88% acid (65). The acid strength at which the rates of desulfonation and resulfonation become equal can thus be approached from both directions. In Chapter 2, this was designated the "π value," in referring specifically to the acid strength at which the sulfonation of a given compound stops because the acid has become too dilute.

Desulfonation is also applicable to nonvolatile materials which remain in the reactor until cleavage is complete. Compounds in this category include hydroxy- and amino-substituted anthraquinones (15, 47), 2, 6-dinitroaniline (57), ion-exchange resins (50), and other compounds mentioned in Sections III-D-3 and III-D-4. Naphthalenedisulfonic acids undergo stepwise cleavage (66). The addition of an inert organic solvent is often helpful when working with unstable, nonvolatile compounds (49).

Hydrochloric and hydrobromic acids are too volatile for use as desulfonation catalysts except in sealed tubes. Sulfuric acid, although nonvolatile, sometimes undesirably oxidizes or decomposes sensitive compounds, or, as stated before, may effect resulfonation. These difficulties have been overcome by using a "flash" procedure, which involves gradual addition of the sodium sulfonate to hot sulfuric acid through which a stream of superheated steam is being passed (61). The desulfonated compound is thus distilled from the reaction mixture after only momentary exposure to the acid medium. Phosphoric acid is being used with increasing frequency in the range 190 - 220°C either at atmospheric pressure (59), or as a 30% aqueous solution in an autoclave (9). Although, as shown in Table 8-1, it is a less active catalyst than either of the other two acids, it is nonvolatile, and has been shown not to oxidize, isomerize, or otherwise alter organic compounds under these conditions. However, phosphoric acid gave unsatisfactory results with hydroxylated petroleum sulfonic acids under some conditions (62), but not under others (9).

B.   Influence of Chemical Structure

The desulfonation temperature is defined as the minimum temperature at which the reaction occurs at a practical rate at atmospheric pressure. The data cited in Table 8-2, from various sources and obtained under varying conditions, give some indication of the variation in the desulfonation temperatures resulting from alterations in chemical structure. It is seen that isomeric compounds react at different temperatures; as discussed below, this provides a basis for isomer separation. Increasing methylation of the ring greatly facilitates de-

TABLE 8-2

Desulfonation Temperatures of Benzenesulfonic Acid Derivatives

Substituent	Desulfonation temperature	Acid	Reference
None	227	H_3PO_4	78
2-CH_3	188	H_3PO_4	78
3-CH_3	155	H_3PO_4	78
4-CH_3	186	H_3PO_4	78
2,4-$(CH_3)_2$	137	H_3PO_4	78
3,4-$(CH_3)_2$	175	H_3PO_4	78
2,4,6-$(CH_3)_3$	80	HCl	36
Pentamethyl	25	H_2SO_4	28
2-SO_3H	180	H_2SO_4	71
3-SO_3H	195	H_2SO_4	71
4-SO_3H	205	H_2SO_4	71
3-Cl	182	H_3PO_4	78
4-Cl	200	H_3PO_4	78
2,4-$(Cl)_2$	155	H_3PO_4	78
4-Br	217	H_3PO_4	78
4-OH	123	H_2SO_4	10
4-OH-3-CH_3	133	H_2SO_4	10
4-OH-2-CH_3	116	H_2SO_4	10
4-OH-2,3-$(CH_3)_2$	115	H_2SO_4	10

sulfonation. The tri- and tetramethylbenzenesulfonic acid isomers with two groups ortho to the sulfonic group can desulfonate even at room temperature or below, whereas the isomers with only one ortho methyl group react less easily (11, 32, 33). Pentamethylbenzenesulfonic acid behaves likewise (32). An ortho hydroxyl group has less effect than methyl in facilitating desulfonation (24).

The desulfonation temperatures quoted in Table 8-2, although indicative, should not be taken too literally, since it has been pointed out that the desulfonation temperature of an individual sulfonic acid will vary considerably with the nature and quantity of the reaction medium and with the conditions used (67). In addition, there may be as much as a 40°C difference between the temperature at which hydrolysis becomes perceptible and that at which the rate is maximum (1). This can lead to the selection of different desulfonation temperatures for one compound. On the other hand, some of the phenolic materials listed in Table 8-2 are stated to desulfonate over a 3°C range (10). In general, however, it appears that the degree of partial hydrolysis at a fixed temperature is a more precise index of comparative hydrolytic stability than the desulfonation temperature. From Table 8-2 it would be concluded that 3-methyl- and 3-chlorobenzenesulfonic acids undergo desulfonation more easily than the other isomers. More recent work with toluene, however, has shown that ease of cleavage decreases in the order ortho-para-meta, since the respective rate constants in 60% H_2SO_4 at 152°C for the three toluenesulfonic acids are 27, 13, and 0.37 x 10^{-5} sec. $^{-1}$ (79). A similar result was noted in 30% HCl at 100°C (64). As shown in Table 8-3, two other ortho-para- directing groups,

TABLE 8-3

Partial Desulfonation of Substituted Benzenesulfonic Acids

Substituent	Temperature	Time (hr.)	Per cent cleavage
2-NH_2	211	4	90
3-NH_2	211	4	0
4-NH_2	211	4	66
2-Cl	163	100	49
3-Cl	163	100	2
4-Cl	163	100	14
3-OH	110	25	0.4
4-OH	110	25	44

chloro and amino, show the same pattern, as does also hydroxyl in the two cases cited (70). However, the figures quoted in Table 8-2 for the chloro compounds would lead to the opposite conclusion. The meta-directing carboxyl and sulfonic acid substituents, on the other hand, decrease the ease of desulfonation in the order ortho-meta-para (71). It thus appears that electron-donating substituents facilitate both sulfonation and desulfonation, while electron-withdrawing groups inhibit both reactions (24). Also, for both types of substituents, ease of sulfonation parallels that of desulfonation for the meta and para positions. This conclusion was reached many years ago for the methylated benzenes (1). For the ortho position steric factors inhibit sulfonation and facilitate desulfonation regardless of the type of substituent.

Recent studies have emphasized the quantitative kinetic aspects, especially for the methylated benzenesulfonic acids. Such data have been reported for the three trimethylbenzenesulfonic acid isomers (37, 40), as summarized in Table 8-4. Another such study of mesitylenesulfonic acid (33) was made at 12.3°C using 72.0 - 77.8% H_2SO_4, conditions under which the two other isomers do not desulfonate. Data for

TABLE 8-4

Hydrolysis Rate Constants for Trimethylbenzenesulfonic Acids in Aqueous Sulfuric Acid

$(k \cdot 10^4 \cdot min.^{-1})$

	1,3,5-Isomer (Mesitylene)			1,2,4-Isomer (Pseudocumene)			1,2,3-Isomer (Hemimellitene)		
% Acid	40.0	49.6	54.6	49.6	64.7	70.2	50	60.5	70
Temp. 80	-	3.9	11.8	-	-	-	-	-	-
100	6.2	33.8	-	-	3.4	4.8	17.3	73.7	185.0
115	-	-	-	1.2	-	-	42.6	188.0	458.3
130	-	-	-	-	54.0	-	-	537.0	1151.2

two of the three tetramethylbenzenesulfonic acid isomers, and for pentamethylbenzenesulfonic acid, are given in Table 8-5 for conditions under which the third tetramethylbenzenesulfonate isomer (1,2,3,4) does not desulfonate (32). Mesitylene, and the three compounds listed in Table 8-5, all have methyl groups on both sides of the sulfonic group, which renders desulfonation easy. Why these compounds should differ to such an extent among themselves has not been explained. Kinetic studies have also been made on 2-chlorobenzenesulfonic acid using $H_2S^{35}O_4$ as tracer at various acid strengths over the temperature range 119 - 150°C (65), as well as on the two other chlorobenzenesulfonic acid isomers (30).

TABLE 8-5

Hydrolysis Rate Constants for Polymethylbenzenesulfonic Acids

(At 12.3°C)

	1,2,4,5-Isomer (Durene)			1,2,3,5-Isomer (Isodurene)			Pentamethylbenzene		
% Acid	76.1	81.2	83.2	70.3	74.9	77.8	57.9	63.3	64.6
$k.10^4.min^{-1}$	10.0	48.0	82.3	22.6	68.5	155.0	12.9	46.4	68.0

C. Sulfonation - Desulfonation - Resulfonation

This phenomenon is characteristic of all aromatic sulfonation reactions conducted under reversible conditions - i.e., with acid or oleum at elevated temperature and/or with prolonged times of reaction. Although specific aspects of it have been studied for some time by Spryskov and co-workers, the generality of this effect has not been appreciated until very recently.

The concepts involved appear well illustrated in the case of naphthalene (63). The following reactions occur:

$$C_{10}H_8 + H_2SO_4 \rightleftharpoons 1\text{-}C_{10}H_7SO_3H + H_2O \qquad (8\text{-}11)$$

$$C_{10}H_8 + H_2SO_4 \rightleftharpoons 2\text{-}C_{10}H_7SO_3H + H_2O \qquad (8\text{-}12)$$

Below 70°C, both reactions will proceed to the right, but not to the left. Between 70 and 113°C, reaction 8-11 goes in both directions, but 8-12 functions only to the right. Above 113°C, both reactions are true equilibria. In spite of steric hindrance, reaction 8-11 proceeds much more rapidly than reaction 8-12, and the 1-sulfonate is, therefore, the main product at 100°C, after a short reaction time. However, after 60 days at the same temperature (cf., Table 2-19), the product comprises

97. 8% 2-isomer and 2. 2% 1-isomer. Thus, the 1-sulfonate, although
the first to be formed, is desulfonated at 100°C, whereas the 2-sulfo-
nate, not being desulfonated, is finally almost the sole product, provided sufficient time is allowed. Heating the 1-sulfonate with C^{14} in
the 1-position at 160°C in 91% H_2SO_4 yields the 2-sulfonate substituted
randomly in all four of the 2-positions (80). This experiment shows
that desulfonation-resulfonation is involved, rather than "rearrangement, " a conclusion also reached independently with toluene (81).

Gore (20) has characterized a similar phenomenon with anthracene
and phenanthrene. Rapid, initial sulfonation occurs at the most reactive, but more sterically hindered positions. This may be the result of
greater electron density, or of greater stability of the σ complex (51).
Thereafter, slow proton-catalyzed desulfonation-resulfonation occurs
with essentially irreversible substitution at the less reactive positions.

It has become recognized more recently that kinetically-controlled
orientation and thermodynamically-controlled orientation are also different with benzene derivatives. As might be expected, the isomers
are present at equilibrium in inverse proportion to their ease of desulfonation as mentioned in the preceding section. As shown in Table 2-
14, toluene rapidly forms 21 - 49% of the sterically hindered ortho sulfonate, but upon further heating, this isomer quickly disappears in
favor of the para isomer, which in turn is partially converted to the
most stable meta compound. At equilibrium, the ortho isomer content
is only 3 to 5%, with 55 - 60% being meta (64, 81). Chlorobenzene
similarly forms an equilibrium mixture comprising 0, 54, and 46% of
the ortho, meta, and para isomers (64), although little meta compound is formed initially. This result is consistent with relative ease
of desulfonation, as indicated in Table 8-3. Phenols behave likewise
(31, 48), as shown in Table 2-16. An initial 36, 0, and 64% content of
the ortho, meta, and para isomers becomes 5, 0, and 95 upon further
heating, and at final equilibrium the meta content is 40%.

Meta- directing groups show a similar effect. Although the meta
isomer is the initial product in the sulfonation of benzenesulfonic acid
to produce the disulfonate, it has long been known that the para isomer
is formed to some extent under more drastic conditions. More recent
work (71a) indicates that equilibrium is attained in 87% acid at 66%
meta and 34% para isomers, but reaction is extremely slow, even at
235°C. The ortho isomer, on the other hand, isomerizes very rapidly
at this temperature. It has also been found that the para disulfonate is
the main product upon heating the meta disodium salt at 300°C under
pressure with a metal catalyst. A similar use of drastic conditions for
preparing the abnormal 4-sulfonate of pyridine is mentioned in Section IV.

The reactions discussed in this section lead to the conclusion that
the classical concept of certain groups being mainly ortho-para directors, and of others being mainly meta directors, should be broadened
to the view that various isomers can be obtained depending upon the extent to which true equilibrium is reached by the desulfonation-resulfonation sequence, and upon relative isomer stability as reflected by ease
of desulfonation.

D. Practical Applications of Desulfonation

1. SEPARATION OF ISOMERS

Sulfonation, followed by desulfonation, has been used to separate mixtures of various types of aromatic compounds not easily separable by distillation or other means. Either or both steps can be selective. In addition, the intermediate sulfonate can be purified by several approaches, including layer separation, removal of residual unsulfonated material, recrystallization of the metallic salts, or other means.

A typical example is the separation of ethyltoluene isomers (36, 38); the data are summarized in Table 8-6. The upper sulfonic acid layer, resulting from the addition of an equal volume of water to the crude sulfonation mixture, was steamed. The absence of ortho isomer in the product is explained by the failure of its sulfonic acid to hydrolyze below 200 °C. The fraction obtained below 160 °C, formed in 41% yield, is fairly pure meta isomer, but the para isomer recovered at 180-200 °C still contains some meta isomer. The 160 - 180 °C fraction could be recycled. It thus appears that, like other separation methods, the degree of purification achieved depends upon the narrowness of the fractions taken. Others (42) have used this approach for purifying the meta ethyltoluene isomer.

TABLE 8-6

Separation of Ethyltoluene Isomers

Hydrolysis temperature	Distillate composition (%)		
	Ortho	Meta	Para
(Initial mixture)	1.4	64.0	34.6
Below 160	0	99.4	0.6
160 - 180	0	77.0	23.0
180 - 200	0	8.4	91.6

The isolation of m-xylene by sulfonation-desulfonation has been studied extensively (11, 29, 42, 56, 84), and operated on a substantial commercial scale (23, 43). The conditions for maximum rate of hydrolysis were determined as follows for the three xylene isomers: ortho: 60% acid at 130 - 45 °C; meta: 65% acid at 130 - 45 °C; para: 70% acid at 100 - 30 °C (39). Other hydrocarbons purified by this method include 3, 5-dimethyl-1-ethylbenzene (13), trimethylbenzenes (60), four meta C2-4 (84) and four ortho C3-6 (12) dialkylbenzenes, 1, 2, 4, 5-tetraethylbenzene (55), and dimethylnaphthalene isomers in coal tar (35). This procedure has also been applied to the di- (74) and trichlorobenzenes (44). In the latter case, the 1, 2, 3-isomer sulfonates more easily than the 1, 2, 4-compound, since the former can react with both ortho positions free, whereas the latter cannot. 3-Chlorotoluene (45), 2, 5-dichlorotoluene (26), trichlorotoluenes (8), and chloroxylenes (14) have been similarly purified. A series of eight cresol and xylenol isomers found in coal tar were separated likewise (10). One isomer - 3, 5-xylenol - did not sulfonate under the conditions used, since each available ring position is flanked by two substituents.

2. ANALYSIS OF SULFONIC ACIDS

The desulfonation reaction has proved an indispensible tool in determining the chemical structures of commercial sulfonated petroleum fractions of the lubricating oil range, both water-soluble ("green acids") and oil-soluble ("mahogany acids"). Hydrolysis gave the parent hydrocarbons, which were then analyzed by chromatography and other standard analytical procedures not applicable to corresponding sulfonic acids. Hydrochloric acid (62), and more recently, 30% phosphoric acid (9) have been used as catalysts. The analysis and determination of the constituent fractions of coal tar, including both phenols and hydrocarbons, have also been effected by sulfonation-desulfonation (10, 35); desulfonation in these cases was effected with sulfuric acid.

3. RAW MATERIAL AND WASTE RECOVERY

In manufacture of the insecticide DDT, oleum is employed as the condensing agent; this results in sulfonation of some of the raw material chlorobenzene as a side reaction. Passage of steam into the spent acid results in hydrolysis of the sulfonic acid, permits recovery of the chlorobenzene, and at the same time partially purifies the acid. In the industrial sulfonation of naphthalene in the 2-position intermediate to the preparation of 2-naphthol, a sulfonate mixture of 85% 2-isomer and 15% 1-isomer is obtained. The 1-sulfonate is removed by steaming at 160 - 5°C to effect cleavage, the 2-isomer being stable (18). Similarly, mixtures of anthraquinonedisulfonate isomers (mainly 1, 7- ; also some 1, 6- ; 1, 5- ; and 1, 8-) are recovered by removing all the sulfo groups in the 1-position, yielding anthraquinone and its 2-sulfonate (15). This is effected by prolonged heating in dilute sulfuric acid at 180 - 200°C. Desulfonation is undoubtedly a main reaction occurring during the steaming (at 125°C or higher) of the sulfuric acid sludges obtained commercially in the refining of various petroleum products (52, 72). The aqueous acid can then be concentrated for re-use, and the hydrocarbon layer separated and burned as fuel.

4. SYNTHETIC APPLICATIONS

Sulfonation-desulfonation has proved a useful tool for preparing ortho-substituted benzene derivatives. The sulfonic group is introduced to block the 4-position opposite a methyl, hydroxyl, or acetylamino group; then a chlorine, bromine, alkyl, or nitro group is introduced ortho to one of these groups. Finally, the sulfonic group is removed; for the case of 2-chlorotoluene, the sequence is as follows (15):

$$+ H_2SO_4 \qquad (8\text{-}13)$$

Other compounds prepared by this general scheme include 2, 6-dichloro- and -dibromoanilines (58), 2-bromophenol (25), 2-sec-butylphenol (4), and 2-cyclohexylphenol (54). In the last two cases, the sulfonate group need not be removed by hydrolysis, but can be replaced by an entering nitro group in a final nitration step. 2, 6-Dinitroaniline (57) is likewise prepared by using the sulfonic group to block the 4-position during nitration.

Some of the desulfonation-resulfonation reactions cited in Section III-C appear suitable for synthesis of "abnormal" isomers. The meta toluene- and chlorobenzenesulfonic acids are thus obtainable in fair yield and purity.

Desulfonation has also found application in the preparation of dye intermediates derived from naphthalene and anthraquinone. The isomeric naphthalenedisulfonic acids have decreasing stability to hydrolysis with sulfuric acid at 100 to 160°C in the following order: 2, 6-; 2, 7-; 1, 3-; 1, 7-; 1, 6-; 1, 5-; (66); as expected, the groups in the α positions are more labile than those placed β. 6-Aminonaphthalene-1, - 3-disulfonic acid is prepared by refluxing the 1, 3, 5-trisulfonate in dilute H_2SO_4 for 4 hr. at 125°C (83). Other hydroxy- and aminonaphthalenesulfonic acids have been desulfonated by heating with hydrochloric, phosphoric, or sulfuric acids in the range 100 - 200°C (40, 49).

In the anthraquinone series, desulfonation is regarded as a technique of some importance for the preparation of dye intermediates (15, 47, 73); cleavage is usually effected by heating with 60 - 85% H_2SO_4. As expected, the 2-sulfonate is more stable than the 1-isomer, in which the sulfonic group is situated ortho to the carbonyl moiety. Those situated ortho to hydroxyl or amino groups are quite labile, and advantage is taken of this in the preparation of several dye intermediates.

In the sulfonation of styrene-divinylbenzene copolymers for the preparation of ion-exchange resins, the rate of reaction is diffusion-controlled, and therefore depends upon pore size. On the other hand, desulfonation of the resin with concentrated HCl is independent of pore size (50). By appropriate combined use of these two approaches, it is possible to prepare resins with sulfonate groups in positions either related, or not related, to pore size. The decomposition of sulfonated polystyrene ion-exchange resins upon heating is thought to result from the action of free sulfuric acid liberated by hydrolytic action of residual water in the resin (53).

IV. HETEROCYCLIC COMPOUNDS

The desulfonation of heterocyclic sulfonates has been studied relatively little.

Xanthene (Formula 8-14-A) has been purified by sulfonation-desulfonation, but the yield is only 33 - 40% (34).

(A)   (B)   (C)   (8-14)

The sulfonation of pyridine, as usually conducted at 275°C, yields the 3-sulfonate. However, at 330°C the 4-isomer is formed. As with the disulfonation of benzene, the reaction is reversible and the 4-isomer is the more stable (22). The 4-position of 1-phenyl-3-methyl-5-pyrazolone (Formula 8-14-B) sulfonates easily, followed by the 4-position on the benzene ring. However, the first group expectedly cleaves more easily, leaving the more stable 1-(4-sulfophenyl) derivative as the main reaction product (27). Others (49) have noted desulfonation of this type of sulfonate at 50°C. A study of the desulfonation of the mono- di-, and trisulfonic acids of carbazole (Formula 8-14-C) has shown that the 3-monosulfonic acid is much more easily desulfonated than any of the other compounds (7). The 2, 3, 6, 8-tetrasulfonate of carbazole was converted to the 2-hydroxy-3, 6, 8-trisulfonate and to the 2, 8-dihydroxy-3, 6-disulfonate by caustic fusion; hydrolytic cleavage of these compounds gave the respective mono- and dihydroxycarbazoles (5).

REFERENCES

1. Armstrong, H. E., and A. K. Miller, J. Chem. Soc., 45, 148 (1884).
2. Asinger, F., Chemie und Technologie der Paraffin-Kohlenwasserstoffe, Akademie Verlag, Berlin, 1956.
3. Baddeley, G., G. Holt, and J. Kenner, Nature, 154, 361 (1944).
4. Barker, C. H., and D. W. Pound, British Patent 650,906; Chem. Abstr., 45, 9561 (1951).
5. Bergdolt, A., and A. Schmelzer, U. S. Patent 1,981,301; Chem. Abstr., 29, 618 (1935).
6. Bornstein, L., and F. Rostler, Mod. Plastics, 19, 72 (1942).
7. Borodkin, V. F., Zh. Prikl. Khim., 23, 1105 (1950); Chem. Abstr., 46, 10148 (1952).
8. Brimelow, H. C., R. L. Jones, and T. P. Metcalfe, J. Chem. Soc., 1951, 1208.
9. Brown, A. B., and J. O. Knobloch, ASTM No. 224, 213 (1958), American Society for Testing Materials, Philadelphia.
10. Brueckner, H., Z. Anal. Chem., 75, 289 (1928); Chem. Abstr., 23, 1738 (1929).
11. Crafts, J. M., J. Am. Chem. Soc., 23, 248 (1901).
12. Elsner, B. B., and H. E. Strauss, J. Chem. Soc., 1957, 583.
13. Elwell, W. E., U. S. Patent 2,541,959; Chem. Abstr., 46, 1037 (1952).
14. Engelbertz, P., German Patent 950,464; Chem. Abstr., 53, 4205 (1959).
15. Fierz-David, H. E., and L. Blangey, Fundamental Processes of Dye Chemistry, Interscience, New York, 1949.
16. Geiseler, G., and R. Kuschmiers, Z. Physik. Chem. (Frankfurt), 33, 264 (1962).
17. Geiseler, G., and H. Reinhardt, Z. Physik. Chem. (Frankfurt), 28, 24 (1961).
18. Gilbert, E. E., and P. H. Groggins, Unit Processes in Organic Synthesis, 5th ed., P. H. Groggins, ed., McGraw-Hill, New York, 1958.
19. Goodman, I., and R. A. Edington, British Patent 834,251; Chem. Abstr., 54, 20986 (1960).
20. Gore, P. H., J. Org. Chem., 22, 135 (1957).
21. Herbrandson, H. F., W. S. Kelly, and J. Versnel, J. Am. Chem. Soc., 80, 3301 (1958).
22. den Hertog, H. J., H. C. vander Plas, and D. J. Buurman, Rec. Trav. Chim., 77, 963 (1958).
23. Hetzner, H. P., and R. J. Miller, U. S. Patent 2,511,711; Chem. Abstr., 44, 8368 (1950).
24. Holt, G., M. Sc. Thesis, Manchester College of Science and Technology, 1944.
25. Huston, R. C., and M. M. Ballard, Organic Synthesis, Vol. 2, Wiley, New York, 1943, p. 97.

26.   IG Farbenindustrie AG, U.S. Dept. Commerce, OTS Rept.,
       PB75, 478.
27.   Ioffe, I.S., and Z. Ya. Khavin, J. Gen. Chem. USSR (English
       Transl.), 17, 528 (1947); Chem. Abstr., 42, 1933 (1948).
28.   Jacobsen, O., Ber., 20, 896 (1887).
29.   Jezl, J. L., and L. D. Hague, U.S. Patent 2, 880, 253; Chem.
       Abstr., 53, 16524 (1959).
30.   Kachurin, O. I., A. A. Spryskov, and L. P. Mel'nikova, Izv. Vysshykh
       Uchebn. Zavedenii Khim. i Khim. Tekhnol., 3, 669 (1960); Chem.
       Abstr., 55, 2544 (1961).
31.   Karavaev, B. I., and A. A. Spryskov, Zh. Obshch. Khim., 33, No.
       6, 1890 (1963); Chem. Abstr., 59, 11221 (1963).
32.   Kilpatrick, M., and M. W. Meyer, J. Phys. Chem., 65, 1312
       (1961).
33.   Kilpatrick, M., M. W. Meyer, and M. L. Kilpatrick, J. Phys. Chem.,
       65, 1189 (1961).
34.   Kruber, O., and H. Lauenstein, Ber., 74, 1693 (1941).
35.   Kruber, O., and R. Oberkobusch, Chem. Ber., 84, 826 (1951).
36.   Leitman, Ya. I., and I. N. Diyarov, Zh. Prikl. Khim., 34, 1868
       (1961); Chem. Abstr., 56, 359 (1962).
37.   Leitman, Ya. I., and I. N. Diyarov, Zh. Prikl. Khim., 34, 1920
       (1961); Chem. Abstr., 56, 2355 (1962).
38.   Leitman, Ya. I., and I. N. Diyarov, Proizv. Benzola, Vses.,
       Nauchn. -Issled. Inst. Neftekhim. Protsessov, 1962, 216; Chem.
       Abstr., 59, 9756 (1963).
39.   Leitman, Ya. I., and M. S. Pevzner, Zh. Prikl. Khim., 32, 2754
       (1959); Chem. Abstr., 54, 9458 (1960).
40.   Leitman, Ya. I., V. I. Sorokin, and I. V. Tselinskii, Zh. Prikl. Khim.,
       33, 1875 (1960); Chem. Abstr., 55, 435 (1961).
41.   Long, F. A., and M. A. Paul, Chem. Rev., 57, 935 (1957).
42.   Mair, B. J., D. J. Termini, C. B. Willingham, and D. Rossini, J.
       Res. Natl. Bur. Std., 37, 229 (1946).
43.   Meek, P. D., in Advances in Petroleum Chemistry and Refining,
       Vol. 4, J. J. McKetta, ed., Interscience, New York, 1961, p. 437.
44.   Merritt, L., U.S. Patent 2, 725, 408; Chem. Abstr., 51, 3661
       (1957).
45.   Miller, R. J., U.S. Patent 2, 523, 707; Chem. Abstr., 45, 1163
       (1951).
46.   Moore, F. J., and G. R. Tucker, J. Am. Chem. Soc., 49, 262
       (1927).
47.   Munro, W. P., in Kirk-Othmer, Encyclopedia of Chemical Tech-
       nology, Vol. 1, 1st ed., Interscience, New York, 1947, p. 947.
48.   Muramoto, Y., Science Ind. (Japan), 29, 315 (1955); Chem.
       Abstr., 50, 9946 (1956).
49.   Muth, F., in Houben-Weyl, Methoden der Organischen Chemie,
       Vol. IX, Thieme Verlag, Stuttgart, 1955.
50.   National Chemical Laboratory, Dept. of Scientific and Industrial
       Research, Annual Rept. 1960, London.

51. Nelson, K. L. , and H. C. Brown, in The Chemistry of Petroleum Hydrocarbons, Vol. 3, Reinhold, New York, 1955, p. 465.

52. Oliver, T. C. , and S. F. Spangler, in The Science of Petroleum, Vol. 3, Oxford University Press, New York, 1938, p. 2764.

53. Polyanskii, N. G. , and P. E. Tulupov, J. App. Chem. USSR (English Transl.), 35, 2281 (1962); Chem. Abstr. , 58, 5837 (1963).

54. Prescott, R. F. , U. S. Patent 2, 112, 543; Chem. Abstr. , 32, 3774 (1938).

55. Rabjohn, N. , J. W. Fronabarger, and W. W. Linstromberg, J. Org. Chem. , 20, 271 (1955).

56. Reif, H. E. , and A. P. Stuart, U. S. Patent 2, 848, 483; Chem. Abstr. , 52, 21062 (1958).

57. Schultz, H. P. , Organic Syntheses, Vol. 31, Wiley, New York, 1951.

58. Seikel, M. K. , Organic Syntheses, Vol. 35, Wiley, New York, 1955, p. 262.

59. Setzkorn, E. A. , and A. B. Carel, J. Am. Oil Chemists' Soc. , 40, 57 (1963).

60. Smith, L. I. , and O. W. Cass, J. Am. Chem. Soc. , 54, 1614 (1932).

61. Smith, L. I. , and A. R. Lux, J. Am. Chem. Soc. , 51, 2994 (1929).

62. Sperling, R. , Ind. Eng. Chem. , 40, 890 (1948).

63. Spryskov, A. A. , J. Gen. Chem. USSR (English Transl.), 16, 2126 (1946); Chem. Abstr. , 42, 894 (1948).

64. Spryskov, A. A. , Zh. Obshch. Khim. , 30, 2449 (1960); Chem. Abstr. , 55, 12336 (1961).

65. Spryskov, A. A. , and O. I. Kachurin, Zh. Obshch. Khim. , 28, 1642 (1958); Chem. Abstr. , 53, 1215 (1959).

66. Spryskov, A. A. , and B. I. Karavaev, Zh. Obshch. Khim, 22, 1871 (1952); Chem. Abstr. , 47, 8710 (1953).

67. Spryskov, A. A. , and N. A. Ovsyankina, Zh. Obshch. Khim. , 20, 1043 (1950); Chem. Abstr. , 44, 9367 (1950).

68. Spryskov, A. A. , and N. A. Ovsyankina, Zh. Obshch. Khim. , 21, 1508 (1951); Chem. Abstr. , 46, 2523 (1952).

69. Spryskov, A. A. , and N. A. Ovsyankina, Sb. Statei Obshch. Khim. , 2, 882 (1953); Chem. Abstr. , 49, 6894 (1955).

70. Spryskov, A. A. , and N. A. Ovsyankina, Zh. Obshch. Khim. , 24, 1810 (1954); Chem. Abstr. , 49, 12342 (1955).

71. Spryskov, A. A. , and S. P. Starkov, Zh. Obshch. Khim. , 26, 2862 (1956); Chem. Abstr. , 51, 8038 (1957).

71a. Spryskov, A. A. , and S. P. Starkov, Zh. Obshch. Khim. , 27, 3067 (1957); Chem. Abstr. , 52, 8072 (1958).

72. Squire, E. S. , D. G. Pigeon, and P. C. Jones, J. Inst. Petrol. , 38, 12 (1952).

73. Stilmar, F. B. , and M. A. Perkins, in The Chemistry of Synthetic Dyes and Pigments, H. A. Lubs, ed. , Reinhold, New York, 1955, p. 337.

74. Stoesser, W. C. , and W. M. Gentry, U. S. Patent 2, 835, 707; Chem. Abstr. , 52, 16295 (1958).

75.   Suter, C. M. , The Organic Chemistry of Sulfur, Wiley, New York, 1944.
76.   Terent'ev, A. P. , and A. I. Gershenovich, Zh. Obshch. Khim. , 23, 204 (1953); Chem. Abstr. , 48, 2568 (1954).
77.   Tiers, G. V. D. , U. S. Patent 2, 951, 051; Chem. Abstr. , 55, 5347 (1961).
78.   Vesely, V. , and T. Stojanova, Collection Czech. Chem. Commun. , 9, 465 (1937); Chem. Abstr. , 32, 1549 (1938).
79.   Vollbracht, L. , H. Cerfontain,   and F. L. J. Sixma, Rec. Trav. Chim. , 80, 11 (1961).
80.   Vorozhtsov, N. N. , Jr. , V. A. Koptyug, and A. M. Komagorov, Zh. Obshch. Khim. , 31, 3330 (1961); Chem. Abstr. , 57, 2152 (1962)
81.   Wanders, A. C. M. , and H. Cerfontain, Proc. Chem. Soc. , 1963, 174.
82.   Weil, J. K. , F. D. Smith, A. J. Stirton, and R. G. Bistline, Jr. , J. Am. Oil Chemists' Soc. , 40, 538 (1963).
83.   Werner, J. , in Kirk-Othmer, Encyclopedia of Chemical Technology, Vol. 9, 1st ed. , Interscience, New York, 1952, p. 258.
84.   Wood, G. F. , and R. E. Plappinger, J. Am. Chem. Soc. , 73, 5603 (1951).

AUTHOR INDEX[*]

A

Abbott Laboratories, 406 (ref. 1), 407 (refs. 2, 2a), 420

Abe, H. , 255 (ref. 1), 310

Abe, K. , 81 (ref. 1), 105

Abe, Y. , 92 (ref. 2), 105, 166 (ref. 1), 181

Abercromby, D. C. , 2 (ref. 1), 25

Aberg, B. , 249 (ref. 668), 336

Abrams, E. L. A. , 84 (ref. 294), 85 (ref. 294), 116

Ackermann, F. , 254 (refs. 2, 3), 255 (refs. 4, 5), 302 (refs. 4, 5), 303 (ref. 5), 310, 408 (refs. 3, 4), 420

Ackermann, H. , 300 (ref. 6), 310

Adams, C. C. , 67 (ref. 159), 110

Adams, C. E. , 51 (ref. 3), 52 (ref. 3), 105, 218 (refs. 1, 170), 230, 236

Adams, D. A. W. , 147 (ref. 2), 181, 212 (ref. 2), 230, 299 (ref. 7), 310

Adams, F. H. , 88 (ref. 243), 114

Adams, P. , 300 (ref. 165), 316

Adams, R. , 160 (refs. 3, 4), 181, 217 (ref. 3), 230, 249 (ref. 8), 310

Adeniran, M. A. , 125 (ref. 4a), 172 (ref. 4a), 181

Adler, E. , 160 (ref. 5), 181

Agawa, T. , 270(ref. 375), 325, 361 (ref. 212), 393

Agfa Wolfen Filmfabrik, 370 (ref. 1), 385

Aguado, L. , 171 (ref. 6), 181

Aiello, T. , 219 (ref. 4), 230

Aiko, I. , 406 (ref. 5), 420

Akiyama, U. , 82 (ref. 4), 105

Aktiebolaget Pharmacia, 357 (ref. 2), 385

Aktien-Gesellschaft vorm, B.

Siegfried, 253 (ref. 9), 310

Aktieselskabet Benzon, A. , 254 (ref. 10), 310

Albertson, N. F. , 2 (ref. 1a), 15 (ref. 1a), 25

Alburn, H. E. , 358 (ref. 3), 385

Alderson, W. L. , 250 (ref. 120), 251 (ref. 120), 314

Aldrich Chemical Co. , 9 (ref. 1b), 25, 278 (ref. 11), 280 (ref. 11), 290 (ref. 11), 292 (ref. 11), 294 (ref. 11), 305 (ref. 11), 306 (ref. 11), 310

Alexander, E. R. , 78 (ref. 5), 79 (ref. 5), 105, 157 (ref. 7), 181

Alexander, S. S. , 23 (ref. 80), 28, 77 (ref. 261), 80 (ref. 261), 115

Alfieri, C. C. , 37-42 (ref. 446), 122, 142 (ref. 433), 197, 276 (ref. 650), 335

Alles, R. , 248 (refs. 12, 13), 310

Allied Chemical Corp. , 2 (ref. 3), 4 (ref. 4), 9 (refs. 2, 4), 11 (refs. 2, 4), 13 (ref. 2), 18 (ref. 4), 25, 36 (ref. 7), 41 (ref. 7), 45 (ref. 7), 52 (ref. 7), 53 (ref. 7), 58 (ref. 6), 60 (ref. 7), 67 (ref. 7), 68 (ref. 7), 71 (ref. 7), 74 (ref. 7), 81 (ref. 7), 82 (ref. 7), 84 (ref. 7), 105, 157 (ref. 8), 181, 269 (ref. 14), 275 (ref. 14), 276 (ref. 15), 277 (ref. 16), 278 (ref. 14), 288 (ref. 15), 294 (ref. 14), 303 (ref. 15), 305 (ref. 14), 306 (ref. 14), 310, 362 (ref. 5), 372 (ref. 5), 373 (ref. 5), 374 (ref. 4), 385, 407 (ref. 6), 420

Allmen, S. V. , 172 (refs. 9, 10), 181

Alphen, J. van, 262 (ref. 17), 310

Alpine Chemische A. G. , 357 (ref. 6), 385

Mohr, R. , 295 (ref. 459), 328
Molteni, H. A. , 262 (ref. 460), 328
Mones, E. M. , 285 (ref. 422), 326
Monsanto Chemical Co. , 255 (ref. 462), 297 (ref. 461), 328
Montonna, R. E. , 171 (ref. 163), 187, 417 (ref. 44), 419 (ref. 44), 421
Mook, H. W. , 34 (ref. 21), 105
Moore, F. J. , 427 (ref. 46), 440
Moore, L. O. , 369 (refs. 257, 258), 395
Moore, M. B. , 154 (ref. 74), 165 (ref. 74), 184, 192
Moore, R. G. D. , 291 (ref. 204), 304 (ref. 204), 318
Moos, J. , 341 (ref. 331), 397
Mora, P. T. , 357 (ref. 417), 401
Moralli, G. J. , 302 (ref. 463), 328
Morgner, M. , 275 (ref. 464), 328
Mori, P. T. , 37 (ref. 449), 39 (ref. 449), 41 (ref. 449), 123, 142 (ref. 438), 197
Mori, S. , 419 (ref. 63), 422
Morita, M. , 407 (ref. 47a), 421
Moriuchi, M. , 140 (ref. 288), 192
Morkved, E. , 56 (ref. 230), 113, 163 (ref. 229), 190
Morris, L. R. , 302 (ref. 248), 319
Morton, M. , 152, 192, 289 (ref. 465), 328
Moses, P. , 250 (ref. 209), 258 (ref. 209), 259 (ref. 209), 318
Mosher, C. W. , 205 (ref. 150), 209 (ref. 150), 235
Mosher, H. S. , 97 (ref. 270), 99 (ref. 271), 115
Mosher, R. A. , 206 (ref. 123), 234
Mothurf, A. , 146 (ref. 290), 192
Motozato, Y. , 141 (ref. 291), 192
Moulton, R. W. , 297 (ref. 611), 334
Moyer, W. W. , 34 (ref. 272), 36 (ref. 273), 115, 413 (ref. 64), 422

Mueller, 146 (ref. 292), 192
Mueller, G. , 170 (ref. 26), 181, 291 (ref. 300a), 321
Mueller, I. F. , 301 (ref. 466), 328
Mueller, M. , 372 (ref. 259), 395
Mueller, P. , 422
Mueller, W. , 274 (ref. 467), 328
Muenz, F. , 58 (ref. 173), 111, 250 (ref. 468), 265 (refs. 263, 264), 294 (ref. 264), 295 (ref. 264), 298 (ref. 263), 320, 328
Mukherji, B. K. , 355 (ref. 36), 386
Mulder, H. , 250 (refs. 36, 37), 252 (ref. 36), 256 (ref. 37), 311
Muller, N. , 100 (ref. 274), 115
Mulligan, B. , 265 (ref. 469), 328
Mundlos, E. , 215 (ref. 99), 233, 267 (ref. 313), 322
Municio, A. M. , 171 (ref. 6), 177 (ref. 11), 181, 213 (refs. 6, 7), 230
Munro, W. P. , 429 (ref. 47), 437 (ref. 47), 440
Muraca, R. , 94 (ref. 481), 124
Murakami, M. , 212 (ref. 151), 235
Muramoto, Y. , 73 (ref. 276), 79 (ref. 275), 115, 434 (ref. 48), 440
Murav'eva, K. M. , 219 (ref. 151a), 235
Murdock, S. A. , 302 (refs. 470, 471), 328
Murphy, A. R. , 90 (ref. 277), 115
Muskett, C. W. , 357 (ref. 151), 390
Mussard, A. , 342 (ref. 187), 392
Mustafa, A. , 56, 115, 280 (refs. 472, 473), 307 (refs. 472, 473), 308 (refs. 472, 473), 328
Muth, F. , 18 (ref. 84), 28, 67 (ref. 279), 70 (ref. 279), 83 (ref. 279), 87 (ref. 279), 89 (ref. 279), 94 (ref. 279), 115, 171, 172 (ref. 293), 173 (ref. 293), 192, 228, 235, 427, 429

P

Squire, E. S. , 436 (ref. 72), 441
Stacey, F. W. , 149 (ref. 407),
  156 (ref. 407), 196
Stacey, G. J. , 210 (ref. 186), 237
Staehler, G. , 274 (ref. 559a), 332
Stalinovy Zavody, 248 (ref. 599),
  333
Stallmann, O. , 102 (ref. 8), 105
Stamicarbon, NV, 209 (ref. 206),
  237
Starkov, S. P. , 69 (ref. 379), 70
  (refs. 376, 377), 119, 224 (ref.
  122), 234, 430 (ref. 71), 432
  (ref. 71), 434 (ref. 71a), 441
Staszewska, D. , 273 (ref. 657),
  336
Stather, F. , 297 (refs. 600, 601),
  333
Stavric, B. , 85 (ref. 380), 119
Stawitzke, A. A. , 360 (ref. 368),
  399
Stayner, R. A. , 267 (ref. 603),
  334, 362 (ref. 365), 399
Stayner, R. D. , 267 (ref. 603),
  298 (ref. 602), 334, 355 (ref.
  364), 362 (ref. 365), 399
Stearns, J. A. , 215 (ref. 57a),
  232
Stedman, G. , 145 (ref. 70), 183
Stedman, R. J. , 14 (ref. 71), 15
  (ref. 71), 28
Steen, E. J. van der, 249 (ref.
  668), 336
Stein, E. , 413 (ref. 91), 423
Stein, W. , 44 (ref. 31a), 106
Stein, W. H. , 297 (ref. 153), 298
  (ref. 153), 315
Steindorff, A. , 259 (ref. 604),
  334
Steinfort, O. , 171 (ref. 277), 191
Steinhauer, A. F. , 80 (ref. 381),
  119
Steinmetz, J. M. , 76 (ref. 115),
  109
Stelling, O. , 157 (ref. 408), 196
Stenlake, J. B. , 223 (ref. 45), 231
Stephen, W. E. , 268 (ref. 549), 300
  (ref. 549), 331

Stephenson, O. , 85 (ref. 42), 106
Stern, R. , 48-50 (ref. 382), 120
Stevens, J. R. , 291 (ref. 204), 304
  (ref. 204), 318
Stevens, W. , 357 (ref. 140), 390
Stewart, A. W. , 158 (ref. 409), 159
  (ref. 409), 196
Stewart, D. , 342 (ref. 366), 399
Stewart, F. D. , 219 (refs. 145,
  207), 235, 238
Stewart, J. M. , 143 (ref. 410),
  161 (ref. 410), 196, 209 (ref.
  210), 210 (refs. 208-210), 222
  (ref. 210), 238, 261 (ref. 605),
  334
Stewart, T. D. , 157 (ref. 411),
  196, 244 (ref. 606), 334
Stiles, A. R. , 129 (ref. 354), 194
Stillich, O. , 277 (ref. 607), 334
Stilmar, F. B. , 437 (ref. 73), 441
Stinemur, S. B. , 291 (ref. 617),
  334
Stipnice, H. , 40 (ref. 165), 111
Stirton, A. J. , 34, 35 (refs. 35,
  384, 473-477), 106, 120, 124,
  215 (ref. 229), 238, 262 (ref.
  685), 278 (ref. 608), 279 (ref.
  608), 334, 337, 345 (ref. 249),
  352 (refs. 35, 249, 407), 360
  (refs. 368, 406), 361 (ref. 406),
  386, 394, 399, 400, 426 (ref.
  82), 442
Stockhausen, J. , 45 (refs. 28, 29),
  58 (refs. 28, 29), 105, 106
Stoesser, S. M. , 76 (ref. 57), 107
Stoesser, W. C. , 436 (ref. 74),
  441
Stoessl, A. , 56 (ref. 230), 113,
  163 (ref. 229), 190
Stogryn, E. L. , 150 (ref. 412),
  196
Stojanova, T. , 430 (ref. 78), 442
Stone, G. C. H. , 140 (ref. 413),
  196, 215 (ref. 211), 238
Strain, B. , 348 (ref. 130), 389
Strakov, A. , 19 (ref. 105a), 29,
  40 (refs. 385-387), 120
Strating, J. , 282 (ref. 609), 292
  (ref. 609), 307 (ref. 609), 334

SUBJECT INDEX

A

Abietic acid, 59
Acetaldehyde, 42, 158, 275
Acetaldehyde-bisulfite, 158, 250-256
Acetaldehydedisulfonic acid, 42, 275
Acetaldehydemonosulfonic acid, 42, 56
  substituted, 54, 61, 275
Acetic acid, 22, 33, 67, 72, 73
Acetic anhydride, 22, 33
Acetoacetic ester, 246, 264
Acetone, 39, 159, 246
Acetonesulfonic acid, 56, 276
Acetone-SO_3 complex, 17
Acetonitrile, 37, 417
Acetyl chloride, 34
  sulfo- (see under Sulfoacetic acid)
Acetylene(s), 59-61, 151-152, 273, 275
Acetylenic alcohols, 151, 152, 360-361
Acetyl sulfate, composition, 22
  preparation, 22, 23, 33
  reactions summarized, 22, 23
  reactions with alkenamine derivatives, 59
  alkenes, 48-52
  amines, 23
  anthracene, 91
  benzene, 69
  benzothiophenes, 97
  castor oil, 59, 365
  cellulose, 359
  diphenyl ether, 80
  fatty oils, 365
  ferrocene, 103, 104
  fluorene, 92
  furan, 93
  guaiazylene, 59
  ketones, 37-41, 55-57

oleic acid, 58
olive oil, 58, 365
phenols, 23
sterols, 39-41, 55, 56
urea, 412
Acid chlorides, reactions with
  2-aminoethanesulfonic acid, 264, 265
  aminomethanesulfonic acid, 258
  2-hydroxyethanesulfonic acid, 261, 262
  metanilic acid, 298
  phenolsulfonic acid, 297
  sulfanilic acid, 298
  sulfonation of aliphatic, 34
  aromatic, 81
Acids, dicarboxylic, aliphatic, 35, 36
  aromatic, 81
  (see also under names of individual acids)
Acids, monocarboxylic, aliphatic, saturated, sulfochlorination, 131
  sulfonation, 33-36
  sulfoxidation, 134
  aliphatic, unsaturated, bisulfite addition to, 148, 150
  sulfation, 363, 365
  sulfonation, 56-59
  aromatic, 80-82
  heterocyclic, 94, 98, 103, 104
  (see also under names of individual acids)
Acids, α-sulfo, 33-36, 278, 279
Acridines, 176
Acrolein, 153, 154, 287
Acrylonitrile, 155, 243, 244, 260, 274, 289, 291, 296
Acyl sulfates, 22, 23
  (see also under Acetyl sulfate)
Adipic acid, 36
Alcohols, amino (see under Amino alcohols)

501